PHYSICS DEPARTMENT
UNIVERSITY of GEORGIA
ATHENS, GEORGIA 30601

Winfield J. Abbe
515 Manzanita Ave.
Sierra Madre, Calif

McGRAW-HILL ELECTRICAL AND ELECTRONIC ENGINEERING SERIES

Frederick Emmons Terman, *Consulting Editor*

ELECTRONIC ENGINEERING

McGraw-Hill Electrical and Electronic Engineering Series

FREDERICK EMMONS TERMAN, *Consulting Editor*
W. W. HARMAN and J. G. TRUXAL, *Associate Consulting Editors*

BAILEY AND GAULT · Alternating-current Machinery
BERANEK · Acoustics
BRUNS AND SAUNDERS · Analysis of Feedback Control System
CAGE · Theory and Application of Industrial Electronics
CAUER · Synthesis of Linear Communication Networks, Vols. I and II
CUCCIA · Harmonics, Sidebands, and Transients in Communication
    Engineering
EASTMAN · Fundamentals of Vacuum Tubes
EVANS · Control-system Dynamics
FEINSTEIN · Foundation of Information Theory
FITZGERALD AND HIGGINBOTHAM · Basic Electrical Engineering
FITZGERALD AND KINGSLEY · Electric Machinery
GEPPERT · Basic Electron Tubes
GLASFORD · Fundamentals of Television Engineering
HAPPELL AND HESSELBERTH · Engineering Electronics
HARMAN · Fundamentals of Electronic Motion
HARRINGTON · Introduction to Electromagnetic Engineering
HAYT · Engineering Electromagnetics
HESSLER AND CAREY · Fundamentals of Electrical Engineering
HILL · Electronics in Engineering
JOHNSON · Transmission Lines and Networks
KRAUS · Antennas
KRAUS · Electromagnetics
LePAGE · Analysis of Alternating-current Circuits
LePAGE AND SEELY · General Network Analysis
MILLMAN AND SEELY · Electronics
MILLMAN AND TAUB · Pulse and Digital Circuits
ROGERS · Introduction to Electric Fields
RÜDENBERG · Transient Performance of Electric Power Systems
RYDER · Engineering Electronics
SEELY · Electron-tube Circuits
SEELY · Electronic Engineering
SEELY · Introduction to Electric and Magnetic Fields
SEELY · Radio Electronics
SISKIND · Direct-current Machinery
SKILLING · Electric Transmission Lines
SKILLING · Transient Electric Currents
SPANGENBERG · Fundamentals of Electron Devices
SPANGENBERG · Vacuum Tubes
STEVENSON · Elements of Power System Analysis
STORER · Passive Network Synthesis
TERMAN · Electronic and Radio Engineering
TERMAN AND PETTIT · Electronic Measurements
THALER · Elements of Servomechanism Theory
THALER AND BROWN · Servomechanism Analysis
THOMPSON · Alternating-current and Transient Circuit Analysis
TRUXAL · Automatic Feedback Control System Synthesis

Electronic Engineering

SAMUEL SEELY, Ph.D.

Professor and Chairman
Department of Electrical Engineering
Syracuse University

New York   Toronto   London

McGRAW-HILL BOOK COMPANY, INC.

1956

ELECTRONIC ENGINEERING

Library of Congress Catalog Card Number 55-5697

v

PREFACE

"Electronic Engineering" and "Radio Electronics" have been written as companion volumes, though they have been produced as independent textbooks. Together they represent a revision and extension of the author's "Electron-tube Circuits." It has been necessary to include a certain amount of material that is common to both books in order to ensure completeness and continuity of text material. Moreover, the common material is the same in each book, in the interests of economy of production. However, the amount of duplicated material has been kept to a minimum, consistent with the desire to have these books independent, and also to provide a complete and continuous development.

This book has as its objective a detailed discussion of a large variety of electronic circuits which are important in such diverse fields as radar, television, electronic control and instrumentation, and computers. Those circuits which have found applications principally in the field of radio are not included in this book, though a number of circuits of interest both in nonradio and in radio applications are included. Most of the text is devoted to the analysis of circuit operation. However, some of the factors that must be considered in circuit and system synthesis are discussed.

Wherever possible, the analysis proceeds in two stages. An effort is made first to present a physical explanation of the operation of the circuits. If feasible, a mathematical analysis of the operation of the circuit is given. Such mathematical analyses have a threefold objective: (1) To illustrate the techniques of analysis. Often, in fact, alternative developments have been included to demonstrate different methods of analysis. (2) To deduce a solution which yields a description of the operation of the circuit. (3) To examine the effects of the various parameters on the operation of the circuit.

In all analyses considerable care has been taken to include the requisite reference conditions for potential polarities, current directions, and transformer-winding sense. These are an essential part of any circuit diagram, and without them the ultimate choice of a positive or negative sign would require a major decision.

Representative types of circuits of widespread use and importance have been discussed and analyzed. It is not possible, of course, to include a

v

discussion of every possible type of circuit of a given class. In fact, a review of the literature will disclose almost as many choices of circuit parameters or tube types as there are groups engaged in this work. In general, the principle of operation is deemed to be of the essence, rather than the choice of a particular set of parameters, and most attention is paid to a discussion of these principles of operation.

Much of the material in this book has been used in courses in electronic circuits and applications at Syracuse University. A considerable amount of new material has been added to that previously available in "Electron-tube Circuits." Thus, not only has there been an addition to the content of the chapters originally available, but an introduction to solid-state theory, the transistor, and the transistor as a circuit element is now available.

To provide the proper acknowledgment of the source of much of this material is impossible. As noted in the preface to "Electron-tube Circuits," much of this material represented circuits in use at the MIT Radiation Laboratory during World War II. Some of the circuits were developed at this laboratory, but many of them were developments at a number of American and British laboratories. In only a few cases was the identity of the groups responsible for any given circuit known. Where direct sources of information have been used, reference is given to these.

The author wishes to acknowledge helpful discussions with many of his colleagues. He is particularly indebted to Dr. Herbert Hellerman for his helpful suggestions relating to Chaps. 15 and 16, and to Richard E. Gildersleeve for his assistance in proofreading the entire text.

SAMUEL SEELY

CONTENTS

CHAPTER 1

CHARACTERISTICS OF ELECTRON TUBES

1-1. Electronic Systems. A unique definition of an electronic system as it will be studied in this text is not possible, owing to the multiplicity and complexity of such systems. For the most part, no consideration will be given to communication systems, as these are covered in the companion volume, "Radio Electronics," although certain of the circuits which are of importance in communication applications are also of considerable importance in essentially noncommunication applications. This text will confine itself principally to a study of a variety of circuits which form the building blocks of a tremendous array of electronic systems for all manner of applications. As part of the study, some discussion will be included of the manner of connecting a variety of such building blocks to perform a specified sequence of operations.

A particular electronic system may impose a demand for electronic circuits to perform a wide diversity of operations. For example, a relatively simple system might easily require the generation of waves of sinusoidal waveshape, of square waveshape, of triangular waveshape, amplifiers which amplify with virtually no distortion, amplifiers which introduce controlled distortion, amplifiers which produce controlled blocking, and a host of others. Some building blocks may consist of relatively simple circuits, and others may require a relatively complex array of components to achieve the desired end.

In order to present the material in a reasonably logical manner, the following chapters present the analyses of the operation of a variety of classes of electronic circuits, without regard for the particular applications, but principally according to the manner of operation and analysis. For this reason, a given chapter may contain circuits which have altogether different applications. The choice of examples and problems will indicate in some measure representative applications. Some discussion will be included in such cases of practical reasons which might influence the preference for one circuit over another for achieving a specified requirement.

1-2. Fundamental Considerations in Electron Tubes. Before one undertakes a study of circuits that incorporate electron tubes, it will be well to examine certain of the physical principles which govern the operation of these tubes. There are two important basic questions that relate to such tubes. One relates to the actual source of the electrons and their liberation; the second relates to the control of the electron beam. A brief discussion of these matters follows.

EMISSION OF ELECTRONS

1-3. Source and Control of Electrons. According to modern theory, all matter is electrical in nature. The atom, which is one of the fundamental building blocks of all matter, consists of a central core or nucleus which is positively charged and which carries nearly all the mass of the atom. Enough negatively charged electrons surround the nucleus so that the atom is electrically neutral in its normal state. Since all chemical substances consist of groups of these atoms which are bound to each other, then all matter, whether it is in the solid, the liquid, or the gaseous state, is a potential source of electrons. All three states of matter do, in fact, serve as sources of electrons. A number of different processes serve to effect the release of electrons, those which are of importance in electron tubes being (1) thermionic emission, (2) secondary emission, (3) photoelectric emission, (4) high field emission, and (5) ionization. These processes will be considered in some detail in what follows.

With the release of the electrons, a means for their control must be provided. Such control is effected by means of externally controlled electric fields or magnetic fields, or both. These fields perform one or both of the following functions: (1) control of the number of electrons that leave the region near the emitter; (2) control of the paths of the electrons after they leave the emitter. Control method 1 is the more common, and such a control method is incorporated in almost all electron tubes, except those of the field-deflected variety. The cathode-ray tube is a very important example of a field-deflected tube. However, even in this latter case, a control of type 1 is incorporated to control the electron-tube current, even though the subsequent motion is controlled by means of electric or magnetic fields, or both.

1-4. Thermionic Emission. Consider matter in the metallic state. Metals are most generally employed in the form of a wire or ribbon filament. If such a filament contains electrons and if these are relatively free to move about in the metal (and this is the case since the application of a small potential difference between the ends of the wire will result in a current flow), it might be expected that some electrons might "leak" out of the metal of their own accord. This does not occur, however.

Consider what happens to an electron as it seeks to escape from a metal. The escaping, negatively charged electron will induce a positive charge on the metal. There will then be a force of attraction between the induced charge and the electron.   Unless the escaping electron possesses sufficient energy to carry it out of the region of influence of this image force of attraction, it will be returned to the metal.*   The minimum amount of energy that is required to release the electron against this attractive force is known as the *work function* of the metal.   This requisite minimum amount of energy may be supplied by any one of a number of different methods.   One of the most important methods is to heat the metal to a high temperature.   In this way, some of the thermal energy supplied to the metal is transferred from the lattice of the heated metal crystals into kinetic energy of the electrons.

An explicit expression relating the thermionic-emission current density and the temperature of the metal can be derived.[1]†   The expression so derived has the form

$$J_{th} = A_0 T^2 e^{-b_0/T} \tag{1-1}$$

where A_0 is a constant for all metals and has the value of 120×10^4 amp/(m²)(°K²) and b_0 is a constant that is characteristic of the metal. The quantity b_0 is related to the work function E_W of the metal by

$$b_0 = 11{,}600 E_W \qquad °K \tag{1-2}$$

It has been found experimentally that Eq. (1-1) does represent the form of the variation of current with temperature for most metals, although the value obtained for A_0 may differ materially from the theoretical value of 120×10^4 amp/(m²)(°K²).

TABLE 1-1

THE IMPORTANT THERMIONIC EMITTERS AND THE
THERMIONIC-EMISSION CONSTANTS

Emitter	A_0, amp/(m²)(°K²)	E_W, ev
Tungsten.....................	60×10^4	4.52
Thoriated-tungsten............	3×10^4	2.63
Oxide-coated.................	0.01×10^4	1

It follows from Eq. (1-1) that metals that have a low work function will provide copious emission at moderately low temperatures.   Unfortunately, however, the low-work-function metals melt in some cases and boil in others, at the temperatures necessary for appreciable thermionic emission.   The important emitters in present-day use are pure-tungsten, thoriated-tungsten, and oxide-coated cathodes.   The thermionic-emission constants of these emitters are contained in Table 1-1.

* A somewhat more detailed discussion of the electron theory of metals is given in Chap. 15.

† Superior numbers refer to citations at the end of some chapters.

Tungsten is used extensively for thermionic filaments despite its relatively high work function. In fact, this material is particularly important because it is virtually the only material that can be used successfully as the filament in high-potential tubes. It is used in high-potential X-ray tubes, in high-potential rectifier tubes, and in the large power-amplifier tubes that are used in radio and communication applications. It has the disadvantage that the *cathode emission efficiency*, defined as the ratio of the emission current in milliamperes to the heating power in watts, is small. Despite this, it can be operated at a sufficiently high temperature, between 2600 and 2800°K, to provide an adequate emission.

It has been found that the application of a very thin layer of low-work-function material on filaments of tungsten will materially reduce the work function of the resulting surface. A thoriated-tungsten filament is obtained by adding a small amount of thorium oxide to the tungsten before it is drawn. Such filaments, when properly activated, will yield an efficient emitter at about 1800°K. It is found desirable to *carbonize* such an emitter, since the rate of evaporation of the thorium layer from the filament is thus reduced by about a factor of 6. Thoriated-tungsten filaments are limited in application to tubes that operate at intermediate potentials, say 10,000 volts or less. Higher-potential tubes use pure-tungsten filaments.

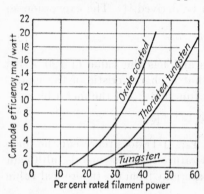

FIG. 1-1. Cathode efficiency curves of an oxide-coated, a thoriated-tungsten, and a pure-tungsten filament.

The oxide-coated cathode is very efficient (about twenty times as efficient as tungsten) and provides a high emission current at the relatively low temperature of 1000°K. It consists of a metal sleeve of konal (an alloy of nickel, cobalt, iron, and titanium) or some other metal, which is coated with the oxides of barium and strontium. These cathodes are limited for a number of reasons to use in the lower potential tubes, say about 1,000 volts or less, although they do operate satisfactorily at higher potentials under pulsed conditions at relatively low-duty cycle. They are used almost exclusively in receiving-type tubes and provide efficient operation with long life.

Curves showing the relative cathode efficiencies of tungsten, thoriated-tungsten, and oxide-coated cathodes are illustrated in Fig. 1-1. It will be seen that tungsten has a considerably lower efficiency than either of the other two emitters.

The thermionic emitters in their practical form in electron tubes may

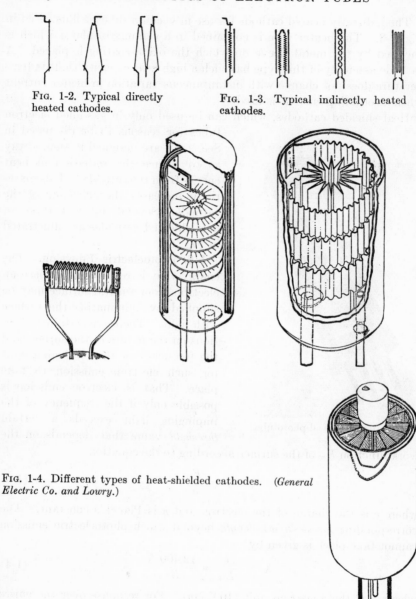

FIG. 1-2. Typical directly heated cathodes.

FIG. 1-3. Typical indirectly heated cathodes.

FIG. 1-4. Different types of heat-shielded cathodes.   (*General Electric Co. and Lowry.*)

be of the directly heated or filamentary type, or of the indirectly heated type, and in the case of gas and vapor tubes the cathode may be of the heat-shielded type.   Typical filamentary cathodes are illustrated in Fig. 1-2.   These filamentary cathodes may be of the pure-tungsten, thoriated-tungsten, or oxide-coated type.

The indirectly heated cathode for use in vacuum tubes is illustrated in Fig. 1-3. The heater wire is contained in a ceramic insulator which is enclosed by the metal sleeve on which the oxide coating is placed. A cathode assembly of this type has such a high heat capacity that its temperature does not change with instantaneous variation in heater current when alternating current is used.

Heat-shielded cathodes, which can be used only in gas-filled electron tubes for reasons to be discussed in Sec. 1-25, are designed in such a way as to reduce the radiation of heat energy from the cathode. This materially increases the efficiency of the cathode. Several different types of heat-shielded cathodes are illustrated in Fig. 1-4.

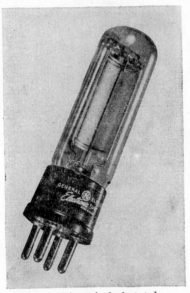

FIG. 1-5. A typical phototube.

1-5. Photoelectric Emission. The energy that is required to release an electron from a metal surface may be supplied by illuminating the surface with light. There are certain restrictions on the nature of the surface and the frequency of the impinging light for such electron emission to take place. That is, electron emission is possible only if the frequency of the impinging light exceeds a certain *threshold* value that depends on the work function E_W of the surface according to the equation

$$f_c = \frac{eE_W}{h} \tag{1-3}$$

where e is the charge of the electron and h is Planck's constant. The corresponding *threshold wavelength* beyond which photoelectric emission cannot take place is given by

$$\lambda_c = \frac{ch}{eE_W} = \frac{12,400 \text{ A}}{E_W} \tag{1-4}$$

where A is the angstrom unit (10^{-8} cm). For response over the entire visible region, 4000 to 8000 A, the work function of the photosensitive surface must be less than 1.54 volts.

The essential elements of a phototube are the photosensitive cathode surface and a collecting electrode contained in a glass envelope that either is evacuated or contains an inert gas at low pressure. A photograph of such a phototube is shown in Fig. 1-5. The number of photoelectrons per square millimeter of area of a photocathode is small, and it is customary to use photocathodes of large area, as shown.

The current characteristics of such phototubes for different collecting potentials between the cathode and the collecting anode, with light intensity as a parameter, are illustrated. Figure 1-6 shows the curves of a

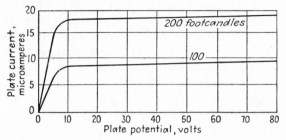

Fig. 1-6. The volt-ampere characteristics of a type PJ-22 vacuum phototube, with light intensity as a parameter.

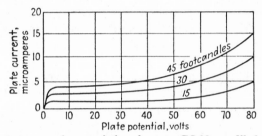

Fig. 1-7. The volt-ampere characteristics of a type PJ-23 gas-filled phototube, with light intensity as a parameter.

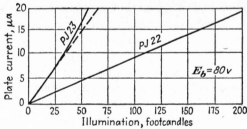

Fig. 1-8. Photocurrent as a function of illumination for a PJ-22 vacuum phototube and a PJ-23 gas-filled cell.

vacuum phototube with light intensity as a parameter. Note that the current reaches near saturation values for very low values of applied potential.

The presence in the glass envelope of an inert gas, such as neon or argon, at low pressure materially alters the volt-ampere curves. A set of characteristic curves for a gas phototube are given in Fig. 1-7. The presence of the gas in a phototube increases the sensitivity of the phototube, the current output for a given light intensity increasing with increased plate potential, whereas the output remains sensibly constant in the vacuum phototube.

A significant comparison of the output from two phototubes, one of the vacuum type and the other of the gas-filled type, other characteristics of the tubes being the same, is contained in Fig. 1-8. Note that the photocurrent for the vacuum phototube is a linear function of the illumination, whereas that for the gas-filled cell shows deviations from the linear at the higher illuminations. However, the greater sensitivity of the gas-filled cell is clearly evident.

1-6. Secondary Emission. It is possible for a particle, either an electron or a positive ion, to strike a metallic surface and transfer all or a part of its kinetic energy in this collision to one or more of the internal electrons. If the energy of the incident particle is sufficiently high, some of the internal electrons may be emitted. Several tubes have been designed which incorporate secondary-emission surfaces as part of the device, and highly sensitive phototubes have such auxiliary elements in them. Frequently the secondary emission that exists is of a deleterious nature. This matter will be discussed in explaining certain features of the characteristics of tetrodes.

1-7. High Field Emission. The presence of a very strong electric field at the surface of a metal will cause electron emission. Ordinarily the field in the average electron tube is too small to induce such electron emission. This process has been suggested to account for the electron emission from a mercury-pool cathode in a mercury rectifier.

1-8. Ionization. The process in which an atom loses an electron is known as *ionization*. The atom that has lost the electron is called a *positive ion*. The process of ionization may occur in several ways.

Electron Bombardment. Consider a free electron, which might have been released from the envelope or from any of the electrodes within the tube by any of the processes discussed above. Suppose that this free electron has acquired enough energy from an applied field so that, upon collision with a neutral atom, it removes an electron. Following this action, two electrons and a positive ion exist. Since there are now two electrons available, both may collide with gas particles and thus induce further ionization. Such a process as this may become cumulative, with consequent large electron release. This process is very important and accounts for the successful operation of gas- and vapor-filled rectifier tubes. It is also the basis of the gas amplification in gas-filled phototubes.

Photoelectric Emission. If the gas is exposed to light of the proper frequency, then this radiant energy may be absorbed by the atom, with resulting electron emission. This process is important in initiating certain discharges.

Positive-ion Bombardment.   The collision between a positive ion and a neutral gas particle may result in electron release, in much the same manner as by electron bombardment.   This process is very inefficient and is usually insignificant in normal gas tubes.

Thermal Emission.   If the temperature of the gas is high enough, some electrons may become dislodged from the gas particles.   However, the gas temperature in electron tubes is generally low, and this process is normally unimportant.

THE HIGH-VACUUM DIODE

1-9. The Potential Distribution between the Electrodes.   Consider a thermionic source situated in a vacuum.   This cathode will emit electrons, most of which have very little energy when they emerge.   Those electrons which first escape will diffuse throughout the space within the envelope.   An equilibrium condition will soon be reached when, because of the mutual repulsion between electrons, the free electrons in the space will prevent any additional electrons from leaving the cathode.   The equilibrium state will be reached when the space charge of the electron cloud produces a strong enough electric field to prevent any subsequent emission.

The inclusion of a collecting plate near the thermionic cathode will allow the collection of electrons from the space charge when this plate is maintained at a positive potential with respect to the cathode; the higher the potential, the higher the current.   Of course, if the thermionic emission is limited, then the maximum current possible is the temperature-saturated value.

In addition to such a simple two-element device, which is the diode, grids may be interposed between the cathode and plate.   If a single grid is interposed, the tube is a triode.   If two grids are present, the tube is a tetrode; three grids yield a pentode, etc.   Details of the characteristics and operation of such devices will be considered in some detail in the following pages.

Consider a simple diode consisting of a plane cathode and a collecting plate, or anode, which is parallel to it.   It is supposed that the cathode can be heated to any desired temperature and that the potential between the cathode and anode may be set at any desired value.   It is desired to examine the potential distribution between the tube elements for various cathode temperatures and fixed anode-cathode applied potential.

Suppose that the temperature of the cathode is high enough to allow some electrons to be emitted.   An electron space-charge cloud will be formed in the envelope.   The density of the electrons and the potential at any point in the interelectrode space are related by Poisson's equation

$$\frac{d^2V}{dx^2} = \frac{\rho}{\epsilon_0} \tag{1-5}$$

where V is the potential in volts, ρ is the magnitude of the electronic-charge density in coulombs per cubic meter, and $\epsilon_0 = 10^{-9}/36\pi$ is the permittivity of space. A study of this expression will yield significant information.

It is supposed that the electrons that are emitted from the cathode have zero initial velocities. Under these conditions, the general character of the results will have the forms illustrated in Fig. 1-9. At the temperature T_1, which is too low for any emission, the potential distribution is a linear function of the distance from the cathode to the anode. This follows from Eq. (1-5), since, for zero-charge density,

$$\frac{d^2V}{dx^2} = 0 \qquad \text{or} \qquad \frac{dV}{dx} = \text{const}$$

This is the equation of a straight line.

At the higher temperature T_2, the charge density ρ is not zero. Clearly, the anode-cathode potential, which is externally controlled, will be independent of the temperature, and all curves must pass through the fixed end points. Suppose that the potential distribution is somewhat as illustrated by the curve marked T_2. All curves must be concave upward, since Eq. (1-5), which may be interpreted as a measure of the curvature, is positive. A positive curvature means that the change in slope dV/dx between two adjacent points must be positive. Moreover, the curvature is greater for larger values of ρ, corresponding to the higher temperatures. It is possible to justify that the maximum current that can be drawn from the diode for a fixed plate potential and any temperature is obtained under the condition of zero electric field at the surface of the cathode. Under these optimum conditions,

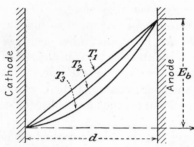

FIG. 1-9. The potential distribution between plane-parallel electrodes, for several values of cathode temperature.

$$\frac{dV}{dx} = 0 \qquad \text{at } x = 0 \tag{1-6}$$

This condition is valid under the assumption of zero initial velocities of emission of the electrons.

1-10. Equations of Space Charge. An explicit relation between the current collected and the potential that is applied between the anode and cathode is possible. In general, the current density is a measure of the rate at which the electrons pass through unit area per unit time in the direction of the field. If v denotes the drift velocity in meters per second, N is the electron density in electrons per cubic meter, and e is the electronic charge in coulombs, then the current density in amperes per square meter is

$$J = Nev = \rho v \tag{1-7}$$

Also, neglecting the initial velocity, the velocity of the electron at any point in the interelectrode space is related to the potential through which it has fallen by the following expression, which is based on the conservation of energy:

$$\tfrac{1}{2}mv^2 = eV \tag{1-8}$$

By combining the foregoing expressions, there results

$$\frac{d^2V}{dx^2} = \frac{JV^{-\frac{1}{2}}}{\epsilon_0(2e/m)^{\frac{1}{2}}} \tag{1-9}$$

This is a differential equation in V as a function of x. The solution of it is given by

$$J = \frac{\epsilon_0}{2.25}\sqrt{2\frac{e}{m}}\frac{V^{\frac{3}{2}}}{x^2} \qquad \text{amp/m}^2 \tag{1-10}$$

For electrons, and in terms of the boundary conditions $V = E_b$ at the anode, there results

$$J = 2.33 \times 10^{-6}\frac{E_b^{\frac{3}{2}}}{d^2} \qquad \text{amp/m}^2 \tag{1-11}$$

This equation is known as the *Langmuir-Childs,* or *three-halves-power, law.* It relates the current density, and so the current, with the applied potential and the geometry of the tube. It shows that the

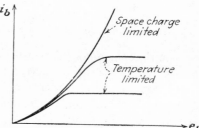

FIG. 1-10. The volt-ampere characteristics of a typical diode.

space-charge current is independent of the temperature and the work function of the cathode. Thus, no matter how many electrons a cathode may be able to supply, the geometry of the tube and the applied potential will determine the maximum current that can be collected by the anode. If the electron supply from the cathode is restricted, the current may be less than the value predicted by Eq. (1-11). The conditions are somewhat as represented graphically in Fig. 1-10.

For the case of a tube that possesses cylindrical symmetry, a similar analysis is possible. The results of such a calculation lead to the following expression for the current,

$$I_b = 14.6 \times 10^{-6} \frac{l}{r_a} \frac{E_b^{3/2}}{\beta^2} \qquad \text{amp} \qquad (1\text{-}12)$$

where l is the active length of the tube and β^2 is a quantity that is determined from the ratio r_a/r_k, the ratio of anode to cathode radius. For ratios r_a/r_k of 8 or more, β^2 may be taken as unity.

Attention is called to the fact that the plate current depends upon the three-halves power of the plate potential both for the plane parallel and also for a diode possessing cylindrical symmetry. This is a general relationship, and it is possible to demonstrate that an expression of the form $I_b = kE_b^{3/2}$ applies for any geometry, provided only that the same restrictions as imposed in the above developments are true. The specific

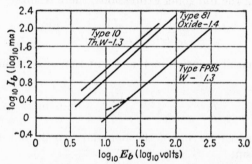

FIG. 1-11. Experimental results to verify the three-halves-power law for tubes with oxide-coated, thoriated-tungsten, and pure-tungsten filaments.

value of the constant k that exists in this expression cannot be analytically determined unless the geometry of the system is specified.

The dependence of the current on the potential for any tube may be determined by plotting the results obtained experimentally on a logarithmic scale. Theoretically one should find, if the expression $I_b = kE_b^{3/2}$ is valid, that

$$\log_{10} I_b = \log_{10} k + \tfrac{3}{2} \log_{10} E_b \qquad (1\text{-}13)$$

The logarithmic plots for three commercial tubes are shown in Fig. 1-11. The type 10 tube is a triode and was converted into a diode by connecting grid and plate together. The other tubes are diodes. It will be observed that the logarithmic plots are straight lines, although the slopes of these lines are all slightly less than the theoretical 1.5.

1-11. Rating of Vacuum Diodes. The current and potential ratings of a diode, i.e., the maximum current that the tube may carry and the maximum potential difference that may be applied between anode and cathode, are influenced by a number of factors.

1. A limit is set to the tube current by the cathode efficiency of the emitter.   Thus, for a given input power to the filament, a maximum current is specified.

2. There is a maximum temperature limit to which the glass envelope of the tube may be safely allowed to rise.   This is the temperature to which the tube was raised during the outgassing process.   This is about 400°C for soft glass and about 600°C for pyrex.   For higher temperatures, the gases adsorbed by the glass walls may be liberated.   Owing to this limitation, glass bulbs are seldom used for vacuum tubes of more than about 1 kw capacity.

3. A very important limitation is set by the temperature to which the anode may rise.   In addition to the fraction of the heat radiated by the cathode that is intercepted by the anode, the anode is also heated by the energy carried by the anode current.   The instantaneous power carried by the anode current and supplied to the anode is given by $e_b i_b$, where e_b is the anode-cathode potential and i_b is the anode current.   The temperature to which the anode rises will depend upon the area of the anode and the material of its construction.

The most common metals used for anodes are nickel and iron for receiving tubes and tantalum, molybdenum, and graphite for transmitting tubes.   The surfaces are often roughened or blackened in order to increase the thermal emissivity.   The anodes of many transmitting tubes may be operated at a cherry-red heat without excessive gas emission. To allow for forced cooling of the anode, cooling coils may be provided, or the tube may be immersed in oil.   The newer type of transmitting tubes are frequently provided with radiator fins for forced-air cooling.   Two different types of transmitting tubes are illustrated in Fig. 1-12.

4. The potential limitation of a high-vacuum diode is also dependent on the type of its construction.   If the filament and anode leads are brought out side by side through the same glass press, some conduction may take place between these leads through the glass.   This effect is particularly marked if the glass is hot, and the resulting electrolysis will cause the glass to deteriorate and eventually to leak.   The highest potential permissible between adjacent leads in glass depends upon the spacing and upon the type of glass but is generally kept below 1,000 volts. Higher-potential tubes are usually provided with filament leads at one end of the glass envelope, with the anode at the other end.

The glass envelope must be long enough so that flashover on the outside of the tube will not occur.   In a diode as a rectifier, no current will exist during the time that the anode is negative with respect to the cathode.   The maximum safe rating of a rectifying diode is known as the *peak-inverse-potential rating*.

Commercial vacuum diodes are made which will rectify current at high potential, up to 200,000 volts. Such units are used with X-ray equipment, with high-potential cable-testing equipment, and with the high-potential equipment for nuclear-physics research. The dimensions and shape of the glass envelope will depend upon the current capacity of the tube and the type of cooling to be used, oil-cooled tubes being generally smaller than air-cooled types.

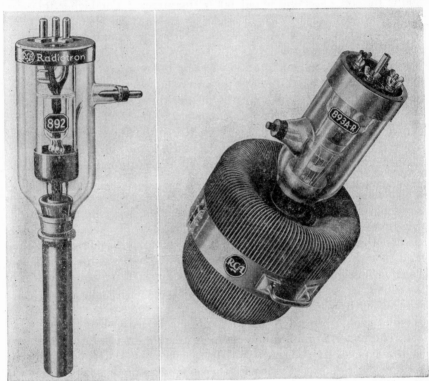

Fig. 1-12. Photographs of two transmitting tubes.   (*RCA Mfg. Co.*)

THE TRIODE

1-12. The Grid. The introduction of a third element between the cathode and plate of the diode by DeForest in 1907 was the start of the extensive developments involving vacuum tubes. This new electrode, called the *control grid*, consists of a wire mesh, or screen, which surrounds the cathode and is situated close to it. The potential applied to the grid in such a tube is usually several volts negative relative to the cathode, whereas the plate is usually maintained several hundred volts positive with respect to the cathode. Clearly, the electric field resulting from the potential of the grid tends to maintain a large space-charge cloud, whereas the field of the plate tends to reduce the space charge. However, owing to its proximity to the cathode, a given potential on the grid will exercise a greater effect on the space charge than the same potential on the plate. This would seem to imply that a proportionality should exist between the relative effectiveness of the grid and plate potentials on the space charge and that the plate current might be represented approximately by the equation

$$i_b = k \left(e_c + \frac{e_b}{\mu} \right)^{3/2} \tag{1-14}$$

where e_b is the plate-cathode potential, e_c is the grid-cathode potential, and the factor μ is a measure of the relative grid-plate potential effectiveness on the tube current. The factor μ is known as the *amplification factor* of the grid.

The validity of Eq. (1-14), which is simply a natural extension of the three-halves-power space-charge equation of the diode, has been verified experimentally for many triodes. No simple, rigorous theoretical derivation of this equation is possible, even for a triode of relatively simple geometry. However, the value of the amplification factor μ can be calculated

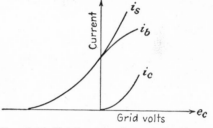

Fig. 1-13. Total space, plate, and grid current in a triode, as a function of grid potential, with fixed plate potential.

with a fair degree of accuracy from equations that are based on electrostatic considerations.

By maintaining the grid at some negative potential with respect to the cathode, it will repel electrons and will, in part, neutralize the attractive field of the anode, thus reducing the anode current. If the grid potential is made positive, the electron stream will increase because of the combined action of both the grid and the plate potentials. But, with a positive potential on the grid, some of the space charge will be attracted to it, and a current in the grid will result. The grid structure must be designed to dissipate the grid power if the grid potential is to be maintained positive; otherwise the grid structure may be seriously damaged. Generally the grid is maintained negative, although positive-grid triodes for power-amplifier applications are available.

The variations of the plate and grid currents with variations of grid potential are illustrated in Fig. 1-13. In this diagram, the plate potential is maintained constant. For sufficiently negative grid potential, cutoff of the plate current occurs. As the grid potential is made less negative, the plate current follows a smooth curve, the variation being expressed analytically by Eq. (1-14).   As the grid potential is made positive, grid current flows, the magnitude of this current increasing rapidly with increasing grid potential.

For positive grid potentials, and with the consequent grid current, Eq. (1-14) no longer represents the plate current, although it does give a good representation of the total space current.   With increasing grid potentials, the grid current increases, and the plate current decreases.

1-13. Triode Parameters.   In view of Eq. (1-14), the dependence of the plate current on the plate and the grid potentials may be represented functionally by the expression

$$i_b = f(e_b, e_c) \tag{1-15}$$

Of course the plate current also depends upon the heater temperature, but as the heater current is usually maintained at rated value (this is

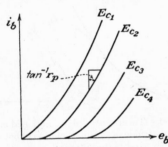

FIG. 1-14. The plate characteristics of a triode.

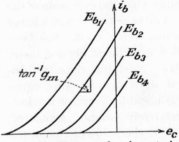

FIG. 1-15. The transfer characteristics of a triode.

such as to provide perhaps five to ten times the normal required current), this term usually does not enter into the functional relationship.   If Eq. (1-15) is plotted on a three-dimensional system of axes, a space diagram representing the function $f(i_b, e_b, e_c) = 0$ is obtained.   The projections of these surfaces on the three coordinate planes give three families of characteristic curves.   These curves are given in Figs. 1-14 to 1-16.

The curves of Fig. 1-14 are known as the *plate characteristics* since they show the variation of the plate current with plate potential for various values of grid bias.   The main effect of making the grid more negative is to shift the curves to the right, without changing the slopes appreciably. This is in accord with what would be expected from consideration of Eq. (1-14).

If the grid potential is made the independent variable, the *mutual*, or *transfer*, characteristics of Fig. 1-15 result. The effect of making the plate potential less positive is to shift the curves to the right, the slopes again remaining substantially unchanged.

The simultaneous variation of both the plate and the grid potentials so that the plate current remains constant gives rise to a third group of characteristics illustrated in Fig. 1-16. These show the relative effects of the plate and grid potentials on the plate current of the tube. But from the discussion of Sec. 1-12 it is the amplification factor that relates these two effects. Consequently, the amplification factor is defined as the ratio of the change in plate potential to the change in grid potential for a constant plate current. Mathematically, μ is given by the relation

$$\mu = -\left(\frac{\partial e_b}{\partial e_c}\right)_{I_b} \tag{1-16}$$

The negative sign takes account of the fact that a decreasing grid potential must accompany an increasing plate potential if the plate current is to remain unchanged.

Consider the variation in the plate current. This is obtained by expanding Eq. (1-15) in a Taylor's expansion. But it is here assumed that the variation is small and that it is adequately represented by the first two terms of the expansion. Subject to this limitation, the expression has the form

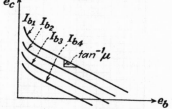

$$\Delta i_b = \left(\frac{\partial i_b}{\partial e_b}\right)_{E_c} \Delta e_b + \left(\frac{\partial i_b}{\partial e_c}\right)_{E_b} \Delta e_c \tag{1-17}$$

FIG. 1-16. The constant-current characteristics of a triode.

This expression indicates simply that changes both in the plate potential Δe_b and in the grid potential Δe_c will cause changes in the plate current.

The quantity $(\partial e_b/\partial i_b)_{E_c}$ expresses the ratio of an increment of plate potential to the corresponding increment of plate current, for constant E_c. This ratio has the units of resistance, is known as the *plate resistance* of the tube, and is designated by the symbol r_p. Clearly, r_p is the slope of the plate characteristics of Fig. 1-14 and has been so indicated there.

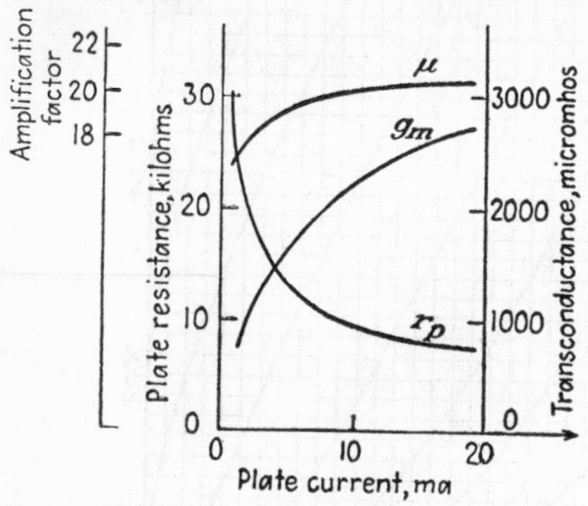

The quantity $(\partial i_b/\partial e_c)_{E_b}$, which gives the ratio of an increment of plate current to the corresponding increment of grid potential for constant plate potential E_b, has units of conductance. It is known

FIG. 1-17. The parameters μ, r_p, and g_m of a 6C5 triode as a function of plate current.

as the *plate-grid transconductance*, or *mutual conductance*, and is designated by the symbol g_m. The mutual conductance g_m is the slope of the mutual-, or transfer-, characteristic curves of Fig. 1-15.

AVERAGE PLATE CHARACTERISTICS

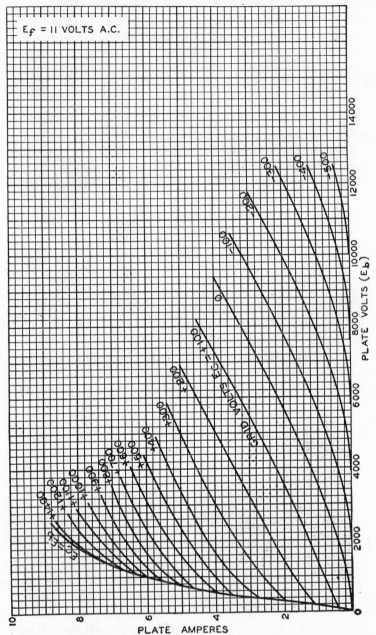

FIG. 1-18. The plate characteristics of a type 889A power triode.

AVERAGE CONSTANT-CURRENT CHARACTERISTICS

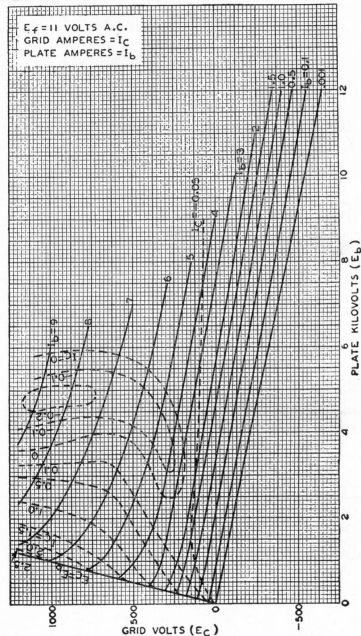

FIG. 1-19. The constant-current characteristics of the power triode of Fig. 1-18.

To summarize, the triode coefficients have the forms

$$\left(\frac{\partial e_b}{\partial i_b}\right)_{E_c} \equiv r_p \qquad \text{plate resistance}$$

$$\left(\frac{\partial i_b}{\partial e_c}\right)_{E_b} \equiv g_m \qquad \text{mutual conductance} \qquad (1\text{-}18)$$

$$-\left(\frac{\partial e_b}{\partial e_c}\right)_{I_b} \equiv \mu \qquad \text{amplification factor}$$

It is easy to show that μ is related to r_p and g_m by the expression

$$\mu = r_p g_m \qquad (1\text{-}19)$$

This is obtained by setting $\Delta i_b = 0$ in Eq. (1-17) and then using the definitions of Eq. (1-18).

The variations of these parameters for a fixed value of plate potential for the 6C5 tube are shown in Fig. 1-17. It is noticed that the plate resistance varies over rather wide limits, being very high at zero plate current, and approaches a constant value at the higher plate currents. The transconductance varies from a very small value at zero plate current and tends toward a constant value at the higher plate currents. The amplification factor remains reasonably constant over a wide range of currents, although it falls off rapidly at the low currents. The corresponding values for other values of E_b may differ numerically, but the general variations will be similar.

High-power triodes are used extensively in transmitters. The grid of such a tube is driven positive with respect to the cathode during part of the cycle, and the current is cut off during part of the cycle. The important characteristics of such tubes are the plate curves and the constant-current curves. The variations over normal operating limits are as illustrated in Figs. 1-18 and 1-19 for a type 889A tube.

MULTIELECTRODE TUBES

1-14. Tetrodes. In the tetrode a fourth electrode is interposed between the grid and the plate. This new electrode is known as the *screen grid*, or *grid* 2, in order to distinguish it from the "control" grid of the triode. Physically, it almost entirely encloses the plate. Because of its design and disposition, the screen grid affords very complete electrostatic shielding between the plate and the control grid. This shielding is such that the grid-plate capacitance is reduced by a factor of about 1,000 or more. However, the screen mesh does not interfere appreciably with the electron flow. The reduction of the grid-plate capacitance is a very important improvement over the triode, and this matter will be considered in some detail in Chap. 2.

Because of the electrostatic shielding of the plate by the screen, the potential of the plate has almost no effect in producing an electric field at the cathode. Since the total space current is determined almost wholly by the field near the cathode surface, the plate exerts little or no effect on the total space charge drawn from the cathode. There is, therefore, a significant difference between the triode and the tetrode. In a triode, the plate performs two distinct functions, that of controlling the total space current, and that of collecting the plate current. In a tetrode, the plate serves only to collect those electrons which have passed through the screen.

The passive character of the plate makes the tetrode a much better potential amplifier than the triode. This follows from the fact that in the triode with a resistance load an increase in load current is accompanied by a decreased plate-cathode potential, which results in a decreased space current. In the tetrode, the decreased plate-cathode potential still exists, but owing to the secondary role of the plate the space current is not materially affected.

The disposition of the cathode and the control grid is nearly the same in both the tetrode and the triode, and therefore the grid-plate transconductance is nearly the same in both tubes. Also, the plate resistance of the tetrode is considerably higher than that of the triode. This follows from the fact that the plate potential has very little effect on the plate current. Thus, with the high plate resistance and with a g_m that is about the same as for the triode, the tetrode amplification factor is very high.

1-15. Tetrode Characteristics. In the tetrode with fixed control-grid and screen-grid potentials, the total space current is practically constant. Hence, that portion of the space current which is not collected by the plate must be collected

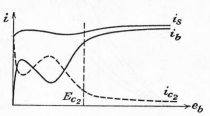

Fig. 1-20. Curves of total space current, plate current, and screen current in a tetrode.

by the screen; where the plate current is large, the screen current must be small, and vice versa. The general character of the results is illustrated in Fig. 1-20.

Although the plate potential does not affect the total space current to a very great extent (although a slight effect is noted in the curve at the lower plate potentials), it does determine the division of the space current between plate and screen. At zero plate potential, few of the electrons have sufficient energy to reach the anode, and the plate current should be small. As the plate potential is increased, a rapid rise occurs in the plate current, with a corresponding reduction of the screen current. When the plate potential is larger than the screen potential, the plate collects almost the entire space current and the screen current approaches zero or a very small value.

An inspection of the curves of Fig. 1-20 shows that the plate current rises very rapidly with increasing plate potential, but this increase is followed by a region of plate-potential variation in which the plate current decreases with increasing plate potential. This region is one of negative plate resistance, since an increasing plate potential is accompanied by a decreasing plate current. The kinks, or folds, in the curves are caused by the emission of electrons from the plate by the process of secondary emission. This results from the impact of the primary electrons with the plate. That is, secondary electrons will be released from the anode, and if this is the electrode with the highest positive potential, the electrons will be collected by the anode, without any noticeable effect. If, however, secondary electrons are liberated from the anode, and if these electrons are collected by some other electrode, then the anode current will decrease, whereas the current to the collecting electrode will increase. It is this latter situation which exists in the tetrode when the plate potential is low and the screen is at a high potential.

When the plate potential is higher than the screen potential, the secondary electrons from the plate are drawn back, without appreciable effect. If under these potential conditions secondary electrons are liberated from the screen, these will be collected by the anode. The corresponding plate current will be greater than that in the absence of secondary emission from the screen.

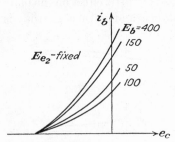

FIG. 1-21. The transfer characteristics of a tetrode, for a fixed screen potential, and with the plate potential as a parameter.

1-16. Transfer Characteristics. Since the plate of a tetrode has no appreciable influence on the space current, it is expected that the cathode, the control grid, and the screen grid should possess characteristics not unlike those of a triode. This is actually the case, as illustrated in Fig. 1-21. These curves show the effect of variations of plate potential on plate current, for fixed E_{c2}. Because of the slight influence of the plate, the transfer curves are bunched together. These curves should be compared with those of the triode in Fig. 1-15, where the transfer curves are widely separated.

The transfer curves become separated for plate potentials below the screen potential, and this is the region of operation which is generally avoided in practice. In fact the transfer characteristic for $E_b = 100$ volts actually falls below that for $E_b = 50$ volts. This anomalous behavior is directly the result of the secondary-emission effects discussed above,

1-17. Tube Parameters. It is expected, on the basis of the foregoing discussion, that the plate current may be expressed as a function of the potential of the various electrodes by an expression of the form

$$i_b = f(e_b, e_{c1}, e_{c2}) \tag{1-20}$$

where e_{c1} is the potential of the first, or control, grid, e_{c2} is the potential of the second, or screen, grid, and e_b is the potential of the plate, all with respect to the cathode. This functional relationship is just a natural extension of that which applies for triodes. In fact, an approximate explicit form of the dependence is possible. This form, which is an extension of Eq. (1-14), may be written as

$$i_b = k \left(e_{c1} + \frac{e_b}{\mu_1} + \frac{e_{c2}}{\mu_2} \right)^{3/2} \tag{1-21}$$

where μ_1 and μ_2 are the control-grid and screen-grid amplification factors, respectively.

The variation in the plate current, second- and higher-order terms in the Taylor expansion being neglected, is given by

$$\Delta i_b = \left(\frac{\partial i_b}{\partial e_b} \right)_{E_{c1},E_{c2}} \Delta e_b + \left(\frac{\partial i_b}{\partial e_{c1}} \right)_{E_b,E_{c2}} \Delta e_{c1} + \left(\frac{\partial i_b}{\partial e_{c2}} \right)_{E_b,E_{c1}} \Delta e_{c2} \tag{1-22}$$

Generally, the screen potential is maintained constant at some appropriate value, and hence $\Delta e_{c2} = 0$. The third term in the expansion may be omitted under these conditions. The partial-differential coefficients appearing in this expression furnish the basis for the definitions of the tube parameters. These are

$$\left(\frac{\partial e_b}{\partial i_b} \right)_{E_{c1},E_{c2}} \equiv r_p \qquad \text{plate resistance}$$

$$\left(\frac{\partial i_b}{\partial e_{c1}} \right)_{E_b,E_{c2}} \equiv g_m \qquad \text{mutual conductance} \tag{1-23}$$

$$-\left(\frac{\partial e_b}{\partial e_{c1}} \right)_{I_b,E_{c2}} \equiv \mu \qquad \text{amplification factor}$$

The two subscripts associated with each term indicate the parameters that are maintained constant during the partial differentiation. It can be shown that here too the relation $\mu = r_p g_m$ is valid. Nominal values for the various parameters that appear in this relationship are $r_p = 10^5$ to 2×10^6 ohms, $g_m = 500$ to $3,000$ μmhos, and $\mu = 100$ to $1,200$.

1-18. Pentodes. Although the insertion of the screen grid between the control grid and the anode in a triode serves to isolate the plate circuit from the grid circuit, the range of operation of the tube is limited owing to the effects of secondary emission. This limitation results from the fact that, if the plate-potential swing is made too large, the instantaneous plate potential may extend into the region of rapidly falling plate current, with a resulting marked distortion in the output.

The kinks, or folds, that appear in the plate-characteristic curves and that limit the range of operation of the tetrode may be removed by inserting a coarse *suppressor*-grid structure between the screen grid and the plate of the tetrode. Tubes that are provided with this extra grid are

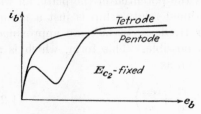

FIG. 1-22. The characteristics of a tube when connected as a tetrode and as a pentode.

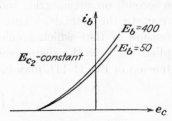

FIG. 1-23. The transfer curves of a pentode for fixed screen potential and with the plate potential as a parameter.

known as *pentodes*. The suppressor grid must be maintained at a lower potential than the instantaneous potential reached by the plate at any time in its potential excursions. Usually the suppressor is connected to the cathode, either externally or internally. Now since both the screen and the anode are positive with respect to the suppressor grid, secondary electrons from either electrode will be returned to the emitting electrode. The main electron stream will not be materially affected by the presence of the suppressor grid. The effects of the insertion of the suppressor grid are shown graphically in Fig. 1-22.

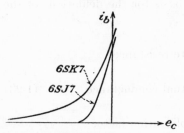

FIG. 1-24. The transfer curves of a 6SJ7 sharp-cutoff pentode and a 6SK7 remote-cutoff pentode.

The pentode has displaced the tetrode in radio-frequency (r-f) potential amplifiers, because it permits a somewhat higher potential amplification at moderate values of plate potential. Likewise it permits a greater plate-potential excursion without distortion. Tetrodes are used extensively in high-power tuned amplifiers.

The transfer curves of a pentode are shown in Fig. 1-23. It is noted that the curves are almost independent of the plate potential.

1-19. Remote-cutoff Tubes. If in a pentode the grid-cathode spacing, the spacing between grid wires, or the diameter of the grid wires is not uniform along the entire length of the control-grid structure, the various portions of the grid will possess different degrees of electrostatic control over the plate current. That is, one portion of the grid may cause electron-flow cutoff, whereas an appreciable current might pass through a more widely spaced section of the grid. As a result, the plate-current control by the grid is considerably less effective than in a conventional pentode. The general character of the results is illustrated in Fig. 1-24. Owing to its construction, a given grid-potential increment results in a plate-current change that is a function of the bias. This means that the mutual conductance is a function of the bias. For this reason, these tubes are called *variable-mu* tubes. They are also known as *remote-cutoff* and *supercontrol* tubes. They have applications in radio receivers and may be used in frequency-modulation (f-m) transmitters. Some applications will be considered in later chapters.

1-20. Hexodes, Heptodes. A number of special-purpose tubes containing more grid elements than the pentode are used extensively. These tubes possess a wide variety of characteristics, depending upon the grids to which fixed potentials are applied and those to which signals might be applied. These tubes are used extensively as converters in superheterodyne receivers and in f-m transmitter and other applications.

1-21. Beam Power Tubes. The suppressor grid is introduced into the pentode in order to extend the range of operation of these tubes beyond that of the tetrode. These tubes are quite satisfactory over wide limits, and the range of operation is limited when the instantaneous plate potential falls to the rapidly falling plate-current region at low potentials. This rapid change in plate current for small changes in plate potential in the region of low plate potential results from the overeffectiveness of the suppressor grid at these low plate potentials.

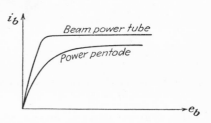

FIG. 1-25. The plate characteristics of a beam power tube and a power pentode.

Because of this, the shape of the suppressor grid in some modern pentodes has been so dimensioned that the effects of secondary emission are just suppressed or only admitted slightly at the low anode potentials. This results in an improved plate characteristic and is manifested by a sharper break in the plate characteristic.

The pentode and tetrode beam power tubes were designed with these considerations specifically in mind, and a plate characteristic is illustrated in Fig. 1-25. It will be noted that the plate current remains independent of plate potential to a lower relative value in the beam power tube than in the power pentode. The essential features of the beam power tube are illustrated in the schematic view of Fig. 1-26. One feature of the design of this tube is that each spiral turn of the screen is aligned with a spiral turn of the control grid. This serves to keep the screen current small and hence leaves the plate current virtually unchanged. Other features are the flattened cathode, the beam-forming side plates (maintained at zero potential), the shape of the plate, the curvature of the grids, and the spacing of the various elements. As a result of these design characteristics, the electrons flow between the grid wires toward the plate in sheets, or beams.

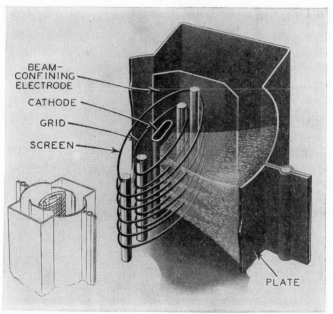

Fig. 1-26. Schematic view of the shapes and arrangements of the electrodes in a beam power tube. (*RCA Mfg. Co.*)

The region between the screen and the plate possesses features which are somewhat analogous to those which exist in the space-charge-limited diode. That is, there is a flow of charge between two electrodes. However, the electrons, when they enter this region do so with an appreciable velocity. For such a case as this, the considerations of Sec. 1-10 would have to be modified to take account of the initial velocity. If this is done, it is found that a potential minimum will exist in the region between the two electrodes. This potential minimum acts as a virtual suppressor grid, and any secondary electrons that are emitted from either the plate or the screen are returned to the emitting electrode.

The actual potential distribution in the screen-plate region will depend on the instantaneous plate potential and the plate current, for a constant screen potential. The resulting variable suppressor action proves to be superior to that possible with a mechanical grid structure, as illustrated.

GAS TUBES

1-22. Electrical Discharge in Gases. There are two important classes of discharge in gases that play roles in electron tubes. One of these is the *glow* discharge, and the second is the *arc* discharge. The glow discharge utilizes a cold cathode and is characterized by a fairly high tube drop and a low current-carrying capacity. The potential drop across the tube over the operating range is fairly constant and independent of the current. The arc discharge is characterized by a low potential drop and a high current capacity. For an arc tube with a thermionic cathode, the temperature-limited cathode emission may be drawn with a tube drop approximately equal to the ionization potential of the gas. For a mercury-pool cathode, extremely high current densities exist (of the order of 5×10^8 amp/m²), with high total currents possible and a tube drop approximately equal to the ionization potential of the mercury atom.

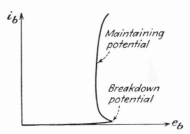

FIG. 1-27. Volt-ampere characteristic of a glow discharge.

Consider a gas tube which consists of a cold cathode and a collecting anode, between which is connected a source of potential through a current-limiting resistance, and an indicating ammeter. The volt-ampere characteristic of such a tube has the form illustrated in Fig. 1-27. This curve shows that breakdown occurs at a potential which is somewhat higher than the maintaining potential but that there is a region where the tube drop remains substantially constant over an appreciable range of currents. Visually, the discharge is characterized by a colored luminous region, the color being a function of the gas present in the tube.

It is desired to explain the mechanism of operation of these tubes. Consider, therefore, that a free electron exists within the tube; such an electron might have been released by ionization due to collision between a gas molecule and a cosmic ray or by photoelectric emission. With the application of the potential between the electrodes, the electron will drift toward the anode. If the field is large enough, the electron may acquire enough energy to ionize a molecule when it collides with it. Now two electrons will be present, the original one and also the electron that has been liberated by the process of ionization, and a positive ion. The two electrons and the positive ion will move in the applied field, the electrons moving toward the anode, and the positive ion toward the cathode. If the field is large enough, the resulting cumulative ionization may continue until *breakdown* occurs. Once breakdown occurs, the potential distribution within the tube is markedly modified, and most of the region of the discharge becomes virtually equipotential or force-free, containing as many positive as negative charges. This is the plasma of the discharge. Almost the entire potential change occurs in the very narrow region near the cathode. Normal values for cathode-fall potential range between about 59 volts (a potassium surface and helium gas) and 350 volts. The presence of a low-work-function coating on the cathode will result in a low cathode fall with any gas. Also, the use of one of the inert gases (helium, neon, argon, etc.) results in a low cathode fall with any cathode material. The cathode fall adjusts itself to such a value that each positive ion, when it falls through this field, will release an electron from the cathode by secondary emission. The positive ion combines with this electron and thus becomes neutralized.

Another feature of a normal glow discharge is that the current density at the cathode remains sensibly constant. For higher currents, a greater portion of the cathode is covered with glow, the area of the glow on the cathode increasing directly with the magnitude of the current. Once the cathode is completely covered with glow, any further current through the tube depends on an excess of secondary emission from the cathode over that required to neutralize the positive ions. This is accompanied by a rising cathode fall. This is the "abnormal" glow and is generally of small practical importance.

The dividing line between an arc and a glow discharge is rather indistinct. The arc discharge allows for the passage of large currents at low potential, the current density at the cathode being high. Nevertheless each discharge has associated with it the cathode fall, the plasma, and the anode fall (which is of minor significance in both types of discharge). The discharges differ in respect to the mechanism by which the electrons are supplied from the cathode. In the glow discharge, as discussed, the electrons are emitted from the cathode by the process of secondary emission resulting from positive-ion bombardment of the cathode. In the arc discharge, the emission of the electrons from the cathode occurs through the operation of a supplementary mechanism other than by positive-ion bombardment. In the thermionic arc, the electrons are supplied by a cathode that is heated to a high temperature, either by the discharge or externally by means of an auxiliary heating circuit. The mechanism for electron release is not fully understood in the arcs that employ a mercury-pool cathode or an arc between metal surfaces. However, in these discharges the primary function of the gas is to supply a sufficient positive-ion density to neutralize the electron space charge. Because of this, the normal potential drop across an arc tube will be of the order of the ionization potential of the gas.

1-23. Glow Tube. A glow tube is a cold-cathode gas-discharge tube which operates in the normal glow-discharge region. The potential drop across the tube over the operating range is fairly constant and independent of the current. When the tube is connected in a circuit, a current-limiting resistor must be used if serious damage to the tube is to be avoided.

One commercial type of tube consists of a central anode wire which is coaxial with a cylindrical cathode, as illustrated in Fig. 1-28. The electrodes are of nickel, the inner surface of the cathode being oxide-coated. The cathode fall is sometimes lowered by sputtering some misch metal (an alloy of cerium, lanthanum, and didymium) on the cathode. The gases that are commonly used are neon, argon, and helium. The tubes containing neon or helium usually contain a small amount of argon. The presence of the argon lowers the starting potential. These tubes are available with normal output potentials of 75, 90, 105, and 150 volts and bear the designations $OA3/VR$-75, $OB3/VR$-90, etc. The normal maximum current is 30 ma. The starting probe that is attached to the cathode, as illustrated in Fig. 1-28, serves to lower the breakdown potential of the tube.

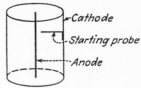

FIG. 1-28. Electrode structure in a VR tube.

FIG. 1-29. Photographs of several low-capacity glow tubes.   (*General Electric Co.*)

Glow lamps are also available for pilot, marker, and test-lamp service. Such tubes are available in several sizes from $\frac{1}{25}$ to 3 watts capacity. Photographs of these are given in Fig. 1-29.

1-24. Cold-cathode Triodes. A cold-cathode triode, or *grid-glow tube*, contains three elements, the cathode, the anode, and a starter, or control, anode. The control electrode is placed close to the cathode. The spacing of the electrodes is such that a discharge takes place from the cathode to the control electrode at a lower potential than is required for a discharge from the cathode to the anode. Once the control gap has been broken down, however, it is possible for the discharge to transfer to the main anode. The cathode-anode potenial that is required for this transfer to occur is a function of the transfer current, the current in the control-electrode–cathode circuit. Such a "transfer," or "transition," characteristic is given in Fig. 1-30.

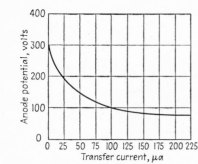

FIG. 1-30. Transfer characteristic of an RCA OA4G cold-cathode triode.

For zero transfer current, which means that the control electrode is not connected in the circuit, the anode potential is equal to the breakdown potential between cathode and anode. It is observed from the curve that the required anode-cathode potential falls rapidly as the transfer current is increased. An increased transfer current indicates the presence of greater ionization. Regardless of the magnitude of the transfer current, however, the anode-cathode potential can never fall below the maintaining voltage for this gap. The transfer characteristic approaches this sustaining potential asymptotically.

1-25. Hot-cathode Gas-filled Diodes. These tubes are thermionic cathode diodes in which there is an inert gas at low pressure or in which mercury vapor is added. In the latter case a few drops of mercury are added to the tube after evacuation. The pressure in the tube is then a function of the mercury-vapor condensation temperature. The relationship between the pressure and the temperature is shown in Fig. 1-31. Under normal operating conditions, the temperature of the tube will be 15 to 20°C above that of the surroundings (ambient temperature).

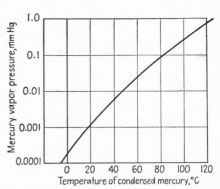

FIG. 1-31. Mercury-vapor pressure as a function of condensation temperature.

As already discussed, the sole function of the gas in these tubes is to provide ions for the neutralization of space charge, thus permitting the current to be obtained at much lower potentials than are necessary in vacuum tubes. If more than saturation current is demanded by the circuit, then gas amplification, resulting from positive-ion bombardment of the cathode, will occur. Under these circumstances the cathode fall increases. The tube drop should not be permitted to exceed the disintegration potential of the cathode (about 22 volts for a mercury diode with either oxide-coated or thoriated-tungsten cathodes); otherwise the cathode may be seriously damaged by the positive-ion bombardment.

Two typical commercial mercury-vapor-filled diodes are illustrated in Fig. 1-32.

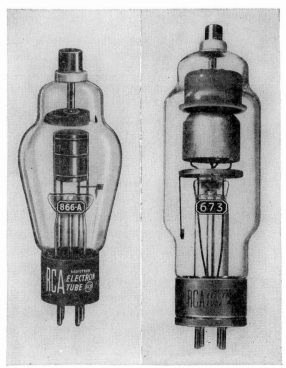

FIG. 1-32. Commercial mercury-vapor diodes of different capacity. (*RCA Mfg. Co.*)

1-26. High-pressure Gas Diodes. Diodes are available which contain argon or a mixture of argon and mercury at a pressure of about 5 cm. The cathodes in such tubes consist of a short, heavy thoriated-tungsten or oxide-coated filament and are located close to heavy graphite anodes. These tubes, which are known as *tungar* or *rectigon* tubes, are used extensively in chargers for storage batteries.

The presence of the fairly high-pressure gas serves a twofold purpose. One is to provide the positive ions for reducing the space charge. The second is to prevent the evaporation of the thorium or the coating from the filament. This second factor is extremely important since the filament is operated at higher than normal temperature in order to provide the large currents from such a simple cathode structure. The high-pressure gas in such a tube imposes a limitation on these tubes, and they are limited to low-potential operation.

1-27. The Thyratron. The thyratron is a three-electrode tube which comprises the cathode, the anode, and a massive grid structure between them. The grid structure is so designed as to provide almost complete electrostatic shielding between the cathode and the anode. In such a tube as this, the initiation of the arc is controlled by controlling the potential of the grid. The grid usually consists of a cylindrical structure which surrounds both the anode and the cathode, a baffle or a series of baffles containing small holes being inserted between the anode and the cathode. The electrode structure of such a tube is illustrated in Fig. 1-33. The shielding by the grid is so complete that the application of a small grid potential before conduction is started is adequate to overcome the field at the cathode resulting from the application of a large anode potential.

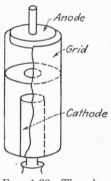

FIG. 1-33. The electrode structure of a negative-control thyratron.

Once the arc has been initiated, the grid loses complete control over the arc. Grid control is reestablished only when the anode potential is reduced to a value less than that necessary to maintain the arc. Once the arc has been extinguished by lowering the plate potential, the grid once more becomes the controlling factor which determines when conduction will again be initiated. That is, if the grid potential is more positive than that necessary for the controlling action to prevail, conduction will take place; if more negative, no conduction will occur. The curve that relates the grid ignition potential with the potential of the anode for conduction just to begin is known as the *critical grid curve*. In fact, a knowledge of this static curve is all that is required to determine completely the behavior of a thyratron in a circuit.

Typical starting-characteristic curves of mercury-vapor thyratrons are given in Fig. 1-34. Two distinct types of characteristics are illustrated, viz., those in which the grid potential must always be positive, and those in which the grid is generally negative, except for very low plate potentials. The physical distinction between these positive and negative control tubes lies essentially in the more complete shielding by the grid in positive control tubes.

In the negative-control tube, where the shielding is far less complete than in the positive-control type, the effect of the plate potential is clearly seen; the higher the plate potential, the more negative must the grid potential be in order to prevent conduction from taking place. For low plate potentials, positive grid potentials must be applied before ionization, and hence conduction, can begin.   If the plate potential is reduced still more, even below the potential necessary for ionization, breakdown can still be obtained by making the grid sufficiently positive.   Now, however, the function of the tube may be destroyed, since the arc may take place between the cathode and the grid, with very little current to the plate.   The thyratron will be converted into a gas diode under these con-

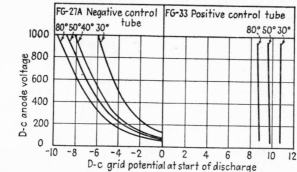

Fig. 1-34. Critical grid characteristics of a positive- and a negative-control thyratron for different temperatures.

ditions, the plate acting as a dummy electrode, the cylindrical grid now serving as the anode.   It is because of this that a large current-limiting resistance is connected in the grid circuit, as it is unwise to draw a large grid current.

In addition to the mercury-vapor- and gas-filled thyratrons of moderate current capacity, small argon-filled low-current-capacity tubes are available.   The shielding between the cathode and the anode is not so complete in these tubes as in the higher-current units.   Also, the critical grid curve is independent of temperature, since the number of gas molecules in the glass envelope remains constant. A typical critical grid curve for an 884 is given in Fig. 1-35.

1-28. Shield-grid Thyratrons.   Before breakdown of the tube occurs, the current to the grid of a thyratron such as the FG-27A is a few tenths of a microampere.   Although this current is entirely negligible for many applications, it will cause trouble in circuits that require very high grid impedances.   This is especially true in circuits that employ phototubes. For this reason, a fourth electrode, or shield grid, has been added to the

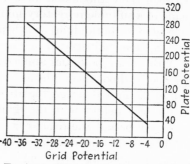

Fig. 1-35. Critical grid characteristic of an 884 argon-filled thyratron.

thyratron. Such a shield-grid thyratron structure is illustrated in Fig. 1-36. The massive cylindrical shield-grid structure encloses the cathode, control grid, and anode. Owing to the shielding, the grid current is reduced to a small fraction of its original value, the preignition current being of the order of 10^{-3} μa.

The critical grid starting characteristics of such a tube are shown in Fig. 1-37. It will be observed that these characteristics are functions of the shield-grid potential.

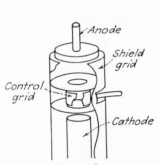

Fig. 1-36. Electrode structure of the FG-98 shield-grid thyratron.

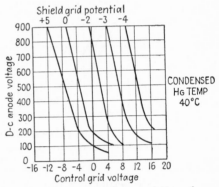

Fig. 1-37. Control characteristics of an FG-98 shield-grid thyratron.

1-29. The Ignitron. The ignitron is a mercury-pool-cathode diode which is provided with a third electrode for initiating the discharge between the cathode and anode. The third electrode, or igniter rod, is made of a suitable refractory material (such as silicon carbide, boron carbide, and carborundum) which projects into the mercury-pool cathode. Such a tube is illustrated in Fig. 1-38.

With an a-c potential applied between the cathode and the anode of the pool-cathode diode, the arc would be extinguished once each alternate half cycle, provided that the arc could be initiated regularly. The application of a potential to the igniter rod at the appropriate point in the cycle will permit the regular ignition of the arc.

There is a fundamental difference between the control action in a thyratron and that of the igniter rod in an ignitron. In thyratrons, the grid prevents the formation of an arc, whereas the igniter initiates the arc. In the former case the electrons already exist in the tube, owing to the presence of an externally heated cathode, but the grid electrostatically prevents the electrons from flowing to the anode until a critical potential is reached. In the ignitron, the tube is in a nonconducting state until the igniter circuit is energized, when conduction is forced.

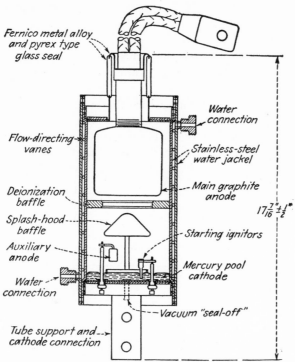

Fernico metal alloy
and pyrex type
glass seal

Flow-directing
vanes

Deionization
baffle

Splash-hood
baffle

Auxiliary
anode

Water
connection

Tube support and
cathode connection

Water
connection

Stainless-steel
water jacket

Main graphite
anode

Starting ignitors

Mercury pool
cathode

Vacuum "seal-off"

$17\frac{7}{16}" \pm \frac{1}{2}"$

FIG. 1-38. Photograph of a water-cooled metal ignitron.   (*General Electric Co.*)

1-30. Tube Ratings—Current, Voltage, Temperature. Gas- and vapor-filled tubes are given average rather than rms current ratings. This rating specifies the maximum current that the tube may carry continuously without excessive heating of any of the parts. The time over which the average is to be taken is also specified by the manufacturer. That the average current is important in such a tube follows from the fact that the instantaneous power to the plate of the tube is given by the product of the instantaneous anode current and the instantaneous tube potential. Since the potential is substantially constant and independent of the tube current, the average power is the product of the tube drop and the average tube current. The tubes are also given peak-current ratings, these ratings specifying the maximum current that the tubes should be permitted to reach in each conducting cycle.

Such tubes are also given peak-inverse-potential ratings. This is the largest safe instantaneous negative potential that may be applied to the tube without the possibility of conduction in the inverse direction arising because of breakdown of the gas in the tube. This potential is also referred to as the *flash-back* potential. The variation of the inverse peak potential with temperature for an 866 diode is shown in Fig. 1-39,

The maximum peak forward potential is a quantity that is significant only for thyratrons. It specifies the largest positive potential that may be applied to the anode before the grid loses its arc-initiating ability. That is, for potentials higher than this, a glow discharge may occur between anode and grid, which will immediately initiate the cathode-anode arc.

The condensed-mercury temperature limits are specified for the safe and efficient operation of mercury-vapor tubes. The range usually extends from about 30 to 80°C. The upper temperature limit is determined by the allowable peak inverse potential. The lower limit is set

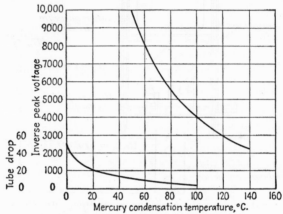

FIG. 1-39. Peak inverse potential and tube drop of an 866 diode as a function of temperature.

by the allowable tube drop, which increases with decreasing temperature and which may cause serious cathode disintegration, as well as a decreased efficiency.

1-31. Deionization and Ionization Times. The ionization time of a tube specifies the time required for conduction to be established once the potentials have been applied. It seldom exceeds 10 μsec and is approximately 0.01 μsec for the 884 thyratron.

The deionization time is a measure of the minimum time that is required after removal of the anode potential before the grid of a thyratron again regains control. It represents the time that is required for the positive ions to diffuse away from the grid and recombine with electrons to form neutral molecules. The deionization time depends on many factors, such as gas pressure, electrode spacing, and exposed areas. For commercial tubes that are operated under rated conditions, it varies between 100 and 1,000 μsec. This is considerably longer than the ionization time and may offer a serious limitation to the use of such tubes in many applications.

CATHODE-RAY TUBES

1-32. Forces on Charged Particles in Electric and Magnetic Fields.
The present section is devoted to a discussion of the operating features
of cathode-ray tubes.   Consequently, the considerations are of limited
scope,* with a detailed study only of those concepts related to the problems which occur in the cathode-ray tube.

Initially, consider a charged particle in an electric field.   The force on
a unit positive charge at any point in an electric field, by definition, is
the electric field intensity $\mathcal{E}$ at that point.   Consequently, the force on
an electron of charge $-e$ in an electric field of intensity $\mathcal{E}$ is given by
$-e\mathcal{E}$, the resulting force being opposite to the direction of the electric
field.   Thus,

$$\mathbf{f} = -e\mathcal{E} \qquad \text{newtons} \qquad (1\text{-}24)$$

where e is in coulombs and $\mathcal{E}$ is in volts per meter.   Boldface type† will
be employed wherever vector quantities (those having both magnitude
and direction) are encountered.

In order to ascertain the path of the electron in an electric field, the
force, given by Eq. (1-24), is related to the mass and acceleration of the
electron by Newton's second law of motion.   Hence

$$\mathbf{f} = -e\mathcal{E} = m\frac{d\mathbf{v}}{dt} \qquad \text{newtons}‡ \qquad (1\text{-}25)$$

where m is in kilograms ($= 9.107 \times 10^{-31}$ kg) and $d\mathbf{v}/dt$ is in meters per
second per second.   The solution of this equation, subject to appropriate
initial conditions, will give the path of the particle under the influence of
the applied electric forces.

To examine the force on a moving charge in a magnetic field, use will
be made of the well-known "motor law."   This law states that the force
on a conductor of length L ms carrying a current of I amps and situated
in a magnetic field of intensity B webers/m² is BIL newtons, provided
that the directions of $\mathbf{I}$ and $\mathbf{B}$ are perpendicular to each other.   Under
these conditions the force is perpendicular to the plane of $\mathbf{I}$ and $\mathbf{B}$ and has
the direction of advance of a right-handed screw which is placed at O
and is rotated from $\mathbf{I}$ to $\mathbf{B}$ (see Fig. 1-40 for the geometry involved).   If
$\mathbf{I}$ and $\mathbf{B}$ are not perpendicular to each other, the force is determined by
the component of $\mathbf{I}$ perpendicular to $\mathbf{B}$.

* For more details see ref. 1.

† Later boldface type will also be used to represent complex numbers. **No diffi-**
culty will ensue, since vectors with complex factors will not occur in this work.

‡ This assumes that the velocity is sufficiently small so that relativistic effects **need**
not be taken into account.

By considering a beam of electrons to make up the current and taking into account the fact that the direction of flow of electrons is opposite to the direction of the conventional current, the force per electron is found to be[1]

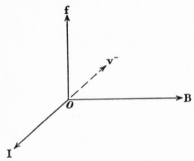

FIG. 1-40. Illustrating the force on a conductor in a magnetic field.

$$\mathbf{f} = e\mathbf{v}^- \times \mathbf{B} \qquad \text{newtons} \qquad (1\text{-}26)$$

The situation is illustrated in Fig. 1-40, where $\mathbf{v}^-$ represents the velocity of the electron.

1-33. Electrostatic Deflection in Cathode-ray Tubes. It is desired to ascertain the deflection of the electron beam in the cathode-ray tube illustrated in Fig. 1-41. It is assumed that a constant potential E_d is applied between the deflecting plates, as shown.

The initial velocity of the electrons v_{0x} results from the accelerating potential E_a. This follows from the fact that, in the cathode-anode region, the electric field intensity $\mathcal{E}$ is produced by the potential E_a. Also the field is directed from anode to cathode, so that the force, accord-

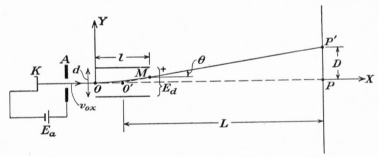

FIG. 1-41. Electrostatic deflection in a cathode-ray tube.

ing to Eq. (1-25), is directed in the positive X direction. Therefore Eq. (1-25) may be written as

$$\frac{-e\mathcal{E}_x}{m} = \frac{dv_x}{dt}$$

Multiply this equation by $dx = v_x\,dt$, and integrate. This leads to

$$\frac{-e}{m}\int_{x_0}^{x}\mathcal{E}_x\,dx = \int_{v_{0x}}^{v}v_x\,dv_x \qquad (1\text{-}27)$$

But the definite integral $\int_{x_0}^{x}\mathcal{E}_x\,dx$ is an expression for the work done by the field in carrying a unit positive charge from point x_0 to x. Also by definition, the potential V of a point x with respect to point x_0 is the work done against the field in taking a unit positive charge from x_0 to x, or

$$V \equiv - \int_{x_0}^{x} \mathcal{E}_x \, dx \qquad \text{volts} \tag{1-28}$$

Hence Eq. (1-27) integrates to

$$eV = \frac{1}{2}m(v_x^2 - v_{0x}^2) \qquad \text{joules} \tag{1-29}$$

This expression shows that the kinetic energy acquired by an electron in falling through a potential difference V is independent of the form of the variation of the field between the points x_0 and x.

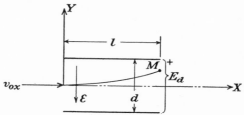

FIG. 1-42. Two-dimensional motion in a uniform electric field.

If the initial velocity of the electrons from the cathode is assumed to be zero, then Eq. (1-29) reduces to

$$eV = \frac{1}{2}mv_x^2$$

from which it follows that

$$v_x = \sqrt{\frac{2eV}{m}} \qquad \text{m/sec} \tag{1-30}$$

and for the electron this becomes

$$v = 5.93 \times 10^5 V^{1/2} \qquad \text{m/sec} \tag{1-31}$$

Now consider the region between the deflecting plates.   The situation is illustrated in Fig. 1-42.   The motion of the electron is to be investigated, subject to the initial conditions

$$\left. \begin{array}{ll} v_x = v_{0x} & x = 0 \\ v_y = 0 & y = 0 \\ v_z = 0 & z = 0 \end{array} \right\} \text{ when } t = 0$$

Since there is no force in the Z direction, the acceleration in that direction is zero.   Hence the component of velocity in the Z direction is unchanged by the field.   But since the initial velocity in this direction is assumed to be zero, it will remain zero.   The motion then takes place entirely in a plane, the plane of the paper in this case.

From similar reasoning, the velocity along the X axis remains constant and equal to v_{0x}, since the acceleration along X is zero.   Thus

$$v_x = v_{0x}$$

from which, by integration, subject to the appropriate initial condition,

$$x = v_{0x}t \qquad (1\text{-}32)$$

The velocity in the Y direction will change, because of the electric field in this direction.   Subject to the specified initial conditions, the force equation in the Y direction yields, for negligible field fringing,

$$v_y = a_y t \qquad (1\text{-}33)$$

Also,

$$y = \tfrac{1}{2} a_y t^2$$

where

$$a_y = -\frac{e\mathcal{E}_y}{m} = \frac{eE_d}{md} \qquad (1\text{-}34)$$

The path of the particle with respect to the point O is determined by combining Eqs. (1-32) and (1-33), the variable t being eliminated.   This leads to

$$y = \frac{1}{2}\frac{a_y}{v_{0x}^2}\, x^2 \qquad (1\text{-}35)$$

This expression shows that the path between the deflecting plates is a parabola.

Now return to considerations of Fig. 1-41.   When the particle leaves the point M, it will travel in a straight line toward the screen, since the region from M to the screen is assumed to be field-free.   The straight-line path is tangent to the parabola at the point M.   The slope of the line at point M is obtained from Eq. (1-35) and is

$$\tan\theta = \frac{dy}{dx}\bigg|_{x=l} = \frac{a_y l}{v_{0x}^2}$$

From the geometry of the figure, the straight-line path MP' is represented by the expression

$$y = \frac{a_y l}{v_{0x}^2}\left(x - \frac{l}{2}\right) \qquad (1\text{-}36)$$

since, at point M, $x = l$ and $y = \tfrac{1}{2}a_y l^2/v_{0x}^2$.

Note that if $y = 0$ in the above expression, $x = l/2$.   This indicates that when the straight-line path MP' is projected backward, it will intersect the tube axis at the point O', the center point of the plates.   This permits one to consider O' as a virtual cathode, and, regardless of the potentials E_d and E_a, the electrons appear to emerge from this point and travel in a straight-line path to the screen.

At the point P' on the screen, $y = D$, and $x = L + l/2$. Equation (1-36) becomes

$$D = \frac{a_y l L}{v_{0x}^2}$$

By inserting the known values of a_y and v_{0x}, this becomes

$$D = \frac{l L E_d}{2 d E_a} \tag{1-37}$$

This shows that the deflection on the screen of a cathode-ray tube is directly proportional to the deflecting potential E_d and varies inversely with the accelerating potential.

A number of idealizations have been made in the foregoing development, such as neglect of initial velocities of the electrons, neglect of the effects of fringing of the electric field between the deflecting plates, and the use of parallel deflecting plates. Owing to these, a considerable correction may be necessary in the deflection given by Eq. (1-37). However, the expression does give the proper dependence on the various parameters.

1-34. The Intensifier Tube. According to Eq. (1-37), the deflection of the cathode-ray beam for a given deflecting potential varies inversely

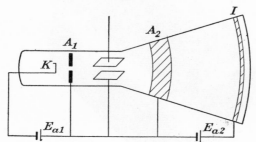

Fig. 1-43. A cathode-ray tube with an intensifier band.

with the accelerating potential. Consequently, greater sensitivity exists for smaller values of E_a. This would seem to indicate the desirability of using low values of accelerating potential. However, the smaller values of E_a cause a decreased luminosity of the spot on the screen, because the luminosity depends on the energy carried by the electron beam. As a result, a compromise must be reached between luminosity and sensitivity in cathode-ray tube design.

The inclusion of an additional electrode, called the *intensifier*, or *post-accelerating*, electrode, near the screen permits a high sensitivity and also a high luminosity. The general appearance of such a tube is shown in Fig. 1-43. The intensifier band is a conducting ring on the inner surface of the glass envelope near the screen. With such a tube, the accelerat-

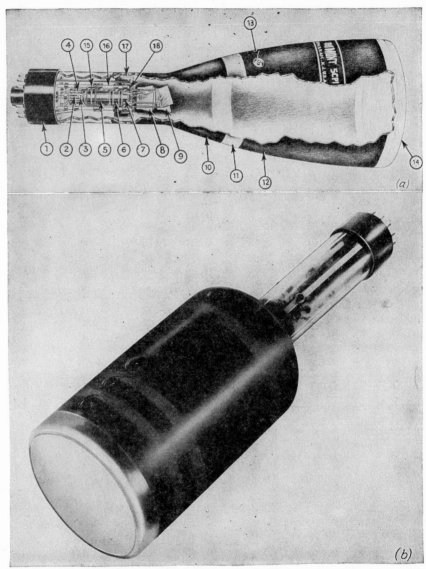

FIG. 1-44. (a) A modern cathode-ray tube. 1, Base; 2, heater; 3, cathode; 4, control grid G; 5, preaccelerating electrode (connected internally to A_2); 6, focusing electrode A_1; 7, accelerating electrode A_2; 8, deflection-plate pair D_3D_4; 9, deflection-plate pair D_1D_2; 10, conductive coating (connected internally to A_2); 11, intensifier gap; 12, intensifier electrode A_3; 13, A_3 terminal; 14, fluorescent screen; 15, getter; 16, ceramic gun supports; 17, mount support spider; 18, deflection-plate structure support. (b) A type 5RP multiband-intensifier cathode-ray tube. (A. B. Du Mont Laboratories, Inc.)

ing potential applied to the first anode A_1 is reduced so as to provide a high sensitivity. The second anode A_2 is maintained at the first-anode potential, as indicated in the figure, so that the deflection in the region of the deflecting plates is controlled by the deflecting potential E_d. After deflection, the electrons are given an additional energy through the use of the intensifier potential E_{a2}. As usually operated, the potential between A_2 and $I(E_{a2})$ is approximately equal to the accelerating potential E_{a1}. This provides full brilliance with a sensitivity almost twice that of a tube of the same characteristics which does not have the intensifier band.

If the ratio of intensifier to accelerating potential is much greater than about 2, it is necessary, in order to reduce the distortions that are introduced by the nonaxial components of electric field caused by the intensifier, to change the tube shape and divide the postaccelerating potential among several intensifier bands. Figure 1-44a is a photograph of a relatively low-potential cathode-ray tube, which includes a single intensifier band. Figure 1-44b is the photograph of a multiband intensifier tube.

1-35. Magnetic Deflection in Cathode-ray Tubes. The essential elements of a magnetically deflected cathode-ray tube are illustrated in

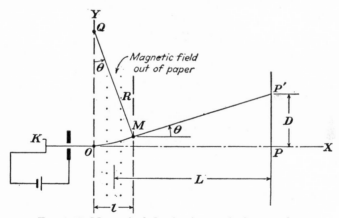

Fig. 1-45. Magnetic deflection in a cathode-ray tube.

Fig. 1-45. As indicated, the constant magnetic field extends over a limited region of the tube and is assumed here to be pointing out of the paper. An application of the principles of Sec. 1-32 will show that the beam is deflected upward, as shown. If the field is uniform, the electron experiences a force of magnitude evB.

In this case, as for the electrostatic tube, the cathode and first anode supply a beam of electrons which enter the region of the magnetic field at the point O with an initial velocity v_{0x}. When the electrons enter the region of magnetic field, a force acts on them. However, the force is perpendicular to v, and so to the motion at every instant. As a result, no work is done on the electrons, and the kinetic energy is not changed. This means that the speed remains unchanged during the electron path in the constant magnetic field. This type of force results in a circular path with constant speed.

To find the radius of the circular path, use is made of the fact that a particle moving in a circular path with constant speed v has an acceleration toward the center of the circle of magnitude v^2/R, where R is the radius of the path. Then

$$\frac{mv^2}{R} = evB$$

from which

$$R = \frac{mv}{eB} \qquad \text{meters} \qquad (1\text{-}38)$$

The corresponding angular velocity is

$$\omega = \frac{v}{R} = \frac{eB}{m} \qquad \text{rad/sec} \qquad (1\text{-}39)$$

This expression shows that the angular velocity is independent of the radius or the speed. This means that faster-moving particles will traverse larger circles in the same time that a slower particle traverses a smaller circle.

On the basis of the foregoing, the path OM in Fig. 1-45 will be a segment of a circle whose center is at Q. The speed of the particle remains constant at its entering value

$$v = v_{0x} = \sqrt{\frac{2eE_a}{m}} \qquad \text{m/sec} \qquad (1\text{-}40)$$

The angle θ is given approximately by

$$\theta \doteq \frac{l}{R} \qquad (1\text{-}41)$$

Also, in most practical cases L is much larger than l, whence little error is made in assuming that the straight line MP' when projected backward will pass through the center O' of the region of the magnetic field. Then

$$D \doteq L \tan \theta \qquad (1\text{-}42)$$

For the conditions chosen, θ is assumed small, thereby permitting the approximation $\tan \theta = \theta$. Combining this result with Eqs. (1-40) to (1-42), there results

$$D = L\theta = \frac{lL}{R} = \frac{lLeB}{mv} = \frac{lLB}{\sqrt{E_a}} \sqrt{\frac{e}{2m}} \qquad \text{meters} \qquad (1\text{-}43)$$

This shows that the deflection on the screen of the cathode-ray tube is directly proportional to the deflecting magnetic field and inversely proportional to the square root of the anode potential. A typical cathode-ray tube with magnetic focusing and deflection is illustrated in Fig. 1-46.

1-36. Comparison of Electric and Magnetic Tubes. Electrostatic tubes are used in practically all oscilloscope applications over a wide frequency range. The upper frequency limit is determined by the capacitance of the leads and deflecting plates. For the higher frequencies, the

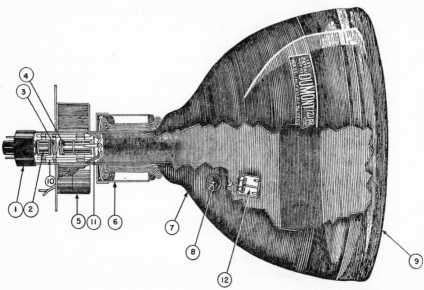

Fig. 1-46. Typical cathode-ray tube with magnetic focusing and deflection. 1, Base; 2, control electrode G_1; 3, screen grid G_2; 4, accelerating electrode A; 5, focusing coil; 6, deflection yoke; 7, anode conductive coating; 8, anode terminal; 9, fluorescent screen; 10, ceramic gun support; 11, mount support spider; 12, getter. (*A. B. Du Mont Laboratories, Inc.*)

deflecting plates are brought out directly through the neck of the glass bulb to coaxial connectors. Owing to their operation, little power is required for deflection, except possibly at the very high sweep speeds. As a result, the sweep and deflection circuit amplifiers are relatively simple.

Owing to the inductance of the deflecting coil, magnetic tubes have a relatively small pass band (about 10 kc). Also, since the sweep speed is controlled by the current in the deflecting yoke, the coil current is critically dependent upon the frequency of the applied potential. For this reason, magnetic deflection is limited essentially to constant-frequency

service, such as that found in television or radar. In these applications
the signal is applied to the grid or cathode to give an intensity-modulated
beam rather than a deflection-type presentation (referred to in radar
applications as an A scope).

Magnetic focusing is generally used with magnetic deflection, since the
focusing possible with a magnetic tube is usually better than with an
electrostatic focusing system. The magnetically deflected, magnetically
focused tube is very desirable, as it provides a high-intensity beam with
a minimum tube length and a minimum distortion of the spot due to the
deflection of the beam. In addition, the magnetic tube is less complicated than the electrostatic type, and the production costs are lower.
Also, from Eq. (1-43), the deflection per unit applied field intensity varies
inversely as the square root of the accelerating potential, whence the
increase in accelerating potential, so as to provide a high-intensity spot,
does not require that the deflecting field, for a given deflection, be
increased proportionately.

REFERENCE

1. For more details, see:
   Millman, J., and S. Seely, "Electronics," 2d ed., McGraw-Hill Book Company, Inc., New York, 1951.

PROBLEMS

1-1. A tungsten filament, 0.0085 in. diameter, $3^{11}\!/_{16}$ in. long, is operated at
2650°K. What is the temperature-limited current? If the temperature is
increased by 50°K, by what percentage does the emission current increase?

1-2. The filament of an FP-400 tungsten-filament tube is 1.25 in. long and
0.005 in. in diameter. If the total emission current is 30 ma, at what temperature
is the filament operating?

1-3. A simple inverted-V oxide-coated cathode is made of tungsten ribbon
0.125 by 0.020 in. and is 1.4 in. long. It is maintained at a temperature of
1100°K. What is the thermionic-emission current?

1-4. An oxide-coated emitter is operating at 1100°K. Calculate the relative
thermionic-emission current if b_0 has the value 12,000; the value 11,000.

1-5. At what temperature will a thoriated-tungsten filament give as much
current as a tungsten filament of the same dimensions which is maintained at
2650°K?

1-6. At what temperature will an oxide-coated cathode give the same emission
as a thoriated-tungsten filament of the same physical dimensions which is maintained at 1750°K?

1-7. Monochromatic light of wavelength 5893 A falls on the following surfaces:
a. Cesium, with a work function 1.8 volts.
b. Platinum, with a work function 5.3 volts.
Is photoelectric emission possible in both cases? Explain.

1-8. A PJ-22 vacuum photocell is to be used to sound an alarm when the light
at a given region of a room falls below 40 ft-c or increases above 120 ft-c. What
are the corresponding photocurrents? A collecting potential of 45 volts is used.

1-9. Plot i_b vs. e_b of the 6H6 diode (see Appendix B) on log paper. From this plot, determine the quantities k and n in the expression $i_b = ke_b^n$.

1-10. The anode current in a type 5U4G diode with 54 volts applied between the plate and cathode is 200 ma. What is the required potential for a current of 100 ma? The tube operates under space-charge conditions.

1-11. Suppose that the FP-400 tube is operating under rated filament power input (see Prob. 1-2). The operating temperature is 2700°K, and the anode diameter is 0.50 in.

a. Calculate the saturation current.

b. At what potential will the current become temperature-saturated?

1-12. Plot i_b vs. $e_b + \mu e_c$ on log paper of the 6J5 triode (see Appendix B). From this curve, find the quantities k and n in the expression $i_b = k(e_b + \mu e_c)^n$.

1-13. The 6J5 triode is operated with $E_b = 135$ volts. Determine and plot curves of μ, g_m, and r_p as a function of e_c.

1-14. The rating of a certain triode is given by the expression

$$i_b = 130 \times 10^{-6}(e_c + 0.125e_b)^{1.58}$$

With $E_c = -20$ volts, $E_b = 350$ volts, find I_b, r_p, g_m, μ.

1-15. The plate and grid characteristics of a type 851 power triode are given in Appendix B. Plot $i_s = i_b + i_c$ vs. $e_b + \mu e_c$ on log paper, and find the quantities k and n in the expression $i_s = k(e_b + \mu e_c)^n$.

1-16. The current in a 6J5 triode for which $\mu = 20$ and which is operating with $E_c = -8$ volts, $E_b = 250$ volts is 8.7 ma. Estimate the current when $E_b = 200$ volts and $E_c = -6$ volts.

1-17. A 6J5 triode for which $\mu = 20$ is operating with $E_b = 250$ volts. What grid potential is required to reduce the current to zero?

1-18. Evaluate the value of μ, g_m, and r_p of the 6SJ7 pentode for $E_c = -3$ volts, $E_{cc2} = 100$ volts, $E_b = 150$ volts.

1-19. Evaluate the values of μ, g_m, r_p, of the 6SK7 supercontrol pentode for $E_{cc2} = 100$ volts, $E_b = 250$ volts, with $E_c = -1$ volts; with $E_c = -10$ volts.

1-20. Plot a curve of g_m vs. E_{c1} of a 6SK7 with $E_{cc2} = 100$ volts, $E_b = 250$ volts.

1-21. Use the plate characteristics of the 6SJ7 and the 6SK7 pentodes to construct mutual characteristics on the same sheet, with $E_b = 200$ volts for each tube. Determine the maximum and minimum values of g_m for each tube in the range of your sketch.

1-22. Plot a curve of g_m vs. E_{c3} of a 6L7 with $E_{cc1} = -6$ volts, $E_{cc2} = 150$ volts.

1-23. Refer to Sec. 1-15 for a discussion of secondary emission caused by electron impact. What happens to the secondary electrons that are produced by the impact of the primary current on the anode in a diode? In a triode?

1-24. The mercury-condensation temperature in a General Electric type FG-57A thyratron is 40°C. If the volume of the tube is 300 cm³, calculate the mass of the mercury vapor in the tube.

1-25. *a.* An OA4G cold-cathode triode is used in the circuit shown, with

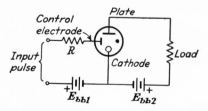

E_{bb1} = 80 volts, E_{bb2} = 120 volts. Determine the largest value of R for which the current will transfer to the main anode, for no input pulse.

b. Determine the value of the load resistance to limit the load current to the rated maximum of 25 ma.

1-26. A VR-105 regulator tube is incorporated in the circuit shown to maintain a constant output potential. The supply potential remains constant at 250 volts, but the load fluctuates between 40 and 60 ma. Find the value of R so that the

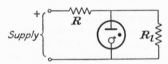

load potential is steady at 105 volts. Assume that the normal operating range of the tube is 5 to 40 ma.

1-27. Suppose that the plate supply potential to a circuit containing a thyratron is sinusoidal. If the rms value of the potential is 220 volts, draw a sketch showing the supply potential and the corresponding critical grid curve for (*a*) a negative-control tube, (*b*) a positive-control tube.

1-28. An electron starts from rest at the negative plate of a plane-parallel capacitor. The potential across the plates is 1,500 volts, and the separation of the plates is 2 cm.

a. How long does it take for the electron to reach a speed of 10^7 m/sec?

b. How far does the electron travel before reaching this speed?

c. Through what potential does the electron fall in acquiring this speed?

1-29. The axial length of the deflecting plates of a cathode-ray tube is 2.5 cm. The accelerating potential is 2,000 volts. A sinusoidal potential is applied to the deflecting plates.

a. What is the maximum frequency of this deflection potential, if the electrons are not to remain in the region between the plates for more than one-half cycle?

b. If the frequency of the deflecting potential is 1,000 cps, for what fraction of the cycle is the electron between the plates?

1-30. A cathode-ray tube that is provided with a postaccelerating anode has the following dimensions: l = 2.4 cm, L = 34.8 cm, d = 0.5 cm. The distance from the center of the plates to anode A_2 is 5.0 cm, the width of band A_2 is 8.0 cm, and the distance from the screen to the intensifier ring is 1.6 cm.

a. Calculate the deflection on the screen when E_{a1} = 2,200 volts, E_d = 200 volts, and E_{a2} = 0 volts.

b. Suppose that E_{a1} = E_{a2} = 1,100 volts. What is the new deflection?

1-31. *a.* Suppose that the deflection of the cathode-ray tube of Prob. 1-30 is produced by a uniform magnetic field acting over the distance l. If the deflection on the screen under conditions of E_{a2} = 0 is 8.0 cm, what is the strength of the magnetic field.

b. If the deflection is produced by a transverse magnetic field acting over the entire length of the cathode-ray tube, what is the magnetic-field intensity?

CHAPTER 2

VACUUM TRIODES AS CIRCUIT ELEMENTS

2-1. Introduction. The analysis of the behavior of a vacuum-tube circuit may be accomplished by two different methods, both of which are to be examined in some detail. In one method, use is made of the static characteristics of the tube. The second method achieves two forms. In one, the tube is replaced by an equivalent potential source and a series resistance. The source potential depends on the amplitude of the input signal, the internal resistance depending on the tube that is used. In the other form, the tube is replaced by an equivalent current source and a shunting conductance. The magnitude of the source current depends on the amplitude of the input signal, the shunting conductance depending on the tube that is used.

Although the second methods assume that the tube characteristics are linear, the ultimate analyses allow a very clear insight into the operation of the circuit. Because of this, the equivalent-circuit methods of analysis are usually considerably more important than the method involving the tube characteristics. Moreover, it is possible to estimate the inaccuracies in the method, when large signal operation is involved. Actually, the form of analysis is dictated in large measure by the bias of the tube, the signal amplitudes, and the characteristics of the load. It must be noted that the equivalent-circuit techniques provide no means for establishing d-c bias and current levels, and direct recourse to the static characteristics is necessary for this purpose.

An introduction of the methods will be made in terms of the operation of the triode, but these will later be extended to the operation of other types of tube.

2-2. Symbols and Terminology. The simple triode amplifier is illustrated in Fig. 2-1. Before proceeding with the analysis, it is necessary to discuss the meaning of the symbols and the general terminology of vacuum-tube circuits.

The input circuit of the amplifier usually refers to all the elements of the circuit that exist between the grid and the cathode terminals of the tube. Similarly, the output, or plate, circuit usually refers to the elements that are connected between the cathode and the plate terminals

49

of the tube. In the circuit illustrated, the input circuit comprises the input potential source e_1, the grid resistor R_g, and the bias battery E_{cc}. The plate circuit consists of the load resistor R_l and the plate-supply battery E_{bb}. In many applications, the input signal e_1 is a sinusoidally varying potential, although the waveshape may be nonsinusoidal, and is frequently very carefully chosen for a particular application.

A variety of potentials, both d-c and varying, are involved simultane-

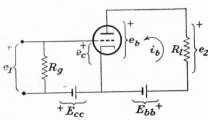

FIG. 2-1. The basic circuit of a triode amplifier.

ously in a vacuum-tube circuit, making it necessary that a precise method of labeling such sources be established. In what follows, lowercase letters will be used to designate instantaneous values, and capital letters will denote either d-c or rms values of sinus-oids. The subscripts c and g will refer to the grid circuit, and the subscripts b and p will refer to the plate circuit. Examples of the nota-tion follow:

E_{cc} = d-c grid, or C bias

E_{bb} = d-c plate supply, or B supply

E_1 = rms value of a-c input excitation potential if this excitation is sinusoidal

E_2 = rms value of a-c output potential for a sinusoidal output

e_1 = instantaneous input signal; measured with respect to the input terminals

e_c = instantaneous signal that appears between grid and cathode of tube

e_g = instantaneous-signal component that appears between grid and cathode of tube

e_2 = instantaneous signal that appears across output element of circuit

e_b = instantaneous potential between plate and cathode of tube

i_p = instantaneous-signal component of plate current; positive in direction from cathode to plate through load

i_b = instantaneous total plate current; positive in direction from cathode to plate through load

I_b = average or d-c current in plate circuit

E_b = average or d-c potential from plate to cathode

Figure 2-1 illustrates the reference positive-potential polarities and the reference direction of current. These reference conditions are an essen-tial part of the diagram.

As a specific illustration of the notation, suppose that the input signal potential to the amplifier of Fig. 2-1 is

$$e_1 = e_g = \sqrt{2}\, E_g \sin \omega t$$

Then the instantaneous grid-cathode potential is

$$e_c = E_{cc} + \sqrt{2}\, E_g \sin \omega t$$

Circuits will be discussed in which no such simple relation between grid driving signal and grid-cathode potential exists, owing to an involved interconnection of circuit elements among the tube elements.

2-3. Graphical Analysis. Refer to Fig. 2-1, and suppose that the grid input signal $e_1 = 0$. Owing to the d-c sources E_{cc} and E_{bb}, it will be supposed that there is a current in the plate circuit. This is true only if the plate supply E_{bb} and the grid supply E_{cc} are properly chosen. The value of this current may be found graphically. In fact, it is essential that a graphical solution be used. This follows from the fact that the plate circuit of Fig. 2-1 yields the relation

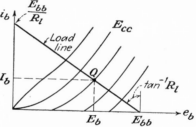

FIG. 2-2. The operating point Q is located at the intersection of the load line and the plate characteristic for $e_c = E_{cc}$.

$$e_b = E_{bb} - i_b R_l \qquad (2\text{-}1)$$

However, this one equation is not sufficient to determine the current corresponding to the potential E_{bb}, since there are two unknown quantities in the expression, e_b and i_b.

A second relation between e_b and i_b is given by the plate characteristics of the triode. The simultaneous solution of Eq. (2-1) and the plate characteristics will yield the desired current. This is accomplished by drawing Eq. (2-1) on the plate characteristics, in the manner illustrated in Fig. 2-2. The line that passes through the points

$$
\begin{aligned}
i_b &= 0 & e_b &= E_{bb} \\
i_b &= \frac{E_{bb}}{R_l} & e_b &= 0
\end{aligned}
\qquad (2\text{-}2)
$$

is known as the *load line*. It is obviously independent of the tube characteristics, for it depends only upon elements external to the tube. The intersection of this line with the curve for $e_c = E_{cc}$ is called the *operating*, or *quiescent*, point Q. The grid-bias supply E_{cc} is usually such as to maintain the grid negative relative to the cathode. The Q current in the external circuit is I_b, and the corresponding plate-cathode potential is E_b.

Suppose that the grid-cathode potential is

$$e_c = E_{cc} + \sqrt{2}\, E_g \sin \omega t$$

The maximum and minimum values of e_c will be $E_{cc} + \sqrt{2}\, E_g$ and

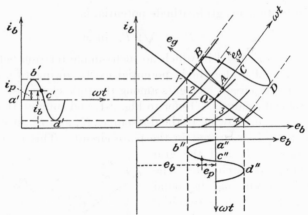

Fig. 2-3. The output current and potential waveforms for a given input grid signal.

$E_{cc} - \sqrt{2}\, E_g$, respectively. The plate current and the plate potential will vary about the values of I_b and E_b. The graphical construction of Fig. 2-3 shows the details of the variations. The values of e_b and i_b for any given value of e_c are obtained from the intersection of the load line and the i_b-e_b curve for the specified e_c. The points a', b', c', etc., of the output current and the points a'', b'', c'', etc., of the output-potential wave correspond, respectively, to the points A, B, C, etc., of the input grid-signal waveform.

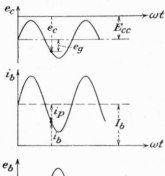

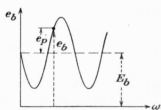

Fig. 2-4. The grid input waveshape and the corresponding output current and potential waveshapes.

It is instructive to show the several waveshapes in their proper phase relation. This is done in Fig. 2-4. It should be noted in particular that the variations about the quiescent values have been labeled. The quantities so labeled are

$$e_g = e_c - E_{cc}$$
$$e_p = e_b - E_b \qquad (2\text{-}3)$$
$$i_p = i_b - I_b$$

These quantities give a measure of the amplification property of the amplifier, as it is a direct measure of the a-c output variations for a given a-c input variation.

The curves of Fig. 2-4 indicate the following very significant results: If the current i_p is sinusoidal, then i_p and e_p are 180 deg out of phase with each other. Also, the grid driving potential e_g and the plate current i_p are in phase with each other. This simply states that, when a positive signal is applied to the grid, the tube current increases. Moreover, with an increased current in the plate circuit, the potential of the plate falls.

A curve of the intersection of the load line with the static-characteristic curves, which is a measure of the current i_b as a function of e_c for the specified E_{bb} and load R_l, is important. It is known as the "dynamic" characteristic of the tube circuit and yields directly the output current for a given input signal. The construction is directly related to the construction of Fig. 2-3 and is given in Fig. 2-5. The corresponding points on both curves are similarly marked.

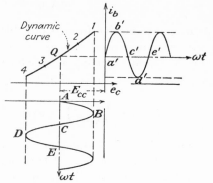

2-4. Potential-source Equivalent Representation of a Triode. In most electron-tube problems, one is interested in the "a-c response" of the tube, rather than in the total

Fig. 2-5. The dynamic curve and its use in determining the output waveshape for a given input signal.

instantaneous variation of the potentials and current. That is, the values of i_p and e_p for a given e_g are ordinarily desired. It is possible to deduce this information directly from the static characteristics of the tube, as discussed in Sec. 2-3. Of course, if the potential variations are small, the accuracy of the results will be poor, as small changes cannot be read with any degree of accuracy from the curves. Moreover, the process may become quite tedious to perform, particularly for a reactive load since the load curve is no longer a straight line.

For small variations in the input potential, the tube parameters μ, r_p, and g_m will remain substantially constant over the operating range. Under such conditions, it will be shown that the graphical solution may be replaced by an analytic one. Actually, the equivalent analytical solution depends on the constancy of the tube parameters, rather than on the magnitude of the signals involved. The analytic method may be used even under large signal operation provided that the tube parameters remain substantially constant.

Reference is made to Eqs. (1-17) and (1-18), which specify the variation in current about the quiescent point in terms of the variation resulting from the changes in the plate and grid potentials. This expression, which is

$$\Delta i_b = \left(\frac{\partial i_b}{\partial e_b}\right)_{E_c} \Delta e_b + \left(\frac{\partial i_b}{\partial e_c}\right)_{E_b} \Delta e_c \tag{2-4}$$

is only approximate. It specifies only the first two terms of the Taylor expansion of the function $i_b = i_b(e_b, e_c)$. In the general case, the result is

$$\Delta i_b = \left(\frac{\partial i_b}{\partial e_b}\right)_{E_c} \Delta e_b + \left(\frac{\partial i_b}{\partial e_c}\right)_{E_b} \Delta e_c + \frac{1}{2!}\left(\frac{\partial^2 i_b}{\partial e_b^2}\right)_{E_c} (\Delta e_b)^2$$
$$+ \frac{1}{2!}\left(\frac{\partial^2 i_b}{\partial e_c^2}\right)_{E_b} (\Delta e_c)^2 + \frac{\partial^2 i_b}{\partial e_b\,\partial e_c} \Delta e_b\,\Delta e_c + \cdots \tag{2-5}$$

A more informative form is possible, by relating the higher-order terms in the expansion explicitly as variations in the plate resistance r_p or in the mutual conductance g_m. Consider the third term in the expansion. By combining this with Eq. (1-18), there results

$$\frac{1}{2}\left(\frac{\partial^2 i_b}{\partial e_b^2}\right)_{E_c} (\Delta e_b)^2 = \frac{1}{2}\left[\frac{\partial(1/r_p)}{\partial e_b}\right]_{E_c} (\Delta e_b)^2 \tag{2-6}$$

When the tube parameters are sensibly constant over the operating range of Δe_b and Δe_c, Eq. (2-4) is an adequate representation of the variation. This may be written, by Eqs. (1-17) and (1-18), as

$$\Delta i_b = \frac{1}{r_p} \Delta e_b + g_m \Delta e_c \tag{2-7}$$

But as the changes about the quiescent values are, respectively,

$$\Delta i_b = i_b - I_b = i_p$$
$$\Delta e_c = e_c - E_{cc} = e_g \tag{2-8}$$
$$\Delta e_b = e_b - E_{bb} = e_p$$

then Eq. (2-7) becomes

$$i_p = \frac{1}{r_p} e_p + g_m e_g \tag{2-9}$$

or

$$e_p = -\mu e_g + i_p r_p \tag{2-10}$$

This expression shows that the potential e_p comprises two components; one is an equivalent generated emf, or electromotance, which is μ times as large as the grid-cathode potential e_g, and the second is a potential difference across the tube resistance r_p resulting from the current i_p through it.

Equation (2-10) may be used as the basis for drawing an equivalent network for the tube. This is done in Fig. 2-6. Observe that the plate circuit of the tube is replaced by a fictitious potential source with an electromotance μe_g and an internal resistance r_p. Two points are emphasized. First, the reference positive polarities and reference current direction are essential parts of the equivalent-network representation. Second, no d-c quantities appear on the diagram, since the equivalent-circuit representation applies only for *changes* about the Q point.

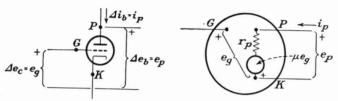

Fig. 2-6. The vacuum triode and its a-c potential-source equivalent representation.

2-5. Current-source Equivalent Representation of a Triode. The current-source equivalent representation of a triode replaces the tube by a constant-current source shunted by a conductance, instead of the potential source with a series resistance. The form of the result is easily obtained by rearranging Eq. (2-9) into the form

$$g_m e_g = i_p - \frac{e_p}{r_p} \tag{2-11}$$

This expression shows that the current i_p comprises two components; one is a generated current which is g_m as large as the grid-cathode potential e_g, and the second is a current through the shunting tube resistance r_p because of the potential e_p across it.

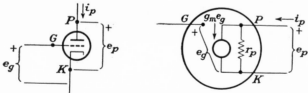

Fig. 2-7. The vacuum triode and its current-source equivalent representation.

Equation (2-11) may be used as the basis for drawing the equivalent network of the tube. This is done in Fig. 2-7. Observe that the plate circuit of the tube is replaced by a current source with generated current $g_m e_g$ and a shunting resistance r_p. Note also that the reference positive polarities and the reference current direction are essential parts of the equivalent-network representation, as before.

The reader will observe a striking parallel between the discussion in this section and that in the previous section, except that one section confines itself to a potential source and a series internal resistance, whereas the present section confines itself to a current source and a shunt conductance (or resistance). This is actually part of a larger pattern which exists in general network analysis and which is given the name of *duality*.*

If the varying quantities are sinusoidally varying ones, and this will ordinarily be assumed unless otherwise explicitly stated, the analysis proceeds most easily in terms of the phasors (sinors and complex-number representation for impedances) of elementary a-c circuit theory. The circuit notation and certain elements of general network analysis which will be found useful in this text are discussed in Appendix A. The reader is urged to refer to this appendix before proceeding. For sinusoidally varying signals, therefore, the tube potentials are expressed in terms of the symbols E_g, E_p, and I_p, where these boldface symbols are employed to

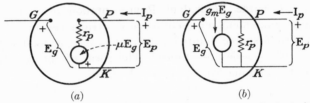

(a)   (b)

Fig. 2-8. (a) The potential-source and (b) the current-source equivalent circuits of the triode for sinusoidally varying quantities.

denote sinor quantities, a symbolism that is adopted in this text. For sinusoidally varying quantities, the vacuum triode is given in the accompanying two equivalent forms (see Fig. 2-8).

2-6. Linear Analysis of Electron-tube Circuits. As discussed in Sec. 2-4, it is possible to determine the a-c response of a vacuum-tube circuit, when the parameters of the tube remain substantially constant over the range of operation, by replacing the tube by either its potential-source equivalent or its current-source equivalent, and then employing the techniques of general network analysis in the complete analysis of the circuit.

The technique of drawing the equivalent network of any tube circuit is a straightforward process, although care must be exercised in carrying out the details. To avoid error, the following simple rules will be found helpful:

1. Draw the actual diagram neatly.

2. Mark the points G, P, and K on this diagram. Locate these points as the start of the equivalent circuit. Maintain the same relative position as in the original circuit.

3. Between points P and K include either the potential-source repre-

---

* Some amplification of the principles of duality is given in Appendix A. Its applications to transistor circuit analysis are given in Chap. 16. For an extensive discussion see W. LePage and S. Seely, "General Network Analysis," McGraw-Hill Book Company, Inc., New York, 1952.

sentation of Fig. 2-8a or the current-source representation of Fig. 2-8b, depending on the preferred form.

4. Transfer all circuit elements from the actual circuit to the equivalent circuit, without altering the relative positions of these elements.

5. Replace each d-c source by its internal resistance, if any.

Several examples will be given to illustrate the foregoing techniques.

Example 1. Calculate the output potential E_2 of the simple amplifier circuit given in Fig. 2-9. Note that the technique of drawing the equivalent circuit is in accord with the rules given above.

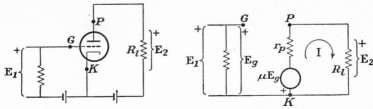

FIG. 2-9. A simple amplifier circuit and its a-c equivalent. The potential-source equivalent of the tube has been used.

A direct application of the Kirchhoff potential law, which requires that the algebraic sum of the potential rises and falls in completing a closed loop must be zero, yields directly

$$\mu E_g + I(r_p + R_l) = 0 \tag{2-12}$$

Note also that

$$E_g = E_1 \tag{2-13}$$

It therefore follows that

$$I = -\frac{\mu E_1}{r_p + R_l} \tag{2-14}$$

and the output potential E_2 is given by

$$E_2 = IR_l = -\frac{\mu R_l E_1}{r_p + R_l} = \frac{-\mu}{1 + r_p/R_l} E_1 \tag{2-15}$$

The ratio of the output to input potentials E_2/E_1 is the amplification, or gain, K of the amplifier. Therefore

$$K = \frac{E_2}{E_1} = \frac{-\mu}{1 + r_p/R_l} \tag{2-16}$$

It is of interest to plot this expression, which has the form given in Fig. 2-10. It should be observed from this diagram that gains which approach μ are quite feasible with moderate R_l/r_p ratios. For values of the ratio $-K/\mu$ which are nearly unity, it is required that R_l be large. In this case, however,

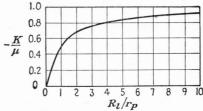

FIG. 2-10. The gain of the amplifier of Fig. 2-9 as a function of load resistance.

for the tube to be operated at the proper d-c quiescent levels, the source E_{bb} must be large, and the heating of the tube or load resistor may become unduly high.

Example 2. Calculate the output potential E_2 of the amplifier circuit given in Fig. 2-11.

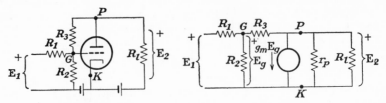

Fig. 2-11. A simple amplifier circuit and its a-c equivalent. The current-source equivalent has been used.

The Kirchhoff current law is applied to the two junctions. This law requires that the sum of the currents at any junction must be zero. The equations are

$$\text{Junction } G: \qquad \frac{E_2 - E_g}{R_3} - \frac{E_g}{R_2} - \frac{E_g - E_1}{R_1} = 0$$

$$\text{Junction } P: \qquad -\left(\frac{E_2 - E_g}{R_3}\right) - g_m E_g - \frac{E_2}{r_p} - \frac{E_2}{R_l} = 0 \qquad (2\text{-}17)$$

Collecting terms gives two equations,

$$\frac{E_1}{R_1} + \frac{E_2}{R_3} - E_g\left(\frac{1}{R_1} + \frac{1}{R_2} + \frac{1}{R_3}\right) = 0$$

$$E_2\left(\frac{1}{R_3} + \frac{1}{r_p} + \frac{1}{R_l}\right) + E_g\left(g_m - \frac{1}{R_3}\right) = 0 \qquad (2\text{-}18)$$

Combine the equations to get, by eliminating E_g,

$$\frac{E_1}{R_1} + E_2\left[\frac{1}{R_3} + \frac{\left(\frac{1}{R_1} + \frac{1}{R_2} + \frac{1}{R_3}\right)\left(\frac{1}{R_3} + \frac{1}{r_p} + \frac{1}{R_l}\right)}{g_m - 1/R_3}\right] = 0 \qquad (2\text{-}19)$$

The output potential is

$$E_2 = \frac{-(g_m - 1/R_3)(1/R_1)}{\dfrac{1}{R_3}\left(g_m - \dfrac{1}{R_3}\right) + \left(\dfrac{1}{R_1} + \dfrac{1}{R_2} + \dfrac{1}{R_3}\right)\left(\dfrac{1}{R_3} + \dfrac{1}{r_p} + \dfrac{1}{R_l}\right)} E_1 \qquad (2\text{-}20)$$

The potential gain of this amplifier is

$$K \equiv \frac{E_2}{E_1} = \frac{-(g_m - 1/R_3)(1/R_1)}{\left(g_m - \dfrac{1}{R_3}\right)\dfrac{1}{R_3} + \left(\dfrac{1}{R_1} + \dfrac{1}{R_2} + \dfrac{1}{R_3}\right)\left(\dfrac{1}{R_3} + \dfrac{1}{r_p} + \dfrac{1}{R_l}\right)} \qquad (2\text{-}21)$$

It should be noted that if the resistors R_1 and R_3 were absent, the circuit will reduce to that of Example 1. Thus, by setting $R_1 = 0$ and $R_3 = \infty$ in Eq. (2-21), the result reduces to that given in Eq. (2-16). Because of the presence of R_1 and R_3, the gain of this amplifier stage is lower than that given in Example 1. A discussion of the effects of introducing these resistors, which have introduced what is known as *negative feedback*, will be deferred until Chap. 5.

2-7. Measurement of Triode Coefficients. As several additional illustrations of the methods of analysis just discussed, the circuits for obtaining the values of μ, r_p, and g_m of a triode will be analyzed. It should be recalled that the triode coefficients, first discussed in Sec. 1-13, were shown to be related to the slope of the static-characteristic curves, according to Figs. 1-14 to 1-16. However, the accuracy with which these quantities can be measured in this way is not high. Not only do the methods now to be discussed yield results which are made under dynamic conditions,

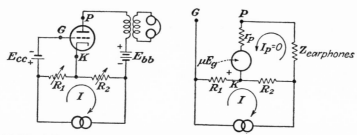

FIG. 2-12. The Miller bridge and its equivalent circuit for determining the amplification factor of a triode under operating conditions.

but the results are usually more accurate than those deduced from the static characteristics.

The amplification factor μ is readily determined by means of the circuit given in Fig. 2-12. The operations involved in balancing the bridge consist simply in varying R_1 and R_2 until no signal from the oscillator is heard in the earphones. When this condition prevails, the plate current $I_p = 0$. Then the potential $E_g = IR_1$. By applying Kirchhoff's law to the plate circuit,

$$-\mu E_g + IR_2 = 0$$

or

$$+\mu E_g = IR_2 = \mu IR_1$$

It follows from this that

$$\mu = \frac{R_2}{R_1} \tag{2-22}$$

This measurement may be effected for any desired d-c current in the tube simply by adjusting the grid bias E_{cc}.

The transconductance g_m is measured by means of a bridge circuit that is a slight modification of Fig. 2-12. The addition of a resistor R_3 between the plate and cathode makes this measurement possible. The schematic and equivalent circuits of this bridge network are given in Fig. 2-13. The measurement is accomplished by adjusting the resistors until no signal is heard in the earphones.

By applying Kirchhoff's law to the several loops, there results

$$I_p R_3 + I_p r_p - \mu E_g = 0$$

But the potential E_g is

$$E_g = IR_1$$

Then

$$I_p(R_3 + r_p) = \mu IR_1 \tag{2-23}$$

Also, it follows that

$$IR_2 - I_p R_3 = 0$$

or

$$IR_2 = I_p R_3 \tag{2-24}$$

The ratio of Eq. (2-23) to Eq. (2-24) is

$$\frac{R_3 + r_p}{R_3} = \mu \frac{R_1}{R_2}$$

from which

$$r_p = R_3 \left(\mu \frac{R_1}{R_2} - 1 \right) \tag{2-25}$$

Although this bridge may be used to evaluate r_p, the result would be dependent on the measurement of μ. If, however, R_1 is chosen in such

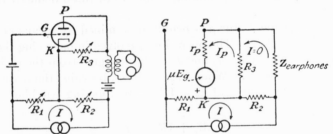

FIG. 2-13. The Miller bridge for determining the transconductance of a triode under operating conditions.

a way that $\mu R_1/R_2 \gg 1$, then approximately

$$r_p \doteq \mu \frac{R_3 R_1}{R_2}$$

or

$$g_m = \frac{\mu}{r_p} = \frac{R_2}{R_3 R_1} \tag{2-26}$$

The plate resistance r_p of the tube can be measured directly by incorporating the plate circuit of the tube as the fourth arm of a Wheatstone bridge, as shown in Fig. 2-14. When the bridge is balanced,

$$r_p = \frac{R_2 R_3}{R_1} \tag{2-27}$$

The above circuits do not yield perfect balance owing to the capacitive effects of the tube, and it is sometimes necessary to provide a means for balancing these effects. Basically, however, the circuits are those given.

2-8. Harmonic Generation in a Tube.
The equivalent-linear-circuit analysis of Sec. 2-4 usually permits an adequate solution of an amplifier circuit when the limitations of the method are not exceeded or if relatively slight differences are considered of no importance. There are occasions when it is desirable to examine critically the effects of the assumptions.

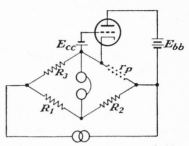

Fig. 2-14. A Wheatstone bridge for determining the plate resistance of a triode under operating conditions.

The assumption of linear operation, which is implied in Eq. (2-4) and which assumed that higher-order terms in the Taylor expansion of the current $i_b(e_b, e_c)$ are negligible, is not always valid. This assumption, which allowed the graphical solution of Fig. 2-5 to be replaced by the analytical one of Fig. 2-6, requires that the dynamic characteristic of the amplifier circuit be linear over the range of operation. Actually, the dynamic characteristic is not linear in general but contains a slight curvature. This nonlinear characteristic arises because the (i_b, e_b) static characteristics (see Fig. 2-3) are not equidistant lines for constant e_c intervals over the range of operation. The effect of this nonlinear dynamic characteristic is a nonsinusoidal output waveshape when the input wave is sinusoidal. Such an effect is known as *nonlinear*, or *amplitude*, distortion.

It is possible to obtain a measure of the degree of nonlinearity that results from the existence of the nonlinear dynamic curve. To do this, it is observed that the dynamic curve with respect to the Q point may be expressed by a power series of the form

$$i_p = a_1 e_g + a_2 e_g^2 + a_3 e_g^3 + \cdots \tag{2-28}$$

Clearly, if all terms in this series vanish except the first, then the linear assumptions of the equivalent-circuit concept result. It will be found that triodes, when operated under normal conditions, may be adequately expressed by retaining the first two terms in the expansion. When a triode is operated with such a large signal that the instantaneous grid-cathode potential becomes positive, or if the triode is operated with such a bias that the very curved portions of the plate characteristics must be employed, more than two terms must be retained in the expansion. Likewise, it is found that the parabolic approximation is not adequate to represent the dynamic curve of a tetrode or a pentode under normal operating conditions. If the dynamic curve contains an extreme curvature or if the operation is over an extreme range, it is sometimes found preferable to devise special methods of analysis. For example, such special methods must be used in the analysis of a tuned class C amplifier.

Suppose that the dynamic curve may be represented as in Eq. (2-28), and consider that the input wave is a simple cosine function of time, of the form

$$e_g = E_{gm} \cos \omega t \qquad (2\text{-}29)$$

By combining this expression with Eq. (2-28) and expanding the higher-order powers of the cosine that appear in the resulting series, the result

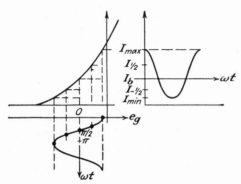

Fig. 2-15. The construction for obtaining the plate-current values to be used in the five-point schedule for determining the Fourier coefficients.

may be shown to have the form

$$i_b = I_b + B_0 + B_1 \cos \omega t + B_2 \cos 2\omega t + B_3 \cos 3\omega t + \cdots \qquad (2\text{-}30)$$

If it is assumed that the excitation potential is a sine function of the time instead of the cosine form chosen, the resulting Fourier series representing the output current will be found to contain odd sine components and even cosine components.

A number of different methods exist for obtaining the coefficients B_0, B_1, B_2, etc. One of the more common methods is best discussed by reference to Fig. 2-15. It will be assumed for convenience that only five terms, B_0, B_1, B_2, B_3, B_4, exist in the resulting Fourier series. In order to evaluate these five coefficients, the values of the current at five different values of e_g are required. The values chosen are I_{max}, $I_{1/2}$, I_b, $I_{-1/2}$, and I_{min} and correspond, respectively, to the following values of e_g: the maximum positive value; one-half the maximum positive value; zero; one-half the maximum negative value; the maximum negative value.

It is evident from the figure that the currents are those chosen as shown at the angles

$$\omega t = 0 \qquad i_b = I_{max}$$

$$\omega t = \frac{\pi}{3} \qquad i_b = I_{\frac{1}{2}}$$

$$\omega t = \frac{\pi}{2} \qquad i_b = I_b \qquad\qquad (2\text{-}31)$$

$$\omega t = \frac{2\pi}{3} \qquad i_b = I_{-\frac{1}{2}}$$

$$\omega t = \pi \qquad i_b = I_{min}$$

By combining these results with Eq. (2-30), five equations containing five unknowns are obtained. The simultaneous solution of these equations yields

$$B_0 = \tfrac{1}{6}\,(I_{max} + 2I_{\frac{1}{2}} + 2I_{-\frac{1}{2}} + I_{min}) - I_b$$
$$B_1 = \tfrac{1}{3}\,(I_{max} + I_{\frac{1}{2}} - I_{-\frac{1}{2}} - I_{min})$$
$$B_2 = \tfrac{1}{4}\,(I_{max} - 2I_b + I_{min}) \qquad\qquad (2\text{-}32)$$
$$B_3 = \tfrac{1}{6}\,(I_{max} - 2I_{\frac{1}{2}} + 2I_{-\frac{1}{2}} - I_{min})$$
$$B_4 = \tfrac{1}{12}\,(I_{max} - 4I_{\frac{1}{2}} + 6I_b - 4I_{-\frac{1}{2}} + I_{min})$$

The percentage of harmonic distortion is defined as

$$D_2 = \frac{B_2}{B_1} \times 100\% \qquad D_3 = \frac{B_3}{B_1} \times 100\% \qquad D_4 = \frac{B_4}{B_1} \times 100\% \quad (2\text{-}33)$$

where D_s ($s = 2, 3, 4, \ldots$) represents the per cent distortion of the sth harmonic and the total distortion is defined as

$$D = \sqrt{D_2^2 + D_3^2 + D_4^2 + \cdots} \qquad\qquad (2\text{-}34)$$

For the case where a three-point schedule is sufficient, and, as already indicated, this would apply for a triode under normal operating conditions, the analysis yields the expressions

$$B_1 = \tfrac{1}{2}\,(I_{max} - I_{min}) \qquad\qquad (2\text{-}35)$$
$$B_2 = B_0 = \tfrac{1}{4}\,(I_{max} - 2I_b + I_{min})$$

PROBLEMS

2-1. A 6C5 triode is used in the circuit of Fig. 2-1, the plate characteristics of which are given in Appendix B.

a. With $E_{bb} = 300$ volts, $E_{cc} = -8$ volts, $R_l = 20$ kilohms, draw the load line, and locate the operating point. Plot the dynamic characteristic of the circuit.

b. If $e_1 = 6 \sin 10{,}000t$, determine the output current graphically and plot the curve as a function of ωt.

c. From these curves, determine and plot the instantaneous plate potential for the same interval as in part *b.* Check the phase relation between a-c components of grid potential, plate current, and plate potential.

2-2. The characteristics of a given triode may be represented by the expression

$$i_b = 8.8 \times 10^{-3}(e_b + 16e_c)^{1.5} \qquad \text{ma}$$

It is to be operated at a plate potential $E_b = 250$ volts and a grid-bias potential $E_c = -9$ volts.

a. Calculate the plate resistance of the tube.

b. If this tube is used in the circuit of Fig. 2-1 with a load resistance $R_l = 10$ kilohms, determine the plate supply potential necessary for the tube to be operating under the specified conditions.

c. Suppose that the grid driving source applies a potential $e_1 = 8 \sin \omega t$ to the grid. Determine the a-c potential across the load resistor.

2-3. Draw the potential-source equivalent circuit of the electron-tube circuits in the accompanying diagrams.

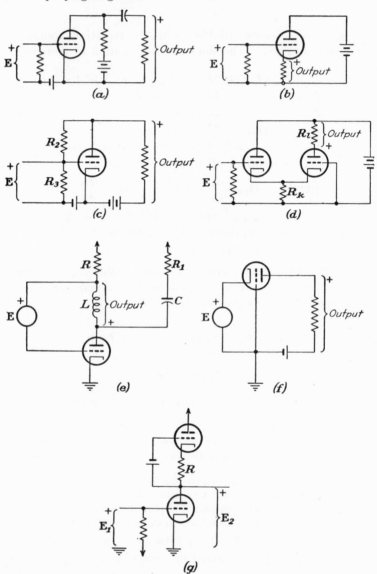

(a)

(b)

(c)

(d)

(e)

(f)

(g)

2-4. A type 6A3 triode is used in an amplifier circuit to supply power to a 3,000-ohm resistor. In this circuit $E_{cc} = -45$ volts, $E_{bb} = 350$ volts. A 45-volt peak a-c signal is applied to the grid.

a. Plot the dynamic curve of the tube.

b. Assume that only the fundamental and a second harmonic exist in the output. Determine the magnitudes of each.

c. Plot a curve showing the output current for the sinusoidal input. On the same sheet, plot the corresponding results from the calculations in part *b.*

2-5. It is possible to obtain a five-point schedule for determining the coefficients B_0, B_1, B_2, B_3, B_4 by almost any sensible choice of angle. Determine the five-point schedule for determining the coefficients B in terms of I_{max}, $I_{0.707}$, I_b, $I_{-0.707}$, I_{min}.

CHAPTER 3

BASIC AMPLIFIER PRINCIPLES

3-1. Classification of Tubes and Amplifiers. The classification of an amplifier is usually somewhat involved, owing to the fact that a complete classification must include information about the tubes that are used, the conditions of the bias, the character of the circuit elements connected to the tubes, the function of the circuit, and the range of operation. Certain of these factors will be discussed here, but many will be deferred for later discussion.

Apart from the wide variety of vacuum tubes of the diode, triode, tetrode, pentode, beam, hexode, heptode, and multiunit types and the varied power capacities of each type, it is possible to classify the tubes according to their principal applications. Tubes may be classified roughly into five groups, viz., potential-amplifier tubes, power-amplifier tubes, current-amplifier tubes, general-purpose tubes, and special-purpose tubes.

1. Potential-amplifier tubes have a relatively high amplification factor and are used where the primary consideration is one of high potential gain. Such tubes usually operate into high impedance loads, either tuned or untuned.

2. Power-amplifier tubes are those which have relatively low values of amplification factor and fairly low values of plate resistance. They are capable of controlling appreciable currents at reasonably high plate potentials.

3. Current-amplifier tubes are those which are designed to give a large change of plate current for a small grid potential; i.e., they possess a high transconductance. These tubes may be required to carry fairly large plate currents. Such tubes find application as both potential and power amplifiers, depending on the tube capacity, and are used extensively in sweep generating circuits.

4. General-purpose amplifier tubes are those whose characteristics are intermediate between the potential- and the power-amplifier tubes. They must have a reasonably high amplification factor and yet must be able to supply some power.

5. Special-purpose tubes include a wide variety of types. The hexode, heptode, and multiunit tubes are of this type.

Amplifiers are classified according to their frequency range, the method of tube operation, and the method of interstage coupling. For example, they may be classed as direct-coupled amplifiers, audio-frequency (a-f) amplifiers, video amplifiers, or tuned r-f amplifiers if some indication of the frequency of operation is desired. Also, the position of the quiescent point and the extent of the tube characteristic that is being used will determine the method of tube operation. This will specify whether the

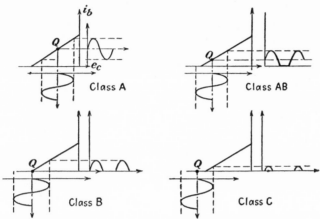

Fig. 3-1. Amplifier classification in terms of the position of the quiescent point of the tubes.

tube is being operated in class A, class AB, class B, or class C. These definitions are illustrated graphically in Fig. 3-1.

1. A class A amplifier is an amplifier in which the grid bias and the a-c grid potentials are such that plate current flows in the tube at all times.

2. A class AB amplifier is one in which the grid bias and the a-c grid potentials are such that plate current flows in the tube for appreciably more than half but less than the entire electrical cycle.

3. A class B amplifier is one in which the grid bias is approximately equal to the cutoff value of the tube, so that the plate current is approximately zero when no exciting grid potential is applied, and such that plate current flows for approximately one-half of each cycle when an a-c grid potential is applied.

4. A class C amplifier is one in which the grid bias is appreciably greater than the cutoff value, so that the plate current in each tube is zero when no a-c grid potential is applied, and such that plate current flows for appreciably less than one-half of each cycle when an a-c grid potential is applied.

To indicate that grid current does not flow during any part of the input cycle, the subscript 1 is frequently added to the letter or letters of the class identification. The subscript 2 is added to denote that grid current does flow during some part of the cycle. For example, the designation class AB₁ indicates that the amplifier operates under class AB conditions and that no grid current flows during any part of the input cycle.

Potential amplifiers, whether tuned or untuned, generally operate in class A. Low-power audio amplifiers may be operated under class A and with special connections, under class AB or class B conditions. Tuned r-f power amplifiers are operated either under class B or under class C conditions. Oscillators usually operate under class C conditions. A detailed discussion is deferred until the appropriate points in the text. When a tube is used essentially as a switch, no classification is ordinarily specified.

3-2. Distortion in Amplifiers. The application of a sinusoidal signal to the grid of an ideal class A amplifier will be accompanied by a sinusoidal output wave. Frequently the output waveform is not an exact replica of the input-signal waveform because of distortion that results either within the tube or from the influence of the associated circuit. The distortions that may exist either separately or simultaneously are nonlinear distortion, frequency distortion, and delay distortion. These are defined as follows:

1. Nonlinear distortion is that form of distortion which occurs when the ratio of potential to current is a function of the magnitude of either.

2. Frequency distortion is that form of distortion in which the change is in the relative magnitudes of the different frequency components of a wave, provided that the change is not caused by nonlinear distortion.

3. Delay distortion is that form of distortion which occurs when the phase angle of the transfer impedance with respect to two chosen pairs of terminals is not linear with frequency within a desired range, the time of transmission, or delay, varying with frequency in that range.

In accordance with definition 1, nonlinear distortion results when new frequencies appear in the output which are not present in the input signal. These new frequencies arise from the existence of a nonlinear dynamic curve and were discussed in Sec. 2-8.

Frequency distortion arises when the components of different frequency are amplified by different amounts. This distortion is usually a function of the character of the circuits associated with the amplifier. If the gain vs. frequency characteristic of the amplifier is not a horizontal straight line over the range of frequencies under consideration, the circuit is said to exhibit frequency distortion over this range.

Delay distortion, also called *phase-shift distortion*, results from the fact that the phase shift of waves of different frequency in the amplifier is different. Such distortion is not of importance in amplifiers of the a-f type, since delay distortion is not perceptible to the ear. It is very objectionable in systems that depend on waveshape for their operation, as, for example, in television or facsimile systems. If the phase shift is proportional to the frequency, a time delay will occur although no distortion is introduced. To see this, suppose that the input signal to the amplifier has the form

$$e_1 = E_{m1} \sin (\omega t + \theta_1) + E_{m2} \sin (2\omega t + \theta_2) + \cdots \tag{3-1}$$

If the gain K is constant in magnitude but possesses a phase shift that is proportional to the frequency, the output will be of the form

$$e_2 = KE_{m1} \sin (\omega t + \theta_1 + \psi) + KE_{m2} \sin (2\omega t + \theta_2 + 2\psi) + \cdots$$

This output potential has the same waveshape as the input signal, but a time delay between these two waves exists. By writing

$$\omega t' = \omega t + \psi$$

then

$$e_2 = KE_{m1} \sin (\omega t' + \theta_1) + KE_{m2} \sin (2\omega t' + \theta_2) + \cdots \tag{3-2}$$

This is simply the expression given by Eq. (3-1), except that it is referred to a new time scale t'. Delay distortion, like frequency distortion, arises from the frequency characteristics of the circuit associated with the vacuum tube.

It is not possible to achieve such a linear phase characteristic with simple networks, but it may be approximated with special phase-equalizing networks.

3-3. The Decibel; Power Sensitivity. In many problems where two power levels are to be compared, it is found very convenient to compare the relative powers on a logarithmic rather than on a direct scale. The unit of this logarithmic scale is called the *bel*. A *decibel*, which is abbreviated db, is $\frac{1}{10}$ bel. By definition, the logarithm to the base 10 of the ratio of two powers is N bels. That is,

$$\text{Number of bels} = \log_{10} \frac{P_2}{P_1}$$

$$\text{Number of db} = 10 \log_{10} \frac{P_2}{P_1} \tag{3-3}$$

or

It should be emphasized that the bel or the decibel denotes a power ratio. Consequently the specification of a certain power in decibels is meaningless unless a reference level is implied or is explicitly specified. In communication applications, it is usual practice to specify 6 mw as the zero reference level. However, any power may be designated as the zero reference level in any particular problem.

Suppose that these considerations are applied to a power amplifier, with P_2 the output power and P_1 the input power. This assumes that the input circuit to the amplifier absorbs power. If the grid circuit does not absorb an appreciable power, then the term *decibel gain* of the amplifier means nothing. Under such conditions, it is customary to speak of *power sensitivity*, which is defined as the ratio of the power output to the square of the input signal potential. Thus

$$\text{Power sensitivity} \equiv \frac{P_2}{E_1^2} \qquad \text{mhos} \tag{3-4}$$

where P_2 is the power output in watts and E_1 is the input signal rms volts.

If the input and output impedances are equal resistances, then $P_2 = E_2^2/R$ and $P_1 = E_1^2/R$, where E_2 and E_1 are the output and input potentials. Under this condition, Eq. (3-3) reduces to

$$\text{Number of db} = 20 \log_{10} \frac{E_2}{E_1} \tag{3-5}$$

In general, the input and output resistances are not equal. Despite this, this expression is adopted as a convenient definition of the decibel potential gain of an amplifier. It is essential, however, when the gain of an amplifier is discussed, that it be clearly stated whether one is referring to potential gain or power gain, as these two figures will be different, in general.

Many of the considerations of the foregoing sections are best illustrated by several examples.

Example 1. Calculate the gain of the grounded-grid amplifier circuit of Fig. 3-2.

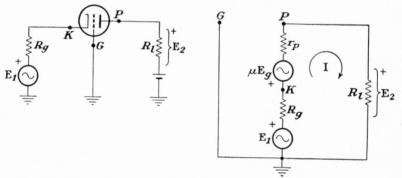

Fig. 3-2. Schematic and equivalent circuits of a grounded-grid amplifier.

Solution. The equivalent circuit of the amplifier is drawn according to the rules of Sec. 2-6 and is that shown in Fig. 3-2b. The application of the Kirchhoff potential law to the equivalent circuit yields

$$\mathbf{E}_1 - \mu\mathbf{E}_g - \mathbf{I}(r_p + R_g + R_l) = 0 \tag{3-6}$$

Also from the diagram

$$\mathbf{E}_g = -\mathbf{E}_1 + \mathbf{I}R_g \tag{3-7}$$

Combine the two equations to find

$$\mathbf{E}_1 - \mu(-\mathbf{E}_1 + \mathbf{I}R_g) - \mathbf{I}(r_p + R_g + R_l) = 0$$

The plate current is then given by

$$\mathbf{I} = \frac{\mathbf{E}_1(\mu + 1)}{r_p + (\mu + 1)R_g + R_l} \tag{3-8}$$

The corresponding output potential is

$$\mathbf{E}_2 = \mathbf{I}R_l = \frac{(\mu + 1)R_l\mathbf{E}_1}{(\mu + 1)R_g + r_p + R_l} \tag{3-9}$$

The gain, or potential amplification of this amplifier, which is the ratio of the output to the input potential, is

$$\mathbf{K} = \frac{\mathbf{E}_2}{\mathbf{E}_1} = \frac{R_l}{R_g + \dfrac{r_p + R_l}{\mu + 1}} \tag{3-10}$$

The input impedance is given as the ratio $\mathbf{E}_1/\mathbf{I}$ and is

$$\mathbf{Z}_1 = \frac{\mathbf{E}_1}{\mathbf{I}} = \frac{r_p + R_l}{\mu + 1} + R_g \tag{3-11}$$

which, for small R_g, is quite small.   This means, of course, that heavy loading of the driving source may exist if R_g is small.

It is of interest to compare the results of this example with Example 1 of Sec. 2-6.   Observe that it is possible to apply the signal either in the grid circuit or in the cathode circuit and still achieve operation of the tube, although the input impedance is different in the two cases.

Example 2.   A type 6J5 triode for which $\mu = 20$, $r_p = 7,700$ ohms is employed in an amplifier, the load of which consists of an inductor for which $R_L = 1,000$ ohms and $L = 1$ henry.   Calculate the gain and phase shift of the amplifier at $\omega = 2,000$ rad/sec and $\omega = 10,000$ rad/sec.   Draw the complete sinor diagram of the system.   The input signal is 6 volts rms.

Solution.   The schematic and equivalent circuits are shown in the accompany-

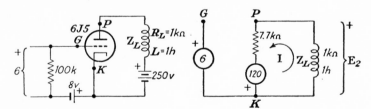

ing diagrams.   At $\omega = 2,000$ rad/sec,

$$\mathbf{I} = \frac{120 + j0}{7,700 + (1,000 + j2,000)} = 13.1 - j3.01 \text{ ma}$$

The output potential is

$$\mathbf{E}_2 = -(1,000 + j2,000)(13.1 - j3.01) \times 10^{-3}$$
$$= -(19.1 + j23.2) = 30.1\underline{/-129.5^\circ}$$

The gain is given by

$$K = \frac{E_2}{E_1} = \frac{30.1/-129.5°}{6/0} = 5.01/-129.5°$$

The potential sinor diagram has the form shown in the sketch.   At $\omega = 10,000$

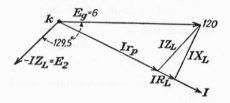

rad/sec,

$$I = \frac{120 + j0}{7,700 + (1,000 + j10,000)} = 5.94 - j6.83 \text{ ma}$$

The output potential is

$$\begin{aligned} E_2 &= -(1,000 + j10,000)(5.94 - j6.83) \times 10^{-3} \\ &= -(74.2 + j52.6) \\ &= 90.8/-144.7° \end{aligned}$$

The gain is given by

$$K = \frac{90.8/-144.7°}{6/0} = 15.1/-144.7°$$

The potential sinor diagram has the form of the accompanying diagram.

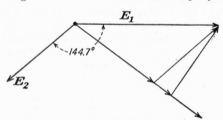

The results are tabulated for convenience.   An examination of the results indicates the presence of frequency distortion, since the gain at $\omega = 2,000$ rad/sec is different from that at $\omega = 10,000$ rad/sec.   Also, phase-shift distortion exists in this amplifier.

ω	Gain and phase	Potential db gain
2,000	$5.01/-129.5°$	14 db
10,000	$15.1/-144.7°$	23.6 db

3-4. Interelectrode Capacitances in a Triode.   It was assumed in the foregoing discussions that with a negative bias on the grid the grid driving-source current was negligible.   This is generally true if one examines only the current intercepted by the grid because of its location within the region of the electron stream. Actually though, owing to the physical proximity of the elements of the tube, interelectrode capacitances between pairs of elements exist. These capacitances are important in the behavior of the circuit, as charging currents do exist.

Owing to the capacitance that exists between the plate and the grid, it is not true that the grid circuit is completely independent of the plate circuit. Since the capacitance between plate and grid is small, the approximation that the plate circuit is independent of the grid circuit is valid at the lower frequencies. However, at the higher frequencies, interelectrode capacitances may seriously affect the operation.

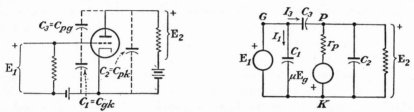

FIG. 3-3. Schematic and equivalent circuits of an amplifier, including the interelectrode capacitances.

A more complete schematic diagram and its equivalent circuit are given in Fig. 3-3. In this circuit, C_{pg} denotes the capacitance between the grid and the plate, C_{gk} is the grid-cathode capacitance, and C_{pk} is the capacitance between the plate and the cathode. The solution for the gain of this circuit is readily obtained with the aid of the Millman theorem (see Appendix A, Sec. A-5b). The point O' corresponds to the plate terminal P, and the point O is the cathode terminal K. Four branches must be considered between these points: the load impedance with zero potential; the capacitor C_2 with zero potential; the potential rise μE_g in series with r_p; the potential E_1 in series with C_3. The capacitor C_1 which exists across the input E_1 does not appear in the equation. The result is

$$E_2 = \frac{-\mu E_g Y_p + E_1 Y_3}{Y_p + Y_l + Y_2 + Y_3} \tag{3-12}$$

where $Y_p = 1/r_p$ is admittance corresponding to r_p

$Y_2 = j\omega C_2$ is admittance corresponding to C_2

$Y_3 = j\omega C_3$ is admittance corresponding to C_3

$Y_l = 1/Z_l$ is admittance corresponding to Z_l

$E_2 =$ potential difference between P and K, or potential across load impedance

Note that $E_1 = E_g$. The potential gain is given by

$$K = \frac{\text{output potential}}{\text{input potential}} = \frac{E_2}{E_1}$$

and may be written in the form

$$K = \frac{Y_3 - g_m}{Y_p + Y_l + Y_2 + Y_3} \tag{3-13}$$

In this expression use has been made of the fact that $g_m = \mu/r_p$.

In this analysis a number of factors have been neglected. It has been assumed that no conduction or leakage currents exist between tube terminals. Such leakage current will depend upon many variable factors, such as the spacing between electrodes, the materials of the base, the conditions of the surface of the glass and the tube base, and perhaps the surface leakage between connecting wires. Ordinarily the error is small in neglecting the effects of this surface leakage. If this assumption is not true, the effect can be taken into account by writing for each interelectrode admittance $g_s + j\omega C_s$ instead of $j\omega C_s$, where g_s takes account of the leakage current and also dielectric losses. Interwiring and stray capacitances must be taken into account. This may be done by considering them to be in parallel with C_1, C_2, and C_3. Additional considerations are necessary at the high frequencies. These are discussed in Sec. 3-8.

The error made in the calculation of the gain by neglecting the interelectrode capacitances is very small over the a-f spectrum. These interelectrode capacitances are usually 10 $\mu\mu$f or less, which corresponds to admittances of less than 2 μmhos at 20,000 cps. This is to be compared with the mutual conductance of the tube of, say, 1,500 μmhos at the normal operating point. Likewise $Y_2 + Y_3$ is usually negligible compared with $Y_p + Y_l$. Under these conditions, the expression for the gain [Eq. (3-13)] reduces to Eq. (2-16).

3-5. Input Admittance of a Triode. Owing to the presence of the interelectrode capacitances, the grid circuit is no longer isolated from the plate circuit. In fact, with an increasing signal on the grid and with the consequent decreasing potential on the plate, an appreciable change of potential appears across the capacitance C_{pg}, with a consequent appreciable current flow. Also, the potential change across the capacitance C_{gk} is accompanied by a current flow. Clearly, therefore, the input-signal source must supply these currents. To calculate this current, it is noted from the diagram that

$$I_1 = E_1Y_1$$

and

$$I_3 = E_{gp}Y_3 = (E_1 - E_2)Y_3$$

But from the fact that

$$E_2 = KE_1$$

then the total input current is

$$\mathbf{I}_i = \mathbf{I}_1 + \mathbf{I}_3 = [\mathbf{Y}_1 + (1 - \mathbf{K})\mathbf{Y}_3]\mathbf{E}_1$$

The input admittance, given by the ratio $\mathbf{Y}_i = \mathbf{I}_i/\mathbf{E}_1$, is

$$\mathbf{Y}_i = \mathbf{Y}_1 + (1 - \mathbf{K})\mathbf{Y}_3 \qquad (3\text{-}14)$$

If $\mathbf{Y}_i$ is to be zero, evidently both $\mathbf{Y}_1$ and $\mathbf{Y}_3$ must be zero, since $\mathbf{K}$ cannot, in general, be $1/\underline{0}$ deg. Thus, for the system to possess a negligible input admittance over a wide range of frequencies, the grid-cathode and the grid-plate capacitances must be negligible.

Consider a triode with a pure resistance load. At the lower frequencies, the gain is given by the simple expression [Eq. (2-16)]

$$\mathbf{K} = \frac{-\mu R_l}{R_l + r_p}$$

In this case, Eq. (3-14) becomes

$$\mathbf{Y}_i = j\omega \left[C_1 + \left(1 + \frac{\mu R_l}{R_l + r_p} \right) C_3 \right] \qquad (3\text{-}15)$$

Thus the input admittance is that from a capacitor between grid and cathode of magnitude

$$C_i = C_1 + \left(1 + \frac{\mu R_l}{R_l + r_p} \right) C_3 \qquad (3\text{-}16)$$

Attention is called to the very large contribution to the input capacitance by the grid-plate capacitance C_3, owing to the fact that its magnitude is multiplied by the amplifier gain. As a result, the total input capacitance is very much higher than any of the interelectrode capacitances. The presence of this input capacitance will be found to affect the operation of the amplifier, and often will make operation impossible, especially at the higher frequencies. Methods of compensation have been devised to overcome this effect, and these will be examined later.

For the general case when the gain of the amplifier $\mathbf{K}$ is a complex quantity, the input admittance will consist of two terms, a resistive and a reactive term. For the case of an inductive load, the gain $\mathbf{K}$ may be written in the form (see Sec. 3-3, Example 2)

$$\mathbf{K} = -(k_1 + jk_2) \qquad (3\text{-}17)$$

and Eq. (3-14) becomes

$$\mathbf{Y}_i = -\omega C_3 k_2 + j\omega[C_1 + (1 + k_1)C_3] \qquad (3\text{-}18)$$

This expression indicates that the equivalent input circuit comprises a resistance (which is negative in this particular case, although it will be positive for a capacitive load) in parallel with a capacitance C_i, as shown in Fig. 3-4. The equivalent elements have the form

$$R_i = -\frac{1}{\omega C_3 k_2}.$$ (3-19)

and the capacitor

$$C_i = C_1 + (1 + k_1)C_3$$ (3-20)

As indicated in the above development, it is possible for the term k_2 to be negative (with an inductive load). Under these circumstances the input resistance R_i will be negative. Physically, this means that power is being fed back from the output circuit into the grid circuit through the coupling provided by the grid-plate capacitance. If this feedback reaches an extreme stage, the amplifier will oscillate. These feedback effects in an amplifier will be examined in some detail in Chap. 5.

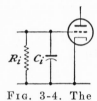

FIG. 3-4. The equivalent input circuit of a triode.

3-6. Input Admittance of a Tetrode. The equivalent circuit of the tetrode is essentially that of the triode, even though a screen grid exists in the tetrode. A schematic diagram of a simple amplifier circuit employing a tetrode is given in Fig. 3-5. In drawing the equivalent circuit, the rules given in Sec. 2-6 have been appropriately extended and employed. This requires the introduction of a point S, the screen terminal, in addition to the points K, G, and P.

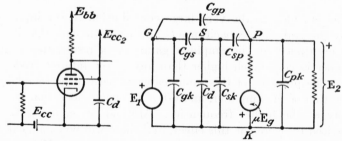

FIG. 3-5. Schematic and equivalent circuits of a tetrode in an amplifier circuit.

Notice that the screen potential is maintained at a fixed d-c potential with respect to cathode and is at zero potential in so far as a-c variations about the Q point are concerned. As indicated in the figure, this effectively places a short circuit across C_{ks} and puts C_{gk} and C_{gs} in parallel. This parallel combination is denoted C_1. The capacitance C_{ps} now appears from plate to cathode and is effectively in parallel with C_{pk}. This parallel combination is denoted C_2. Also, from the discussion in Sec. 1-14, the shielding action of the screen is such that the capacitance C_{pg} between grid and plate is very small. If this capacitance is assumed to be negligible, and it is less than 0.001 $\mu\mu$f in the average potential tetrode, then Fig. 3-5 may be redrawn in the form shown in Fig. 3-6. In this figure, the capacitances have the values

$$C_1 = C_{gk} + C_{gs}$$
$$C_2 = C_{ps} + C_{pk}$$
(3-21)

The input admittance of the tube is then

$$\mathbf{Y}_i = j\omega C_1$$
(3-22)

The mere substitution of a tetrode for a triode may not result in a very marked improvement in the amplifier response. This follows from the fact that the stray and wiring capacitances external to the tube may allow significant grid-plate coupling. It is necessary that care be exercised in order that plate and grid circuits be shielded or widely separated from each other in order to utilize the inherent possibilities of the tube.

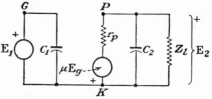

FIG. 3-6. The ideal equivalent circuit of a tetrode amplifier.

3-7. Input Admittance of a Pentode. The discussion in Sec. 1-14 showed that, even though the tetrode had a significantly smaller grid-plate capacitance than the triode, the presence of the screen grid was accompanied by the effects of secondary emission from the plate when the instantaneous plate potential fell below the screen potential. As discussed, the effect of this is overcome by the insertion of a suppressor grid between the screen grid and the plate.

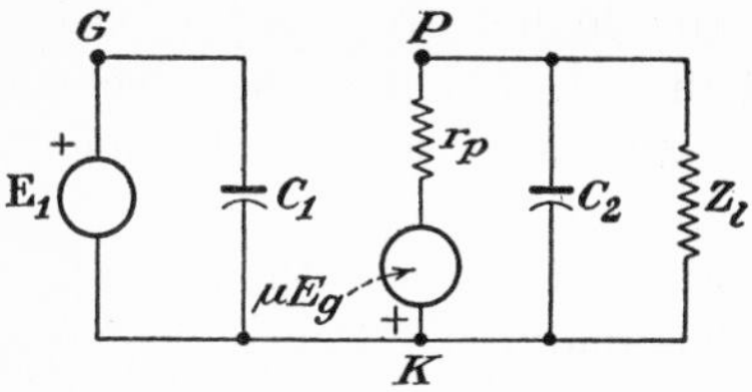

When used in a circuit as a potential amplifier, the pentode is connected in the circuit exactly like the tetrode with the addition that the suppressor grid is connected to the cathode. By drawing the complete equivalent circuit of the pentode amplifier, by appropriately extending the rules of Sec. 2-6, and by including all tube capacitances, it is easy to show that the equivalent circuit reduces to that shown in Fig. 3-7. In this diagram

FIG. 3-7. The equivalent circuit of a pentode amplifier.

$$C_1 = C_{gk} + C_{gs}$$
$$C_2 = C_{pk} + C_{ps} + C_{p3}$$
(3-23)

where C_{p3} is the plate-grid No. 3 capacitance.

The plate load impedance $\mathbf{Z}_l$ is frequently much smaller than the plate resistance of the tube, and it is convenient to use the current-source

equivalent-circuit representation of the tube, as shown.   For the range
of frequencies over which the input and output capacitances C_1 and C_2
are negligible, and with $r_p \gg Z_l$, the total generator current passes

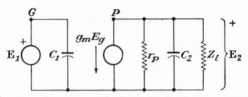

Fig. 3-8. The current-source equivalent circuit of the pentode amplifier.

through Z_l.   Under these circumstances the output potential is

$$\mathbf{E}_2 = -g_m \mathbf{E}_1 \mathbf{Z}_l$$

and the gain is given by the simple form

$$\mathbf{K} = -g_m \mathbf{Z}_l \qquad (3\text{-}24)$$

If the assumed conditions are not valid, then the gain becomes

$$\mathbf{K} = -g_m \mathbf{Z} \qquad (3\text{-}25)$$

where $\mathbf{Z}$ is the combined parallel impedance in the output circuit.

3-8. High-frequency (H-F) Considerations.

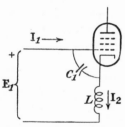

FIG. 3-9. Circuit for examining the effect of cathode lead inductance in a pentode.

In addition to the effects of the interelectrode
capacitances in affecting the performance of an
amplifier, several other factors are of importance,
particularly at the higher frequencies.   Some
were mentioned in Sec. 3-4, plus the effects of
lead inductances and also the effects due to
transit time.

To examine the effect of the cathode lead inductance, Fig. 3-9 is analyzed.   For convenience,
it will be assumed that the grid is negative
throughout the cycle and that transit-time
effects are negligible.   Then for $\mathbf{I}_2 \gg \mathbf{I}_1$

$$\mathbf{I}_2 = g_m \mathbf{E}_g$$

and

$$\mathbf{E}_g = \frac{\mathbf{I}_1}{j\omega C_1}$$

Also

$$\mathbf{E}_1 = \frac{\mathbf{I}_1}{j\omega C_1} + jg_m \mathbf{E}_g \omega L$$

Combine equations to get

$$E_1 = \frac{I_1}{j\omega C_1} + jg_m\omega L\,\frac{I_1}{j\omega C_1}$$

$$= \frac{I_1}{j\omega C_1}\,(1 + jg_m\omega L)$$

The input admittance is

$$Y_i = \frac{I_1}{E_1} = \frac{j\omega C_1}{1 + jg_m\omega L} = \frac{j\omega C_1(1 - j\omega g_m L)}{1 + \omega^2 g_m^2 L^2} \tag{3-26}$$

If $\omega^2 g_m^2 L^2 \ll 1$, then

$$Y_i = \omega^2 g_m L C_1 + j\omega C_1 \tag{3-27}$$

Observe, therefore, that the cathode lead inductance introduces an input conductance of amount $\omega^2 g_m L C_1$.

A second component of input conductance arises because of the transit time of the electrons between cathode and plate. An exact calculation is difficult, but a qualitative explanation is possible which indicates the grid-loading effects involved. To understand grid loading, consider an electron that has left the cathode and is approaching the grid in its flight to the anode. Suppose that the grid potential is negative relative to the cathode so that no electrons are collected by the grid. As the electron approaches the grid, a changing image-charge density will be induced on the grid (see Sec. 1-4 for a discussion of image charges). This changing image charge represents an instantaneous grid current, the direction of flow of charge being such as to charge the bias battery. The power for this charging process is supplied by the moving electron, and as a result the electron is decelerated.

Once the electron has passed the grid, the process is reversed, and the moving electron receives energy from the grid, and it is accelerated thereby. The amount of energy lost by the electron as it approaches the grid is just equal to that which it gains as it moves away, and the net energy change is zero. As a result, the net grid loading is zero.

If the transit time of the electron in the cathode-anode space is of the order of the frequency of the applied grid potential, the grid loading becomes important, for now the electron can no longer be considered to be in a field which is constant in time. It is possible for the energy that is supplied to the grid by the moving electron to exceed the amount of energy that is returned by the grid in its interelectrode flight, with a resultant net energy loss in the grid circuit. This energy is supplied by the grid driving source, and it represents a load on this source.

From a circuits point of view, the foregoing may be described in terms of an induced current in the grid. At the lower frequencies, the induced grid current is 90 deg out of phase with the grid potential, with a consequent zero net power loss. At the higher frequencies, an inphase component exists. This inphase component reduces the input resistance, and this may produce an appreciable loading of the input circuit.

The foregoing concepts may be employed to indicate in a qualitative way the effect of the various factors on the input resistance. If T denotes the transit time, f denotes the frequency of the applied grid potential, and g_m is the mutual conductance of the tube, it is expected that the grid current I_g is proportional to T and f, since I_g is small if either of these is small. Also, I_g should be proportional to g_m, since g_m determines the a-c component of plate current for a specified E_g, and the total grid current is proportional to this a-c component of the plate current. If α denotes the transit angle, which is now less than 90 deg, then the inphase component of I_g is $I_g \sin \alpha$, which is simply $I_g \alpha$ for small deviations from 90 deg. But α is also proportional to T and f. Thus the inphase component of I_g is proportional to $g_m T^2 f^2$, or

$$g_i = k g_m f^2 T^2 \tag{3-28}$$

where k is a constant depending on the geometry of the tube and electrode potentials. This relationship agrees with the complete analyses of Ferris.*

It will be seen from Eqs. (3-27) and (3-28) that g_i and the conductance component of the cathode inductance depend on the frequency in the same way. Consequently, these components cannot be separated readily in measurement of input resistance or conductance.

Tubes for use at the high frequencies are made in a manner to reduce transit time, interelectrode capacitances, and lead inductances. This is done by means of very close electrode spacing, and generally small physical dimensions of electrodes. Among such tubes are the so-called "acorn," "doorknob," "pencil," and "disk-seal," or "lighthouse," tubes, with upper limits in frequency of approximately 2,000, 1,700, 3,000, and 3,500 Mc, respectively. These names are indicative of the external envelope shape, the first three possessing essentially cylindrical electrode structures, the last being essentially of a planar construction. The first two have the leads brought out of the envelopes at widely spaced points, in order to reduce capacitances. The latter two bring the leads out in the form of disks. At the higher frequencies these tubes are incorporated in coaxial line resonators, lead inductances being unimportant as these form part of the resonant cavities.

3-9. Potential Sources for Amplifiers. A number of different potential sources are required in an amplifier. These are: the filament, or A, supply; the plate, or B, supply E_{bb}; the grid-bias, or C, supply E_{cc}; the screen supply E_{cc2}. These potentials are supplied in different ways.

* W. R. Ferris, *Proc. IRE*, **24**, 82 (1936).

The Filament, or A, Supply.   The most common method of heating the cathodes of indirectly heated tubes is from a low-potential winding on a transformer which operates from the a-c supply lines.   Storage batteries may be used if d-c heating is necessary, but this is ordinarily not necessary except in special applications.   Special low-drain tubes are available for use in portable radio sets and are fed from dry batteries.

The Plate, or B, Supply E_{bb}.   Most equipments involving the use of electron tubes are operated from the a-c supply mains, and the d-c plate supply is then secured by means of a rectifier and filter unit (see Chaps. 12 and 13 for details).   For applications with severe requirements on regulation or low ripple, the power supply must be electronically regulated.   For low-drain requirements, dry batteries may be used.

The Grid, or C, Supply E_{cc}.   The grid circuit of most amplifiers ordinarily requires very little current, and hence low-power dry batteries may be used.   In most cases, however, self-bias is used (although this is restricted to class A and class AB amplifiers).   Self-bias is achieved by including a resistor R_k in the cathode of the amplifier tube and shunting this resistor with a

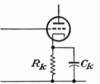

Fig. 3-10. Obtaining self-bias by means of a cathode resistor.

capacitor C_k, the reactance of which is small compared with R_k over the operating frequency range.   The quiescent current I_b flows through this resistor, and the potential difference provides the grid bias.   The correct self-biasing resistance $R_k = E_{cc}/I_b$.

The capacitor C_k serves to by-pass any a-c components in the plate current, so that no a-c component appears across the resistor R_k.   If such an a-c component, or varying bias, does exist, then clearly there is a reaction between the plate circuit and the input circuit.   Such a "feedback" effect will receive detailed consideration in Chap. 5.   If this effect is to be avoided, large-capacitance capacitors may be required, particularly if the frequency is low.   High-capacitance low-potential electrolytic capacitors are available for this specific service and are quite small physically.

The Screen Supply E_{cc2}.   The screen supply is ordinarily obtained from the plate-supply source.   In many cases the screen potential is lower than the plate supply, and it is usual practice to connect the screen to the plate supply through a resistor.   The resistor is chosen of such a size that the potential drop across it due to the screen current will set the screen at the desired potential.   A capacitor is then connected from the screen to the cathode so as to maintain this potential constant and independent of B-supply variations or variations in the screen current.

It is customary to use a common B supply for all tubes of a given amplifier circuit.   Because of this, the possibility for interactions among the stages through this common plate supply does exist and might be troublesome unless the effective output impedance of the power-supply unit is very small. It is necessary in some applications to include *RC* combinations known as *decoupling filters* so as to avoid this interaction.

A typical resistance-capacitance coupled-amplifier circuit which is provided with self-bias, decoupling filters, and screen dropping resistors is illustrated in Fig. 3-11.

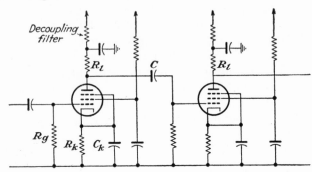

Fig. 3-11. Resistance-capacitance coupled amplifier, with self-bias, decoupling filters, and screen dropping resistors.

PROBLEMS

3-1. Two waves, one of amplitude 10 volts and frequency 1,000 cps, the second of amplitude 5 volts and frequency 3,000 cps, are applied to the input of a certain network. The two waves are so phased that they both pass through zero in the positive direction together.

   a. Sketch the resulting input potential.

   b. Suppose that the fundamental component suffers a phase delay of 10 deg on the fundamental scale and that the third-harmonic component suffers a 50-deg delay on the third-harmonic scale, although neither amplitude is affected. Sketch the output wave.

3-2. *a.* The output potential of a given amplifier is 18 volts when the input potential is 0.2 volt at 5,000 cps. What is the decibel potential gain of the amplifier?

   b. The output potential is 7 volts when the input potential is 0.2 volts at 18,000 cps. By how many decibels is the response of the amplifier at 18 kc below that at 5 kc?

3-3. Prepare a table giving the power sensitivity of the following tubes (assume that the output power and the grid excitation are those specified in the tube manual): 6A3, 6F6, 6V6, 6L6, 6AG7.

3-4. An a-c excitation potential of 5 volts rms at a frequency of 2,000 cps is applied to a 6J5 tube for which $\mu = 20$, $r_p = 7,700$ ohms. The load is a pure resistance of 15,000 ohms. Calculate the following:

   a. The a-c current in the plate circuit.

   b. The a-c output potential.

   c. The gain of the amplifier.

   d. The a-c power in the load resistor.

3-5. Repeat Prob. 3-4 if the load is an inductive reactance of 15,000 ohms.

3-6. Find expressions for the indicated quantity in the accompanying circuits.

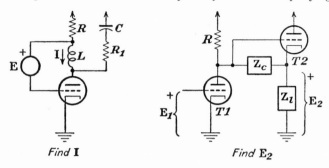

Find **I**   Find **E₂**

3-7. A type 6SF5 high-mu triode is operated as a simple amplifier under specified conditions at 30,000 cps.   The important factors are

$$\mu = 100 \qquad r_p = 66,000 \text{ ohms} \qquad C_{gp} = 2.4 \ \mu\mu\text{f} \qquad C_{gk} = 4.0 \ \mu\mu\text{f}$$
$$C_{pk} = 3.6 \ \mu\mu\text{f}$$

a. Calculate the input capacitance and the input resistance of the tube alone
when the load is a resistor $R_l = 100$ kilohms.

b. Repeat when the load impedance is of the form $60,000 + j60,000$ ohms.

3-8. A type 6J5 triode is operated as a simple amplifier under specified conditions at 22,000 cps.   The important factors are

$$\mu = 20 \qquad r_p = 7,700 \text{ ohms} \qquad C_{gp} = 3.4 \ \mu\mu\text{f} \qquad C_{gk} = 3.4 \ \mu\mu\text{f}$$
$$C_{pk} = 3.6 \ \mu\mu\text{f}$$

a. Calculate the input capacitance and the input resistance of the tube when
the load is a resistor $R_l = 20$ kilohms.

b. Repeat when the load is an impedance of the form $10,000 + j10,000$ ohms.

3-9. A type 6J5 tube is operated in the circuit of the accompanying diagram.
Calculate the output potential.   (See Prob. 3-8 for the important factors of the
tube.)

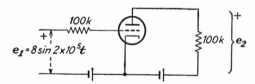

3-10. Show that Fig. 3-7 does represent the complete equivalent circuit of the
pentode.

3-11. A type 6SJ7 pentode is operated as a simple amplifier under specified
conditions.

a. When connected as a pentode, with $R_l = 25$ kilohms, the important factors
are

$$g_m = 1,575 \ \mu\text{mhos} \qquad r_p = 0.7 \text{ megohms} \qquad C_{gp} = 0.005 \ \mu\mu\text{f} \qquad C_{\text{input}} = 6.0 \ \mu\mu\text{f}$$
$$C_{\text{output}} = 7.0 \ \mu\mu\text{f}$$

Calculate the input capacitance of the amplifier.

b. When this tube is reconnected as a triode, the factors become

$$\mu = 19 \qquad r_p = 8{,}000 \text{ ohms} \qquad C_{gp} = 2.8\ \mu\mu\text{f} \qquad C_{gk} = 3.4\ \mu\mu\text{f} \qquad C_{pk} = 11\ \mu\mu\text{f}$$

Calculate the input capacitance with $R_l = 25$ kilohms, and compare with the results of part *a*.

3-12. A 6AC7 pentode is to be used as a class A amplifier with $E_b = 250$ volts. Determine the value of the self-biasing cathode resistor to set $E_{cc} = -2$ volts; the screen dropping resistor to set E_{c2} at 150 volts if $E_{bb} = 350$.

CHAPTER 4

UNTUNED POTENTIAL AMPLIFIERS

4-1. Basic Considerations. It is frequently necessary to achieve a higher gain in an amplifier than is possible with a single amplifier stage. In such cases, the amplifier stages are cascaded to achieve this higher gain, the output potential from one stage serving as the input potential to the next stage.

A number of factors influence the number and the characteristics of the individual stages which must be used to meet certain previously specified requirements. Among the factors which must be taken into account in amplifier design are the total over-all gain required, the shape of the frequency-response characteristic, and the over-all bandwidth. Certain factors exist which impose limits to the sensitivity which may be achieved, among these being the inherent noise generated in such devices. The requirements for stability of operation impose severe practical restrictions on the techniques of construction. Because of the several factors that play a part in amplifier design, gains in excess of about 10^6, or 120 db potential gain, are extremely difficult to achieve. Depending on the bandwidth considerations, amplifiers seldom exceed six to nine stages in cascade for stable operation. Extreme caution is required in the design of such multistage amplifiers.

To calculate the over-all gain and frequency response of a multistage amplifier, the equivalent circuit of the amplifier must be drawn. The rules for accomplishing this are given in Sec. 2-6. The resultant equivalent network is then analyzed as a conventional problem in a-c circuit analysis.

A variety of coupling networks between the cascaded stages are possible, and a few have become very common, either because of their simplicity or because of some especially desirable characteristic. A number of the more common types will be considered in this chapter in some detail.

4-2. Resistance-Capacitance (RC) Coupled Amplifier. The resistance-capacitance (RC) coupled amplifier, illustrated in Fig. 4-1, is one of the more common and more important amplifier circuits. This amplifier circuit is used when a sensibly constant amplification over a wide range of frequencies is desired. By the use of tubes with high amplification factors, it is possible to achieve a gain of 50 or more per stage. It will be found that high-gain triodes possess certain inherent disadvantages, and it is frequently desirable to use pentodes instead. If pentodes are used, the screen potential must remain constant; otherwise the following analysis will no longer be valid.

The capacitors C_1, C_2, and C_3 in this schematic diagram are known as *coupling*, or *blocking*, capacitors and serve to prevent any d-c potentials that are present in one stage from appearing in another stage. That is, capacitor C_1 serves to prevent any d-c potential in the input from appearing across the grid resistor R_{g1} and thus changing the d-c operating level of the amplifier. Capacitor C_2 serves a similar function in coupling stage 1 to stage 2. The value of the coupling capacitors is determined primarily by the l-f amplification. They ordinarily range from about

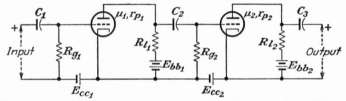

FIG. 4-1. Schematic diagram of a two-stage RC coupled amplifier.

0.001 to 0.1 μf for conventional a-f stages. The resistor R_g, which is known as the *grid resistor*, furnishes a path by which the grid-bias supply is applied to the grid. It also serves as a leak path through which any electrons that may be collected by the grid from the electron stream within the tube may be returned to the cathode. If such a leak path were not provided, the grid would acquire a negative potential with the collection of the electrons, thus influencing the operation of the tube. A negative-bias supply potential is ordinarily used, and the grid current is usually very small. This permits the use of relatively large resistances for R_g, say from 50 kilohms to 2 megohms. Large values of R_g are desirable in achieving a wide frequency response. The load resistor R_l is determined principally by the gain and the frequency bandwidth that are desired, as will be shown below.

The equivalent circuit of the amplifier of Fig. 4-1 is shown in Fig. 4-2. This circuit is valid for triodes, tetrodes, or pentodes provided that the screen potential of the latter two is maintained constant. In this circuit E_1 denotes the a-c input potential applied to the grid of the first stage. This potential appears across the parallel combination consisting of the resistor R_{g1} in parallel with the input impedance to the amplifier. The interelectrode capacitances are not shown on the diagram, but their effect is contained in the effective input capacitance C_g to each stage. That is, the input impedance of the stage is considered to comprise a resistance (assumed positive) in parallel with the input capacitance. It is also supposed that the impedance of the driving source is low, so that the loading by the total input impedance of the first stage does not affect the input potential.   The output circuit of the first stage consists of the load resistance, the coupling capacitance C_2, output tube and wiring capacitances, and the total input impedance of the second stage.   This is denoted as R_g and C_g for the total resistive and capacitive components.   The output of the amplifier is the potential across the output impedance, which is denoted by the symbol $\mathbf{Z}$.   This impedance

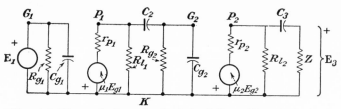

Fig. 4-2. The equivalent circuit of the RC amplifier of Fig. 4-1.

cannot be specified more completely until the nature of the output circuit is known.

The coupling between the grid and the plate of the tubes through the interelectrode capacitances can be neglected over a wide frequency range with pentodes and over the a-f range with triodes.   Consequently each stage may be considered as independent of the following stage, but the output of one stage is the input to the next stage.   As a result, it follows that since

$$\mathbf{K}_1 = \frac{\mathbf{E}_2}{\mathbf{E}_1} = \frac{\text{output potential of 1st stage}}{\text{input potential to 1st stage}}$$

and

$$\mathbf{K}_2 = \frac{\mathbf{E}_3}{\mathbf{E}_2} = \frac{\text{output potential of 2d stage}}{\text{input potential to 2d stage}}$$
$$= \frac{\text{output potential of 2d stage}}{\text{output potential of 1st stage}}$$

then the resultant over-all gain is

$$\mathbf{K} = \frac{\mathbf{E}_3}{\mathbf{E}_1} = \frac{\text{output potential of 2d stage}}{\text{input potential to 1st stage}}$$

It follows from these expressions that

$$\mathbf{K} = \mathbf{K}_1 \mathbf{K}_2 \tag{4-1}$$

By taking twenty times the logarithm of the magnitude of this expression

$$20 \log_{10} K = 20 \log_{10} K_1 + 20 \log_{10} K_2 \tag{4-2}$$

It follows from this that the total decibel potential gain of the multistage amplifier is the sum of the decibel potential gains of the separate stages.   This fact is independent of the type of interstage coupling.

4-3. Analysis of RC Coupled Amplifier.   A typical stage of the RC coupled amplifier is considered in detail.   This stage might represent any of a group of similar stages of an amplifier chain, except perhaps the output stage.   Representative subscripts have been omitted.   The equivalent circuit is given in its two forms in Fig. 4-3.

The typical stage will be analyzed by two methods in order to show the features of the methods.   One method will employ the Millman theorem,

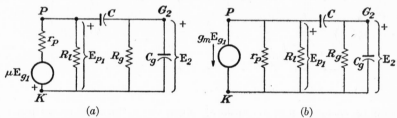

(a)   (b)

FIG. 4-3. A typical stage of an RC coupled amplifier.   (a) Potential-source and (b) current-source equivalents.

as applied to Fig. 4-3a.   The second method will employ a straightforward junction solution of Fig. 4-3b.

A direct application of the Millman theorem between the points G_2 and K yields the expression

$$E_2 = \frac{E_{p1}Y_C}{Y_C + Y_{R_g} + Y_{C_g}} \tag{4-3}$$

where $Y_C = j\omega C$, $Y_{R_g} = 1/R_g$, $Y_{C_g} = j\omega C_g$.   An application of this theorem between the points P_1 and K yields the expression

$$E_{p1} = \frac{-\mu E_{g1}Y_p + E_2Y_C}{Y_p + Y_l + Y_C} \tag{4-4}$$

where $Y_p = 1/r_p$ and $Y_l = 1/R_l$.   By combining Eq. (4-3) with Eq. (4-4) and solving for the gain $K = E_2/E_{g1}$, since $E_{g1} = E_1$, there results

$$K = \frac{-\mu Y_p Y_C}{(Y_C + Y_{R_v} + Y_{C_g})(Y_p + Y_l) + Y_C(Y_{R_g} + Y_{C_g})} \tag{4-5}$$

This is the complete expression for the potential gain of such an amplifier stage.   If the constants of the circuit are known, the gain and phase-shift characteristics as a function of frequency may be calculated.

Now refer to Fig. 4-3b, and apply the standard techniques of junction analysis.   The controlling equations, obtained from considerations of the

Kirchhoff current law, are

$$(Y_p + Y_l + Y_c)E_{p1} - Y_cE_2 = -g_mE_{g1} \qquad (4\text{-}6)$$
$$-Y_cE_{p1} + (Y_c + Y_{c_g} + Y_{R_g})E_2 = 0$$

By determinantal methods, it follows that

$$K = \frac{E_2}{E_1} = \frac{\begin{vmatrix} Y_p + Y_l + Y_c & -g_m \\ -Y_c & 0 \end{vmatrix}}{\begin{vmatrix} Y_p + Y_l + Y_c & -Y_c \\ -Y_c & Y_c + Y_{c_g} + Y_{R_g} \end{vmatrix}} \qquad (4\text{-}7)$$

The expansion of these determinants by Cramer's rule yields Eq. (4-5), as it must.

It will be found convenient to analyze the response of the amplifier for limiting regions of frequency instead of attempting an interpretation of

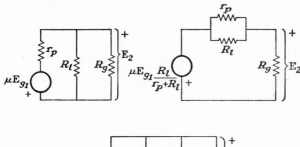

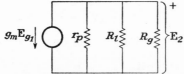

Fig. 4-4. The mid-frequency equivalent circuits of the RC amplifier.

Eq. (4-5) directly. In fact, in many cases it is more convenient to analyze the appropriate equivalent circuit, rather than attempt the analysis from Eq. (4-5).

Intermediate Frequencies. The intermediate frequencies, or mid-frequencies, are those for which Y_C is large and Y_{C_g} is small. Subject to these conditions, the equivalent circuits of Fig. 4-3 reduce to those shown in Fig. 4-4.

For the range of frequencies over which this equivalent circuit is valid, the expression for the gain becomes

$$K = K_0 = \frac{-g_m}{Y_p + Y_l + Y_{R_g}} \qquad (4\text{-}8)$$

This expression for the gain is independent of the frequency, since no reactive elements appear in the circuit. Each parameter in the equation is a conductance, and because of the negative sign the relative phase angle between the input and output potentials is constant and equal to 180 deg.

L-F Region. At the low frequencies the effect of C_g is negligible, and Y_{C_g} may be made zero. The effect of the coupling capacitor C becomes very important. The equivalent circuit under these conditions has the form shown in Fig. 4-5. The general expression for the gain [Eq. (4-5)]

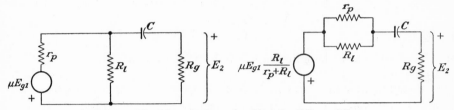

FIG. 4-5. The l-f equivalent circuit of the *RC* amplifier.

reduces to

$$\mathbf{K} = \mathbf{K}_1 = \frac{-\mu \mathbf{Y}_p \mathbf{Y}_C}{\mathbf{Y}_C(\mathbf{Y}_p + \mathbf{Y}_l + \mathbf{Y}_{R_g}) + \mathbf{Y}_{R_g}(\mathbf{Y}_p + \mathbf{Y}_l)} \tag{4-9}$$

It is found convenient to examine the l-f gain relative to the mid-frequency gain. The ratio $\mathbf{K}_1/\mathbf{K}_0$ becomes

$$\frac{\mathbf{K}_1}{\mathbf{K}_0} = \frac{1}{1 + \dfrac{\mathbf{Y}_{R_g}(\mathbf{Y}_p + \mathbf{Y}_l)}{\mathbf{Y}_C(\mathbf{Y}_p + \mathbf{Y}_l + \mathbf{Y}_{R_g})}} \tag{4-10}$$

This may be written in the simple form, for any frequency f,

$$\frac{\mathbf{K}_1}{\mathbf{K}_0} = \frac{1}{1 - j(\mathbf{f}_1/f)} \tag{4-11}$$

where

$$\mathbf{f}_1 \equiv \frac{\mathbf{Y}_{R_g}(\mathbf{Y}_p + \mathbf{Y}_l)}{2\pi C(\mathbf{Y}_p + \mathbf{Y}_l + \mathbf{Y}_{R_g})} \tag{4-12}$$

Equations (4-11) and (4-12) are meaningful only if the load is a pure resistance, since then $\mathbf{f}_1$ is a real number and

$$\frac{K_1}{K_0} = \frac{1}{\sqrt{1 + (f_1/f)^2}}$$

where

$$f_1 = \frac{1}{2\pi C \left[R_g + \dfrac{r_p R_l}{r_p + R_l} \right]} \tag{4-13}$$

This shows that the parameter f_1 represents the frequency at which the gain falls to $1/\sqrt{2}$, or 70.7 per cent of its mid-frequency value. This frequency is usually referred to as the *l-f cutoff* frequency of the amplifier.

The relative phase angle θ_1 is given by

$$\tan \theta_1 = \frac{f_1}{f} \tag{4-14}$$

This approaches 90 deg as the frequency approaches zero.

It should be noted that the l-f cutoff value [Eq. (4-12)] depends, among other terms, on the size of the coupling capacitor C. Since the value of C appears in the denominator of the expression for f_1, then, for a decreased l-f cutoff, larger values of C must be chosen. Of course, the gain must ultimately fall to zero at zero frequency.

There are several practical limitations to the size of the coupling capacitance that may be used. The capacitor must be of high quality so that any leakage current will be small. Otherwise a conduction path from the plate of one stage to the grid of the next stage may exist. But good-quality capacitors in sizes greater than 0.1 μf are physically large and are relatively expensive. Also, if the coupling capacitance is large, a phenomenon known as *blocking* may result. This arises when the time constant CR_g is much larger than the period of the highest frequency to be passed by the amplifier. Thus if an appreciable charge flows into the capacitor with the application of the input signal and if this cannot leak off quickly enough, a charge will build up. This may bias the tube highly negatively, perhaps even beyond cutoff. The amplifier then becomes inoperative until the capacitor discharges. This condition is sometimes desirable in special electron-tube circuits and will be the subject of a detailed discussion in Chap. 7. However, it is a condition that must be avoided in an amplifier that is to reproduce the input signal in an amplified form.

The grid resistance R_g must be made high to keep the gain high, since R_g of one stage represents a loading across the plate resistance R_l of the previous stage. The upper limit to this value is set by the grid current. Ordinarily the grid current is small, particularly when the grid bias is negative. But if the grid resistance is made too high, and several megohms is the usual limit, the potential across this resistance will act as a spurious bias on the tube. While special low-grid-current tubes are available, these are designed for special operations and would not ordinarily be used in conventional circuits.

H-F Region. At the high frequencies, the admittance of C is very large, and the admittance of C_g becomes important. The equivalent circuit corresponding to these conditions becomes that shown in Fig. 4-6. The general expression for the gain reduces to

$$\mathbf{K} = \mathbf{K}_2 = \frac{-\mu \mathbf{Y}_p}{\mathbf{Y}_p + \mathbf{Y}_l + \mathbf{Y}_{R_g} + \mathbf{Y}_{C_g}} \tag{4-15}$$

The gain ratio K_2/K_0 becomes

$$\frac{K_2}{K_0} = \frac{1}{1 + \dfrac{Y_{C_g}}{Y_p + Y_l + Y_{R_g}}} \tag{4-16}$$

This expression may be written in a form similar to Eq. (4-11) for the l-f case. It becomes

$$\frac{K_2}{K_0} = \frac{1}{1 + j(f/f_2)} \tag{4-17}$$

where

$$f_2 \equiv \frac{Y_p + Y_l + Y_{R_g}}{2\pi C_g} \tag{4-18}$$

In this expression C_g denotes the total capacitance from grid to cathode and comprises the input capacitance of the following stage, the output wiring, and the output tube capacitance.

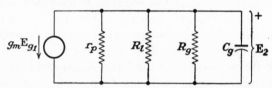

Fig. 4-6. The h-f equivalent circuit of the RC amplifier.

If the load is a pure resistance, then f_2 is a real number and the magnitude of the relative gain becomes

$$\frac{K_2}{K_0} = \sqrt{\frac{1}{1 + (f/f_2)^2}} \tag{4-19}$$

It follows from this that f_2 represents that frequency at which the h-f gain falls to $1/\sqrt{2}$, or 70.7 per cent, of its mid-frequency value. This frequency is usually referred to as the *h-f cutoff* of the amplifier. The relative phase angle θ_2 is given by

$$\tan \theta_2 = -\frac{f}{f_2} \tag{4-20}$$

This angle approaches -90 deg as the frequency becomes very large compared with f_2.

Note from Eq. (4-18) that the h-f cutoff value depends on the value of C_g, among other factors. Since the value of C_g appears in the denominator of the expression, then clearly a high h-f cutoff requires a small value of C_g. Moreover, since the input capacitance of a pentode is appreciably less than that of a triode, the pentode possesses inherently better possibilities for a broad frequency response than does the triode. It will be found in Sec. 5-11, in the discussion of the cathode-follower amplifier, that triodes with cathode-follower coupling stages also possess broad-band capabilities, although this is accomplished at the expense of a tube. Note above that the h-f cutoff is improved by the use of large Y_p, Y_l, and Y_{R_g}, which implies the use of small values of resistance R_l, R_g and a tube with a small plate resistance.

4-4. Universal Amplification Curves for RC Amplifiers.[1] The fore-going analysis shows that the gain of an RC coupled amplifier is substantially constant over a range of frequencies and falls off at both the

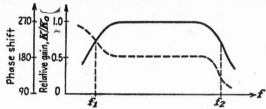

FIG. 4-7. A typical frequency response and phase characteristic of an RC coupled amplifier.

high and the low frequencies. A typical frequency-response curve has the form sketched in Fig. 4-7.

Since the relative gain and the relative phase-shift characteristics depend only upon the two parameters f_1 and f_2, it is possible to construct curves which are applicable to any such amplifier. Such universal curves are given in Fig. 4-8.

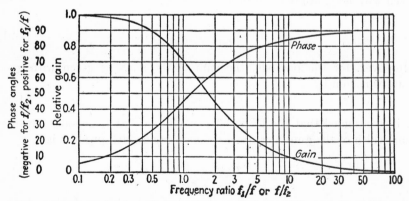

FIG. 4-8. Universal gain and phase-shift curves for an RC coupled amplifier.

The frequency-response characteristics of any RC coupled amplifier can easily be obtained with the aid of these curves. The first step in the analysis is to calculate the values of the parameters f_1 and f_2 from Eqs. (4-12) and (4-18). Then the values of the relative gain and the relative phase angle are obtained from the curves for a number of values of the ratio f_1/f and f/f_2. These are plotted as a function of f. It must be remembered in using Fig. 4-8 that the ordinate is K_1/K_0 or θ_1 when the abscissa is f_1/f. Also, the ordinate is K_2/K_0 or θ_2 when the abscissa is f/f_2.

4-5. Gain-Bandwidth Product. Suppose that it is desired to extend the h-f response of an RC coupled amplifier. According to the universal gain characteristic, this requires that the quantity f_2 be increased. By Eq. (4-18) this increase in f_2 may be accomplished by increasing any of the terms $\mathbf{Y}_p$, $\mathbf{Y}_l$, or $\mathbf{Y}_{R_g}$ or by decreasing C_g. It is desired to examine the effect of varying these parameters.

Consider the factor $\mathbf{Y}_p$. An increase in $\mathbf{Y}_p$ implies that the plate resistance r_p is reduced. This would seem to favor the use of triodes with low values of r_p. However, tubes of this type are power triodes, which are low-μ tubes. Consequently, in addition to the low gain inherent in such tubes, and the corresponding high grid driving signal that would be required for reasonable output potential, the use of a triode is inadvisable because of the relatively large total input capacitance which such a stage would possess [see Eq. (3-16)], so that the influence of the increase in C_g would more than overcome the gain possible by increasing $\mathbf{Y}_p$.

An increase in $\mathbf{Y}_l$, which implies a reduction in the load resistance R_l, will also be accompanied by an increased value of f_2. Thus while there is an increase in the bandwidth of the amplifier, the gain is thereby reduced. Suppose that the tube that is used is a pentode, and this is generally the case for a broad-band amplifier. Since r_p is large (and of the order of 1 megohm) and R_g may also be made large, the h-f cutoff value is given with good approximation by

$$f_2 = \frac{Y_l}{2\pi C_g} = \frac{1}{2\pi R_l C_g} \tag{4-21}$$

Moreover, for the pentode, the gain of the stage is given with good approximation by

$$K_2 = g_m R_l \tag{4-22}$$

If it is assumed that the l-f cutoff is small, so that f_2 denotes the total bandwidth of the amplifier, then the gain-bandwidth product is

$$K_2 B = \frac{g_m}{2\pi C_g} \tag{4-23}$$

Observe from this expression that the gain-bandwidth product of the RC coupled amplifier is a constant that depends only on the tube. This means that, by changing a circuit parameter to increase the gain, the bandwidth of the system is reduced; one is obtained at the expense of the other for a given tube and a given circuit configuration.

Since the gain of the stage is proportional to g_m of the tube, and since the bandwidth, for a given gain, is proportional to $1/C_g$ in a given circuit configuration, the limit to the bandwidth is dictated fundamentally by the interelectrode capacitances of the tube. Thus even if the wiring and socket capacitances were reduced to zero, an impossible practical situation, the sum of the output capacitance of the one tube and the input capacitance to the following stage would provide the ultimate limitation. That is, the ultimate limit is imposed by an effective capacitance C_t, which is the output capacitance of one tube and the input capacitance to the next tube, or,

$$K_2 B = \frac{g_m}{2\pi(C_{in} + C_{out})} = \frac{g_m}{2\pi C_t} \tag{4-24}$$

From this expression, a quantity M is defined as

$$M \equiv \frac{g_m}{C_t} \tag{4-25}$$

M is known as the *figure of merit* of the tube.

For service requiring a large gain-bandwidth product, the tube should possess a large transconductance in proportion to the input plus output electrode capacitances. The 6AK5 and the 6AC7 are both highly satisfactory in this respect, the 6AK5 being slightly superior to the 6AC7 When allowance is made for socket and wiring capacitances, an average 6AK5 has a gain-bandwidth product of approximately 55 Mc (for the tube capacitances alone this figure is approximately 117 Mc) and an average 6AC7 has a corresponding value of 50 Mc.

4-6. Cascaded Stages. When identical stages are connected in cascade, a higher gain is provided, as required by Eq. (4-1). However, this higher gain is accompanied by a narrower bandwidth. It is desired to obtain expressions which show the effect of cascading identical amplifiers. This is done piecewise for the important frequency regions.

Consider that n identical stages are connected in cascade. In the mid-frequency range the resultant gain is constant and is given by

$$K_{0n} = (K_0)^n \tag{4-26}$$

For the l-f region, the relative gain for the n stages is given by

$$\left(\frac{K_1}{K_0}\right)^n = \frac{1}{[1 + (f_1/f)^2]^{n/2}} \tag{4-27}$$

The resulting l-f cutoff value is defined as that value for which the relative gain is reduced by $1/\sqrt{2}$. This requires that

$$\left[1 + \left(\frac{f_1}{f}\right)^2\right]^{n/2} = 2^{1/2} \tag{4-28}$$

from which

$$1 + \left(\frac{f_1}{f}\right)^2 = 2^{1/n}$$

so that

$$\frac{f_1}{f_{1n}} = \sqrt{2^{1/n} - 1} \tag{4-29}$$

The relative h-f gain for the n-stage amplifier is obtained exactly as for the l-f region and is given by

$$\left(\frac{K_2}{K_0}\right)^n = \frac{1}{[1 + (f/f_2)^2]^{n/2}} \tag{4-30}$$

The corresponding h-f cutoff value is then

$$\frac{f_{2n}}{f_2} = \sqrt{2^{1/n} - 1} \tag{4-31}$$

Table 4-1 gives the values of the cutoff frequency reduction function $\sqrt{2^{1/n} - 1}$. It is seen, for example, that the h-f cutoff value of two

TABLE 4-1

BANDWIDTH REDUCTION FACTOR $\sqrt{2^{1/n} - 1}$

n	$\sqrt{2^{1/n} - 1}$
1	1.0
2	0.643
3	0.510
4	0.435
5	0.387
6	0.350

identical stages in cascade is reduced by a factor 0.643. Correspondingly, the l-f cutoff value is increased by this same factor. This means, of course, that the total bandwidth of the amplifier decreases as the number of cascaded stages increases. To achieve specified over-all h-f and l-f cutoff values, the single-stage cutoff values must be correspondingly high and low, respectively.

4-7. Direct-coupled Amplifier.[2] It is possible to build a type of cascaded amplifier without reactive elements and, in principle at least, secure a very broad-band amplifier. The potential gain of such an amplifier does not depend on the frequency, at least to a first approximation. However, the effect of tube and wiring capacitances imposes the same limitations on the h-f cutoff of the amplifier as in the RC coupled amplifier. It might appear that such amplifiers would find very widespread use because of these desirable characteristics. However, such amplifiers do possess certain disadvantages, and their use is limited, though they find extensive employment as d-c amplifiers and as amplifiers for very slowly varying inputs.

A battery-coupled cascade-amplifier circuit of basic design, together with the equivalent plate circuit for small changes in potential and current, is shown in Fig. 4-9. The gain of such an amplifier stage is readily found to be

$$\mathbf{K} = \frac{-\mu R_l}{r_p + R_l} \tag{4-32}$$

It will be observed that the circuits are quite like the RC coupled amplifier except that the coupling (blocking) capacitors are absent. Because of the fact that the grid of one stage is directly connected to the plate circuit of the previous stage, it is necessary to include d-c sources at the various critical points in the circuit in order that the quiescent conditions be those of class A operation.

The battery-coupled amplifier has the outstanding feature that it will amplify a steady component in the input voltage, but it suffers from

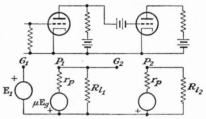

Fig. 4-9. Basic battery-coupled amplifier circuit.

three main disadvantages. The first is the cost of the relatively high-potential grid-bias batteries. These are required when a common plate and a common filament supply are used. In an alternative arrangement, indirectly heated cathodes having different potentials are used, thus obviating the necessity for large grid-bias potentials. However, separate plate supplies are required in this case.

The second disadvantage of the direct-coupled amplifier is the inherent instability associated with direct coupling. The characteristics of the tubes in the circuit change slightly with time; the battery potentials or the a-c line-operated rectified power supplies, likewise change with time. Since such changes are amplified, the d-c amplifier is not feasible unless precautions can be taken which tend to overcome this instability. For this reason, balanced circuits and circuits with degenerative feedback are used, since they tend to minimize this difficulty.

The third disadvantage arises from the capacitance between the grid-bias batteries and the cathodes. This, plus the interelectrode capacitances, stray wiring capacitance, and stray inductance, influences the transient-response time and materially affects the rapidity with which the amplifier output responds to rapid changes of input potential. In consequence, even though the amplifier is direct-coupled, precautions must be taken to ensure a broad h-f response in order to provide a short response time.

It is possible to build a direct-coupled amplifier that uses a positive plate supply, a negative bias supply, and resistance coupling networks. This overcomes the first disadvantage. The circuit of such an amplifier is illustrated in Fig. 4-10. The equivalent circuit of a typical stage of this amplifier is given in Fig. 4-11. The gain of such an amplifier is

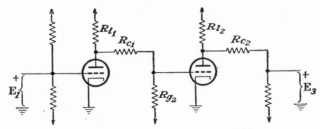

Fig. 4-10. A resistance-coupled amplifier.

readily found to be

$$K = -\frac{\mu R_{g2} \dfrac{R_{l1}}{R_{l1} + R_{c1} + R_{g2}}}{r_p + \dfrac{R_{l1}(R_{c1} + R_{g2})}{R_{l1} + R_{c1} + R_{g2}}} \qquad (4\text{-}33)$$

For an appreciable potential gain, the parallel combination of R_{l1} and $R_{c1} + R_{g2}$ should be large compared with r_p, and R_{g2} should be large compared with R_{c1}. This will necessitate the use of a large bias supply.

Direct-coupled amplifiers are used extensively as the amplifier in a circuit the grid exciting source of which has a very high internal resistance or which is capable of supplying only a very small current. In this case, the grid current must be very small. In particular, the grid current is significant when the grid-cathode resistance of the tube, though high, might not be large in comparison with the resistance of the circuit that supplies the grid signal voltage. Special electrometer tubes in which the grid current is of the order of 10^{-15} amp are available for such applications. The grid current of the typical negative-grid tube is of the order of 10^{-8} amp with normal rated potential applied to the tube electrodes. With the electrode potentials at very low values, the grid current may be reduced as low as 10^{-12} amp. More will be said about the applications of such amplifiers in Chap. 14.

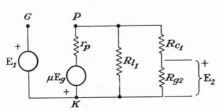

Fig. 4-11. The equivalent circuit of a typical stage of the resistance-coupled amplifier of Fig. 4-10.

4-8. The Cathode-coupled Amplifier. A two-tube circuit which is used extensively as a direct-coupled amplifier, owing to certain self-balancing features, and which is often used as an a-c amplifier, is illustrated in Fig. 4-12.   This circuit overcomes the first disadvantage of the previous section and permits the use of a common battery supply for all stages.

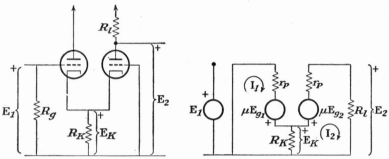

Fig. 4-12. A cathode-coupled amplifier and its equivalent circuit.

To analyze the operation of the circuit, the Kirchhoff potential law is applied to the loop circuits shown.   The tubes are assumed to be identical.   Hence, there follows

$$\begin{aligned}
\mathbf{E}_{g1} &= \mathbf{E}_1 - \mathbf{E}_k = \mathbf{E}_1 - (\mathbf{I}_1 - \mathbf{I}_2)R_k \\
\mathbf{E}_{g2} &= -\mathbf{E}_k = -(\mathbf{I}_1 - \mathbf{I}_2)R_k \\
\mathbf{I}_1 r_p &- \mu\mathbf{E}_{g1} + \mathbf{E}_k = 0 \\
\mathbf{I}_2(r_p + R_l) &+ \mu\mathbf{E}_{g2} - \mathbf{E}_k = 0
\end{aligned} \tag{4-34}$$

Write the equations in the form

$$\mathbf{I}_1[r_p + (\mu + 1)R_k] - \mathbf{I}_2(\mu + 1)R_k = \mu\mathbf{E}_1$$
$$-\mathbf{I}_1(\mu + 1)R_k + \mathbf{I}_2[r_p + (\mu + 1)R_k + R_l] = 0$$

The solution of these equations yields, for current $\mathbf{I}_2$,

$$\mathbf{I}_2 = \frac{\mu(\mu + 1)R_k\mathbf{E}_1}{[r_p + (\mu + 1)R_k][r_p + (\mu + 1)R_k + R_l] - [(\mu + 1)R_k]^2} \tag{4-35}$$

The output potential $\mathbf{E}_2$ is

$$\mathbf{E}_2 = \mathbf{I}_2R_l = \frac{\mu(\mu + 1)R_kR_l\mathbf{E}_1}{[r_p + (\mu + 1)R_k][r_p + (\mu + 1)R_k + R_l] - [(\mu + 1)R_k]^2} \tag{4-36}$$

Now write this as

$$\mathbf{E}_2 = \frac{\mu R_l\mathbf{E}_1}{2r_p + \dfrac{r_p(r_p + R_l)}{(\mu + 1)R_k} + R_l} \tag{4-37}$$

If the parameters are so chosen that $r_p + R_l \ll (\mu + 1)R_k$, then approximately

$$\mathbf{E}_2 = \frac{\mu R_l\mathbf{E}_1}{2r_p + R_l} \tag{4-38}$$

which is a form quite like that for the ordinary single-tube amplifier, except for the appearance of the factor $2r_p$ in the denominator instead of simply r_p. Note also that the output potential has the same phase as the input potential. A typical circuit showing a cascade cathode-coupled amplifier is given in Fig. 4-13.

It may be shown that the h-f cutoff value for cascaded stages, which results from the effects of the interelectrode wiring, and distributed capacitances, is considerably higher than in a single-tube amplifier. However, such amplifier stages are not used for broad-band or video amplifiers, since a pentode proves to be superior, both as regards gain and

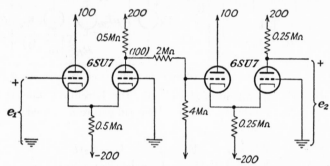

FIG. 4-13. A multistage d-c amplifier employing cathode-coupled amplifiers.

bandwidth possibilities. Moreover, pentodes are seldom used in this circuit from bandwidth considerations alone. Such cathode-coupled amplifiers are used for very l-f or d-c amplifier service.

4-9. H-F Compensation of Video Amplifiers. The untuned potential amplifiers that are discussed in the foregoing sections possess flat frequency-response characteristics over a range of frequencies. Frequently, however, the region of uniform amplification must be wider than is possible with the simple circuits. Also, the question of the phase response becomes quite important in many broad-band amplifiers. Extending the h-f range of an amplifier has received considerable attention, different services requiring different solutions. For example, radar receivers may require a uniform response of 2 to 8 Mc, depending upon the service, although the l-f response in these is not too critical. Television receivers require a sensibly uniform amplification over the range from 30 cps to 4.5 Mc. Such broad-band amplifiers may be achieved by compensating the simple amplifier at both the l-f and the h-f ends of the frequency scale; by the use of tubes as coupling devices, these being connected ordinarily as cathode followers; or by the use of circuits from which the primary cause of the frequency distortion has been eliminated.

4-10. Compensated Broad-band Amplifiers.[3] It is possible to compensate for the drooping of the frequency-response characteristic of a resistance-capacitance coupled amplifier at both the h-f and the l-f ends of the curve. A number of methods exist for accomplishing these results, and several of the more important of these will be considered below in some detail. However, it is advisable to examine roughly what occurs in these several methods of compensation before undertaking a complete analysis.

In the shunt-peaked method of h-f compensation, an inductor is inserted in series with the load resistor. The circuit has the form illustrated in Fig. 4-14. The inductance L_c is chosen of such a value that it

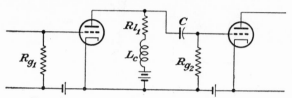

Fig. 4-14. A shunt-peak video amplifier stage.

resonates with the total effective capacitance of the output of one tube and the input of the following tube in the neighborhood of the frequency at which the response would otherwise begin to fall appreciably. In this way, the h-f end of the response curve can be appreciably extended. The choice of the value of L_c is critical; otherwise a peak in the response curve may occur. Such overcompensation must be avoided in most applications.

4-11. H-F Compensation. To study the gain characteristics of an amplifier that is provided with a shunt compensating circuit, the equivalent circuit of Fig. 4-15 is drawn.

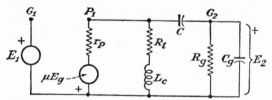

Fig. 4-15. The equivalent circuit of an RC amplifier with an inductor in series with the plate resistor for h-f compensation.

As the series inductance L_c is small (20 to 50 μh), its presence does not affect the l-f or the mid-frequency gains of the amplifier. Consequently for this amplifier, Eq. (4-8) for the mid-frequency gain and Eqs. (4-13) and (4-14) for the l-f gain are still valid. These expressions are rewritten here for convenience.

$$\mathbf{K}_0 = \frac{-\mu \mathbf{Y}_p}{\mathbf{Y}_p + \mathbf{Y}_l + \mathbf{Y}_{R_g}}$$

$$\frac{\mathbf{K}_1}{\mathbf{K}_0} = \frac{1}{\sqrt{1 + (f_1/f)^2}} \Big/ \tan^{-1}\frac{f_1}{f}$$

(4-39)

Broad-band amplifiers usually employ pentodes with relatively small plate-load resistances, as discussed in Sec. 4-5. Because of this, the discussion here will be confined to amplifiers of this type. But for pentodes,

$$r_p \gg R_l \qquad R_{g2} \gg R_l \qquad (4\text{-}40)$$

and the equivalent circuit of Fig. 4-15 reduces to the form of Fig. 4-16.

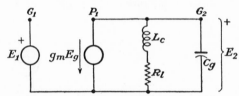

FIG. 4-16. The approximate equivalent circuit of Fig. 4-15 at the mid- and high frequencies.

It follows directly from this that the mid-frequency gain is

$$\mathbf{K_0} = -g_m R_l \qquad (4\text{-}41)$$

and the h-f gain becomes

$$\mathbf{K_2} = \frac{-\mu Y_p}{Y_p + Y_l + Y_{R_g} + Y_{C_g}} \doteq \frac{-g_m}{Y_l + Y_{C_g}} \qquad (4\text{-}42)$$

The h-f- to mid-frequency-gain ratio is

$$\frac{\mathbf{K_2}}{\mathbf{K_0}} = \frac{1}{R_l(Y_l + Y_{C_g})} \qquad (4\text{-}43)$$

Use is made of the quantity f_2, the half-power frequency without compensation, which is, from Eq. (4-18),

$$f_2 = \frac{Y_p + Y_l + Y_{R_g}}{2\pi C_g} \doteq \frac{1}{2\pi R_l C_g} \qquad (4\text{-}44)$$

Also, it is convenient to define the quantity Q_2 as

$$Q_2 \equiv \frac{L_c}{R_l^2 C_g} = \frac{\omega_2 L_c}{R_l} \qquad (4\text{-}45)$$

This is the Q of the series load circuit at the frequency f_2. Equation (4-43) may then be written in the form

$$\frac{\mathbf{K_2}}{\mathbf{K_0}} = \frac{1}{\dfrac{1}{1 + j(\omega/\omega_2)Q_2} + j\dfrac{\omega}{\omega_2}} \qquad (4\text{-}46)$$

This expression is expanded thus:

$$\frac{\mathbf{K_2}}{\mathbf{K_0}} = \frac{1 + j(\omega/\omega_2)Q_2}{[1 - (\omega/\omega_2)^2 Q_2] + j(\omega/\omega_2)}$$

which may be written as

$$\frac{K_2}{K_0} = \sqrt{\frac{1 + (\omega/\omega_2)^2 Q_2^2}{[1 - (\omega/\omega_2)^2 Q_2]^2 + (\omega/\omega_2)^2}} \bigg/ \tan^{-1} \frac{\omega}{\omega_2} Q_2 - \tan^{-1} \frac{\omega/\omega_2}{1 - (\omega/\omega_2)^2 Q_2}$$

$$(4-47)$$

The significance of this equation is best understood by examining curves of gain and phase shift for various values of Q_2. A set of gain curves is given in Fig. 4-17.

It is ordinarily desired that the potential gain be practically constant up to a certain designated high frequency. An inspection of Fig. 4-17

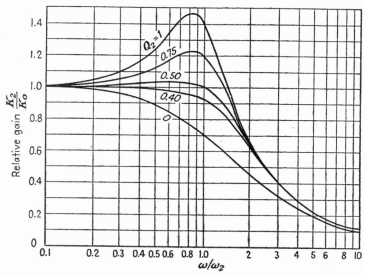

FIG. 4-17. Dimensionless relative-gain curves for the shunt-compensated amplifier. [*Adapted from A. V. Bedford and G. L. Fredendall, Proc. IRE*, **27**, 277 (1939).]

shows that this is best achieved by choosing Q_2 to have a value approximately 0.45. Actually the optimum value for Q_2 is found to be 0.414, under which condition $dK/df = d^2K/df^2 = 0$ for the low frequencies. For the optimum value of Q_2 the response curve remains flat without overshoot over the greatest possible frequency range ω/ω_2 and is therefore known as the *maximally flat* response. From Eqs. (4-44) and (4-45), this requires approximately that

$$R_l = \frac{1}{\omega_2 C_g}$$

$$\omega_2 L_c = \frac{R_l}{2}$$

$$(4-48)$$

That is, approximately constant gain is achieved when the load resistance is approximately equal to the reactance of the effective shunt capacitance and when the inductive reactance is equal approximately to one-half the load resistance at the frequency ω_2.

In order to preserve the waveform of the signal in an amplifier, not only must the relative amplitudes of the various frequency components be maintained, but also their phase relations must be held constant. If this is not so, then phase distortion results. The phase shift through the

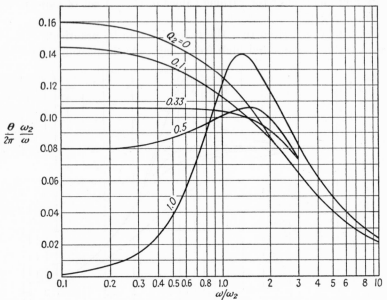

Fig. 4-18. Dimensionless curves of θ/ω as a function of ω/ω_2 for shunt-compensated amplifiers.

amplifier is contained in Eq. (4-47), which is

$$\theta = -\tan^{-1}\frac{\omega}{\omega_2}\left[1 - Q_2 + \left(\frac{\omega Q_2}{\omega_2}\right)^2\right] \qquad (4\text{-}49)$$

Evidently, for the waveform to be preserved, either the phase shift of the various components through the amplifier must be zero, or else the phase of all the frequency components must be changed by the same amount in time. In this way the relative phase relations among the harmonics in the waveform will be preserved. A criterion for zero phase distortion is that θ/ω be a constant. A plot of the dimensionless or normalized time delay $\theta\omega_2/2\pi\omega$ vs. ω/ω_2 is contained in Fig. 4-18.

Figure 4-18 shows a family of dimensionless curves which apply to any amplifier. With ω/ω_2 and Q_2 given, the phase shift at any frequency is readily determined. It will be observed that the curve for $Q_2 = 0.33$ appears to show the least variation of θ/ω and so would introduce the least phase distortion or time delay. Actually, by taking the derivative of θ with respect to ω and equating the coefficients for constant delay in the circuit, the optimum value of Q_2 is found to be 0.32.   On the other hand, the curve for $Q_2 = 0.414$ yields the least variation in gain.   In general, therefore, it would appear that the value of Q_2 should lie in the range from 0.32 to 0.41.   Frequently a value of Q_2 of 0.5 is used, for reasons now to be discussed.

The curve for $Q_2 = 0.5$ yields a relatively uniform amplification over as wide a frequency range as for any value of Q_2. For this case, the relative gain increases by about 3 per cent ($= 0.3$ db) at $\omega/\omega_2 = 0.70$. This is frequently a tolerable increase if only a few stages are used. Moreover, the time-delay errors of the individual stages are additive and would be tolerable in many applications.   If many stages are to be used, then the situation changes.   For example, a 10-stage amplifier designed with $Q_2 = 0.50$ would have a 3-db (41 per cent) bump in the gain curve, with a corresponding serious time-delay error.   Such characteristics might not be tolerable, and a value of Q_2 of 0.41 or lower would then be used.

Clearly, therefore, the acceptable value of Q_2 will be determined by the maximum allowable variation in gain and the tolerable time-delay error.   If one can tolerate the resulting variation in gain, then a given number of stages with $Q_2 = 0.50$ will provide a given gain with a broader bandwidth than is possible with $Q_2 = 0.41$.   This means that the requirement for maximum flatness sacrifices bandwidth for a more uniform amplification curve and less time-delay or phase distortion.

It should perhaps be emphasized that the inclusion of an inductance as a compensating network has resulted in a rather remarkable improvement in response.   That such a simple correcting network does not provide both optimum gain and constant-phase characteristics for the same conditions should not be surprising or unexpected.   More elaborate h-f compensating networks that provide better gain characteristics have been devised.   A number of these are discussed later.

4-12. Transient Response of Shunt-peaked Amplifier.   Some clarification of the need for a broad frequency-response characteristic is possible by examining the transient-response characteristic of such an amplifier. In particular, suppose that the amplifier is to amplify a narrow pulse, say one that lasts for a microsecond or less.   Pulses of this time duration are found in television receivers and also in radar receivers.   It is desired to examine and relate the transient-response characteristic with the h-f characteristics of the amplifier.

Consider first the uncompensated amplifier to which a step function of potential is applied.   The approximate equivalent circuit, the form of the applied input potential and the form of the output potential are given in Fig. 4-19. If the potential step-function is applied at $t = 0$ when the capacitor is uncharged, the output is easily shown to be

$$e_2 = - \frac{\mu E R_l}{r_p + R_l} (1 - e^{-t/R_l C_g}) \doteq -g_m R_l E(1 - e^{-t/R_l C_g}) \qquad (4\text{-}50)$$

which shows that the output will not follow the applied potential but will

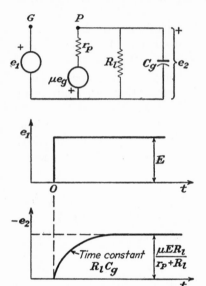

approach the steady-state value in the customary exponential manner.

The rise time of such an amplifier is often taken as the time required for the amplifier to change from 0.1 of its final value to 0.9 of this value. By inserting these values into Eq. (4-50) and solving for the corresponding value of t, it is found that, at the 0.1 point, the time is $0.1R_l C_g$ and, at the 0.9 point, the time is $2.3R_l C_g$. The

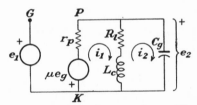

Fig. 4-19. The uncompensated amplifier and its transient response to an input step-function potential.

Fig. 4-20. The shunt-peak amplifier circuit.

rise time is then given by

$$t_{\text{rise}} = 2.2 R_l C_g = \frac{2.2}{2\pi f_2} = \frac{0.35}{f_2} \qquad (4\text{-}51)$$

Thus t_{rise} is seen to be inversely proportional to the band pass of the amplifier. Suppose, for example, that f_2 is 1 Mc. It will then require 0.35 μsec for the potential to rise from 0.1 to 0.9 of its final value. A 1-μsec pulse will be distorted, but it will retain some semblance of its original form. However, a 0.1-μsec pulse will be completely distorted if f_2 is only 1 Mc, a value of 10 Mc being required if the same relative shape is required as with a 1-μsec pulse and a 1-Mc amplifier.

For the case of the shunt-peaked amplifier, the network to be evaluated is that given in Fig. 4-20. The network equations have the operational form

$$(r_p + R_l + L_c p)i_1 - (R_l + L_c p)i_2 = -\mu e_1$$

$$-(R_l + L_c p)i_1 + \left(R_l + L_c p + \frac{1}{C_g p}\right) i_2 = 0 \qquad (4\text{-}52)$$

where p is the symbol for the time derivative operator d/dt. The resulting differential equation relating i_2 with the applied potential e_1 and the network parameters is

$$i_2 = \frac{-\mu(R_l + L_c p)}{(r_p + R_l + L_c p)\left(R_l + L_c p + \dfrac{1}{C_g p}\right) - (R_l + L_c p)^2}\, e_1 \quad (4\text{-}53)$$

The output potential is then related to the input potential by the differential equation

$$e_2 = \frac{-\mu(R_l + L_c p)}{C_g p\left[(r_p + R_l + L_c p)\left(R_l + L_c p + \dfrac{1}{C_g p}\right) - (R_l + L_c p)^2\right]}\, e_1 \quad (4\text{-}54)$$

The solution of this equation is somewhat complicated[4]; the results are best given in graphical form. This is done in Fig. 4-21, which gives

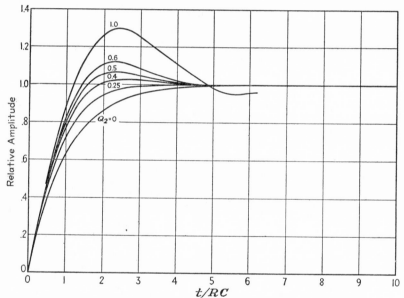

FIG. 4-21. The step-function response of the shunt-peaked amplifier.

the step-function response for various values of Q_2, for C_g initially uncharged.

The foregoing analysis can be extended to the case of such amplifier stages in cascade. The procedure is straightforward, though the resulting equations are complicated. The results for two identical stages in cascade are given in Fig. 4-22, and the results for three identical stages in cascade are given in Fig. 4-23. It is observed from these sets of curves that the rise time of the amplifier decreases with higher values of Q_2.

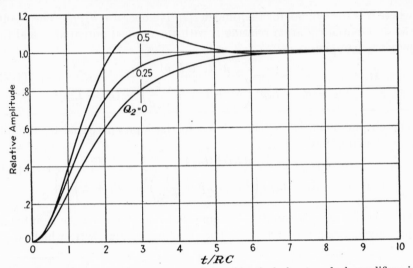

FIG. 4-22. The step-function response of two identical shunt-peaked amplifiers in cascade.

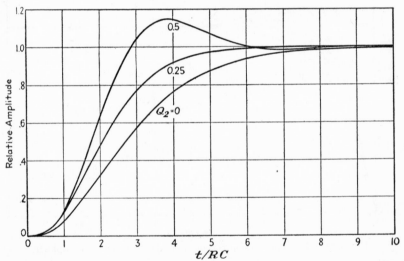

FIG. 4-23. The step-function response of three identical shunt-peaked amplifiers in cascade.

However, the fastest rise time with negligible overshoot occurs for the value of Q_2 which gives the most linear-phase characteristic.

The foregoing considerations suggest a simple direct experimental method of obtaining the band pass of an amplifier. The input to the amplifier is a square wave, and the output is observed on an oscilloscope. The rise time as herein defined is then measured and is related to the band pass through Eq. (4-51).   The square wave is used as a repeating transient source in order to permit sufficient intensity for direct observation on the face of the oscilloscope.   Of course, the square wave must have a very small rise time, and the oscilloscope must possess a sufficiently high frequency response compared with the amplifier under test not to influence the results.   An accurate sweep calibrator would be used for measuring the rise time.

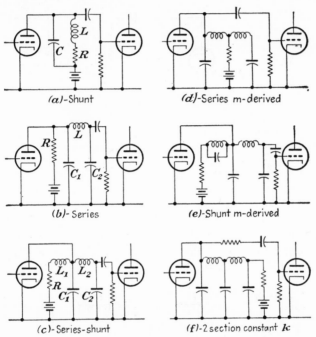

FIG. 4-24. Various h-f compensating coupling circuits.   (*D. L. Jaffee, Electronics, April*, 1942.)

A number of other methods of compensating the h-f response character of an amplifier exist, some of which are superior to the simple shunt-compensated amplifier discussed in detail.   Some of these are illustrated in Fig. 4-24.   The transient response of these more elaborate networks is generally not markedly superior to that of the simple shunt-peaking compensation.   This results from the fact that the amplification and phase-shift characteristics do not deteriorate so rapidly in the shunt-peaked circuit as in other h-f compensating systems having the same h-f limit.   Consequently the apparent advantage of these circuits is largely eliminated.   Specifically,[5] the rise time for the simple shunt-compensated amplifier of Fig. 4-24a with $L = \frac{1}{4}CR^2$ is $1.57RC$; for the series-compensated amplifier (Fig. 4-24b), with $C_1 + C_2 = C$, $C_1 = C/9$, $C_2 = 8C/9$,

$L_1 = 3CR^2/8$, the rise time is $1.40RC$; for the series-shunt compensation of Fig. 4-24c, with $C_1 + C_2 = C$, $C_1 = C/5$, $C_2 = 4C/5$, $L_1 = CR^2/16$, $L_2 = 25CR^2/64$, the rise time is $1.24RC$.

4-13. L-F Compensation. The l-f end of the frequency-response curve may be extended by the use of a capacitance across a portion of the load resistance, as illustrated in Fig. 4-25. In this method, the load resistance is effectively R_l at the high frequencies, owing to the shunting

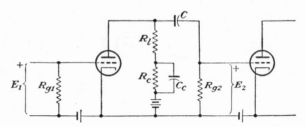

Fig. 4-25. Low-frequency compensation by use of a capacitor across a portion of the load.

action of the capacitance C_c across R_c. At the low frequencies, the shunting effect of C_c is negligible, and the load resistance is effectively $R_l + R_c$. The increased gain of the stage resulting from the increased effective load impedance thus compensates for the loss of gain resulting from the potential-divider action of the coupling capacitor and the grid resistor. In this case, as for the h-f compensation, care must be exercised in the choice of circuit constants.

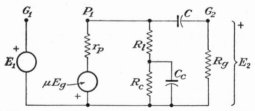

Fig. 4-26. The equivalent circuit of an l-f-compensated RC amplifier.

The equivalent circuit, given in Fig. 4-26, is to be analyzed. Use is again made of the fact that pentodes are generally used in video amplifiers, whence r_p is greater than the combined output load impedance **Z**. Also, in general, the grid resistance of the following stage R_g is large compared with the load resistance R_l.

The mid-frequency gain assumes that the reactances of C_c and C are small compared with R_l and R_g, respectively. The gain expression is then simply

$$\mathbf{K}_0 = -g_m R_l \tag{4-55}$$

The l-f gain is readily obtained from an examination of Fig. 4-26. The expression is

$$\mathbf{K}_1 = -g_m \mathbf{Z} \frac{R_g}{R_g + 1/j\omega C} \tag{4-56}$$

where $\mathbf{Z}$ is the total effective impedance of the output network at the low frequencies. By inserting the known value of $\mathbf{Z}$ in Eq. (4-56) and combining with Eq. (4-55), there results

$$\frac{\mathbf{K}_1}{\mathbf{K}_0} = \frac{1}{R_l \left(\dfrac{1}{R_l + \dfrac{1}{\dfrac{1}{R_c} + j\omega C_c}} + \dfrac{1}{R_g + \dfrac{1}{j\omega C}} \right)} \frac{R_g}{R_g + \dfrac{1}{j\omega C}} \tag{4-57}$$

or

$$\frac{\mathbf{K}_1}{\mathbf{K}_0} = \frac{1}{\dfrac{1}{1 + \dfrac{R_c}{R_l + j\omega C_c R_c R_l}} + \dfrac{j\omega C R_l}{1 + j\omega C R_g}} \frac{1}{1 + \dfrac{1}{j\omega C R_g}}$$

or

$$\frac{\mathbf{K}_1}{\mathbf{K}_0} = \frac{1}{\dfrac{R_l + j\omega C_c R_c R_l}{R_l + R_c + j\omega C_c R_c R_l} + \dfrac{j\omega C R_l}{1 + j\omega C R_g}} \frac{1 + j\omega C R_g}{j\omega C R_g}$$

which is

$$\frac{\mathbf{K}_1}{\mathbf{K}_0} = \frac{1}{\dfrac{R_l}{R_g} + \dfrac{R_l + j\omega C_c R_c R_l}{R_l + R_c + j\omega C_c R_c R_l} \dfrac{1 + j\omega C R_g}{j\omega C R_g}} \tag{4-58}$$

But ordinarily the ratio $R_l/R_g \ll 1$, and Eq. (4-58) becomes

$$\frac{\mathbf{K}_1}{\mathbf{K}_0} = \frac{1}{\dfrac{R_l}{R_l + R_c} \dfrac{1 + j\omega C_c R_c}{1 + j\omega C_c \dfrac{R_c R_l}{R_c + R_l}} \dfrac{1 + j\omega C R_g}{j\omega C R_g}} \tag{4-59}$$

Three time constants appear in this expression, viz.,

$$C_c R_c \qquad C_c \frac{R_c R_l}{R_c + R_l} \qquad C R_g \tag{4-60}$$

By choosing the parameters such that

$$C R_g = C_c \frac{R_c R_l}{R_c + R_l} \tag{4-61}$$

Eq. (4-59) becomes

$$\frac{\mathbf{K}_1}{\mathbf{K}_0} = \frac{1}{\dfrac{R_l}{R_l + R_c} \dfrac{1 + j\omega C_c R_c}{1 + j\omega C R_g} \dfrac{1 + j\omega C R_g}{j\omega C R_g}}$$

which is

$$\frac{K_1}{K_0} = \frac{1}{(1 + j\omega C_c R_c)(1/j\omega C_c R_c)} = \frac{1}{1 - j(1/\omega C_c R_c)} \qquad (4\text{-}62)$$

This may be written in the form

$$\frac{K_1}{K_0} = \frac{1}{\sqrt{1 + (X_{Cc}/R_c)^2}} \Big/ \tan^{-1} \frac{X_{C_e}}{R_c} \qquad (4\text{-}63)$$

It is noted that this choice of parameters yields exactly the same form for the l-f response for the compensated case as that of the uncompensated amplifier, and the universal amplification curves may be used if the correct interpretations are made.   In the present case the l-f response is controlled by the time constant $R_c C_c$ rather than by the output time constant $R_g C$.   The l-f cutoff value now occurs at the value

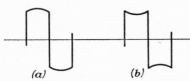

(a)   (b)

Fig. 4-27. The transient response of an (a) l-f-overcompensated, (b) l-f-undercompensated video amplifier.

$$f = \frac{R_l}{R_c + R_l} f_1 \qquad (4\text{-}64)$$

Hence, the higher the value of R_c, the better the compensation.

If the circuit parameters are not chosen according to Eq. (4-61), overcompensation or undercompensation may occur, a rise or a fall occurring in the frequency-response characteristic at the low frequencies.   The effect of overcompensation is readily manifest in the transient response, the output waveshape for a square-wave input having the rounded output shown in Fig. 4-27a.   The corresponding effect for undercompensation has the waveform shown in Fig. 4-27b.

REFERENCES

1. Terman, F. E., *Electronics*, **10**, 34 (June, 1937).
2. Artzt, M., *Electronics*, **18**, 112 (August, 1945).
3. Bedford, A. V., and G. L. Fredendall, *Proc. IRE*, **27**, 277 (1939).
   Kallman, H. E., R. E. Spencer, and C. P. Singer, *Proc. IRE*, **33**, 169, 482 (1945).
   Arguimbau, L. B., "Vacuum Tube Circuits," Chap. IV, John Wiley & Sons, Inc., New York, 1948.
4. Goldman, S., "Transformation Calculus and Electrical Transients," Sec. 12-3, Prentice-Hall, Inc., New York, 1949.
   Cuccia, C. L., "Harmonics, Sidebands, and Transients in Communication Engineering," pp. 198ff., McGraw-Hill Book Company, Inc., New York, 1952.
5. Emms, E. T., and E. Jones, *Electronic Eng.*, **22**, 408 (1950).

PROBLEMS

4-1. The important constants of one of a chain of RC coupled amplifier stages employing pentodes (see Fig. 4-3) are

$$R_l = 75 \text{ kilohms} \qquad r_p = 10^6 \text{ ohms} \qquad g_m = 1,600 \ \mu\text{mhos} \qquad C = 0.01 \ \mu\text{f}$$
$$C_{gk} = 11 \ \mu\mu\text{f} \qquad C_{pk} = 8 \ \mu\mu\text{f} \qquad R_g = 500 \text{ kilohms}$$

a. Calculate the mid-frequency gain and the upper and lower cutoff frequencies.
b. Between what frequencies is the amplifier-stage phase 180 ± 15 deg?

4-2. The frequency response of a three-stage cascaded RC amplifier employing pentodes is to be constant within 0.5 db up to 18 kc. Calculate the h-f cutoff of each stage.

4-3. Consider a chain of similar triode circuits in cascade. Show that the limiting gain-bandwidth product is given by

$$K^2 B = \frac{g_m}{2\pi C_t}$$

What can be said about the use of triodes in a cascaded chain?

4-4. Compute the figure of merit of the following tubes: 6AK5, 6AC7, 6J6, 6F4 triodes; 6AK5, 6AC7 pentodes. (See any tube handbook for characteristics.)

4-5. A 6AC7 tube is used as one of a chain in a video amplifier that is shunt-compensated at the high frequencies and is also l-f compensated. The circuit of this amplifier is shown in the accompanying diagram. Calculate the value of

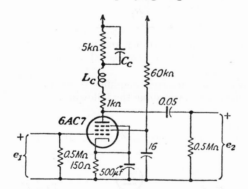

L_c that will yield the same gain at the upper frequency f_2 as at the mid-band. Assuming the stray wiring capacitances to be 20 $\mu\mu$f, the tube capacitances of the 6AC7 are $C_{gp} = 0.015$, $C_{pk} = 5 \ \mu\mu$f, $C_{gk} = 11 \ \mu\mu$f. Calculate f_1 under the optimum conditions for the l-f compensation.

4-6. A video amplifier stage is constructed using a 6AC7. An experimental test shows that the potential amplification drops to 0.707 of the mid-frequency gain at $f_2 = 1$ Mc with $R_l = 6$ kilohms.

a. For what value of R_l will the h-f cutoff value be 3 Mc?
b. What value of L_c is required for flattest gain under the conditions of (a)?
c. What value of L_c is required for "compromise" gain?
d. What is the mid-frequency gain?
e. What is the phase angle for flattest gain when $f = 0.8f_2$?

4-7. A video amplifier using 6AC7 tubes is to provide an over-all gain of 20,000 with a 3-Mc over-all band width. If the total stage shunt capacitance is 25 $\mu\mu$f and with $g_m = 9,000$ μmhos:

   a. Calculate the number of stages required, for $Q_2 = 0.414$.

   b. If 6SJ7 tubes are used ($g_m = 1,600$ μmhos), how many stages are required?

4-8. A five-stage shunt-peak video amplifier is to be built.

   a. If the amplification must not rise more than 1 db above the mid-frequency gain, estimate the value of Q_2 to be used. All stages are identical.

   b. If the time delay at the h-f cutoff point is to be within 10 per cent of the mid-frequency value, what range of Q_2 is permissible?

4-9. Refer to Fig. 4-10 showing a resistance-coupled amplifier. The circuit constants are $R_{l1} = 250$ kilohms, $R_{g2} = 500$ kilohms, $R_{c1} = 500$ kilohms. If $I_{b1} = 0.5$ ma, $E_{bb} = 300$ volts, what must be the value of E_{cc} if E_c of $T2$ is to be -8 volts?

4-10. Calculate the gain of the series balanced d-c amplifier shown in the diagram.

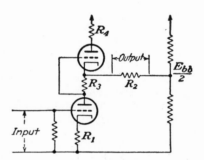

4-11. Calculate the input admittance and the effective internal impedance of the cathode-coupled amplifier when connected as shown in Fig. 4-12. Neglect tube and wiring capacitances.

4-12. The circuit of the inverted amplifier is shown. (Batteries have been omitted for convenience.) Determine the following:

   a. Gain.

   b. Input impedance.

   c. Ratio of output to input power if Z_g and Z_l are resistors.

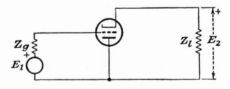

CHAPTER 5

FEEDBACK IN AMPLIFIERS*

5-1. Principles of Feedback.[1] When a part of the output signal is combined with the input signal, feedback is said to exist. If the net effect of the feedback is to increase the effective input signal, the feedback is called *positive, direct,* or *regenerative.* If the resultant input signal is reduced by the feedback potential, the feedback is called *negative, inverse,* or *degenerative.*

The principle of feedback is illustrated in the schematic diagram of Fig. 5-1. For simplicity, series injection is shown at the input, but other

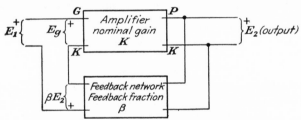

Fig. 5-1. The principle of feedback in amplifiers.

forms of network coupling may be employed. In the diagram shown, a potential E_1 is applied to the input terminals of the amplifier. Suppose that the resultant potential at the output terminals is E_2. Now suppose that a fraction β of this output is fed back in series with the input signal in such a way that the resultant signal that appears between the grid and cathode terminals has the form

$$E_g = E_1 + \beta E_2 \tag{5-1}$$

But the *nominal gain* of the amplifier is given by

$$K \equiv \frac{\text{output potential}}{\text{potential between grid and cathode}} = \frac{E_2}{E_g}$$

Then

$$E_2 = KE_g \tag{5-2}$$

Observe that the nominal gain requires the injection of a potential E_g

* Part of the contents of this chapter was originally prepared with Dr. J. Millman for the second edition of "Electronics," McGraw-Hill Book Company, Inc., New York, 1951, although the material was not included in this text.

between the grid-cathode terminals, with an evaluation of the output potential E_2, with the β network acting as part of the total output load of the circuit.

Equation (5-2) is combined with Eq. (5-1) to yield

$$E_2 = KE_1 + K\beta E_2$$

from which it follows that

$$E_2 = \frac{KE_1}{1 - K\beta} \tag{5-3}$$

The *resultant gain* of the amplifier with feedback is defined as

$$K_f \equiv \frac{\text{output potential}}{\text{input signal potential}} = \frac{E_2}{E_1}$$

Therefore it follows that

$$K_f = \frac{K}{1 - K\beta} \tag{5-4}$$

This equation expresses the resultant gain of the amplifier with feedback K_f in terms of the nominal gain of the amplifier without feedback K, and the feedback fraction β.

It can be seen that if $|1 - K\beta|$ is greater than unity, then K_f is less than K. The feedback is then said to be negative, or degenerative. The application of negative feedback to an amplifier results in a number of characteristics that are highly desirable in the amplifier. It tends to flatten the frequency-response characteristic and to extend the range of uniform response. It materially reduces nonlinear and phase distortion. It improves the stability of the amplifier, making the gain less dependent on the operating potentials or on variations of the tube characteristics. Also, it tends to make the gain less dependent on the load, so that load variations do not seriously influence the operating characteristics of the amplifier. The use of feedback networks of special design will provide selective attenuation, thus permitting a frequency response of desired characteristic. A detailed discussion of the foregoing features will be given later.

Conversely, if $|1 - K\beta|$ is less than unity, then K_f is greater than K. The feedback is now termed positive, or regenerative. The application of positive feedback has effects opposite to those with negative feedback. Thus positive feedback tends to sharpen the frequency-response curve and to decrease the range of uniform response. This permits an increased gain and selectivity. Positive feedback in any amplifier is critical of adjustment. Too much regenerative feedback in any system may result in oscillation. Ordinarily, negative feedback is more common than positive feedback in amplifiers, although oscillators of the feedback variety depend for their operation on the presence of positive feedback.

Observe that, for the case when $K\beta = 1 + j0$, the gain becomes infinite. In this case the amplifier becomes an oscillator, and the output potential is independent of any external signal potential.

Attention is called to the fact that the action of a feedback path depends upon the frequency of operation. That is, the feedback may remain regenerative or degenerative throughout the range of operation of the circuit, although the magnitude and phase angle of the feedback signal may vary with the frequency. It is also possible for the feedback to be positive over a certain range of frequencies and negative over another range of frequencies.

Example. The circuit of a simple triode amplifier with an impedance in the cathode lead is illustrated in Fig. 5-2. This circuit is to be analyzed by two methods. One method is a direct application of the feedback equation [Eq.

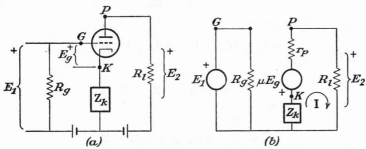

Fig. 5-2. A simple amplifier with cathode degeneration.

(5-4)]. The second method is a direct application of electron-tube circuit principles.

Solution. Refer to the equivalent circuit of the amplifier which is given in Fig. 5-2b. Observe that a part of the output is fed back into the input circuit through the impedance Z_k. It follows from the figure that

$$E_g = E_1 + IZ_k \tag{5-5}$$

But since

$$I = \frac{E_2}{R_l} \tag{5-6}$$

then

$$E_g = E_1 + \frac{Z_k}{R_l} E_2 \tag{5-7}$$

If this expression is compared with Eq. (5-1), which defines the feedback fraction, it is seen that

$$\beta = \frac{Z_k}{R_l} \tag{5-8}$$

Note also that

$$E_2 = IR_l = -\frac{\mu E_g}{r_p + Z_k + R_l} R_l \tag{5-9}$$

and the nominal gain then becomes

$$K = \frac{E_2}{E_g} = \frac{-\mu R_l}{r_p + Z_k + R_l} \tag{5-10}$$

The resultant gain is, by Eq. (5-4),

$$K_f = \frac{K}{1 - K\beta} = \frac{-\mu R_l/(r_p + Z_k + R_l)}{1 - \dfrac{-\mu R_l}{r_p + Z_k + R_l}\dfrac{Z_k}{R_l}} = \frac{-\mu R_l}{r_p + (\mu + 1)Z_k + R_l} \tag{5-11}$$

These results follow of course from direct considerations of the equivalent circuit. The plate circuit yields the expression

$$\mu E_g + I(r_p + Z_k + R_l) = 0 \tag{5-12}$$

But

$$E_g = E_1 + IZ_k \tag{5-13}$$

The solution of these equations gives

$$\mu(E_1 + IZ_k) + I(r_p + Z_k + R_l) = 0$$

from which

$$I = \frac{-\mu E_1}{r_p + (\mu + 1)Z_k + R_l} \tag{5-14}$$

and the resultant gain is

$$K_f = \frac{E_2}{E_1} = \frac{-\mu R_l}{r_p + (\mu + 1)Z_k + R_l} \tag{5-15}$$

which is the same as above.

Often Z_k consists of the parallel combination of R_k and C_k, the value of R_k being so chosen that $I_b R_k$ is just equal to E_c, the quiescent d-c bias of the tube. The capacitance C_k is so chosen that its reactance is very small over the operating range of the amplifier. As a result, Z_k is very small and may be omitted in the above expression. In this case, the usual simple amplifier formula is obtained, since the feedback factor β is zero, and no feedback exists.

5-2. Feedback Amplifier Characteristics. The presence of negative feedback in an amplifier results in a number of desirable characteristics. These are discussed below.

1. *Stability of Amplification.* Suppose that the feedback is negative and that the feedback factor $K\beta$ is made large compared with unity. The resultant gain equation (5-4) becomes

$$K_f \doteq -\frac{K}{K\beta} = -\frac{1}{\beta} \tag{5-16}$$

This means that when the magnitude $K\beta \gg 1$, the actual amplification with negative feedback is a function of the characteristics of the feedback network only. In particular, if β is independent of frequency, then the overall gain will be independent of the frequency. This permits a substantial reduction of the frequency and phase distortion of the amplifier. In fact, by the proper choice of feedback network, it is possible to achieve a wide variety of frequency characteristics.

Note that if $K\beta \gg 1$, then $K_f \doteq -K/K\beta \ll -K$, so that the over-all gain of the amplifier with inverse feedback is less than the nominal gain without feedback. This is the price that must be paid to secure the advantages of negative feedback. This is not a serious price to pay, since the loss in gain can be overcome by the use of additional tubes.

Clearly, if $K\beta$ is greater than unity, then Eq. (5-16) shows that the over-all gain will not change with tube replacements or with variations in battery potentials, since β is independent of the tube. Even if Eq. (5-16) is not completely valid, a substantial improvement results in general stability. This follows from the fact that a change in the nominal gain $d\mathbf{K}$ for whatever reason results in a change $d\mathbf{K}_f$ in the resultant gain by an amount

$$\frac{d\mathbf{K}_f}{\mathbf{K}_f} = \frac{1}{|1 - \mathbf{K}\beta|}\frac{d\mathbf{K}}{\mathbf{K}} \tag{5-17}$$

where $|1 - \mathbf{K}\beta|$ represents the magnitude of the quantity $1 - \mathbf{K}\beta$. This equation is the logarithmic derivative of Eq. (5-4). In this expression, $d\mathbf{K}_f/\mathbf{K}_f$ gives the fractional change in $\mathbf{K}_f$, and $d\mathbf{K}/\mathbf{K}$ gives the fractional change in $\mathbf{K}$. If, for example, the quantity $|1 - \mathbf{K}\beta| = 5$ in a particular feedback amplifier, then the variation in any parameter that might cause a 5 per cent change in the nominal gain will result in a change of only 1 per cent in the resultant gain of the amplifier.

2. *Reduction of Frequency and Phase Distortion.* It follows from Eqs. (5-4) and (5-16) that the over-all gain of the amplifier is almost independent of frequency, provided that β is frequency-independent. In such cases the frequency and phase distortion of an amplifier are materially reduced below the nonfeedback value.

3. *Reduction of Nonlinear Distortion.* One effect was omitted in the above considerations. It was implicitly assumed that the dynamic curve was linear and that the output potential was of the same waveshape as the input. If an appreciable nonlinear distortion exists, then the output contains harmonic components in addition to the signal of fundamental frequency. Suppose, for simplicity, that only a second-harmonic component B_2 is generated within the tube when a large signal potential is impressed on the input. Because of the feedback, the second-harmonic component B_2' that appears in the output is different from that generated within the tube. To find the relationship that exists between B_2' and B_2, the procedure parallels that for the gain considerations. Thus, for a second harmonic B_2' in the output, a fraction $\beta B_2'$ is supplied to the input. As a result, the output actually must contain two components of second-harmonic frequency, the component B_2 that is generated within the tube

and the component $K\beta B_2'$ that arises from the signal that is fed back to the input. This requires that

$$K\beta B_2' + B_2 = B_2'$$

or

$$B_2' = \frac{B_2}{1 - K\beta} \qquad (5\text{-}18)$$

Note that since both K and β are functions of the frequency, in general, the appropriate values that appear in this equation must be evaluated at the second-harmonic frequency.

It should be pointed out that this derivation has assumed that the harmonic distortion generated within the tube depends only upon the grid swing of the fundamental signal potential. The small amount of additional distortion that might arise because a fraction of the second-harmonic component is returned to the input has been neglected. Ordinarily this procedure will lead to little error, although a more exact calculation taking these successive effects into account is readily possible.[2]

Another feature of Eq. (5-18) should be noted. According to this expression, if $|1 - K\beta| = 10$, then the second-harmonic distortion with feedback is only one-tenth its value without feedback. This is the situation when the total output-potential swing is the same in each case; otherwise the harmonic generation within the tube could not be directly compared. This requires that the signal, when feedback is applied, must be $|1 - K\beta|$ times that in the absence of feedback. As a practical consideration, since appreciable nonlinear distortion is generated only when the signal potential is large, then the full benefit of the feedback amplifier in reducing nonlinear distortion is obtained by applying negative feedback to the large-signal stages.

4. *Reduction of Noise.* Considerations such as those leading to Eq. (5-18) for the resultant nonlinear distortion in a feedback amplifier will show that the resultant noise generated in the input to an amplifier chain is reduced by the factor $1 - K\beta$, when feedback is employed. This would seem to represent a real reduction in noise. However, if the requirement is for a specified output signal, the resultant gain with feedback will have to be adjusted, by adjustment of the circuit parameters, or by the addition of amplifier stages, to give the same over-all gain as the amplifier without feedback. Consequently, the noise will be amplified as well as the signal. Moreover, since the noise is independent of the signal, additional amplifier stages to compensate for the loss of gain due to feedback will introduce additional noise. In such cases, the over-all noise of the amplifier with feedback might be higher than that of one without feedback. If the required gain is achieved by the readjustment of the circuit parameters, a reduction in noise will result in the negative feedback amplifier.

5. *Modification of Input and Output (Effective Internal) Impedances.*
These topics will be the subject of detailed consideration in several of
the following sections.

5-3. Feedback Circuits. The potential fed back from the output of
the amplifier into the input may be proportional either to the potential
across the load or to the current through the load.   In the first case, the
feedback is called *potential feedback;* in the second case, it is called *current feedback.*   In either case, the feedback may be positive or negative,
depending upon the connection.   Often the feedback loops are so
involved and interconnected that it is not possible to specify directly

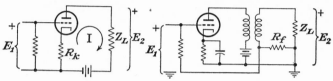

Fig. 5-3. Circuits employing current feedback.

whether the feedback is of the potential or the current types or whether
a combination of both exists.

It is possible to state rules which help to specify more uniquely the
existence of potential or current feedback.   Consider the circuits of Fig.
5-3, which illustrate two amplifiers employing current feedback.   The
first of these diagrams is identical with that of the illustrative example
of the foregoing section, except that the cathode impedance is now shown
as a resistance R_k.   As in the example, the feedback ratio is $\beta = R_k/Z_l$.
Note that, for large feedback ratios, the resultant gain approaches

$$\mathbf{K}_f = -\frac{1}{\beta} = -\frac{Z_l}{R_k} \tag{5-19}$$

Therefore the output potential is

$$\mathbf{E}_2 = -\frac{Z_l}{R_k}\mathbf{E}_1 \tag{5-20}$$

which is proportional to the load impedance.   Also, the output current
is given by

$$\mathbf{I} = \frac{\mathbf{E}_2}{Z_l} = -\frac{\mathbf{E}_1}{R_k} \tag{5-21}$$

which is seen to be independent of the load impedance.   These conditions are characteristic of current feedback.   Hence in current feedback
*the ratio of the feedback potential to the load current is independent of the
load impedance.*

The condition that the output current should be independent of the
load impedance is fulfilled when the internal impedance of the generator

is high compared with the impedance of the external load. Consequently, negative current feedback has the property of increasing the internal impedance of the network. In fact, from the complete expression for the current, from Eq. (5-14), namely,

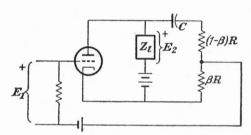

$$I = \frac{-\mu E_1}{r_p + (\mu + 1)R_k + Z_l}$$

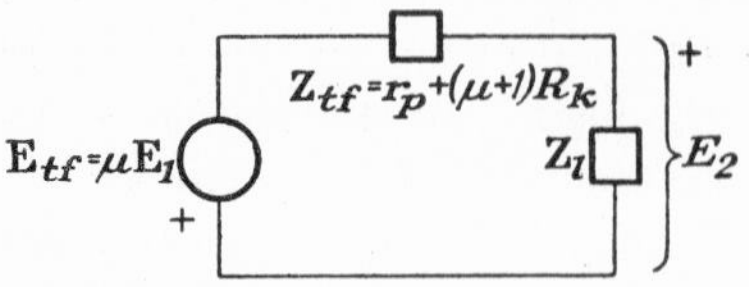

Fig. 5-4. The equivalent circuit of Fig. 5-2a.

it is possible to draw Fig. 5-4, which is the equivalent of Fig. 5-2a. It follows from this that the circuit including feedback comprises a potential source $E_{tf} = \mu E_1$ with an internal impedance $Z_{tf} = r_p + (\mu + 1)R_k$. Since the internal impedance without feedback is simply $r_p + R_k$, the effect of the feedback is to increase the internal impedance by the term uR_k. The ratio of internal impedances with and without feedback is given by

$$\frac{Z_{tf}}{Z_t} = \frac{r_p + (\mu + 1)R_k}{r_p + R_k} = 1 + \frac{\mu R_k}{r_p + R_k} \tag{5-22}$$

A circuit which employs potential feedback is given in Fig. 5-5. In this circuit, the resistance combination $\beta R + (1 - \beta)R = R$ which

Fig. 5-5. Circuit employing potential feedback.

shunts the output is made large compared with the load impedance Z_l. The capacitor C has a reactance that is negligible compared with R at the frequencies to be employed. Its sole purpose is to block the d-c potential from the plate circuit from appearing in the grid circuit.

The feedback ratio is shown as β in the diagram. Also for large feedback ratios, the resultant gain approaches

$$K_f = -\frac{1}{\beta}$$

The output potential is, therefore,

$$E_2 = -\frac{1}{\beta} E_1$$

which is seen to be independent of the load impedance, since β is independent of Z_l. Observe therefore that potential feedback is directly proportional to the output potential, and the *ratio β of the feedback potential to the output potential is independent of the load.* A generator whose output potential is substantially independent of the load impedance must possess a very low internal impedance. Consequently negative potential feedback has the property of decreasing the internal impedance of the amplifier.

To obtain an expression for the resultant gain of the amplifier, the feedback method will be employed. By neglecting the shunting effect of the feedback resistance network on the load impedance, it follows that the nominal gain of the amplifier is given by

$$\mathbf{K} = \frac{-\mu Z_l}{r_p + Z_l} \tag{5-23}$$

Then the resultant gain with feedback is

$$\mathbf{K}_f = \frac{\mathbf{K}}{1 - \mathbf{K}\beta} = \frac{-\mu Z_l}{r_p + Z_l + \beta \mu Z_l} \tag{5-24}$$

This expression may be transformed to the form

$$\mathbf{K}_f = \frac{-\mu' Z_l}{r_p' + Z_l} \tag{5-25}$$

where $\mu' = \dfrac{\mu}{1 + \mu\beta} \qquad r_p' = \dfrac{r_p}{1 + \mu\beta}$

But this is exactly the output that is obtained from the circuit of **Fig. 5-6.**

Consequently, the circuit behaves like a potential source $E_{tf} = \dfrac{\mu}{1 + \mu\beta} E_1$ with an internal impedance $Z_{tf} = r_p/(1 + \mu\beta)$.

The effective internal impedance of the amplifier without feedback is simply $Z_t = r_p$. The effect of potential feedback is to reduce the internal impedance in the ratio

$$\frac{Z_{tf}}{Z_t} = \frac{1}{1 + \mu\beta} \tag{5-26}$$

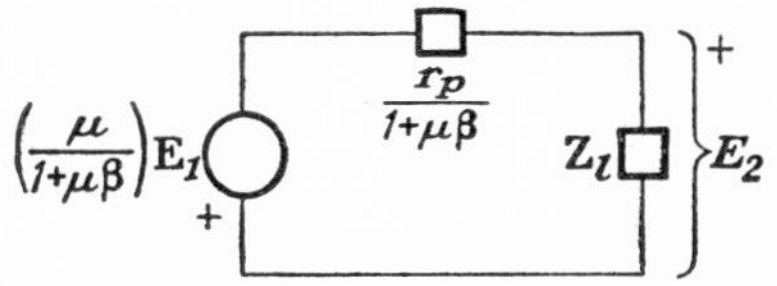

Fig. 5-6. The equivalent circuit of Fig. 5-5.

From the form of Eq. (5-25), the circuit gain appears to be that obtained from a tube whose amplification factor is μ' and whose plate resistance is r_p'. Note that the effective amplification factor is reduced in the same ratio as the plate resistance of the tube. This indicates that a tube possessing a high plate resistance can be effectively converted into a low-plate-resistance tube and thereby permit an impedance match to a low impedance load. This is accomplished, of course, at the expense of effectively converting the tube into a triode, with low μ and low r_p.

The combination of current and potential feedback in an amplifier is frequently called compound, or bridge, feedback. The circuit of such an amplifier is given in Fig. 5-7. The feedback fraction is found to be

$$\beta = \beta_1 + \frac{R_k}{Z_l} = \beta_1 + \beta_2 \tag{5-27}$$

As in the analysis of Fig. 5-5, it is assumed that the resistance combination R is much greater than Z_l and that the reactance of the capacitor is

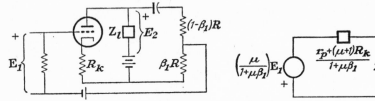

FIG. 5-7. A circuit employing bridge, or compound, feedback.

FIG. 5-8. The equivalent network of Fig. 5-7.

negligible over the frequency range of operation. The resultant gain of the amplifier has the form

$$K_f = \frac{-\mu Z_l}{r_p + (\mu + 1)R_k + (1 + \mu\beta_1)Z_l}$$

This may be written in the form

$$K_f'' = \frac{-\mu'' Z_l}{r_p'' + Z_l}$$

where

$$\mu'' = \frac{\mu}{1 + \mu\beta_1} \tag{5-28}$$

$$r_p'' = \frac{r_p + (\mu + 1)R_k}{1 + \mu\beta_1}$$

The corresponding equivalent circuit shown in Fig. 5-8 gives rise to exactly this expression for the gain and is therefore the equivalent of Fig. 5-7. The effect of the feedback is seen to reflect itself as a change in the effective μ and r_p of the tube. The effective potential and internal impedance are given by the expression

$$E_{tf} = \frac{\mu}{1 + \mu\beta_1} E_1$$

$$Z_{tf} = \frac{r_p + (\mu + 1)R_k}{1 + \mu\beta_1} \tag{5-29}$$

Owing to the form of the expression for Z_{tf}, this quantity may be made greater than, equal to, or less than its value without feedback.

Feedback can be effected over several stages and need not be limited to a stage-by-stage practice. A two-stage RC-coupled amplifier which combines current feedback in the first stage through resistor R_1 and potential feedback between stages is illustrated in Fig. 5-9. A careful consideration of the polarity of the potentials which are fed back will show that both types of feedback are negative.

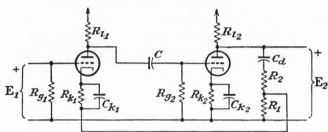

FIG. 5-9. A two-stage RC coupled amplifier with current feedback in the first stage and potential feedback between stages.

It is not always evident what type of feedback is being employed in a given amplifier. The following tests will serve to clarify the situation:

1. If the ratio of feedback potential $\mathbf{E}_f$ to output potential $\mathbf{E}_2$ is nearly independent of the load impedance, then potential feedback is employed. This ratio is the feedback fraction $\beta = \mathbf{E}_f/\mathbf{E}_2$.

2. If the ratio of feedback potential $\mathbf{E}_f$ to load current $\mathbf{I}$ is nearly independent of the load impedance, then current feedback is employed. The ratio $\mathbf{Z}_f = \mathbf{E}_f/\mathbf{I}$ is the feedback impedance.

3. If the feedback potential $\mathbf{E}_f$ is the sum of two terms of the form

$$\mathbf{E}_f = \beta\mathbf{E}_2 + \mathbf{Z}_f\mathbf{I}$$

where *both* β and $\mathbf{Z}_f$ are nearly independent of the load impedance, then compound feedback is employed.

5-4. Effective Internal Impedance with Feedback. The discussion in the foregoing section has shown that the effective internal impedance of the equivalent plate circuit of an electron-tube circuit with feedback depends on the type of feedback that is employed. As shown, current feedback increases the effective internal impedance, and potential feedback decreases the effective internal impedance. These results will be generalized.

The following notation, some of which has already appeared, will apply in the following development:

β is feedback ratio

$\mathbf{K}$ is potential gain without feedback, with load connected

$\mathbf{K}_f$ is potential gain with feedback, with load connected

$\mathbf{K}_t$ is potential gain without feedback, with load open-circuited

$\mathbf{E}_t$ is effective internal potential source without feedback (this is the Helmholtz-Thévenin potential source obtained on open circuit)

E_{tf} is effective internal potential source with feedback

Z_1 is input-terminal impedance without feedback

Z_{1f} is corresponding input-terminal impedance with feedback

Z_t is effective internal impedance without feedback (this is the Thévenin impedance of the equivalent network and is the impedance looking back into the output terminals of the amplifier, with the load open-circuited)

Z_{tf} is corresponding effective internal impedance with feedback

Z_0 is output-terminal impedance without feedback

Z_{0f} is output-terminal impedance with feedback

E_2 is output potential

E_1 is input potential to amplifier

E_f is feedback potential

(Refer to Appendix A for a general discussion of the Helmholtz-Thévenin theorem.) Refer to Fig. 5-10, which shows a general feedback network

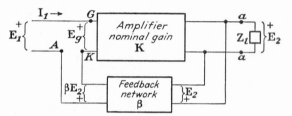

Fig. 5-10. The general potential or parallel feedback circuit.

which is provided with potential feedback. An expression for the internal impedance Z_{tf} of this feedback network will be derived in terms of the internal impedance Z_t without feedback.

Consider first the amplifier with the feedback potential removed. This is accomplished by removing lead A from the feedback network and connecting it to the cathode K. The Thévenin potential-source equivalent of this circuit is given in Fig. 5-11. Z_t in this diagram is the effective internal impedance without feedback, and K_t is the gain without feedback on open circuit (with Z_l omitted from the diagram).

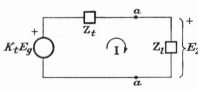

Fig. 5-11. The equivalent circuit of Fig. 5-10 with feedback removed.

To deduce the equivalent circuit of Fig. 5-10 with feedback present, note that the effect of feedback appears in the form of the potential E_g. Without feedback, $E_g = E_1$. With feedback, $E_g = E_1 + \beta E_2$. Clearly, from this discussion, the equivalent circuit of Fig. 5-10 with feedback present is that shown in Fig. 5-12. It should be noted that this figure, even though it is the equivalent circuit of Fig. 5-10 when feedback is present, is not a Thévenin potential-source equivalent representation, because both Z_t and $K_t(E_1 + \beta E_2)$ are functions of the load. Note from the diagram that

$$E_2 = K_t(E_1 + \beta E_2) - IZ_t$$

Therefore

$$E_2(1 - \beta K_t) = K_t E_1 - IZ_t$$

or

$$E_2 = \frac{K_t}{1 - \beta K_t} E_1 - \frac{Z_t}{1 - \beta K_t} I \qquad (5\text{-}30)$$

The Thévenin equivalent network for the circuit with feedback is, according to this expression, that shown in Fig. 5-13.

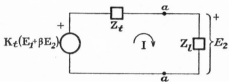

Fig. 5-12. The equivalent circuit of Fig. 5-10 with feedback present.

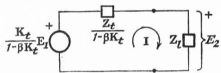

Fig. 5-13. The Thévenin equivalent network of Fig. 5-10.

As a check of these results, it is noted that $K_t E_1/(1 - \beta K_t)$ represents the open-circuit potential with feedback, $K_f E_1$. This agrees with the result obtained in Eq. (5-4) that $K_f = K/(1 - \beta K)$. The internal impedance with potential feedback is

$$Z_{tf} = \frac{Z_t}{1 - \beta K_t} \qquad (5\text{-}31)$$

Since, for negative feedback, $1 - \beta K_t$ is greater than unity, the impedance with feedback is less than that without feedback. Note, moreover, that the effective internal impedance is reduced by the same factor as the gain, when feedback is applied.

It is interesting to apply these results to the potential-feedback circuit of Fig. 5-5. If the load is open-circuited, then the magnitude of the gain of the circuit is simply the μ of the tube and $K_t = -\mu$. Also, the internal impedance without feedback is r_p, whence $Z_t = r_p$. The results so obtained agree with those in Fig. 5-6.

It is now desired to examine the results of current or series feedback on the effective internal impedance. Refer to Fig. 5-14, which shows a

general feedback circuit with current feedback. Although the impedance Z_f is shown isolated from the remainder of the circuit, it is a part
of the feedback circuit and is not part of the external load Z_l. The
equivalent circuit will be of the form shown in Fig. 5-15. In this dia-

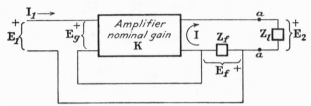

Fig. 5-14. The general current or series feedback circuit.

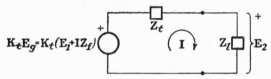

Fig. 5-15. The equivalent circuit of Fig. 5-14 with feedback present.

gram Z_t is the total internal impedance looking back from the load and
includes the effect of Z_f. From Fig. 5-15 it follows that

$$K_t(E_1 + IZ_f) = I(Z_t + Z_l)$$

from which

$$I = \frac{K_t E_1}{Z_t - Z_f K_t + Z_l}$$

But this is the current that exists in the circuit of Fig. 5-16, which is the
Thévenin equivalent with current feedback.

The effective internal impedance of the equivalent Thévenin generator
with current feedback is thus seen
to be

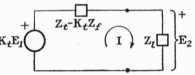

Fig. 5-16. The Thévenin equivalent of
Fig. 5-14.

$$Z_{tf} = Z_t - K_t Z_f \qquad (5\text{-}32)$$

Note that the open-circuit potential
with feedback is $K_t E_1$, which equals
the open-circuit potential without
feedback, in view of the significance
of K_t. This result is consistent with the observation that if Z_l is removed
from Fig. 5-16, an open circuit results, and I, and so the feedback, is
zero.

These results are applied to Fig. 5-3. If the output is removed, the
open-circuit gain is $K_t = -\mu$. The internal impedance without feedback is $Z_t = r_p + R_k$. Hence

$$Z_{tf} = r_p + R_k + \mu R_k$$

which agrees with the previous result.

Example 1.   Analyze the amplifier of Fig. 5-17 by the use of feedback methods, when the output is taken across $\mathbf{R}_l$.

Solution.   The equivalent circuit is given in Fig. 5-17b.   It is first noted that the grid-cathode potential $\mathbf{E}_g$ is given by the expression

$$\mathbf{E}_g = \mathbf{E}_1 - \mathbf{E}_k$$

But since $\mathbf{E}_k = \mathbf{I}R_k$, then

$$\mathbf{E}_k/\mathbf{I} = R_k$$

which is independent of the load impedance.   This indicates, according to the criterion given in Sec. 5-3, that current feedback exists.

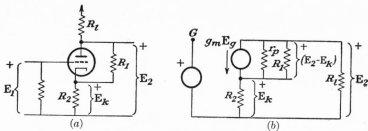

(a) (b)

Fig. 5-17. The circuit of a specific example.

To analyze the circuit completely, it is desired to calculate both $\mathbf{K}_f$ and $\mathbf{Z}_{tf}$. To evaluate these requires an evaluation of β, $\mathbf{K}$, $\mathbf{K}_t$, and $\mathbf{Z}_t$.   Note from the equivalent circuit that

$$\beta = -\frac{\mathbf{E}_k}{\mathbf{E}_2} = \frac{R_2}{R_l}$$

The nominal gain is found by noting that

$$g_m\mathbf{E}_g + (\mathbf{E}_2 - \mathbf{E}_k)\left(\frac{1}{r_p} + \frac{1}{R_1}\right) = -\frac{\mathbf{E}_2}{R_l}$$

But

$$\mathbf{E}_k = -\frac{\mathbf{E}_2}{R_l}R_2$$

Then

$$g_m\mathbf{E}_g + \mathbf{E}_2\left(1 + \frac{R_2}{R_l}\right)\left(\frac{1}{r_p} + \frac{1}{R_1}\right) + \frac{\mathbf{E}_2}{R_l} = 0$$

or

$$g_m\mathbf{E}_g + \mathbf{E}_2\left[\frac{1}{R_l} + \frac{1}{R_l}\frac{(R_l + R_2)(R_1 + r_p)}{r_pR_1}\right] = 0$$

Therefore

$$\mathbf{K} = \frac{\mathbf{E}_2}{\mathbf{E}_g} = \frac{-g_m}{\dfrac{1}{R_l}\left[\dfrac{r_pR_1 + (R_l + R_2)(R_1 + r_p)}{r_pR_1}\right]} \tag{5-33}$$

The equivalent gain on open circuit is simply

$$\mathbf{K}_t = \frac{-\mu R_1}{r_p + R_1} \tag{5-34}$$

Also the equivalent impedance Z_t is

$$Z_t = R_2 + \frac{r_p R_1}{r_p + R_1} = \frac{(r_p + R_1)R_2 + r_p R_1}{r_p + R_1} \tag{5-35}$$

It follows from these expressions that the gain with feedback is

$$K_f = \frac{\dfrac{-g_m R_l}{r_p R_1 + (R_l + R_2)(R_1 + r_p)}}{r_p R_1}}{1 + \dfrac{R_2}{R_l} \dfrac{\dfrac{g_m R_l}{r_p R_1 + (R_l + R_2)(R_1 + r_p)}}{r_p R_1}}$$

This reduces to

$$K_f = \frac{-\mu R_l R_1}{r_p(R_1 + R_2 + R_l) + (\mu + 1)R_1 R_2 + R_1 R_l} \tag{5-36}$$

Also, the effective internal impedance is

$$Z_{tf} = Z_t - K_t Z_f$$
$$= \frac{(r_p + R_1)R_2 + r_p R_1}{r_p + R_1} + \frac{\mu R_1}{r_p + R_1} R_2$$
$$Z_{tf} = \frac{r_p(R_1 + R_2) + (\mu + 1)R_1 R_2}{r_p + R_1} \tag{5-37}$$

It is of some interest to examine the effects of the feedback on the gain and on the effective internal impedance. The gain ratio, given by the ratio of Eq. (5-36) to Eq. (5-33), is found to be

$$\frac{K_f}{K} = \frac{r_p(R_1 + R_2 + R_l) + R_1 R_l + R_1 R_2}{r_p(R_1 + R_2 + R_l) + R_1 R_l + (\mu + 1)R_1 R_2}$$

which may be written in the form

$$\frac{K_f}{K} = \frac{1}{1 + \dfrac{\mu R_1 R_2}{r_p(R_1 + R_2 + R_l) + R_1 R_l + R_1 R_2}}$$

This expression shows that the resultant gain with feedback is less than that without feedback, as expected.

In a somewhat similar way, the effective internal impedances may be compared, to examine the effects of the feedback. By Eqs. (5-37) and (5-35), the ratio is readily found to be

$$\frac{Z_{tf}}{Z_t} = 1 + \frac{\mu R_1 R_2}{r_p(R_1 + R_2) + R_1 R_2}$$

The effect of the feedback is to increase the effective internal impedance, which is characteristic of current feedback.

Example 2.   Analyze the circuit of Example 1 when the output is taken across the cathode resistor R_2.

Solution. In the present case, since E_k is the output potential, then since

$$E_g = E_1 - E_k$$

it follows that

$$\beta = -1$$

But since β is independent of the load, then potential feedback now exists.

The nominal gain is obtained from a study of the equivalent circuit of Fig. 5-17b. It is observed that

$$g_m E_g + (E_2 - E_k)\left(\frac{1}{r_p} + \frac{1}{R_1}\right) = \frac{E_k}{R_2}$$

Also

$$E_2 = -\frac{R_l}{R_2} E_k$$

Then

$$g_m E_g - E_k\left(1 + \frac{R_l}{R_2}\right)\left(\frac{1}{r_p} + \frac{1}{R_1}\right) - \frac{E_k}{R_2} = 0$$

or

$$g_m E_g - E_k\left[\frac{1}{R_2} + \frac{1}{R_2}\frac{(R_2 + R_l)(R_1 + r_p)}{r_p R_1}\right] = 0$$

Therefore

$$K = \frac{E_k}{E_g} = \frac{g_m}{\dfrac{1}{R_2}\dfrac{r_p R_1 + (R_l + R_2)(R_1 + r_p)}{r_p R_1}}$$

which is

$$K = \frac{\mu R_1 R_2}{r_p R_1 + (R_l + R_2)(R_1 + r_p)} \tag{5-38}$$

The equivalent gain on open circuit is

$$K_t = \frac{\mu R_1}{r_p + R_1} \tag{5-39}$$

Also the equivalent impedance Z_t is

$$Z_t = R_l + \frac{r_p R_1}{r_p + R_1} = \frac{(r_p + R_1)R_l + r_p R_1}{r_p + R_1} \tag{5-40}$$

It follows from these expressions that under feedback conditions

$$K_f = \frac{\mu R_1 R_2 / [r_p R_1 + (R_l + R_2)(R_1 + r_p)]}{1 + \mu R_1 R_2 / [r_p R_1 + (R_l + R_2)(R_1 + r_p)]}$$

which reduces to

$$K_f = \frac{\mu R_1 R_2}{r_p(R_1 + R_2 + R_l) + (\mu + 1)R_1 R_2 + R_1 R_l} \tag{5-41}$$

The corresponding effective internal impedance is

$$Z_{tf} = \frac{Z_t}{1 - \beta K_t} = \frac{\dfrac{(r_p + R_1)R_l + r_p R_1}{r_p + R_1}}{1 + \dfrac{\mu R_1}{r_p + R_1}}$$

or

$$Z_{tf} = \frac{(r_p + R_1)R_l + r_p R_1}{r_p + (\mu + 1)R_1} \qquad (5\text{-}42)$$

While it is possible to draw certain conclusions from a comparison of the results obtained in Examples 1 and 2, the same conclusions are possible from the simplified circuit illustrated in Fig. 5-18, in which $R_l = R_2$, and R_1 is set to infinity, or an open circuit. This circuit is known as a single-tube "paraphase" amplifier and provides two equal output potentials of opposite polarity from a single excitation source. For the case when the output potential is E_2, the significant expressions deduced from Eqs. (5-36) and (5-37) are the following:

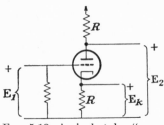

Fig. 5-18. A single-tube "paraphase" amplifier.

$$K_f = \frac{-\mu R_l}{r_p + (\mu + 2)R_l}$$
$$Z_{tf} = r_p + (\mu + 1)R_l \qquad (5\text{-}43)$$

When the output potential is E_k, the appropriate expressions become, from Eqs. (5-41) and (5-42),

$$K_f = \frac{\mu R_l}{r_p + (\mu + 2)R_l}$$
$$Z_{tf} = \frac{r_p + R_l}{\mu + 1} \qquad (5\text{-}44)$$

It will be observed that the gain of the amplifier with respect to each output pair of terminals is the same. However, it is also noted that the effective internal impedances looking back from these terminals are quite different, one being much higher than the other.

5-5. Effect of Feedback on the Output-terminal Impedance. The output-terminal impedance of a circuit is the impedance looking back into the output terminals of the network when the load impedance is in place, but with the input potential reduced to zero. Clearly, the output impedance of an amplifier is the parallel combination of the effective internal impedance and the load impedance. Since the equivalent internal impedance Z_{tf} depends on the type of feedback that is incorporated in the amplifier, then the output impedance will also depend on the type of feedback. The situation is illustrated schematically in Fig. 5-19.

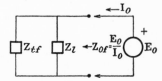

Fig. 5-19. The output-terminal impedance of the general feedback amplifier.

The output impedance Z_{0f}, which is given as the ratio of the current I_0 into the output terminals when a potential E_0 is impressed, is clearly

$$Z_{0f} = \frac{Z_{tf}Z_l}{Z_{tf} + Z_l} \qquad (5\text{-}45)$$

where, for the case of potential feedback, by Eq. (5-31)

$$Z_{tf} = \frac{Z_t}{1 - \beta K_t}$$

and for the case of current feedback, by Eq. (5-32), is

$$Z_{tf} = Z_t - K_t Z_f$$

It is desired to obtain an expression for Z_{0f} in terms of the output impedance without feedback, Z_0, where

$$Z_0 = \frac{Z_t Z_l}{Z_t + Z_l} \qquad (5\text{-}46)$$

a. Potential Feedback. Suppose that the input source to the general
feedback amplifier is reduced to zero and that a potential source is applied

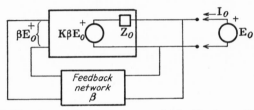

Fig. 5-20. The modifications of the general potential feedback amplifier for calculating
the output-terminal impedance.

to the output terminals.   The situation is illustrated in Fig. 5-20.   This
diagram is Fig. 5-1 appropriately modified for output-impedance deter-
minations.   In view of Fig. 5-11, which gives the equivalent circuit of
the general amplifier with potential feedback, then Z_0 has the form of
Eq. (5-46).

The current I_0 from the applied source is seen to be

$$I_0 = \frac{E_0 - K\beta E_0}{Z_0}$$

and the effective output impedance with feedback is

$$Z_{0f} = \frac{E_0}{I_0} = \frac{Z_0}{1 - K\beta} \qquad (5\text{-}47)$$

which is similar in form to Eq. (5-4).   This shows that the output impedance is reduced by the same factor as the potential gain with the application of potential feedback.

b. Current Feedback. The calculation for the output impedance of an
amplifier which employs current feedback follows a similar pattern.   In
this case, as before, the input signal is reduced to zero, and a potential
source is applied to the output terminals.   The current-feedback circuit

for the output-terminal impedance calculation then becomes that shown in Fig. 5-21.

In this circuit Z_0 denotes the output impedance of the circuit without feedback and includes the effect of Z_f. K is the gain without feedback, but with Z_l in position. The potential E_g is the drop across Z_f and is $I_f Z_f$.

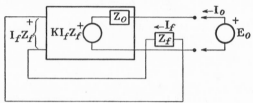

Fig. 5-21. The modifications to the general current feedback circuit for output-terminal impedance determination.

It follows from the diagram, by taking account of the current through the load impedance, that

$$E_0 = I_0 Z_0 - K I_f Z_f$$

But this becomes

$$E_0 = I_0 Z_0 - K Z_f \left(I_0 - \frac{E_0}{Z_l} \right)$$

This gives

$$I_0(Z_0 - K Z_f) = E_0 \left(1 - K \frac{Z_f}{Z_l} \right)$$

from which it follows that the effective output impedance with feedback is

$$Z_{0f} = \frac{Z_0 - K Z_f}{1 - K(Z_f/Z_l)} = Z_0 \frac{1 - K(Z_f/Z_0)}{1 - K(Z_f/Z_l)} \tag{5-48}$$

5-6. Effect of Feedback on the Input-terminal Impedance. It is of some importance to examine how the input impedance of an amplifier is affected by the presence of feedback. It will be found that the effective input impedance increases for both potential and current feedback.

a. Potential Feedback. It follows directly from Fig. 5-10 that the input-terminal impedance with feedback is simply

$$Z_{1f} = \frac{E_1}{I_1}$$

This may be written as

$$Z_{1f} = \frac{E_g - \beta E_2}{I_1} = \frac{E_g}{I_1} (1 - K\beta)$$

But the input impedance without feedback is

$$Z_1 = \frac{E_g}{I_1}$$

Then

$$Z_{1f} = Z_1(1 - K\beta) \tag{5-49}$$

Therefore, owing to the feedback, the input impedance with feedback is greater than the input impedance without feedback, and in the same degree as the gain and distortion decrease.

As a specific example, suppose that Z_1 is the impedance due to a capacitance between the grid-cathode terminals, and this may be the actual tube capacitance modified by the Miller effect. Since the impedance increases with feedback, this means that the effective input capacitance is decreased. Clearly, therefore,

$$C_{1f} = \frac{C_1}{1 - K} \tag{5-50}$$

b. Current Feedback. By proceeding as in (*a*) for the potential feedback, but now with reference to Fig. 5-14 for the general current-feedback circuit,

$$Z_{1f} = \frac{E_1}{I_1} = \frac{E_g - IZ_f}{I_1}$$

$$= \left(E_g - \frac{E_2}{Z_l} Z_f \right) \frac{1}{I_1}$$

But

$$\beta = \frac{Z_f}{Z_l} \qquad E_2 = KE_g$$

Then it follows that

$$Z_{1f} = Z_1(1 - K\beta) \tag{5-51}$$

Note that the input impedance with current feedback is greater than the input impedance without feedback in the same degree as for the case of potential feedback.

5-7. Feedback and Stability. A great deal of information about the stability of an amplifier can be obtained from an analysis of the factor $1 - K\beta$ that appears in the general gain expression [Eq. (5-3)]. This is best analyzed through the use of the polar plot of the expression $K\beta$. Attention is first called to the significance of the quantity $K\beta$. This is best examined by reference to the diagram of Fig. 5-22. Observe that $K\beta$ is the total open-loop gain, in-

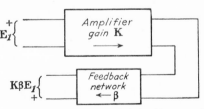

Fig. 5-22. To illustrate the significance of the factor $K\beta$.

cluding the amplifier and the feedback network, but with the feedback connection open. In network parlance, this is the open-loop transfer function of the amplifier and the feedback network. In essence, therefore, consideration of the open-loop performance of the amplifier and feedback network is to be used to provide significant information regarding the performance of the amplifier under closed-loop operation.

Kβ is a function of the frequency, and, in general, points in the complex plane are obtained for the values of Kβ corresponding to all values of f from 0 to ∞. The locus of all these points forms a closed curve.

As a particular example, suppose that the locus of Kβ in the complex plane is drawn for the amplifier illustrated in Fig. 5-5. To do this, the complete expression for the nominal gain, including the effect of the feedback circuit, must be written, rather than the simple form given in Eq.

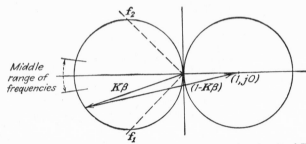

Fig. 5-23. The locus in the complex plane of Kβ for the circuit of Fig. 5-5.

(5-23). Also, the value of β must include the effects of the blocking capacitor C. Certain of the features of the response of this amplifier are known. At the mid-frequencies, the gain is substantially constant and has a phase of 180 deg. For the low and high frequencies, the gain falls to zero, and the phase approaches ±90 deg, respectively. At the l-f and h-f cutoff values the phase is ±135 deg, respectively. It may be shown that the general locus of Kβ of this amplifier for all frequencies is a circle. The result is shown in Fig. 5-23.

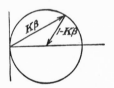

Fig. 5-24. A plot of $|1 - Kβ| = 1$ in the complex plane.

Suppose that a phasor is drawn from the polar locus to the point $(1,j0)$. This is the quantity $1 - Kβ$, as shown. For this particular case, its magnitude is greater than unity for all frequencies, and it has its maximum magnitude at the middle range of frequencies. Moreover, since the resultant gain varies inversely with $1 - Kβ$, then the effect of the feedback is to cause a general flattening of the frequency-response characteristic.

The criterion for positive and negative feedback is evident on the complex plane. First note that the quantity $|1 - Kβ| = 1$ represents a circle of unit radius with its center at the point $(1,j0)$, as illustrated. Clearly, if for a given amplifier $|1 - Kβ| > 1$, then the feedback is negative, with an over-all reduction of gain. Likewise, if $|1 - Kβ| < 1$, there is an over-all increase in gain and the feedback is positive. These considerations show that if Kβ extends outside of the unit circle for any frequency, then the feedback is negative at that frequency. If $K\beta$ lies within the unit circle, then the feedback is positive. If $K\beta$ passes through the point $(1,j0)$ then $1 - K\beta = 0$, and, as will later be shown, the amplifier is unstable and oscillates. A more general analysis by Nyquist[1,3] shows that the amplifier will oscillate if the curve $K\beta$ encloses the point $(1,j0)$ and is stable if the curve does not enclose this point. That is, if the magnitude of $K\beta$ is less than unity when its phase angle is zero, no oscillations are possible.

As a specific example for discussion, suppose that the plot of a given amplifier is that illustrated in Fig. 5-25. The feedback is negative for this amplifier in the frequency range from 0 to f_1. Positive feedback exists in the frequency range from f_1 to ∞. Note, however, that since the locus of $K\beta$ does not enclose the point $(1,j0)$, then, according to the Nyquist criterion, oscillations will not occur.

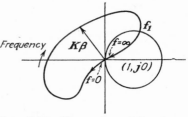

FIG. 5-25. The polar plot of an amplifier.

The Nyquist criterion is actually more extensive than that implied here and applies to the general case of a multiloop feedback system. In this latter case stability is inferred from the number of times that the open-loop transfer-function plot encircles the point $(1,j0)$ as the frequency is varied from $-\infty$ to $+\infty$. (The region of negative frequency introduces no particular complication as the open-loop transfer-function plot for the negative frequencies from $-\infty$ to 0 is the mirror image of that for the positive-frequency range from 0 to $+\infty$, since the function $K\beta$ at frequency $-f$ is the complex conjugate of that at the frequency f.) Also required in ascertaining stability in the multiloop case is the location of the poles of the open-loop transfer function. [A pole of a network function is the generalized frequency at which the function becomes infinite. That is, if a network function is written in the form

$$Z(s) = \frac{(s - S_1)(s - S_2) \cdots}{(s - s_1)(s - s_2) \cdots}$$

then poles exist for $s = s_1$, $s = s_2$, etc.] For the single-loop feedback amplifiers to be considered here (amplifiers with single feedback loops) it is generally necessary to consider only the frequency range 0 to ∞, as the gain is ordinarily zero at each limit. This is not necessarily true for the case of direct-coupled amplifiers, and the complete plot from $-\infty$ to $+\infty$ would then be required. For the single-feedback-loop case, stability is determined in the manner discussed above.

5-8. The Cathode Follower.[4] The cathode follower is illustrated in Fig. 5-26a, the equivalent circuit being given in Fig. 5-26b. This feedback circuit is singled out for detailed consideration because of its extensive use in a variety of applications. These applications stem from the fact that the cathode follower possesses a high input impedance and a low output impedance and may therefore be used as a coupling device between a high impedance source and a low impedance load.

The cathode follower is similar to the single-tube paraphase amplifier of Fig. 5-18, but with a zero plate load. The equivalent circuit is that shown in Fig. 5-26b. The grid circuit is isolated, since interelectrode

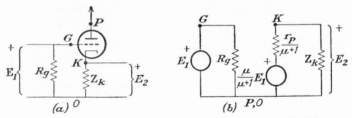

FIG. 5-26. Schematic and equivalent circuit of the cathode follower.

capacitances are neglected, and the input impedance is R_g. The effective internal impedance is $Z_{tf} = r_p/(\mu + 1)$, which is very low. In fact, if $\mu \gg 1$, then $Z_{tf} = r_p/\mu = 1/g_m$. But since g_m for most tubes varies from 1,000 to 10,000 μmhos, then Z_{tf} is of the order of 1,000 to 100 ohms. A double cathode-follower circuit has been devised which has a greatly reduced effective internal impedance.[5]

The gain is obtained from an analysis of Fig. 5-26b and is given by

$$\mathbf{K} = \frac{\mu Z_k}{r_p + (\mu + 1)Z_k} = \frac{\mu}{(\mu + 1) + (r_p/Z_k)} \qquad (5\text{-}52)$$

Clearly $\mathbf{K}$ approaches the limiting value $\mu/(\mu + 1)$ as the ratio r_p/Z_k approaches zero, or as $Z_k \gg r_p$. For tubes with large value of μ, and with $Z_k \gg r_p$, the gain approaches unity. For values of Z_k and r_p found in most normal cases, $\mathbf{K}$ is of the order of 0.9 or higher. In fact, it is because of this unity-gain feature that the circuit derives its name, since the output potential is almost equal to the input potential, whence the cathode and grid rise and fall together in potential by almost equal amounts (or the cathode follows the grid).

The interelectrode and wiring capacitances have been neglected in the above discussions, as their effects are usually negligible for frequencies below about 1 Mc/sec. For purposes of our study, these will be taken into account. The schematic and equivalent circuits are now given in Fig. 5-27.

The expression for the gain of the amplifier is deduced by analyzing the circuit. It is noted that

$$E_2 = \frac{E_1 Y_{C_{gk}} + \mu E_g Y_p}{Y_{C_{gk}} + Y_p + Y_{C_{pk}+C_{fk}} + Y_{Z_k}} \tag{5-53}$$

But it follows that

$$E_g = E_1 - E_2$$

and Eq. (5-53) becomes

$$E_2 = \frac{j\omega C_{gk} E_1 + \mu Y_p (E_1 - E_2)}{j\omega(C_{gk} + C_{pk} + C_{fk}) + 1/r_p + 1/Z_k} \tag{5-54}$$

Solving for the gain K_f which is given by $K_f = E_2/E_1$, there results

$$K_f = \frac{(j\omega r_p C_{gk} + \mu)Z_k}{j\omega r_p Z_k (C_{gk} + C_{pk} + C_{fk}) + r_p + (\mu + 1)Z_k} \tag{5-55}$$

For those values of Z_k which are normally used, the effect of the inter-electrode and wiring capacitances on the potential amplification is negligible for frequencies below about 1 Mc, as already noted. That this is

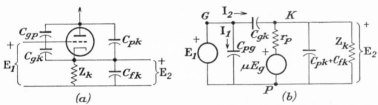

FIG. 5-27. Schematic and equivalent circuits of the cathode follower including the interelectrode capacitances.

so is seen by writing Eq. (5-55) in the form

$$K_f = \frac{(g_m + j\omega C_{gk})Z_k}{1 + \left(\dfrac{\mu + 1}{r_p} + j\omega C_T\right) Z_k} \tag{5-56}$$

where $C_T = C_{gk} + C_{pk} + C_{fk}$. But the effect of the capacitances will become important only for those frequencies for which ωC_T becomes comparable with $(\mu + 1)/r_p \doteq g_m$. If C_T is taken as 30 $\mu\mu f$ and $g_m = 1,000$ μmhos, then $f \doteq g_m/2\pi C_T \doteq 5$ Mc.

To find an expression for the input capacitance of the cathode follower, refer to Fig. 5-27b. It is seen that the current flowing through the source comprises two components. One of these is the current through the capacitance C_{gp} and is

$$I_1 = j\omega C_{gp} E_1 \tag{5-57}$$

The second is the current through the capacitance C_{gk}. This is

$$I_2 = j\omega C_{gk} E_g \tag{5-58}$$

But as $E_g = E_1 - E_2$ and $K_f = E_2/E_1$, then

$$I_2 = j\omega C_{gk}(1 - K_f)E_1 \qquad (5\text{-}59)$$

The total current is

$$I = I_1 + I_2 = j\omega[C_{gp}E_1 + (1 - K_f)C_{gk}E_1]$$

and the effective input capacitance is

$$C_i = C_{gp} + (1 - K_f)C_{gk} \qquad (5\text{-}60)$$

Since in many circuits K_f is approximately 0.9, then C_i has the approximate value

$$C_i = C_{gp} + 0.1C_{gk} \qquad (5\text{-}61)$$

A comparison of this expression with the corresponding form given by Eq. (3-16) for the conventional amplifier stage shows a roughly similar dependence on the tube capacitances, although the numerical value for the cathode follower is considerably smaller than that for the conventional amplifier stage.

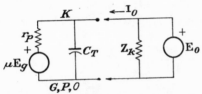

FIG. 5-28. The equivalent output circuit of the cathode follower.

The effective internal impedance Z_{tf} can be determined by finding the current I_0 as a consequence of the application of an a-c potential E_0 to the output terminals of Fig. 5-27. The grid exciting potential is made zero. The equivalent circuit is that drawn as Fig. 5-28, if the internal impedance of the grid driving source is low. The effective internal admittance of the tube alone is found from

$$I_0 = E_0 Y_T + \frac{E_0 - \mu E_g}{r_p} \qquad (5\text{-}62)$$

But under the conditions specified

$$E_g = -E_0$$

Then

$$Y_{tf} = \frac{I_0}{E_0} = Y_T + Y_p + g_m \qquad (5\text{-}63)$$

where $Y_T = j\omega C_T$. It is of interest to compare this result with that which applies without capacitances being considered, viz.,

$$Y_{tf} = \frac{1}{Z_{tf}} = \frac{\mu + 1}{r_p} = g_m + Y_p$$

The effect of the interelectrode capacitances is the addition of the term Y_T to the terms $Y_p + g_m$. Here, as for the gain, Y_T does not become comparable with the other terms except at the higher video frequencies.

5-9. Graphical Analysis of the Cathode Follower. Suppose that the cathode impedance is a resistance R_k, and this is the usual situation. A graphical solution of the operation of the circuit is possible on the plate characteristics of the tube. This necessitates drawing the dynamic characteristic of the circuit from the known plate characteristics. Refer to Fig. 5-29 for notation. The controlling equations of the grid and plate circuits are

$$e_n = e_{cn} + i_{bn}R_k \qquad (5\text{-}64)$$

and

$$E_{bb} = e_{bn} + i_{bn}R_k \qquad (5\text{-}65)$$

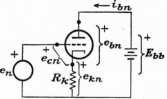

Equation (5-65) is the equation of the load line for the plate supply E_{bb} and the load resistance R_k. The procedure for constructing the dynamic characteristic follows:

FIG. 5-29. The cathode follower with a cathode resistor.

1. On the plate characteristics draw the load line specified by Eq. (5-65). This is illustrated in Fig. 5-30.

2. Note the plate current at each point of intersection of the load line with the plate characteristics. For example, the current at the intersection of the load line with E_{c2} is labeled i_{b2}.

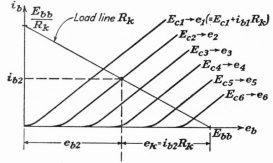

FIG. 5-30. Graphical construction for finding the dynamic characteristic of a cathode follower with cathode resistor R_k.

3. Now relabel the plate characteristics with the appropriate symbol e, according to Eq. (5-64). Thus

$$E_{c1} \rightarrow e_1(\equiv E_{c1} + i_{b1}R_k)$$
$$E_{c2} \rightarrow e_2(\equiv E_{c2} + i_{b2}R_k)$$

etc.

4. The dynamic characteristic is a plot of the (i_{bn}, e_n) characteristic, where i_{bn} is the current corresponding to the input e_n. This requires calculating the value of e_n for each value of E_{cn}, and its corresponding i_{bn}.

Often the complete dynamic curve is not required, but only the current I_b for a specified value of e, say E. By Eq. (5-64) this is

$$I_b = \frac{E - E_c}{R_k}$$

For several values of e_c (and the available E_c values are used), the value of i_b is calculated, and noted on the plate characteristics, as shown in Fig. 5-31. The intersection of the load line and the line connecting the calculated points is the appropriate current I_b for the specified E.

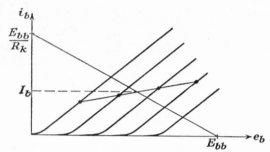

FIG. 5-31. Graphical construction for obtaining the value of I_b for a specified input potential E_1.

It should be specifically noted that the value of the input signal E will be quite large before E_c, the actual grid-cathode potential, becomes positive with the consequent grid current. That is, since the cathode potential follows the grid potential rather closely (for a gain almost equal to unity), the input signal may swing considerably positive before the onset of grid current. The larger the value of R_k, the larger will be the allowable positive swing. When cutoff occurs, no potential difference appears across R_k. Consequently, the applied signal required to reach cutoff is independent of R_k.

Example.   Consider a 6J5 tube with $E_{bb} = 300$ volts and $R_k = 10,000$ ohms. Find the maximum positive and negative input swings for positive grid-cathode potential and cutoff, respectively.

Solution.   From the plate characteristics of the 6J5 (see Appendix B-9) and the specified E_{bb} and R_k, the following data are found:

$$\text{For } E_c = 0: \qquad I_b = 15.7 \text{ ma}$$
$$\text{For } E_c = -18: \quad I_b = 0$$

This shows that the cathode follower may swing from $+157$ volts to -18 volts without drawing grid current or driving the tube beyond cutoff.

Clearly, the operation of the cathode-follower circuit of Fig. 5-29 is unsymmetrical. For small potential excursions, this causes no difficulty. Also, if only positive signals are to be used, no difficulty exists. However, if large negative signals are to be applied, it is necessary to establish the grid at a large positive potential with respect to the bottom end of R_k (ordinarily ground), although the actual tube bias E_c will still be negative. This bias may be achieved in several ways, as illustrated in Fig. 5-32. For symmetrical operation, the bias will be established to set the d-c level across R_k at about half of the peak-peak potential swing.

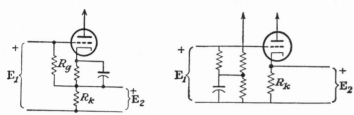

Fig. 5-32. Two ways of achieving more symmetrical operation of a cathode follower.

5-10. The Anode Follower. A circuit which possesses roughly the same gain and impedance properties as the cathode follower, but which also provides phase reversal between the output and input potentials, is often called an *anode follower*. This is perhaps an unfortunate choice of name, since, unlike the cathode follower in which the cathode-potential variations follow the grid-potential variations rather closely, i.e., these potential variations are in the same phase, the anode of the anode follower falls when the grid potential rises. Clearly, no "following"

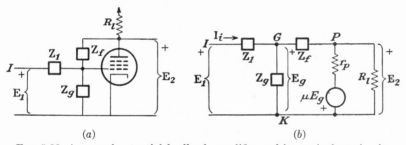

(a)   (b)

Fig. 5-33. A general potential feedback amplifier and its equivalent circuit.

occurs. Because of the almost equal potential changes in the grid and plate potentials, but with the reverse phase, the circuit has been called the *seesaw* circuit. Whatever the most suitable choice of name, the circuit is of value and importance.

The circuit of the anode follower is given in Fig. 5-33. Actually, this is one adaptation of a general operational feedback amplifier, other applications being examined in considerable detail in Chap. 6. It is a simple amplifier which is provided with potential feedback through the impedance Z_f. An analysis of the equivalent circuit is readily carried out. An application of the Millman network theorem between the points K

and G yields

$$E_g = \frac{E_1 Y_1 + E_2 Y_f}{Y_1 + Y_f + Y_g} \tag{5-66}$$

When applied between K and P, the network theorem yields

$$E_2 = \frac{E_g Y_f - \mu E_g Y_p}{Y_f + Y_p + Y_l} = \frac{E_g (Y_f - g_m)}{Y_f + Y_p + Y_l} \tag{5-67}$$

By combining these expressions, there results

$$E_2 = \frac{Y_f - g_m}{Y_f + Y_p + Y_l} \frac{E_1 Y_1 + E_2 Y_f}{Y_1 + Y_g + Y_f} \tag{5-68}$$

By solving for the gain, the result is

$$K_f = \frac{E_2}{E_1} = \frac{Y_1 (Y_f - g_m)}{(Y_f + Y_p + Y_l)(Y_1 + Y_f + Y_g) - Y_f (Y_f - g_m)}$$

which may be written in the form

$$K_f = \frac{Y_1 (Y_f - g_m)}{(Y_1 + Y_f + Y_g)(Y_p + Y_l) + Y_f (Y_1 + Y_g + g_m)} \tag{5-69}$$

To obtain an expression for the output impedance of this general feedback circuit, the procedure followed is substantially that used in Sec. 5-8.

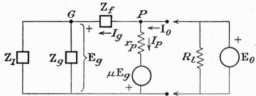

Fig. 5-34. The equivalent circuit for calculating the effective internal impedance of the feedback circuit of Fig. 5-33.

In the present case the equivalent circuit for this calculation becomes that shown in Fig. 5-34. The output admittance is given by

$$Y_{tf} = \frac{I_0}{E_0} = \frac{I_p + I_g}{E_0} \tag{5-70}$$

This may be written in the form

$$Y_{tf} = \frac{1}{E_0} \left[\frac{E_0 + \mu E_g}{r_p} + E_g (Y_g + Y_1) \right]$$

which is

$$Y_{tf} = \frac{1}{E_0} [(Y_1 + Y_g + g_m) E_g + Y_p E_0] \tag{5-71}$$

But from the diagram

$$E_g = \frac{Y_f}{Y_1 + Y_f + Y_g} E_0 \tag{5-72}$$

Hence the expression for the effective internal admittance becomes

$$Y_{tf} = Y_p + Y_f \frac{Y_1 + Y_g + g_m}{Y_1 + Y_f + Y_g} \tag{5-73}$$

An expression for the input admittance is readily obtained. It follows directly from Fig. 5-33b that

$$Y_{1f} \equiv \frac{I_i}{E_1} = \frac{E_1 - E_g}{Z_1 E_1} = Y_1 \left(1 - \frac{E_g}{E_1}\right) \tag{5-74}$$

But by Eqs. (5-66) and (5-69)

$$E_g = \frac{E_1 Y_1 + K_f E_1 Y_f}{Y_1 + Y_g + Y_f} = E_1 \frac{Y_1 + K_f Y_f}{Y_1 + Y_g + Y_f} \tag{5-75}$$

Then

$$Y_{1f} = Y_1 \left(1 - \frac{Y_1 + K_f Y_f}{Y_1 + Y_g + Y_f}\right)$$

which may be written in the form

$$Y_{1f} = \frac{Y_1}{Y_1 + Y_g + Y_f} [Y_g + (1 - K_f)Y_f] \tag{5-76}$$

A numerical comparison of the cathode follower, the anode follower, a conventional amplifier circuit under normal operating conditions, and a conventional amplifier with the plate resistance so chosen as to give the same gain as the cathode follower is very interesting. These data are given in Table 5-1, which assumes the use of a 6J5 tube, with $\mu = 20$, $r_p = 7,700$ ohms, R_l or $R_k = 10,000$ ohms, and $R_g = 1$ megohms in all cases.

TABLE 5-1

COMPARISON OF OPERATING FEATURES OF 6J5 TUBE IN
VARIOUS CIRCUIT CONFIGURATIONS

Circuit	Gain	C_i, $\mu\mu f$	R_i, megohms	Z_{tf}, ohms	Z_{of}, ohms
1. Cathode follower	0.918	3.7	1	366	365
2. Anode follower $(Z_1 = Z_f = 0.5$ megohm)	-0.818	9.6	0.538	853	785
3. Conventional amplifier	-11.3	45.2	1	7,700	4,350
4. Conventional amplifier (low-gain)	-0.918	9.9	1	7,700	353

It is first noted, by comparing the cathode follower with the anode follower, that the gain of each is roughly the same, and approximately equal to unity; the cathode-follower effective internal impedance and output-terminal impedances are approximately one-half those of the anode follower; the input impedance of the cathode follower is approximately twice that of the anode follower.

By comparing the cathode follower with the conventional grounded cathode circuit, the results bear out the statements made in Sec. 5-8, namely, that the gain is reduced; the effective input capacitance is less; the output-terminal impedance is less.

A comparison of the cathode follower with the conventional grounded-cathode circuit, but with the plate resistance chosen to yield numerically the cathode-follower gain, gives a somewhat better comparison between these two circuits. The input capacitance of the latter circuit is more than twice the former. However, this value of capacitance is not excessive. Also, the output-terminal impedance is nearly the same in both cases, although the effective internal impedance of the cathode follower is low, while that of the conventional amplifier circuit is high.

The question may then be raised whether there is any real advantage to be gained from using the cathode follower rather than a conventional amplifier with such a low plate resistance that the gain is intentionally made approximately equal to unity. The real advantage of the cathode follower and the anode follower over the conventional grounded-cathode amplifier with adjusted gain lies principally in the advantages attendant on feedback amplifiers, as discussed in Sec. 5-2.

The cathode follower is extensively used. It is usually employed when a high input impedance or low output impedance or both are required. For example, it is used as the input stage to almost all good-quality cathode-ray oscilloscopes. It is used when it is required to transmit a signal over a relatively long distance. The low output-terminal impedance of the cathode follower tends to minimize the capacitive loading of the long wires or shielded cable, i.e., a low RC time constant results, and transient signals are not seriously distorted. Moreover, with the proper choice of tube, an output-terminal impedance which provides a good impedance match with the characteristic impedance of a coaxial cable is possible.

It is worth noting that for the case of large amplitude signals with an appreciable load capacitance neither the cathode follower nor the anode follower provides the same positive and negative response characteristics. The cathode follower provides a faster positive- than a negative-output change, whereas the anode follower provides a faster negative- than a positive-output change. The reasons for this action are to be found in the fact that the circuits cannot be treated accurately as linear circuits for large signal amplitudes. The replacement of the single tube by a series-connected push-pull pair overcomes this effect. Such a circuit is given[6] in Fig. 5-37.

An interesting physical explanation of the operation of the anode follower is possible,[6] and this discussion is examined analytically in some detail in Sec. 6-2 in connection with summing circuits and in Sec. 6-3 as an approximate analysis of the general operational feedback amplifier. If R_1, R_g, and the tube circuit are considered as elements of a summing network and the circuit of the anode follower is drawn in Fig. 5-35 to stress this summing-network character, then R_g acts as a comparator, the potential across it being the difference between the input and the output

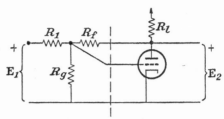

FIG. 5-35. The anode follower drawn in a manner to emphasize the summing-circuit character of the amplifier.

potentials. The action of the amplifier is to tend to make the difference zero, higher amplifier gain being accompanied by a smaller difference, or closer equality. In the extreme case when $R_1 = R_f$, and with very high

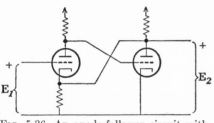

FIG. 5-36. An anode-follower circuit with an amplifier comparator.

amplifier gain, the difference between the input and output potentials is zero, the resultant system gain being unity. The increased gain may be included in the output stage (by using the high-gain tube of Fig. 5-35), or it may be included to provide a more selective comparator. A circuit in which the difference signal is compared at the anode of the comparator stage after amplification is given in Fig. 5-36. Considerable improvement is effected in this circuit.

Another fact to be noted from Eqs. (5-73) and (5-76) is that an increase in Y_f (a reduction in Z_f) results in an increase in the effective input

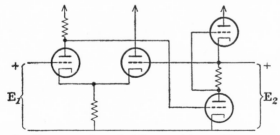

FIG. 5-37. A push-pull-connected anode follower with amplifier comparator and tube feedback path.

impedance, and a decrease of the effective output-terminal impedance. The substitution of a tube impedance for the shunt resistance R_f of the feedback path improves these characteristics. A circuit of this type is given in Fig. 5-37 and also in Fig. P 5-34.

5-11. The Cathode-follower Amplifier. Owing to the high input impedance and low output-terminal impedance of the cathode follower, it is anticipated that the use of such a device as the coupling amplifier between stages will provide an amplifier with a broad frequency-response range. This matter is examined analytically.

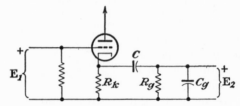

Fig. 5-38. An RC coupled cathode-follower stage.

When used as a coupling amplifier between stages, the cathode-follower circuit becomes essentially that illustrated in Fig. 5-38. In this circuit, C_g is the sum of the effective output capacitance of the cathode follower and the effective input capacitance of the next stage.

The gain of this amplifier will be examined for the various frequency ranges. These follow directly from Eq. (5-52) with the proper interpretation of $\mathbf{Z}_k$.

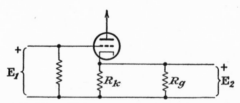

Fig. 5-39. The mid-frequency cathode-follower circuit.

Mid-frequency Gain. The interelectrode capacitances are negligible over the mid-frequency band, whence C_g may be neglected. Also the coupling capacitor C is assumed sufficiently large so that its reactance is negligible. The resulting circuit becomes that of Fig. 5-39. The mid-frequency gain becomes

$$\mathbf{K}_0 = \frac{\mu \mathbf{Z}_k'}{r_p + (\mu + 1)\mathbf{Z}_k'} = \frac{\mu}{\mu + 1 + r_p/\mathbf{Z}_k'} \qquad (5\text{-}77)$$

where

$$\frac{1}{\mathbf{Z}_k'} = \frac{1}{R_k} + \frac{1}{R_g} \qquad (5\text{-}78)$$

H-F Gain. At the h-f end of the response curve, the coupling capacitor may be omitted, although the effect of C_g becomes important. The equivalent circuit has the form shown in Fig. 5-40. The gain equation

[Eq. (5-52)] now becomes

$$K_2 = \frac{\mu}{\mu + 1 + r_p/Z_k''} \tag{5-79}$$

where

$$\frac{1}{Z_k''} = \frac{1}{R_k} + \frac{1}{R_g} + j\omega C_g \tag{5-80}$$

The gain ratio K_2/K_0 becomes

$$\frac{K_2}{K_0} = \frac{1}{1 + \dfrac{j\omega C_g r_p}{\mu + 1 + r_p/Z_k'}}$$

which is

$$\frac{K_2}{K_0} = \frac{1}{1 + j\omega r_p' C_g} = \frac{1}{1 + j(f/f_2)} \tag{5-81}$$

where

$$r_p' = \frac{r_p}{\mu + 1 + r_p/Z_k'} \qquad f_2 = \frac{1}{2\pi r_p' C_g} \tag{5-82}$$

It should be noted that this expression has substantially the same form as Eq. (4-17) for the conventional RC circuit. However, since the product $r_p' C_g$ for the cathode follower is much smaller than $r_p C_g$ of the RC

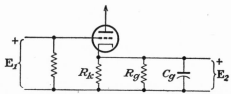

Fig. 5-40. The h-f circuit of the cathode-follower amplifier.

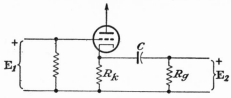

Fig. 5-41. The l-f circuit of the cathode-follower amplifier.

amplifier, then the upper frequency limit of uniform response is much greater for the cathode follower than for the conventional RC stage. Because of this, it is possible to achieve a high h-f limit even when the cathode follower is followed by a stage having a high input capacitance. This means that a rather wide frequency response is possible under these conditions even with a following triode stage.

L-F Gain. At the low frequencies, C_g may be neglected, and the effect of the coupling capacitor becomes very important. Equation (5-52) appropriately modified becomes

$$K_1 = \frac{\mu}{\mu + 1 + r_p/Z_k'''} \frac{R_g}{R_g + 1/j\omega C} \tag{5-83}$$

This expression may be written in the form

$$K_1 = \frac{\mu}{\mu + 1 + \dfrac{r_p}{Z_k'} - \dfrac{r_p}{R_g(1 + j\omega C R_g)}} \frac{j\omega C R_g}{1 + j\omega C R_g} \tag{5-84}$$

where use has been made of the fact that

$$\frac{1}{Z_k'''} = \frac{1}{R_k} + \frac{1}{R_g + 1/j\omega C} = \frac{1}{Z_k'} - \frac{1}{R_g(1 + j\omega C R_g)} \tag{5-85}$$

The gain ratio becomes

$$\frac{K_1}{K_0} = \frac{1}{\mu + 1 + \dfrac{r_p}{Z_k'} - \dfrac{r_p}{R_g(1 + j\omega C R_g)}} \frac{j\omega C R_g}{1 + j\omega C R_g} \left(\mu + 1 + \frac{r_p}{Z_k'} \right)$$

which reduces to the form

$$\frac{K_1}{K_0} = \frac{1}{1 - j(1/\omega C R_1)} = \frac{1}{1 - j(f_1/f)}$$

where
$$R_1 = \frac{R_g}{1 - \dfrac{r_p/R_g}{\mu + 1 + r_p/Z_k'}} \qquad f_1 = \frac{1}{2\pi C R_1} \tag{5-86}$$

This expression has substantially the same form as Eq. (4-11) for the l-f gain of the RC-coupled amplifier, and under typical operating conditions the value of f_1 is much the same for the cathode follower as for the RC amplifier.

REFERENCES

1. Black, H. S., *Elec. Eng.*, **53**, 114 (1934).
   Peterson, E., J. G. Kreer, and L. A. Ware, *Bell System Tech. J.*, **13**, 680 (1934).
2. Feldkeller, R., *Teleg. fersnp. Tech.*, **25**, 217 (1936).
3. Nyquist, H., *Bell System Tech. J.*, **11**, 126 (1932).
   Bode, H. W., "Network Analysis and Feedback Amplifier Design," D. Van Nostrand Company, Inc., New York, 1945.
   Goldman, S., "Transformation Calculus and Electric Transients," Prentice-Hall, Inc., New York, 1949.
4. Reich, H. J., "Theory and Application of Electron Tubes," 2d ed., sec. 6-11, McGraw-Hill Book Company, Inc., New York, 1944.
   Reich, H. J., *Proc. IRE*, **35**, 573 (1947).
   Kraus, H. L., *Electronics*, **20**, 116 (January, 1947).
   Schlesinger, K., *Electronics*, **21**, 103 (February, 1948).
5. Hammoch, C., *MIT Radiation Lab. Rept.* 469 (1943).
6. Keen, A. W., *Wireless Engr.*, **30**, 5 (1953).

PROBLEMS

5-1. An amplifier has a gain $3,000/0$. When negative feedback is applied, the gain is reduced to $2,000/0$. Determine the feedback network.

5-2. An amplifier without feedback gives an output of 46 volts with 8 per cent second-harmonic distortion when the input is 0.16 volt.

   a. If 1 per cent of the output is fed back into the input in a degenerative circuit, what is the output potential?

   b. If an output of 46 volts with 1 per cent second-harmonic distortion is permissible, what is the input potential?

5-3. Given the amplifier stage with cathode degeneration shown in the accompanying diagram,

$$E_{bb} = 250 \text{ volts} \qquad R_l = 100 \text{ kilohms}$$
$$g_m = 1,200 \ \mu\text{mhos} \qquad \mu = 70$$
$$R_g = 1 \text{ megohms}$$

   a. What should be the value of R_k to give an over-all gain of 8?

   b. What is the value of E_{cc}, and the largest value of e_g to yield an output without distortion?

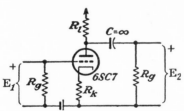

5-4. Plot the gain as a function of frequency of the simple amplifier shown in the accompanying figure. Also plot on the same sheet the gain of the stage when fixed bias is used.

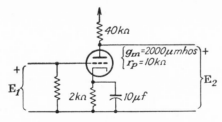

5-5. The first stage of the circuit of Fig. 5-9 uses a 6SJ7 pentode with

$$E_b = 250 \text{ volts} \qquad E_{cc1} = -3 \text{ volts} \qquad E_{cc2} = 100 \text{ volts} \qquad I_b = 3 \text{ ma}$$

The second stage is a 6C5, with $E_b = 250$ volts, $E_{cc1} = -8$ volts, $I_b = 8$ ma. The other factors are

$$R_{l1} = 100 \text{ kilohms} \qquad R_{g1} = R_{g2} = 250 \text{ kilohms} \qquad R_{l2} = 25 \text{ kilohms}$$
$$C = 0.04 \ \mu\text{f} \qquad C_{k1} = 10 \ \mu\text{f} \qquad C_{k2} = 2.5 \ \mu\text{f} \qquad C_d = 0.1 \ \mu\text{f} \qquad R_1 = 200 \text{ ohms}$$
$$R_2 = 150 \text{ kilohms}$$

a. Specify the values of R_{k1}, R_{k2}, E_{bb}.

b. Draw the complete mid-frequency equivalent circuit.

c. The total shunting capacitance across R_{g2} is 80 $\mu\mu f$.   Calculate and plot a gain-frequency-response curve over the range from 20 to 50,000 cps.

d. Repeat (c) if $R_1 = 0$, $R_2 = 150$ kilohms.

5-6. Given the two-stage circuit which is provided with negative-potential feedback, the tubes having $r_p = 10^6$ ohms, $g_m = 1,200$ $\mu mhos$.

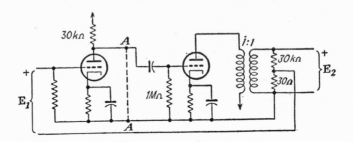

a. Calculate the output impedance.

b. Calculate the impedance between points AA.

5-7. Given a simple pentode amplifier stage as illustrated, the screen by-pass capacitor being omitted.   Derive an expression for the gain of the amplifier stage. Assume that I_b is independent of E_b and that μ_{sg} of the screen grid is the same relative to plate and to screen currents.

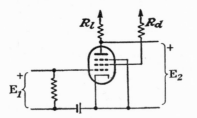

5-8. Calculate the gain of the inverse feedback pair.*   Assume that the tubes are identical and that $R_g \gg R_l$.

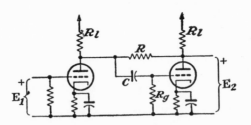

5-9. Obtain an expression for the output potentials of the cathode-coupled two-tube circuit shown in the accompanying figure.

* G. R. Mezger, *Electronics,* **17,** 126 (April, 1944).

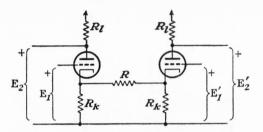

5-10. An RC coupled amplifier has a mid-frequency gain $K_0 = -27$. Potential feedback is applied, the amount of feedback being such as to reduce the lower half-power frequency to one-tenth its no-feedback value.

a. Find the feedback fraction β.

b. Find the resulting mid-frequency gain under feedback conditions.

5-11. Given a three-stage RC coupled amplifier, each stage of which has an l-f cutoff of 20 cps, an h-f cutoff of 84 kc, and a mid-frequency gain of 220. Plot the locus of the complex potential gain.

5-12. The locus of the complex potential amplification of a certain amplifier is illustrated. If 1 per cent negative feedback is applied, determine the value of the gain K at the following frequencies: 100 cps, 10 kc, 40 kc. Assume that β is independent of frequency and that the potential fed back is in phase with the output potential.

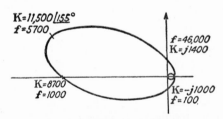

5-13. Three identical RC coupled amplifier stages are connected in cascade, inverse feedback being provided between the output and input, as indicated in

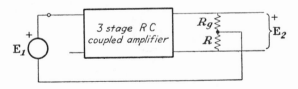

the accompanying diagram. The per stage constants are (see Fig. 4-3 for a typical stage)

$$R_l = 20 \text{ kilohms} \qquad C = 0.01 \ \mu\text{f}$$
$$C_g = 20 \ \mu\mu\text{f} \qquad R_g = 1 \text{ megohm}$$
$$\text{Tube:} \quad r_p = 1 \text{ megohm} \qquad g_m = 1{,}000 \ \mu\text{mhos}$$

a. Determine the maximum value of R for which the amplifier will operate without oscillations.

b. Calculate the mid-band gain under these conditions.

5-14. Consider the amplifier stage illustrated in the accompanying figure.

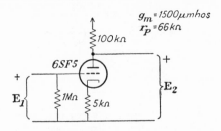

Calculate the following (neglect the effects of interelectrode capacitances):

a. Input impedance Z_{1f}.   Compare this with the value R_g.

b. Effective internal impedance Z_{tf}.

c. Output-terminal impedance Z_{0f}.

5-15. The circuit of Prob. 5-14 is rearranged by connecting the grid resistor to the cathode rather than to ground, as shown.   Repeat Prob. 5-14 for the rearranged circuit.

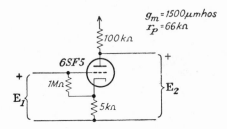

5-16. a. Refer to the cascode circuit illustrated.   Find expressions for the following: gain K, output-terminal impedance Z_{0f}.

b. Compare the results under (a) with the corresponding results when tube $T1$ and its cathode resistor R are replaced by a resistor R_l.

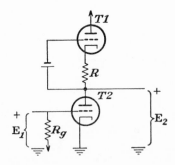

5-17. Calculate the effective input impedance at 10 kc of the circuit in the accompanying figure.   Each tube has the value $g_m = 2,000$ μmhos, $r_p = 10$ kilohms.   Neglect all tube and wiring capacitances.

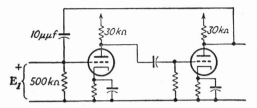

5-18. Derive an expression for the effective input impedance of the cathode-coupled amplifier shown. Under what conditions is this impedance negative?

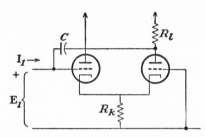

5-19. What must be the value of R_k in Fig. 5-26 if $Z_{0f} = 300$ ohms at 1,000 cps? A 6J5 tube is used.

5-20. Given the cathode-follower circuit with the grid resistor R_g tied from grid to cathode, as shown in the accompanying figure. Derive expressions for the effective input impedance Z_{1f} and the output-terminal impedance Z_{0f}. Neglect tube capacitances. Show that Z_{1f} can be written in the form $Z_{1f} = R_g/(1 - K)$. Find an expression for K.

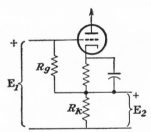

5-21. Compare the values of gain, effective input impedance, effective internal impedance of the two cathode-follower stages illustrated.

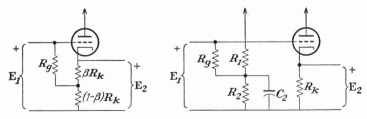

5-22. Calculate and plot as a function of frequency on semilog paper the gain, output impedance, and input impedance of the cathode-follower amplifier of

Fig. 5-38 at the following values of ω: 250; 2,500; 250,000; 2.5×10^6; 5×10^6 rad/sec. Choose a 6J5 tube for which

$r_p = 7,700$ ohms $\mu = 20$ $C_{gp} = 3.4\ \mu\mu f$ $C_{gk} = 3.4\ \mu\mu f$ $C_{pk} = 3.6\ \mu\mu f$

Also choose

    $R_k = 10$ kilohms $R_g = 200$ kilohms $C = 0.01\ \mu f$ $C_g = 40\ \mu\mu f$

5-23. Consider the circuit shown in the accompanying diagram. Determine:

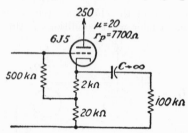

a. The positive signal that will drive e_c to zero.

b. The negative signal to drive the tube to cutoff.

c. The mid-frequency gain.

d. The input admittance when $C_{gp} = 3.4\ \mu\mu f$, $C_{gk} = 4\ \mu\mu f$.

5-24. Repeat Prob. 5-23 when the tube is changed to a 6AC7 pentode. The tube operates in its linear region, with $g_m = 9,000\ \mu$mhos, $r_p = 1$ megohm.

5-25. Plot the dynamic characteristic of a 6J5 tube in a simple cathode-follower circuit, with $E_{bb} = 250$ volts, for the following values of cathode resistance R_k: 5,000 ohms; 25,000 ohms; 100,000 ohms.

5-26. A video amplifier is coupled to a cathode follower, as shown in the figure.

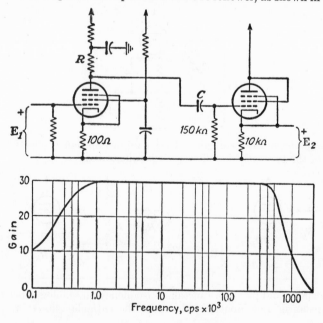

The frequency-response curve of this amplifier is also sketched. Choose the transconductance $g_m = 9,000$ μmhos.

a. Calculate the approximate value of the coupling capacitor between the two stages.

b. Calculate the approximate value of the total shunt capacitance.

5-27. The essentials of a double cathode follower[5] are illustrated.

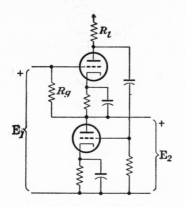

a. Show that the expression for the gain is

$$\mathbf{K}_f = \frac{\mu^2 + \mu r_p/R_l}{(\mu^2 + \mu + 1) + (\mu + 2)r_p/R_l}$$

b. Show that the output admittance is

$$\mathbf{Y}_{0f} = \frac{\mu + 1}{r_p + R_l} + \frac{1 + \dfrac{\mu(\mu + 1)}{1 + r_p/R_l}}{r_p} \doteq \mu g_m$$

5-28. Consider the double cathode follower shown in the diagram. Calculate the gain and effective output-terminal impedance of this amplifier.

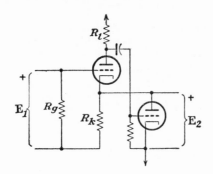

5-29. An alternative double cathode follower which provides for an improved input impedance has been suggested. This is illustrated in the accompanying diagram. The tube in the cathode lead provides, in effect, a high dynamic cathode resistance, thereby permitting a system gain of nearly unity.

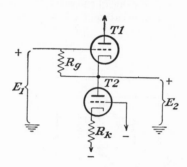

a. Show that the effective input impedance is given by $Z_{1f} = R_g/(1 - K)$. Find an expression for the gain. Show for identical tubes and the usual choice of parameters that $1 - K \doteq 1/\mu$. This may be shown to be approximately one-half that when a resistor R_k is used (see Prob. 5-20).

b. Find an expression for the output-terminal admittance. Show that this reduces to $Y_{0f} \doteq g_{m1}$, which is the same as for the simple cathode follower.

5-30. A form of series double cathode follower is illustrated.* This circuit, like that in Prob. 5-29, provides for an improved input impedance, the gain of the system being more nearly unity than the simple circuit of Prob. 5-20.

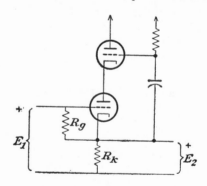

a. Show that the effective input impedance is given by $Z_{1f} = R_g/(1 - K)$. Find an expression for the gain. Show for identical tubes and the usual choice of circuit parameters that $1 - K \doteq 1/g_{m1}R_k$.

b. Find an expression for the output admittance. Show that this is approximately $Y_{2f} \doteq g_{m1}$, the value of the simple cathode follower.

5-31. The two circuits of Probs. 5-29 and 5-30 may be combined to provide a circuit of very high input impedance.† Compute the effective input impedance of the circuit shown.

---

* J. R. MacDonald, *Rev. Sci. Instr.*, **25**, 144 (1954).

† *Idem.*

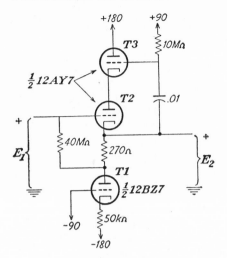

5-32. The circuit of a triode follower* is illustrated. Calculate the effective input impedance and the output admittance of this circuit.

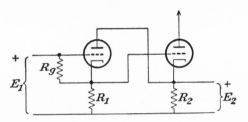

5-33. Show that the h-f cutoff of the anode-follower amplifier is approximately one-half that of the cathode follower. Show also that the l-f cutoff is approximately the same as that of the cathode-follower amplifier, for $\mathbf{Z}_1 = R_g$ in Fig. 5-38.

5-34. Consider the direct-coupled anode-follower circuit illustrated.[6] For the case where $T1$ and $T2$ are identical tubes:

a. Find an expression for the over-all gain of the circuit.

b. Find an expression for the output-terminal impedance $\mathbf{Z}_{0f}$.

c. Choose $R_{l1} = R_{l3} = R_k = 10$ kilohms, $\mu_1 = \mu_3 = 20$, $r_{p1} = r_{p3} = 7{,}700$ ohms; find the numerical value of $\mathbf{Z}_{0f}$.

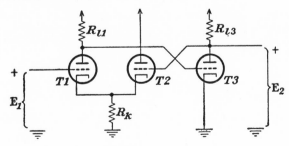

* S. Krakauer, *Rev. Sci. Instr.*, **24**, 496 (1953).

5-35. Calculate the gain, effective input impedance, output-terminal impedance of the grounded-grid input anode-follower circuit[6] shown.

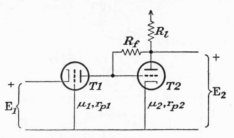

5-36. Evaluate the effective input- and effective output-terminal impedances of the circuit of Fig. 5-37.

5-37. As a simple example of a multiple-loop feedback system, consider a two-stage amplifier with potential feedback over all. If the stage gains are K_1 and K_2, respectively, and the feedback fraction is β,

a. Deduce an expression for the total effective gain.

b. Discuss the question of stability over the pass band and outside of the pass band.

Suppose now that current feedback is applied to stage 1 by means of a cathode resistor R_k.

c. Repeat (*a*) and (*b*) under the present circumstances.

d. Discuss the relative possibility of instability in the two cases.

CHAPTER 6

ELECTRONIC COMPUTING CIRCUITS

Several basic methods are used in computer design. Some are entirely mechanical in character and operation, some are electromechanical, and others are essentially electrical. The electrical types are divided into two general classes, the digital and the analog types. Some circuits of importance in analog-type computers are to be examined in this chapter.

Analog computers are those in which electrical quantities which can be varied and measured conveniently, usually potentials, are made to obey differential equations which are identical in form to those of the system under survey. This permits the use of purely electrical principles and components to yield information concerning the behavior of a wide variety of physical problems.

Among the circuits to be examined are those which perform such basic mathematical operations as addition, subtraction, differentiation, integration, multiplication, division, etc. In some cases, these circuits depend for their operation on the special shapes of the tube characteristics. In other cases, feedback is applied in special ways to achieve the desired results. Certain operations are performed by a combination of circuits.

6-1. Difference Amplifiers. Several circuits exist in which the output potential is the difference between two input signals. Figure 6-1 is the

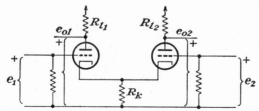

FIG. 6-1. The common cathode difference amplifier.

cathode-coupled difference amplifier. It will be noted that both inputs have a common ground connection. The operation of this circuit will be analyzed for the case of identical tubes.

To analyze the operation of this circuit requires its equivalent circuit. In this case a simple approach is to view the circuit from the cathode-

161

ground terminals and draw the Thévenin equivalents looking into each tube.   This yields Fig. 6-2.

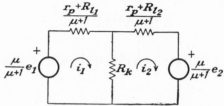

Fig. 6-2. The equivalent circuit of Fig. 6-1.

From general network considerations, the following set of equations results:

$$\left(\frac{r_p + R_{l1}}{\mu + 1} + R_k\right) i_1 - R_k i_2 = \frac{\mu}{\mu + 1} e_1$$

$$-R_k i_1 + \left(\frac{r_p + R_{l2}}{\mu + 1} + R_k\right) i_2 = - \frac{\mu}{\mu + 1} e_2$$

(6-1)

A solution of this set of equations by determinantal methods yields, for i_1,

$$i_1 = \frac{+\mu \left[\left(\dfrac{R_{l2} + r_p}{\mu + 1} + R_k\right) e_1 - R_k e_2 \right]}{\dfrac{(R_{l1} + r_p)(R_{l2} + r_p)}{\mu + 1} + R_k(R_{l1} + R_{l2} + 2r_p)}$$

(6-2)

and, for the current i_2,

$$i_2 = \frac{-\mu \left[R_k e_1 - \left(\dfrac{R_{l1} + r_p}{\mu + 1} + R_k\right) e_2 \right]}{\dfrac{(R_{l1} + r_p)(R_{l2} + r_p)}{\mu + 1} + R_k(R_{l1} + R_{l2} + 2r_p)}$$

(6-3)

The output potentials follow from these and are, respectively,

$$e_{01} = -i_1 R_{l1} = \frac{-\mu R_{l1} \left[\left(\dfrac{R_{l2} + r_p}{\mu + 1} + R_k\right) e_1 - R_k e_2 \right]}{\dfrac{(R_{l1} + r_p)(R_{l2} + r_p)}{\mu + 1} + R_k(R_{l1} + R_{l2} + 2r_p)}$$

(6-4)

and

$$e_{02} = -i_2 R_{l2} = \frac{+\mu R_{l2} \left[R_k e_1 - \left(\dfrac{R_{l1} + r_p}{\mu + 1} + R_k\right) e_2 \right]}{\dfrac{(R_{l1} + r_p)(R_{l2} + r_p)}{\mu + 1} + R_k(R_{l1} + R_{l2} + 2r_p)}$$

(6-5)

Under those particular conditions of operation for which the ratio

$(R_l + r_p)/(\mu + 1) \ll R_k$, Eqs. (6-4) and (6-5) reduce to

$$e_{01} = \frac{-\mu R_{l1}}{R_{l1} + R_{l2} + 2r_p} (e_1 - e_2) \qquad (6\text{-}6)$$

$$e_{02} = \frac{+\mu R_{l2}}{R_{l1} + R_{l2} + 2r_p} (e_1 - e_2) \qquad (6\text{-}7)$$

It will be observed from these equations that the output potentials are given in terms of an amplified difference between the two input potentials.

For the case when the plate resistances are equal, $R_{l1} = R_{l2} = R_l$, Eqs. (6-6) and (6-7) reduce to

$$e_{01} = \frac{-\mu R_l}{2(R_l + r_p)} (e_1 - e_2) \qquad (6\text{-}8)$$

$$e_{02} = \frac{+\mu R_l}{2(R_l + r_p)} (e_1 - e_2) \qquad (6\text{-}9)$$

These expressions show that the two output potentials are of equal magnitude but of opposite polarity. Also, appreciable amplification is pro-

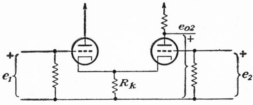

Fig. 6-3. A modification of Fig. 6-1 to yield a single output potential.

vided by the circuit. Note that the difference between the two output potentials is

$$e_{01} - e_{02} = \frac{-\mu R_l}{R_l + r_p} (e_1 - e_2) \qquad (6\text{-}10)$$

Although this expression was obtained from expressions that are only approximate, this result is actually exact. That this is so may be verified by using Eqs. (6-4) and (6-5) directly, and not the approximate forms [Eqs. (6-6) and (6-7)].

If a single output is desired, the circuit may be modified to the form shown in Fig. 6-3. The output from this circuit is obtained by setting $R_{l1} = 0$ in Eqs. (6-6) and (6-7). The result is

$$e_{02} = \frac{\mu R_l}{R_l + 2r_p} (e_1 - e_2) \qquad (6\text{-}11)$$

It should be noted that no restrictions have been placed on the input potentials e_1 and e_2, and the results are therefore independent of the waveshapes and amplitudes, except that the amplitudes must not be so large as to vitiate the linear equivalent circuit of the tubes. This result should be compared with that given in Eq. (4-38).

Attention is directed to the restriction on the validity of Eq. (6-11) which was imposed in going from Eqs. (6-4) and (6-5) to Eqs. (6-6) and (6-7), viz., that $R_l + r_p \ll (\mu + 1)R_k$. The exact difference condition is valid only for $R_k \to \infty$, an impossible practical condition. In all cases, therefore, a slight error exists, although this may be minimized by slight changes in R_{l1} and R_{l2}. A circuit* which does not suffer from this limitation is given in Fig. 6-4, which differs from Fig. 6-3 by the presence of a resistor from the plate of tube 2 to the cathode.

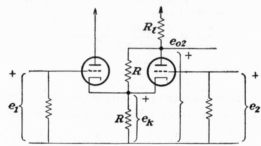

Fig. 6-4. A circuit of an exact difference amplifier.

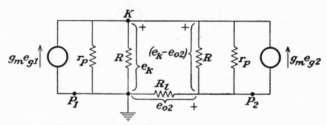

Fig. 6-5. The equivalent circuit of Fig. 6-4.

The analysis of the operation of this amplifier best proceeds from the current-source equivalent circuit, which is given in Fig. 6-5. From the diagram,

$$e_{g1} = e_1 - e_k$$
$$e_{g2} = e_2 - e_k \tag{6-12}$$

By an application of the junction analysis, the following two expressions result:

$$-(Y_l + Y + Y_p)e_k + Y_l(e_k - e_{02}) = -g_m(e_1 - e_k)$$
$$Y_l e_k - (Y_l + Y + Y_p)(e_k - e_{02}) = -g_m(e_2 - e_k) \tag{6-13}$$

Combine terms to get

$$(g_m + Y + Y_p)e_k + Y_l e_{02} = g_m e_1$$
$$(g_m + Y + Y_p)e_k - (Y_l + Y + Y_p)e_{02} = g_m e_2 \tag{6-14}$$

* The author is indebted to Dr. Richard McFee for calling this circuit to his attention. [See also R. McFee, *Rev. Sci. Instr.*, **21**, 770 (1950)]

Now subtract the second equation from the first.   This gives

$$(Y + Y_p + 2Y_l)e_{02} = -g_m(e_2 - e_1) \tag{6-15}$$

or finally

$$e_{02} = \frac{-g_m}{1/R + 1/r_p + 2/R_l}(e_2 - e_1) = \frac{\mu R R_l}{r_p R_l + R R_l + 2 r_p R}(e_1 - e_2) \tag{6-16}$$

Note that no approximations were made in this development.

A third form of difference amplifier is illustrated in Fig. 6-6.   Note that one of the input potentials is isolated from ground.   To analyze the

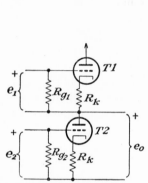

FIG. 6-6. A series, or "cascode," type of difference amplifier.

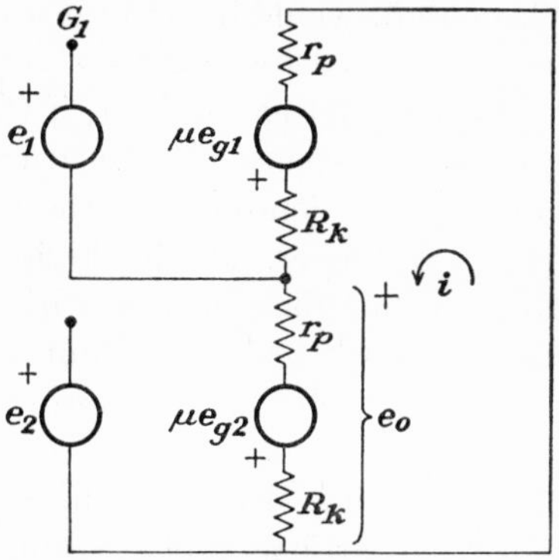

FIG. 6-7. The equivalent of the cascode circuit of Fig. 6-6.

operation of the circuit, recourse is had to the equivalent circuit, which is given in Fig. 6-7.   From the diagram

$$\begin{aligned} e_{g1} &= e_1 - iR_k \\ e_{g2} &= e_2 - iR_k \end{aligned} \tag{6-17}$$

Also, it is seen that

$$i = \frac{\mu(e_{g1} + e_{g2})}{2(r_p + R_k)}$$

which becomes, by combining with Eqs. (6-17),

$$i = \frac{\mu}{2}\frac{e_1 + e_2 - 2iR_k}{r_p + R_k}$$

from which

$$i = \frac{\mu(e_1 + e_2)}{2[r_p + (\mu + 1)R_k]} \tag{6-18}$$

The output potential is then given by

$$\begin{aligned} e_0 &= i(r_p + R_k) - \mu e_{g2} \\ &= i(r_p + R_k) - \mu(e_2 - iR_k) \end{aligned}$$

or

$$e_0 = i[r_p + (\mu + 1)R_k] - \mu e_2 \qquad (6\text{-}19)$$

Combine this expression with Eq. (6-18) to find

$$e_0 = \frac{\mu}{2}(e_1 + e_2) - \mu e_2$$

or finally

$$e_0 = \frac{\mu}{2}(e_1 - e_2) \qquad (6\text{-}20)$$

which shows an exact relationship without approximations.

This circuit would be quite satisfactory in many applications, although there is the need for one input potential which is isolated from ground. This requirement can be met, if the input is an a-c potential of nominal frequency, by the use of an isolating transformer. For waveshapes which might have h-f components, the isolating transformer might cause difficulties. Moreover, at the high frequencies, an unbalance will arise because of the tube and stray wiring capacitances. Difficulties in the use of this circuit will also be encountered at the very low frequencies, owing to the isolation problem. In most cases the circuits of Fig. 6-3 or 6-4 would be preferred.

6-2. Summing Circuits. Suppose that it is desired to add a number of potentials of arbitrary phase, amplitude, and frequency. A number of circuits exist for effecting this addition. Perhaps the simplest method is to effect the summation by means of the resistor network of Fig. 6-8.

A direct application of the Millman theorem yields the expression

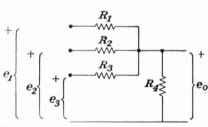

$$e_0 = \frac{e_1 Y_1 + e_2 Y_2 + e_3 Y_3}{Y_1 + Y_2 + Y_3 + Y_4} \qquad (6\text{-}21)$$

If the resistances are all chosen equal so that $R_1 = R_2 = R_3 = R_4 = R$, then Eq. (6-21) becomes

Fig. 6-8. A resistance summing network.

$$e_0 = \frac{1}{4}(e_1 + e_2 + e_3) \qquad (6\text{-}22)$$

This shows that addition is accomplished, but the network gain depends on the number of resistors in the network.

Ordinarily the resistances are high in order to avoid not only the loading of the sources but also interaction among the sources through these resistors. As a result, the effective internal impedance relative to the output terminals is high. In order to avoid loading of the network by the output, the network should feed the grid of a tube circuit.

A feedback summing amplifier which essentially comprises the resistance summing network and the anode follower is illustrated in Fig. 6-9. From considerations only of effective input impedance of the amplifier circuit, the cathode follower could be incorporated in the circuit in place of the anode follower.   However, more is gained than low loading, since a unity-gain system, independent of the number of inputs, is possible.

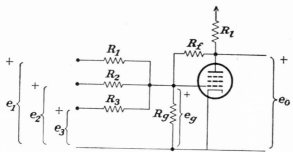

FIG. 6-9. A feedback summing amplifier.

A direct application of the Kirchhoff current law at the grid of the tube of Fig. 6-9 yields

$$\frac{e_1 - e_g}{R_1} + \frac{e_2 - e_g}{R_2} + \cdots + \frac{e_n - e_g}{R_n} + \frac{e_0 - e_g}{R_f} = \frac{e_g}{R_g} \qquad (6\text{-}23)$$

from which

$$\frac{e_1}{R_1} + \frac{e_2}{R_2} + \cdots + \frac{e_n}{R_n} = e_g \left(\frac{1}{R_g} + \frac{1}{R_f} + \frac{1}{R_1} + \cdots + \frac{1}{R_n} \right) - \frac{e_0}{R_f}$$

If the resistances are chosen to be

$$R_1 = R_2 = \cdots = R_n = R_f = R_g = R$$

the above equation becomes

$$\frac{1}{R} \sum_n e_n = \frac{n + 2}{R} e_g - \frac{e_0}{R} \qquad (6\text{-}24)$$

Now, making use of the fact that the nominal gain of the amplifier is

$$K = \frac{e_0}{e_g}$$

the above equation becomes

$$\frac{1}{R} \sum_n e_n = \frac{e_0}{K} \frac{n + 2}{R} - \frac{e_0}{R} \qquad (6\text{-}25)$$

But the nominal gain of the amplifier will be high, particularly if a pentode is used.   For the case of a pentode, and with n ordinarily small,

Eq. (6-25) reduces to the approximate form

$$\frac{1}{R} \sum_n e_n \doteq -\frac{e_0}{R}$$

from which

$$e_0 = -\sum_n e_n \tag{6-26}$$

If the feedback and input resistances are not made equal, Eq. (6-26) becomes

$$e_0 = -R_f \sum_n \frac{e_n}{R_n} \tag{6-27}$$

The appropriate choice of input impedance will permit multiplying the corresponding input potential by the value R_f/R_n. In case any one of the input potentials is required to have a sign opposite to the others, an anode follower or other sign-reversing amplifier can be used before the potential is applied to the appropriate input resistor of the summing amplifier.

A circuit for the addition of potentials in the cathode circuit of a chain of stages is shown in Fig. 6-10. An analysis of this circuit is readily

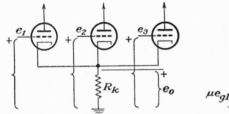

FIG. 6-10. A common cathode summing chain.   FIG. 6-11. The equivalent circuit of Fig. 6-10.

effected if it is assumed that identical tubes are used. In this case the equivalent circuit attains the form shown in Fig. 6-11. An application of the Millman theorem yields

$$e_0 = \frac{\mu e_{g1} Y_p + \mu e_{g2} Y_p + \cdots + \mu e_{gn} Y_p}{n Y_p + Y_k}$$

or

$$e_0 = \frac{\mu Y_p}{n Y_p + Y_k} (e_{g1} + e_{g2} + \cdots + e_{gn}) \tag{6-28}$$

But the grid potentials are

$$e_{g1} = e_1 - e_0$$
$$\cdots \cdots \cdots \cdots$$
$$e_{gn} = e_n - e_0$$
$$\tag{6-29}$$

Combine with Eq. (6-28) to get

$$e_0 = \frac{\mu Y_p}{n Y_p + Y_k} (e_1 + \cdots + e_n - n e_0)$$

or

$$e_0 = \frac{\mu Y_p}{n(\mu + 1) Y_p + Y_k} \sum_n e_n \qquad (6\text{-}30)$$

which is given, with good approximation, by

$$e_0 \doteq \frac{\mu}{n(\mu + 1)} \sum_n e_n \qquad (6\text{-}31)$$

This circuit permits potential summation with very little interaction among the potential sources, owing to the effective isolation afforded by each tube.   However, it does so at the expense of a tube for each potential source.   For this reason, the circuit of Fig. 6-9 with large series resistances would ordinarily be preferred.

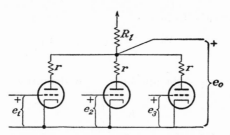

FIG. 6-12. A common plate summing chain.

Addition is also possible by connecting a chain of tubes through a common plate resistor, as illustrated in Fig. 6-12.   The resistors r in each plate lead are small suppressor resistors, to avoid oscillation.   It may be shown that the output potential from such a plate summing chain is given by the expression

$$e_0 = \frac{-\mu}{n + r_p/R_l} \sum_n e_n \qquad (6\text{-}32)$$

Here, as in the case of the common cathode summing chain, a tube is required for each potential source in the adding group.   Some over-all gain is effected in the circuit.

6-3. General Operational Feedback Amplifier—Approximate Analysis. [1] A number of computing elements utilize feedback circuits in order to achieve their desired results.   A circuit that is used extensively in such applications is given in Fig. 6-13.   The equivalent circuit is also given. This circuit, with appropriate choice of parameters, was examined in Sec.

5-10 as the anode follower.   An exact analysis is contained in Sec. 5-10, although an approximate analysis yields important information.   This will be examined before the exact analysis is discussed.

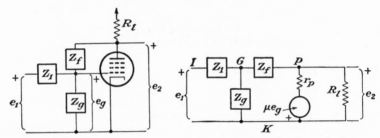

Fig. 6-13. A general feedback circuit and its plate-circuit equivalent.

An application of the Millman network theorem yields directly

$$e_g = \frac{e_1 Y_1 + e_2 Y_f}{Y_1 + Y_f + Y_g} \tag{6-33}$$

This is rewritten in the form

$$e_2 = \frac{Y_1 + Y_f + Y_g}{Y_f} e_g - \frac{Y_1}{Y_f} e_1 \tag{6-34}$$

But the nominal gain of the amplifier is, by definition,

$$K = \frac{e_2}{e_g} \tag{6-35}$$

and the resultant gain with feedback is

$$K_f = \frac{e_2}{e_1} \tag{6-36}$$

Then Eq. (6-34) becomes

$$K_f = \frac{Y_1 + Y_f + Y_g}{Y_f} \frac{e_g}{e_1} - \frac{Y_1}{Y_f} \tag{6-37}$$

or

$$K_f = \frac{Y_1 + Y_f + Y_g}{Y_f} \frac{K_f}{K} - \frac{Y_1}{Y_f}$$

Solving for K_f yields

$$K_f \left(1 - \frac{Y_1 + Y_f + Y_g}{Y_f} \frac{1}{K} \right) = - \frac{Y_1}{Y_f} \tag{6-38}$$

This becomes

$$K_f = - \frac{Y_1}{Y_f} \frac{1}{1 - \frac{1}{K} - \frac{Y_1 + Y_g}{Y_f} \frac{1}{K}} \tag{6-39}$$

or, equivalently,

$$K_f = -\frac{Z_f}{Z_1}\frac{1}{1 - \dfrac{1}{K} - Z_f\dfrac{Z_1 + Z_g}{Z_1 Z_g}\dfrac{1}{K}} \tag{6-40}$$

Some important results can be obtained from this expression. As an approximation, suppose that the grid impedance $Z_g \gg Z_1$. Equation (6-40) becomes

$$K_f \doteq -\frac{Z_f}{Z_1}\frac{1}{1 - 1/K - (Z_f/Z_1)(1/K)} \tag{6-41}$$

For convenience, the quantity K_f' is defined as the ratio

$$K_f' \equiv \frac{Z_f}{Z_1} = Z_f Y_1 \tag{6-42}$$

Then

$$K_f = -K_f'\frac{1}{1 - 1/K - K_f'/K} \tag{6-43}$$

This expression shows that the resultant gain of the amplifier is slightly less than the quantity K_f' defined in Eq. (6-42). Moreover, if it is assumed that the gain of the tube as defined in Eq. (6-35) is large, and this is generally true for a pentode, then Eq. (6-43) becomes approximately

$$K_f = -K_f' \tag{6-44}$$

This means that as long as e_g is negligibly small, the gain of the system is solely dependent on the ratio of the network impedances Z_f/Z_1; that is, it is independent of the changing characteristics of the amplifier so long as $K \gg 1 + Z_f/Z_1$.

Now combine Eqs. (6-44) and (6-36). The resulting expression is written in the form

$$e_2 = -[Z_f Y_1]e_1 \tag{6-45}$$

This expression is very important, as it contains an explanation to the name, *operational amplifier*, that has been applied to the circuit of Fig. 6-13.

Reference to the development leading to Eq. (6-45) will show that at no time was there a requirement imposed that the potentials be sinusoidal functions of time. Consequently the impedance functions that appear in the equations are functions of the general differential operator p ($= d/dt$). This is to say that the foregoing development has actually been a manipulation of the controlling differential equation relating the output potential and the input potential. Equation (6-45) is the approximate form of this controlling differential equation. If one considers the factor $[Z_f Y_1]$ to be an operator, then the basis for the name of the amplifier is clear. Of course, if the applied potential is sinusoidal, then p ($= d/dt$) is replaced by $j\omega$, $Z_f Y_1$ is a function of $j\omega$, and e_2 and e_1 become E_2 and E_1, respectively. In this case Eq. (6-45) is the steady-state relationship

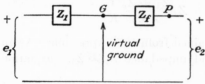

Fig. 6-14. An approximate equivalent circuit of the operational amplifier of Fig. 6-13.

$$E_2 = -Z_f Y_1 E_1$$

Equation (6-45) permits a very convenient approximate circuit to be drawn of the operational amplifier. This approximate circuit is given in Fig. 6-14. The presence of the virtual ground in the diagram is to emphasize the fact that the change in potential on the grid e_g is so small that, as a first approximation, it can be assumed to be zero. A second diagrammatic form for the operational amplifier which is frequently used is given in Fig. 6-15.

A number of special applications of this circuit will be considered, and the corresponding, more detailed analyses of several of these applications will be carried out below. Among others, the direct adaptation of this circuit for integration is very important.

a. *Multiplication by a Constant.* If the impedances Z_f and Z_1 are equal resistances or, in fact, equal impedances of any form, then by Eq. (6-45) the output potential will be the negative of the input potential.

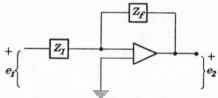

Fig. 6-15. An alternate form of the operational amplifier.

For the case of equal resistances the result is the anode follower, which has already been discussed in detail in Sec. 5-10, and the amplifier performs the simple operation of sign changing.

If the impedances Z_f and Z_1 are unequal resistances, then the output potential e_2 for $Z_f = kZ_1$ will be k times the input potential e_1 and of opposite sign. Since k may be a positive number either greater or less than unity, the magnitude of the output potential can be made larger or smaller than the input potential. In practice the multiplication or division by a constant factor greater than about 20 should be avoided, except in special cases.

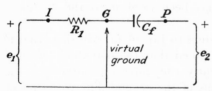

Fig. 6-16. The operational integrating amplifier.

b. *Integrating Circuit.* If the impedance elements in the circuit of Fig. 6-13 are chosen as shown in the accompanying diagram (Fig. 6-16), then $Z_1 = R_1$ and Z_f is the operational expression $Z_f = 1/C_f p$, where $p \ (= d/dt)$ is the usual symbol for the time-derivative operator. Thus $1/p$ denotes integration with respect to time. An application of Eq. (6-45) requires that

$$e_2 = \frac{-1}{R_1 C_f p} e_1$$

which is

$$e_2 = - \frac{1}{R_1 C_f} \int e_1 \, dt \tag{6-46}$$

This shows that the output potential is related to the integral of the input potential.

For the particular case in which the input potential is sinusoidal and of the form

$$e_1 = E_m \sin \omega t$$

then

$$e_2 = - \frac{1}{R_1 C_f} \int E_m \sin \omega t \, dt = \frac{E_m}{\omega R_1 C_f} \cos \omega t$$

if the constant of integration is chosen to be zero. With the constants of the circuit so chosen that

$$R_1 C_f = \frac{1}{\omega}$$

then the output potential is

$$e_2 = E_m \cos \omega t = E_m \sin (\omega t + 90)$$

This permits an output potential which is of the same amplitude as the input, but shifted by 90 deg in phase. Such circuits may be adjusted to yield the 90-deg phase shift to within 10 min or less. Of course, if the factor $R_1 C_f$ is different from $1/\omega$, the amplitude will be different from E_m.

Suppose that there is a small percentage of higher harmonics in the input signal, such as noise. Owing to the appearance of a frequency factor ω appropriate to the signal frequency that will appear in the denominator of each term in the expression for e_2, the higher-harmonic terms will be appreciably reduced in the output. Consequently noise or other h-f spurious signals will not seriously effect the output signal.

An important input potential to such an amplifier is a constant, $-E$. The output is a linear function of time, since

$$e_2 = - \frac{1}{R_1 C_f} \int (-E) \, dt = \frac{E}{R_1 C_f} t$$

Actually, it will be found that the variation follows an exponential law, the start of which is a linear function of time. The input and output waveforms will be somewhat as illustrated in Fig. 6-17.

Attention is called to the extensive use of integrating circuits for the production of saw-tooth waveforms for use as the sweep-deflection potentials in cathode-ray tubes. Chapter 10 contains a detailed discussion of many specific circuits for such applications, and this chapter might well be referred to in reading the present section. Also, simple passive integrating circuits are extensively used as elements of clamping circuits (see Sec. 7-3).

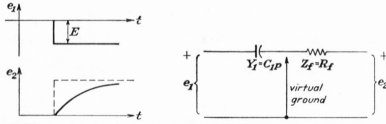

Fig. 6-17. The input and output poten-   Fig. 6-18. The operational differentiating
tials of an integrator.   amplifier.

c. *Differentiating Circuits.* If the circuit elements are chosen as illustrated in Fig. 6-18, then Eq. (6-45) becomes

$$e_2 = -C_1 R_f p e_1 = -C_1 R_f \frac{de_1}{dt} \qquad (6\text{-}47)$$

This expression shows that the output potential is the time derivative of the input potential.

Suppose that the input potential e_1 is sinusoidal and of the form

$$e_1 = E_m \sin \omega t$$

The output potential will be

$$e_2 = -C_1 R_f \omega E_m \cos \omega t$$

If the circuit constants are so chosen that $C_1 R_f = 1/\omega$, then the magnitudes of the input and output signals are equal. It would appear that the differentiating circuit may be used with the same ease as the integrating circuit. Actually this is not so, as will be explained.

Suppose that there is a small percentage of higher harmonics in the input signal. Owing to the appearance of a frequency factor ω appropriate to each component term in the input, the amplitude of the higher-harmonic terms in the output will be appreciably amplified relative to the principal component in the input. As a result, the differentiating circuit is particularly sensitive to noise and other spurious h-f signals. Because of this, it has been found advisable to avoid using the operational amplifier as a differentiator. A simple passive differentiating network is often adequate for many applications and is extensively used, for example, in peaking circuits (see Sec. 7-2).

6-4. The Integrating Circuit.   The equations of Sec. 5-10 contain an exact analysis of the operational amplifier.   The adaptation of this as a common integrating circuit is shown in Fig. 6-19.   The general expression for the output is given by Eq. (5-69).   If the parameters are so chosen as indicated, and for the use of a pentode, then

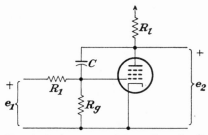

$$Z_1 = R_1 \qquad R_g \gg R_1, R_l$$
$$Z_g = R_g \qquad r_p \gg R_1, R_l$$
$$Y_f = Cp$$

FIG. 6-19. A common integrating circuit.

where, as before, p is the time-derivative operator.   Equation (5-69) reduces to the approximate form shown,

$$e_2 \doteq \frac{Y_1(Cp - g_m)}{(Y_1 + Cp)Y_l + g_mCp} e_1 \qquad (6\text{-}48)$$

This expression may be written in the form

$$e_2 = \frac{Y_1\left(p - \dfrac{g_m}{C}\right)}{(g_m + Y_l)\left[p + \dfrac{Y_1Y_l}{C(g_m + Y_l)}\right]} e_1 \qquad (6\text{-}49)$$

from which it follows that the output is related to the input potential by the operational expression

$$e_2 = A \frac{p - a}{p + b} e_1 \qquad (6\text{-}50)$$

where

$$a = \frac{g_m}{C} \qquad b = \frac{Y_1Y_l}{(g_m + Y_l)C} \qquad A = \frac{Y_1}{g_m + Y_l} \qquad (6\text{-}51)$$

For the application of a step function of potential $e_1 = E$, the potential e_2 is obtained either by classical methods of solving differential equations or by Laplace-transform methods.   The result is

$$e_2 = E_b e^{-bt} + \frac{EAa}{b}(1 - e^{-bt}) \qquad (6\text{-}52)$$

This expression has the form illustrated in the accompanying diagram (Fig. 6-20).   If the constant b is small, a condition that is readily achieved, then Eq. (6-52) reduces to the approximate expression

$$e_2 \doteq E_b + (EAa - E_b b)t \qquad (6\text{-}53)$$

The effective internal impedance of this circuit is of some interest.

Equation (5-73) may be approximated as

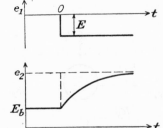

$$Y_{tf} = Y_p + Y_f \frac{Y + Y_g + g_m}{Y_1 + Y_g + Y_f}$$

$$\doteq \frac{g_m Y_f}{Y_1 + Y_g + Y_f}$$

or, more specifically,

$$Y_{tf}(p) = \frac{g_m C p}{Y_1 + Y_g + C p}$$

Correspondingly,

$$Z_{tf} = \frac{Y_1 + Y_g + C p}{g_m C p} = \frac{1}{g_m} + \frac{Y_1 + Y_g}{g_m C p}$$

(6-54)

FIG. 6-20. The input and output waveshapes from an integrating amplifier.

A circuit that gives rise to an expression of this form is that illustrated in Fig. 6-21. This circuit consists of a relatively low series resistance $1/g_m$, which would ordinarily be of the order of several thousand ohms or less,

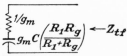

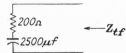

FIG. 6-21. The equivalent internal circuit of the operational integrator.

FIG. 6-22. The equivalent internal circuit of a particular operational integrator.

and a capacitor, the value of which can be made very large. For example, suppose that the tube and circuit constants are the following:

$$g_m = 5,000 \times 10^{-6} \text{ mho}$$
$$C = 1 \ \mu f$$
$$R_1 = R_g = 1 \text{ megohm}$$

The equivalent circuit then becomes as shown in Fig. 6-22. Such a circuit as this may be used as a potential stabilizer, since a ripple of almost any frequency that appears in E_{bb} would be eliminated in the output of this circuit, owing to the very large effective shunting capacitance across the output.

A circuit of this type finds extensive application as the reactance-tube modulator of an f-m transmitter and depends on the fact that the effective

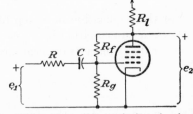

FIG. 6-23. A differentiating circuit.

output capacitance of the circuit varies directly with g_m of the tube, a quantity that can be controlled by an input signal.

6-5. Differentiating Circuit. The basic differentiating circuit is illustrated in Fig. 6-23. This is substantially the circuit discussed in Sec.

6-3, except for the presence of the series input resistance R. The respective impedance elements contained in Eq. (5-69) are chosen to be

$$Z_1 = R + \frac{1}{Cp} \quad \text{or} \quad Y_1 = \frac{1}{R}\frac{p}{p+a} \quad a = \frac{1}{RC}$$
$$Z_f = R_f$$
$$Z_g = R_g$$

There results, subject to the approximations possible when a pentode is used,

$$e_2 \doteq \frac{-Y_1 g_m}{(Y_1 + Y_f + Y_g)Y_l + Y_f(Y_1 + g_m)} e_1$$

$$= \frac{-Y_1 g_m}{Y_1(Y_l + Y_f) + Y_f(Y_l + g_m) + Y_g Y_l} e_1$$

$$= \frac{-g_m p}{p(Y_l + Y_f) + R(p+a)[Y_f(Y_l + g_m) + Y_g Y_l]} e_1$$

$$e_2 = -\frac{g_m p}{p[Y_l + Y_f + R(Y_f Y_l + Y_f g_m + Y_g Y_l)] + aR[Y_f(Y_l + g_m) + Y_g Y_l]} e_1$$
$$(6\text{-}55)$$

This operational expression may be written in the form

$$e_2 = A \frac{p}{p+b} e_1 \qquad (6\text{-}56)$$

where $\qquad A = \dfrac{-g_m}{Y_l + Y_f + R(Y_f Y_l + Y_f g_m + Y_g Y_l)}$

and $\qquad b = \dfrac{1}{C}\dfrac{Y_f Y_l + Y_f g_m + Y_g Y_l}{(Y_l + Y_f) + R(Y_f Y_l + Y_f g_m + Y_g Y_l)} \qquad (6\text{-}57)$

$$= \frac{1/C}{R + \dfrac{Y_l + Y_f}{Y_f Y_l + Y_f g_m + Y_g Y_l}}$$

The application of a step function e_1 to the input, as shown in Fig. 6-24, yields the expected result illustrated, and specified by the expression

$$e_2 = E_b + Ae^{-bt} \qquad (6\text{-}58)$$

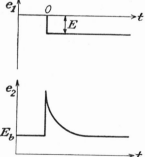

Fig. 6-24. The input and output waveshapes in a differentiating amplifier.

Reference is made to Sec. 6-3c, where it is indicated that it is generally inadvisable to use an operational amplifier as a differentiator owing to gain and phase-shift difficulties that may arise.

6-6. Solving a Simple Differential Equation. A number of circuits have been described for performing a variety of different mathematical operations. This does not include all operations, and, in fact, the very important operations of multiplication and division, and a variety of others which may be obtained through the use of multipliers and dividers, have not yet been considered. It appears desirable to examine the applicability of some of the foregoing circuits before proceeding with an examination of the additional class of circuits. It will be seen that the circuits already examined permit a variety of differential equations to be solved.

Consider the differential equation of motion for a body traveling with an acceleration $f(t)$, a function of time,

$$\frac{d^2y}{dt^2} = f(t) \qquad (6\text{-}59)$$

This differential equation includes a variety of different motions. Thus, if $f(t)$ is zero, the body moves with constant velocity. If $f(t)$ is a constant, the body moves with constant acceleration. For $f(t)$ a function

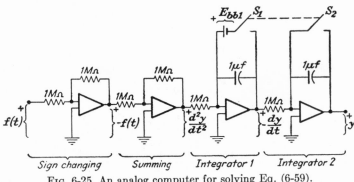

Fig. 6-25. An analog computer for solving Eq. (6-59).

of time, the acceleration varies according to some prescribed variation with time.

Suppose that an analog computer is to be assembled to solve this equation, subject to the initial conditions that $y = 0$ at $t = 0$, and $dy/dt = 6$ ft/sec at $t = 0$. Also, $f(t)$ will be set at -1.5 ft/sec², a constant deceleration. One form of computer for solving this differential equation is illustrated in Fig. 6-25.[2] Four operational amplifiers are used, the function of each being indicated on the diagram. The operation of this computer is best understood when Eq. (6-59) is written in the form

$$\frac{d^2y}{dt^2} - f(t) = 0 \qquad (6\text{-}60)$$

If the output of integrating amplifier 2 is assumed to be y, then the input to this amplifier must have been proportional to $-dy/dt$. In fact, for the choice of R_1 and C_f of this stage indicated, the product R_1C_f is unity, and according to Eq. (6-46) the proportionality factor is unity. The input is indicated on the diagram.

In a similar manner, it follows that the input to the integrating amplifier 1 is d^2y/dt^2, since the multiplying factor has again been chosen to be unity. Note that this input function is the output of the summing amplifier. The function $f(t)$ which is applied to the input of the sign-changing amplifier (the anode-follower circuit) yields an output function $-f(t)$, since, for the choice of parameters, the gain of the amplifier is

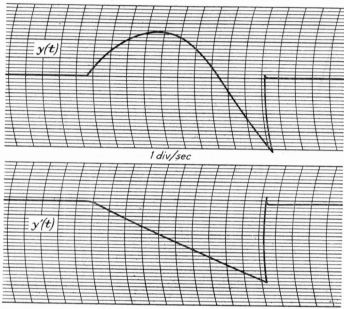

Fig. 6-26. The solution of Eq. (6-59). (*After Hagelbarger, Howe, and Howe. Reprinted, by permission, from UMM-28, published by the Engineering Research Institute of the University of Michigan.*)

unity. The summing amplifier serves to combine the two functions $-f(t)$ and d^2y/dt^2. Actually the first two stages are superfluous in this particular case. They have been included to establish a basic circuit which, by appropriate feedback connections, will solve more complicated equations. In fact, such a modified circuit for solving Eq. (6-61) is given in Fig. 6-27.

It is necessary to provide means for incorporating the initial conditions into the solution. This is accomplished in the following way: Observe that the output potential y of the second integrating amplifier is, for practical purposes, the same as the potential across the feedback capacitor C_f of this amplifier. The output potential y can be made equal to zero by closing switch S_2, which short-circuits the capacitor.

Similarly, of course, the output potential $-dy/dt$ from integrator 1 is substantially the same as the potential across its feedback capacitor. The appropriate initial potential, representing the initial velocity, can be applied by including the d-c supply E_{bb1}, in this case of 6 volts potential, and closing the switch S_1.

The acceleration function $f(t)$ is given its proper value by applying a potential to the input of the sign-changing amplifier of the proper value, -1.5 volts in this case.

The solution of the problem is obtained by opening switches S_1 and S_2 simultaneously and observing the output potential y as a function of time. Of course, if it is desired to observe the velocity dy/dt, it is necessary only to connect the output of integrator 1 to a sign-changing amplifier and observe the output. The results obtained for the solution of this particular problem by Hagelbarger, Howe, and Howe are given in Fig. 6-26.

Attention is called to the fact that if the initial conditions were to require such magnitudes of potential as to cause cutoff of any of the tubes or operation in the nonlinear range of the tube characteristics, appropriate scaling of the potentials would be necessary.

6-7. Differential Equations with One Independent Variable. As a second example of an analog computer for solving a differential equation

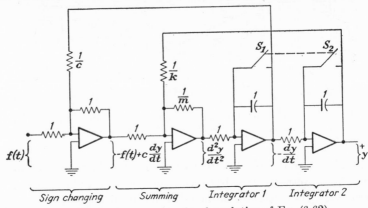

FIG. 6-27. Analog computer for the solution of Eq. (6-62).

with constant coefficients, this section will be concerned with the solution of the equation

$$m \frac{d^2y}{dt^2} + c \frac{dy}{dt} + ky = f(t) \qquad (6\text{-}61)$$

which represents the equation of motion of a mass m supported by a spring with an elastic constant k, the system being subject to a viscous damping force $c\, dy/dt$, and where $f(t)$ represents the driving function.

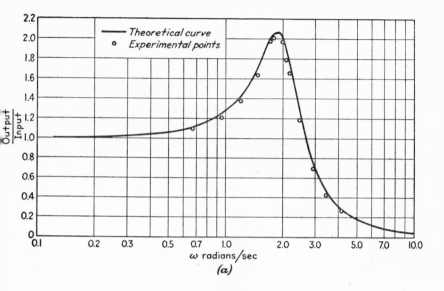

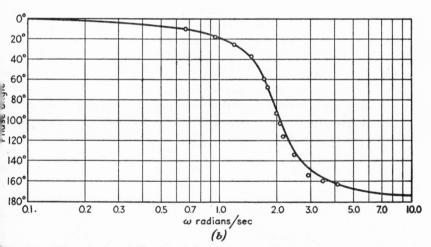

Fig. 6-28. The solution of Eq. (6-62) from the analog computer in Fig. 6-27.   (a) Absolute value of gain vs. ω.   (b) Phase angle of gain vs. ω.   (After Hagelbarger, Howe, and Howe.   Reprinted, by permission, from UMM-28, published by the Engineering Research Institute of the University of Michigan.)

An analog computer for the solution of Eq. (6-61), which is written in the form

$$m \frac{d^2y}{dt^2} + c \frac{dy}{dt} + ky - f(t) = 0 \qquad (6\text{-}62)$$

is shown in Fig. 6-27. Its operation is quite similar to the computer illustrated in Fig. 6-25. For this computer, the initial conditions are $y = 0$ and $dy/dt = 0$. If the initial conditions were other than zero, battery sources would be included in series with the switches S_1 and S_2, with magnitude and polarity determined by the analog scale and sign of the initial conditions.

In this computer, the summing amplifier has fed into it potentials which are proportional to y, dy/dt, d^2y/dt^2, and $f(t)$. These potentials are fed through input resistances $1/k$, $1/c$, $1/m$, and -1, respectively, to take care of the coefficients of the several terms of the equation. The sign-changing amplifier is required for the phase reversal of $f(t)$ in the equation. The solution of the problem is started by the simultaneous opening of the two switches and the application of the driving function $f(t)$. As desired, y, dy/dt, or d^2y/dt^2 may be observed as a function of $f(t)$ at the appropriate terminals.

The results obtained by Hagelbarger, Howe, and Howe for the case of $m = 0.25$, $c = 0.25$, and $k = 1$ and for steady-state operation at various frequencies of an applied sinusoidal waveform for $f(t)$ are given in Fig. 6-28. This necessitated applying a sinusoidal input potential and measuring the output potential after transients had disappeared. The results shown were obtained from records of the amplitude and phase of the output potential for a known amplitude and phase of the input potential. The theoretical curve was obtained by direct evaluation of the steady-state solution of Eq. (6-61).

6-8. Multiplication. The foregoing sections of this chapter have been concerned with a study of a class of linear computing elements and the use of the operational amplifier in such applications. An equally important class of computing elements are of a nonlinear type, many of which incorporate the process of multiplication.

A variety of methods have been used to effect the multiplication of two or more potentials. The degree of precision of the operation and the speed of the operation depend on the method used and the characteristics of the elements of the circuit.

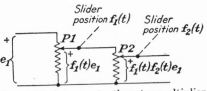

FIG. 6-29. A two-potentiometer multiplier.

a. Two-potentiometer Multiplier. It is of some interest and importance to examine first the two-potentiometer method for multiplication. Consider two potentiometers to be connected as illustrated in Fig. 6-29. For convenience, it is assumed that potentiometer $P2$ does not load potentiometer $P1$. As shown in the diagram, the output from $P2$ is related to the product of the position of the slider on each potentiometer. Clearly, therefore, if a cam is cut of such a shape that when the cam is rotated it moves the sliding contact of a linear rheostat to vary its resistance according to the desired function, then the circuit of Fig. 6-29 with two such cam-operated variable resistances will generate a specified product function.

An alternative means for controlling the position of the slider on each potentiometer, and this method is more important than that which requires the preparation of cams and its associated mechanical linkage, incorporates a small instrument servo, the angular position of the output shaft, and so of the potentiometer slider, being controlled by the magnitude and sense of the applied potential.

The two-potentiometer method produces satisfactory results in many instances, but there are definite limitations to its use. The accuracy can be no better than the linearity of the potentiometer, the precision of the cam or of the connecting link, or the precision of the servo, if one is used. Also, there is a definite limit to the ratio between the maximum and minimum resistances that can be obtained with accuracy.

In some instances cam-operated linear potentiometers are replaced by nonlinear potentiometers which are driven at constant speed. Such nonlinear potentiometers are obtainable with a wide variety of resistance vs. rotation, e.g., sine, cosine, tangent, square root, logarithmic, etc., an accuracy of about 1 per cent being possible.

b. R-F Carrier Systems. A variety of multiplying circuits have been used for years in radio-engineering applications, in the processes of modulation and demodulation. It is the function of the modulator in an a-m system to effect the multiplication of the carrier potential and the modulating-signal potential to yield an amplitude-modulated carrier wave. Likewise, in the demodulating circuit, the modulated carrier wave is combined with the carrier wave to yield the modulating signal. In general, the outputs in each of these applications include a wide array of other multiplication products which arise because the tube characteristic depends in a complicated way on the electrode potentials. The miscellaneous multiplication products which are not desired are usually suppressed by means of tuned circuits in the output, the resulting output being a function of the product of the input potentials. Some of these circuits lend themselves for use in computer applications, although they often require complicated systems to extract the desired product function.

Multiplication for computer applications has been achieved in a combined f-m–a-m system.[3] Here an r-f carrier centered at ω_c is frequency-modulated, the frequency deviation being proportional to one of the multiplicands e_1. This f-m wave is then amplitude-modulated, the modulating index being proportional to the second multiplicand e_2. The resulting carrier is applied to a phase discriminator from which can be extracted a potential which is proportional to the product $e_1 e_2$.

c. *Sampling Techniques.* Pulse techniques[4] have been used to effect multiplication of two different potentials. One method which yields fairly accurate results provides a pulse, the height of which is proportional to the instantaneous value of one potential, the width of which is proportional to the instantaneous value of a second potential. The product is obtained by integration techniques to yield the area under the pulse. This method requires that the potentials to be multiplied be sampled at a relatively high rate, the rate being high enough compared with the normal variation times of the waveforms to be multiplied so

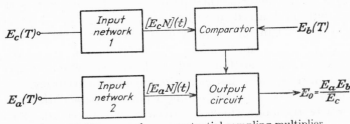

FIG. 6-30. Diagram of sweep-potential sampling multiplier.

that the sampled product curve is a good approximation to the normal instantaneous product of the two potentials.

A method of multiplication and division which samples the potentials to be multiplied at a rapid rate, and uses a comparison technique for obtaining the desired result, has been devised.[5] The essentials of the method are illustrated in Fig. 6-30. Two potentials "sweep" from zero to some maximum value. The sweeps are identical in form and might both be linear, exponential, sinusoidal, etc. The amplitudes of the sweeps are made proportional to two of the multiplier inputs at the sampling instant. A third input potential is compared with one of the sweeping potentials in such a way that when the sweep potential is equal to the third input, the second sweep potential is sampled. The value of the potential at this instant is proportional to the product of two inputs divided by the third, as indicated on the diagram.

The accuracy possible with both general sampling techniques is high, although complicated circuits are required to effect the desired operations.

d. *Nonlinear Tube Characteristics.* Several systems of multiplication have been devised which depend upon the availability of tubes which possess prescribed tube characteristics.

In principle, at least, a simple multiplier would be possible in which the input signals are converted into logarithmic form, the resultant potentials then being added, the sum being passed through an antilog circuit, thereby yielding the desired quantity. The elements of such a system are shown in the block diagram of Fig. 6-31. Such a system may actually be constructed, since the output characteristics of a supercontrol tube, such as the 6SK7, is a logarithmic function of the input signal, over a substantial range of input potential. Also, an antilog circuit has been devised.[6] However, since the logarithmic function is not defined for

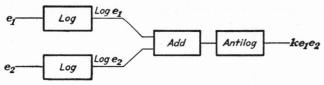

Fig. 6-31. The elements of a logarithmic multiplier.

negative values of the argument, the logarithmic multiplier is restricted in its applicability to a single quadrant.

Simple multiplication without the introduction of undesired terms would theoretically be possible in a multigrid tube, if the application of a potential on one grid controlled the gain so that it was directly proportional to that potential, while the signal output depended directly on the potential applied to a second grid. This is really the tube counterpart of the two-potentiometer multiplier. For the system envisaged, the gain of the amplifier K is assumed proportional to a potential e_3, so that

$$K = me_3$$

Also, the output potential e_0 is assumed directly proportional to the input signal e_1 according to the relation

$$e_0 = Ke_1$$

Then the application of the two signals e_1 and e_3 simultaneously will yield an output

$$e_0 = me_1e_3 \tag{6-63}$$

Some tubes possess characteristics which closely approximate the requirements herein imposed and so may be used for multiplication purposes. In Fig. 6-32 are illustrated the mutual-conductance curves of a 6L7 pentagrid tube as a function of the potential applied to grid 3. It will be noted that g_m is a linear function of the applied potential over a wide range of potential variation. Equation (6-63) is satisfied over this linear range of tube characteristic.

Another method for multiplying two quantities makes use of what has been called the "quarter-square" method. This depends on the fact that the product of two quantities may be expressed by an equation of the form

$$e_1 e_2 = \frac{(e_1 + e_2)^2}{4} - \frac{(e_1 - e_2)^2}{4} \tag{6-64}$$

Consequently multiplication is reduced to the basic requirement for a squaring system. In general, however, this is not particularly easier than direct multiplication.

A block diagram which shows the elements required for a quarter-square multiplier is given in Fig. 6-33. The required squaring circuit

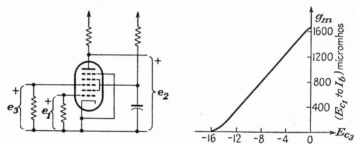

FIG. 6-32. The connections and g_m of a 6L7 tube for use in a multiplying circuit.

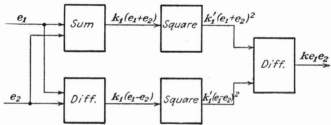

FIG. 6-33. The "quarter-square" method of performing the multiplication of two quantities.

that is necessary for the operation of the system illustrated may be the circuit of Fig. 6-32 with the two input leads connected together, since, with the same input potential to each terminal, the output potential will be proportional to the square of the input potential. An alternate circuit for squaring is discussed in the next section.

The details of two systems which operate on this principle are readily available.[7]

6-9. Squaring Circuits. A squaring circuit is one in which the output potential is proportional to the square of the input potential. A circuit which makes use of the curvature of the tube characteristics of two tubes to accomplish this squaring operation is given by the schematic diagram of Fig. 6-34. It will be observed that this circuit consists of a single tube paraphase amplifier (refer to Sec. 5-4 for a detailed discussion of this circuit) which provides two signals that differ in phase by 180 deg. These signals are applied to the grids of two amplifier stages which are so connected that the odd-harmonic terms cancel in the output. This stage should be compared with a normal push-pull amplifier in which the even-harmonic terms are canceled in the output. As a result of this connection the odd harmonics cancel and, the even-harmonic terms become the important ones in the output.

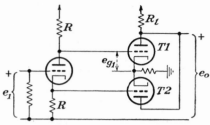

Fig. 6-34. A squaring amplifier.

It is assumed that the plate current in tube $T1$ may be represented by a series of the form

$$i_{p1} = a_1 e_{g1} + a_2 e_{g1}^2 + a_3 e_{g1}^3 + \cdots \tag{6-65}$$

Likewise, the plate current in tube $T2$ will then be given by the series

$$i_{p2} = a_1(-e_{g1}) + a_2(-e_{g1})^2 + a_3(-e_{g1})^3 + \cdots \tag{6-66}$$

The total plate current

$$i_p = i_{p1} + i_{p2} \tag{6-67}$$

becomes

$$i_p = 2a_2 e_{g1}^2 \tag{6-68}$$

if it is assumed that the first three terms of the series representation adequately represent the relation between the input potential and output current. The output potential is then of the form

$$e_0 = i_p R_l = 2a_2 R_l e_{g1}^2 \tag{6-69}$$

An explicit expression for the amplitude factor a_2 appearing in this equation is possible in terms of the tube characteristics. If use is made of the Taylor expansion of the current in terms of the grid potential, viz.,

$$i_p = g_m e_g + \frac{1}{2!} \frac{\partial g_m}{\partial e_g} e_g^2 + \frac{1}{3!} \frac{\partial^2 g_m}{\partial e_g^2} e_g^3 + \cdots \tag{6-70}$$

then clearly the coefficient a_2 is related to $\partial g_m / \partial e_g$ and the output potential is given by the form

$$e_0 = R_l \frac{\partial g_m}{\partial e_g} e_g^2 \tag{6-71}$$

But since the gain of the paraphase amplifier is approximately unity [see Eq. (5-43)], then finally

$$e_0 \doteq R_l \frac{\partial g_m}{\partial e_g} e_1^2 \tag{6-72}$$

This expression shows that, for the output to be proportional to the square of the input potential, it is essential that the coefficient $\partial g_m / \partial e_g$

remain constant over the range of operation of the tube. This condition requires that the composite characteristic of the amplifier must be of the square-law type.

A number of tubes have been examined in order to ascertain which yield satisfactory characteristics for such squaring operations. It has been found that the 6B8 and the 6SK7 tubes are satisfactory when grid-driven and the 6U7G and the 6D6 are quite satisfactory when screen-driven.

6-10. Difference of Squares. It is possible to combine several of the foregoing circuits to yield a number of circuits for performing other

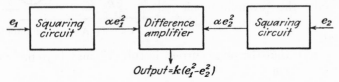

$$Output = k(e_1^2 - e_2^2)$$

FIG. 6-35. Circuit for obtaining the difference of squares.

mathematical operations. For example, the combination of two squaring circuits and a difference amplifier, according to the block diagram of Fig. 6-35, will yield an output that is the difference of the squares of the input signals. This circuit is a simple combination of the basic circuits that are required to perform the separated indicated operations.

6-11. Square-root Circuit. A block diagram showing the elements for yielding the square root of a given potential is illustrated in Fig. 6-36. The input to the circuit is e_1, which is applied to one input of a difference

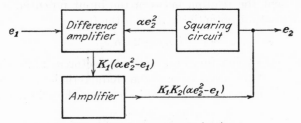

FIG. 6-36. A square-root circuit.

amplifier of the type illustrated in Fig. 6-3. Likewise, it is supposed that a potential e_2 appears at the input of a squaring circuit, the output of which is applied to the second input to the difference amplifier. The output from the difference amplifier, which is the input to a simple amplifier of gain K_2, is then $K_1(\alpha e_2^2 - e_1)$. But the output from the amplifier is actually the source of the potential e_2 which appears at the input to the squaring circuit. This requires, therefore, that

$$K_1 K_2 (\alpha e_2^2 - e_1) = e_2$$

But for large amplifier gain K_2,

$$\frac{e_2}{K_1 K_2} \doteq 0$$

which requires therefore that

$$\alpha e_2^2 - e_1 = 0$$

It follows from this that the output potential e_2 is then related to the input potential by the relation

$$e_2 = \sqrt{\frac{e_1}{\alpha}} \tag{6-73}$$

6-12. Division.   A block diagram showing the elements of a circuit for yielding an output which is proportional to the ratio of two given potentials is given in Fig. 6-37.   In this circuit the two input potentials are

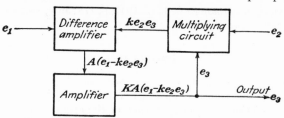

FIG. 6-37. A circuit that divides two potentials.

e_1 and e_2, one of which is applied to the difference amplifier, the second of which is applied to a multiplying circuit.   An examination of the circuit shows that the output from the amplifier, which provides the output and also furnishes one input to the multiplying circuit, is

$$e_3 = KA(e_1 - ke_2e_3)$$

If the amplifier provides a high gain, then it follows that

$$\frac{e_3}{KA} = 0$$

from which, therefore,

$$e_1 - ke_2e_3 = 0$$

or finally

$$e_3 = k' \frac{e_1}{e_2} \tag{6-74}$$

Attention is called to the sampling technique discussed in Sec. 6-8c for multiplication, which is also adaptable for division.

REFERENCES

1. Williams, F. C., F. J. U. Ritson, and T. Kilburn, *J. IEE*, **93**, 1275 (1946).
2. Hagelbarger, D. W., C. W. Howe, and R. M. Howe, *Univ. Mich. Eng. Research Inst. Rept.* UMM-28 (Apr. 1, 1949).
3. Somerville, M. J., *Electronics Eng.*, **24**, 78 (1952).
4. Greenwood, I. A., Jr., J. V. Holdam, Jr., and D. MacRae, Jr., "Electronic Instruments," Massachusetts Institute of Technology Radiation Laboratory Series, vol. 21, pp. 50–53, McGraw-Hill Book Company, Inc., New York, 1948.
   Morrill, C. D., and R. V. Baum, *Electronics*, **25**, 139 (December, 1952).

5. Broomall, J., and L. Riebman, *Proc. IRE*, **40**, 568 (1952).
   Freeman, H., and E. Parsons, *Sperry Eng. Rev.*, **7**, 14 (1954).
6. Snowden, F. C., and H. T. Page, *Rev. Sci. Instr.*, **21**, 179 (1950).
7. Chance, B., J. Busser, and F. C. Williams, *Phys. Rev.*, **79**, 244 (1950).
   Chance, B., and F. C. Williams, *Rev. Sci. Instr.*, **22**, 683 (1951).
8. As general references, consult:
   Greenwood, *op. cit.*
   Korn, G. A., and T. M. Korn, "Electronic Analog Computers," McGraw-Hill Book Company, Inc., New York, 1952.
   Hagelbarger, *op. cit.*
   Ragazzini, J. R., R. H. Randall, and F. A. Russell, *Proc. IRE*, **35**, 444 (1947).
   Mynall, D. J., *Electronic Eng.*, June, 1947, p. 178; July, 1947, p. 214; August, 1947, p. 259; September, 1947, p. 283.

PROBLEMS

6-1. Derive Eq. (6-32) for the common plate summing chain.

6-2. Determine the transfer functions which specify the character of the mathematical operation performed by each of the operational amplifiers shown in the figure.

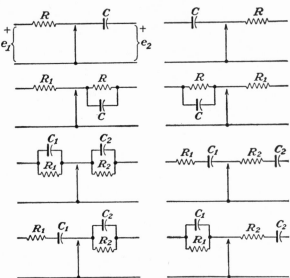

6-3. Sketch an analog computer in the manner of Fig. 6-25 which will solve the differential equation

$$\frac{dy}{dx} + \alpha y = 0$$

6-4. Sketch an analog computer in the manner of Fig. 6-25 which will solve the differential equation

$$\frac{d^2y}{dx^2} + k^2y = 0$$

6-5. The analog computer[2] for a simple servomechanism is illustrated. Deduce the differential equation of which this is the computer analog.

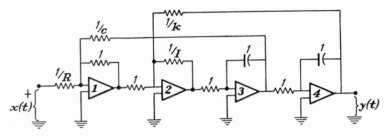

6-6. The analog computer[2] for determining the motion of a particular airplane for which the airplane has an angle of pitch θ for a change of elevator angle δ is illustrated. Observe that this is somewhat like the computer in Prob. 6-5

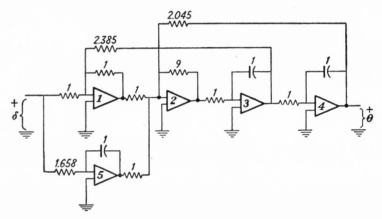

except for the appearance of two functions of the input excitation within the system. Deduce the differential equation of which this is the computer analog.

6-7. Deduce the differential equation which is solved by the computer* shown in the accompanying figure.

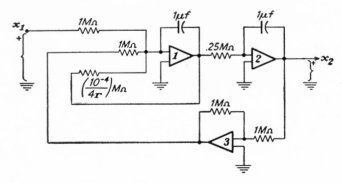

* See ref. 8, Korn and Korn, p. 64.

6-8. The normal mode of oscillation of a beam with free ends has been shown to be expressed by an equation of the form[2]

$$y(x,t) = X(x)e^{j\lambda t}$$

where $X(x)$ is the solution of a differential equation of the form

$$c\frac{d^4X}{dx^4} - X = 0$$

An analog-computer circuit for the solution of this equation is suggested in the diagram. Verify that this computer solves the equation shown.

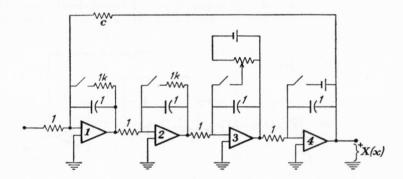

6-9. An analog computer[2] for solving the Bessel equation

$$\frac{d^2y}{dx^2} + \frac{1}{x}\frac{dy}{dx} + \left(1 - \frac{n^2}{x^2}\right)y = 0$$

which involves the use of time-varying changes of resistance to produce the desired functions x and x^2, is illustrated. Verify that this computer solves the Bessel equation.

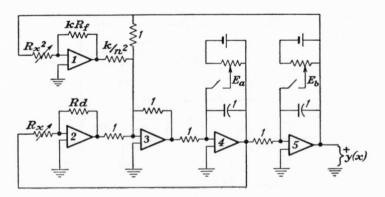

6-10. Show that the output of the operational amplifier circuit illustrated has

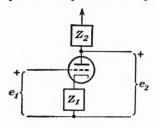

the form

$$e_2 = -[Z_2 Y_1]e_1$$

6-11. Analyze the differentiating circuit shown in the figure.*

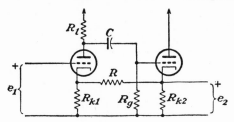

6-12. Analyze the differentiating circuit shown in the figure.

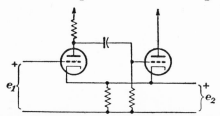

6-13. Analyze the integrating circuits shown in the figures for this problem.

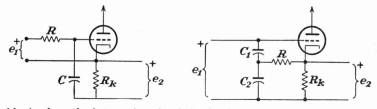

6-14. Analyze the integrating circuit in the diagram.

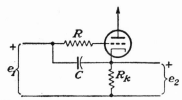

* O. H. Schmitt and W. E. Tolles, *Rev. Sci. Instr.*, **13**, 115 (1942).

6-15. Analyze the integrating circuit shown in the accompanying figure.

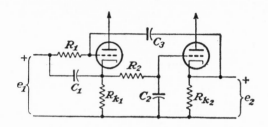

6-16. Show that in the indicated network the output potential is related to the

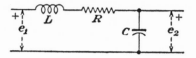

input potential by the equation

$$e_1 = e_2 + RC\frac{de_2}{dt} + LC\frac{d^2e_2}{dt^2}$$

6-17. Show that in the circuit shown the output potential is related to the

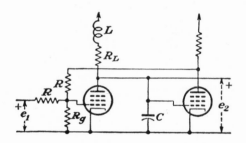

input potential by the expression

$$e_2 = e_1 + R_LC\frac{de_1}{dt} + LC\frac{d^2e_1}{dt^2}$$

6-18. Deduce the differential equation which is solved by the computer given in the accompanying figure.

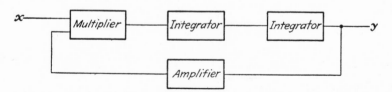

6-19. Determine the differential equation that is solved by the computer sketched.

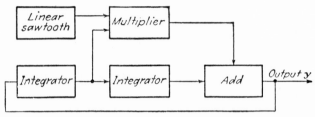

6-20. Show that the output of the circuit e_3 in the diagram is proportional to the ratio e_2/e_1.

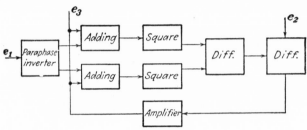

6-21. What equation does the computer in the figure solve?

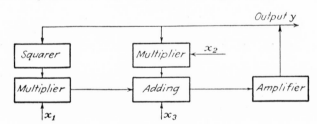

6-22. What equation does the computer in the diagram solve?

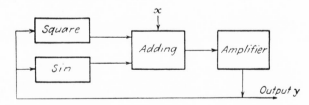

6-23. Sketch block diagrams of computers that will solve the following equations:

a. $$x_1^2 + x_2 = y$$
b. $$x_1^3 + x_1^2 = y$$

c. $$x_1 x_2 + \frac{x_2}{x_1} = y$$

CHAPTER 7

SPECIAL ELECTRONIC CIRCUITS

A wide variety of special electronic circuits have been devised. Among those to be studied in this chapter are limiting and clipping amplifiers, peaking circuits, and clamping circuits.

7-1. Limiting and Clipping Amplifiers. In addition to the various amplifiers that are intended to reproduce a given waveform with a minimum of distortion, there are other forms of circuits which are designed to alter the waveshape of an input wave in some predetermined manner.

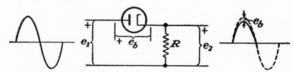

FIG. 7-1. A series diode used to limit negative signals.

Limiting or clipping circuits are designed to remove by electronic means one or the other extremity of an input wave.

A limiter is used when it is desired to square off the extremities of an applied signal. For example, it may be used as one stage in a chain to obtain a substantially rectangular waveform from a sine-wave signal. A limiter may also be used to eliminate either the positive or the negative portion of a wave. Such circuits also find application in f-m receivers to limit to a constant value the amplitude of the signal that is applied to the detection system. This application is discussed in the author's companion volume, entitled "Radio Electronics."

Limiting and clipping may be accomplished by the use of diodes, triodes, or multielectrode tubes. For triodes and multielectrode tubes, the limiting may be accomplished either in the grid or in the plate circuits. The general features of a number of such limiting circuits will be examined below.

a. Series-diode Limiting. The circuit of the series-diode limiter is given in Fig. 7-1. It will be observed that this circuit is precisely that of a diode as used in a rectifier circuit. Since the tube conducts only when the plate is at a positive potential with respect to the cathode, then only the positive portion of the applied wave will pass through the tube, the negative portion of the wave being eliminated. By neglecting the relatively small drop across the tube during conduction, the output wave form is simply the positive portion of the applied waveform. If the diode connections are reversed, then the positive portion of the wave will be eliminated and only the negative portion of the wave will pass through to the output.

The series-diode circuit possesses the feature that it tends to isolate the driving circuit from the output circuit and thus prevents feedback.

b. *Shunt-diode Limiting.* A diode may be connected in shunt across the load for limiting action. In such cases, the diode may be looked upon as an infinite impedance for polarities opposite to that necessary for

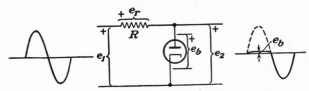

Fig. 7-2. A shunt-diode positive-limiting circuit.

conduction and as a virtual short circuit for the polarity in the conducting direction. The diode is then acting as a switch which will short-circuit a given load for a certain polarity and amplitude of the applied potential.

The connections of a shunt diode for limiting the positive signals at approximately ground potential are shown in Fig. 7-2. With the cathode maintained at ground potential, the diode conducts throughout the entire positive half cycle. During the portion of the cycle when the diode is conducting, the current passes through the series resistor R. With R large compared with the drop across the tube, practically the entire input potential is developed across R, and the output potential is only the small drop across the diode. On the negative portion of the input voltage, the diode does not conduct, and the potential that appears across the output is then determined by the resistance R and the resistance of the load.

If the connections to the diode are reversed, with the anode held at ground potential, the tube will conduct only when the input potential is negative with respect to ground. As a result, the negative potential will appear across the series resistance, except for the small tube drop, which may ordinarily be neglected.

An input potential can be limited to any desired positive or negative value by maintaining the proper diode electrode at the desired potential. Two circuits for limiting about a desired potential are shown in Fig. 7-3.

In the circuit of Fig. 7-3a for positive limiting, it is observed that the cathode is maintained at a fixed potential E above the input. As a result, the diode does not conduct until the positive potential on the anode exceeds E, when the action becomes exactly like that of Fig. 7-2.

The input potential during the conducting portion of the cycle appears across the series resistance R.

The operation of the circuit of Fig. 7-3b is essentially like that of Fig. 7-3a except that conduction of the diode occurs when the cathode falls below the value $-E$. The input portion of the potential during conduction appears across the resistance R.

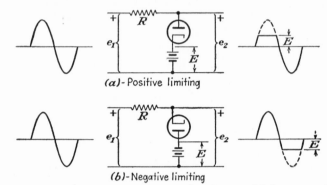

(a)- Positive limiting

(b)- Negative limiting

Fig. 7-3. Positive and negative limiting above and below ground.

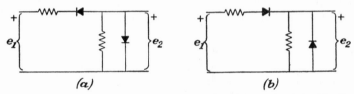

(a)   *(b)*

Fig. 7-4. Double-diode limiters for removing (a) all positive potentials, (b) all negative potentials.

c. Series-Shunt Limiting. The effectiveness of the limiting possible with both the series-diode and the shunt-diode limiters is dependent on the diode possessing a very high resistance when it does not conduct and a very low resistance when it does conduct. Vacuum-tube diodes possess these general properties and operate quite satisfactorily in one or the other limiting circuits. Crystal diodes usually possess poor back resistances, and often the series and shunt limiting circuits are combined into a single circuit in order to improve the limiting. Figure 7-4 illustrates the double-diode series-shunt circuit.

d. Double-diode Limiting. It is possible to limit both amplitude extremities of a waveform at any desired levels by placing two diodes in the circuit, one of which acts to limit the positive peaks, and the other of which acts to limit the negative peaks. The circuit for such double-diode operation is given in Fig. 7-5. In this circuit, diode $T1$ conducts whenever the input potential exceeds the positive bias potential E_1.

Diode $T2$ conducts when the input potential falls below the negative
bias potential $-E_2$.

e. Grid-circuit Limiting. Limiting in the grid circuit of a triode, tetrode, or pentode is possible in exactly the same way as in the plate-cath-

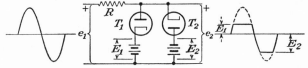

FIG. 7-5. Double-diode limiting circuit.

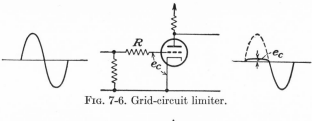

FIG. 7-6. Grid-circuit limiter.

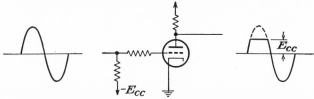

FIG. 7-7. Grid-circuit limiting about a fixed potential level.

ode circuit of the diode circuit of Fig. 7-2. The series resistance R in
the grid line is large compared with the grid-cathode resistance during
grid conduction. This resistance is essentially the diode resistance of
the grid during the period when it is drawing current. The circuit is
given in Fig. 7-6.

If a bias potential is used, as in Fig. 7-7,
limiting occurs about the bias level, precisely in the manner of the circuit of Fig.
7-3a. It is possible to use self-bias instead
of fixed bias for setting the potential level
about which the positive portion of the
wave is limited. The basic circuit of such
a limiter is given in Fig. 7-8.

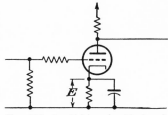

FIG. 7-8. A self-biased grid-circuit
limiter.

f. Saturation Limiting. Limiting action
may also be effected in the plate circuit of a pentode amplifier by employing a large load resistance in conjunction with a low value of plate potential. Such limiting action arises from the peculiar characteristics of
pentodes with low applied potentials which make the operation fall below

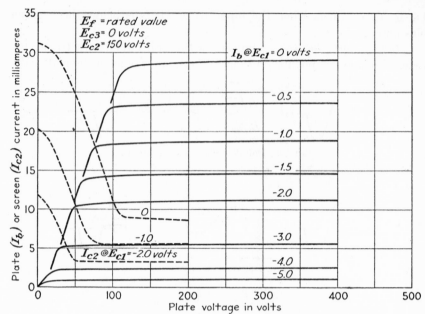

FIG. 7-9. A 6CB6 pentode family of plate characteristics.

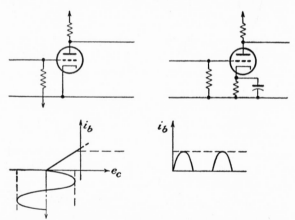

FIG. 7-10. Cutoff limiting in a strongly biased amplifier.

the knee of the plate characteristic. The plate current becomes independent of the amplitude of the grid potential over wide ranges. Figure 7-9 shows a typical plate characteristic. For the small values of E_{bb}, the current remains I_b for any value of e_c more positive than about -4 volts.

To optimize the sensitivity as well as the performance as a limiter, a sharp-cutoff pentode is used with low screen potential and extremely low

plate potential.   Under these conditions the tube is driven to cutoff with
1 or 2 volts of grid drive.

  g. *Cutoff Limiting.*   If a tube is operated in the class B region by so
setting the bias that the current in the tube is nominally near cutoff, then
the application of a sine-wave grid signal will give rise to an output current that possesses features not unlike the current from a diode rectifier.
This results from the fact that a small negative potential will drive the

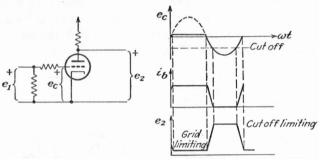

FIG. 7-11. Formation of a square wave by grid-circuit and cutoff limiting.

tube beyond cutoff and that no current will flow for any potential below
this value.   The operation is made evident by an examination of the
dynamic characteristic of the tube as illustrated in Fig. 7-10.

  h. *Combination of Limiting Actions.*   A combination of grid limiting
and cutoff limiting may be employed in an amplifier to produce a substantially square wave from a sine wave or other comparable waveshape.
The action is illustrated in Fig. 7-11.   During the positive portion of the
swing, the grid-circuit limiting is effec-
tive; the plate current reaches its maximum, and the output potential reaches
its minimum.   During the negative
portion of the grid swing, the tube is cut
off, whence the plate current falls to
zero and the plate potential is at its
maximum.

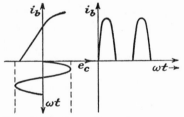

FIG. 7-12. Formation of a square
wave by saturation and cutoff limiting. The overdriven amplifier.

  A combination of saturation limiting
and cutoff limiting in a tube is called an
overdriven amplifier.   The operation is
substantially like that of the circuit with grid-circuit limiting, except that
the grid circuit limits by virtue of the high grid potential, which causes a
high grid current and hence a small grid-cathode resistance.   The operation is illustrated in Fig. 7-12.

  7-2. Peaking Circuits.   Electronic control systems frequently require
the accurate synchronization of two or more events relative to each

other. Often this synchronization is accomplished by generating sharp
triggering pulses in the proper time sequence and having each triggering
pulse initiate the operation of some portion of the total circuit in the
proper order. As a rule these triggering pulses should be of short duration and should have an extremely sharp leading edge. Such pulses can
be generated in specially designed pulse-forming circuits, and a number
of these will be examined in Chap. 9. It is also possible to produce
them in a *peaking* circuit. Such a circuit is capable of distorting an
input signal wave in such a way as to produce an output waveform in
which the time duration is shortened and in which the leading edge is
made as nearly vertical as possible.

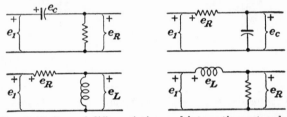

FIG. 7-13. Several differentiating and integrating networks.

The choice of peaking circuit used will depend primarily upon the input
waveshape. One of the common methods is to use sufficient limiting and
amplification so that a substantially rectangular wave is available and
then apply this square wave to an *RC* differentiating circuit. A number
of such differentiating circuits exist, the feedback operational differentiator having been examined in some detail in Chap. 6. The requirements
imposed by this application are not very stringent in general, and simple
forms of so-called *passive differentiating networks* may be used.

The forms of circuit in common use for differentiation and integration
are shown in Fig. 7-13. In the *RC* network, the instantaneous behavior
for an applied potential e is governed by the equations

$$e_R = iR = RC \frac{de_C}{dt}$$

$$e_C = \frac{1}{C} \int i \, dt = \frac{1}{RC} \int e_R \, dt$$

(7-1)

The corresponding equations for the *LR* circuits are

$$e_L = L \frac{di}{dt} = \frac{L}{R} \frac{de_R}{dt}$$

$$e_R = iR = \frac{R}{L} \int e_L \, dt$$

(7-2)

But the sum of the potentials appearing across the capacitance and the
resistance in series must be equal, at every instant, to the applied poten-

tial.   If e_C is very small compared with e_R, then e_R must be approximately equal to the applied potential.   It therefore follows that (1) e_C is approximately proportional to the time integral of the applied potential when e_C/e_R is small and (2) e_R is approximately proportional to the time derivative of the applied potential when e_R/e_C is small.

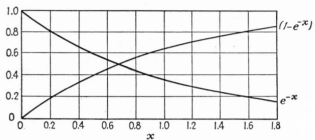

Fig. 7-14. The exponential characteristics of the transient solutions of Eqs. (7-3a) and (7-3b).

If a perfect differentiating and integrating network were used, then the output potential could be specified directly.   Thus the data of the accompanying table follow.

Input	Differentiation	Integration
Square.........	Vertical lines above and below base line	Triangular
Saw-tooth......	Horizontal line on one side of base line; spike on other side of base line	Parabolic
Triangular.....	Square wave	Parabolic half cycles

The behavior of the circuits for an applied d-c potential $e_1 = E_0$ is governed, respectively, by the equations

a. For RC Circuit   *b. For RL Circuit*

$$i = \frac{E_0}{R} e^{-t/RC}$$
$$e_R = E_0 e^{-t/RC} \qquad (7\text{-}3a)$$
$$e_C = E_0(1 - e^{-t/RC})$$

$$i = \frac{E_0}{R}(1 - e^{-Rt/L})$$
$$e_L = E_0 e^{-Rt/L} \qquad (7\text{-}3b)$$
$$e_R = E_0(1 - e^{-Rt/L})$$

$$e = e_R + e_C \qquad (7\text{-}4a)$$

$$e = e_L + e_R \qquad (7\text{-}4b)$$

A plot of the general characteristics of these equations is given in Fig. 7-14.

Equations (7-3a) are obtained by imposing the physical condition that in the RC circuit the current through a capacitor may change instantaneously, but the potential across it cannot change suddenly.   The latter requirement arises from the fact that for an instantaneous change in potential across a capacitor the current source must be infinite, according to the relation $i_c = C\,de_c/dt$, a condition that cannot be achieved with any physical system. This means that a capacitor acts like a short circuit for sudden changes in current.

Similarly in Eqs. (7-3b) for the RL circuit, the physical condition that the current cannot change instantaneously has been imposed. This arises from the relation $e_L = L\,di_L/dt$, which, for instantaneous current changes, requires an infinite potential source, an impossible physical sit-

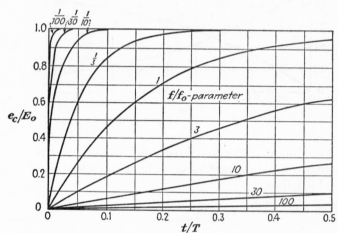

Fig. 7-15. The potential across the capacitor in a simple RC network as a function of time, with f/f_0 as a parameter.

uation. However, an instantaneous change in potential may exist across the inductor.

If a recurring square wave is applied to the RC circuit, instead of a d-c potential, the potential across each element of the circuit will begin to increase with the application of the potential. The increase proceeds exponentially with the time constant of the circuit. When the applied potential reverses, the circuit potentials also reverse. Curves showing the character of the increase, with the ratio f/f_0 as a parameter, where f is the frequency of the applied square wave and is $f = 1/T$, where T is the period of the applied square wave, and where $f_0 = 1/2\pi RC$ is the quantity defined by the time constant of the circuit, are given in Fig. 7-15. These curves are essentially a plot of the function

$$e_C = E_0(1 - e^{-t/RC})$$

or

$$\frac{e_C}{E_0} = 1 - e^{-2\pi(f_0/f)(t/T)} \tag{7-5}$$

For example, if the quantity f_0 of the circuit is 3,000 cps and a 1,000-cps square wave is applied, f/f_0 is $\frac{1}{3}$ and the capacitor potential will rise in accordance with the curve marked $\frac{1}{3}$ and will reach 90 per cent of its full value in about 0.13 cycle.

To obtain the complete response for a given applied square wave, a careful application of the curves of Fig. 7-15 must be made. This gives the form for e_C. The set of curves for e_R is obtained from the known forms of e_1 and e_C, since $e_R = e_1 - e_C$. The results have the form illustrated in Fig. 7-16. A complete analysis for the case when an unsymmetrical pulse is impressed on the circuit is given in Sec. 7-4.

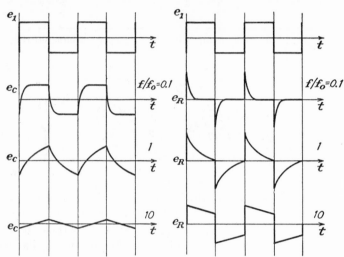

FIG. 7-16. The potential forms e_C and e_R for an applied square wave on a differentiation circuit, with f/f_0 as parameter.

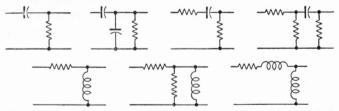

FIG. 7-17. Differentiation circuits with similar response characteristics.

Theoretically it is of no consequence whether the circuit is composed of inductance and resistance or resistance and capacitance. Apart from the higher cost, it is ordinarily not advisable to use an inductive differentiation circuit if it can be avoided because the effective resistance of the coil is usually large enough to change the output character of the results. When an RC differentiating circuit is used, the series capacitance should be large compared with any distributed capacitances that may exist in the circuit. In particular, if the output of such a differentiating circuit is to feed the grid of a tube, the series capacitance should be large compared with the input capacitance of the tube; otherwise, the time constant may be appreciably altered by an indefinite amount.

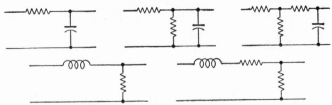

Fig. 7-18. Integrating circuits with similar response characteristics.

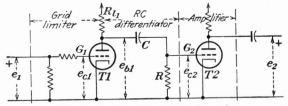

Fig. 7-19. A typical application of an RC differentiator as a peaker.

A number of circuits exist which give transient-response curves that are similar to those represented by Eqs. (7-3a) and (7-3b). The circuits of Fig. 7-17 give transient-response curves similar to those represented by Eqs. (7-3a), and the circuits of Fig. 7-18 give results similar to those of Eqs. (7-3b).

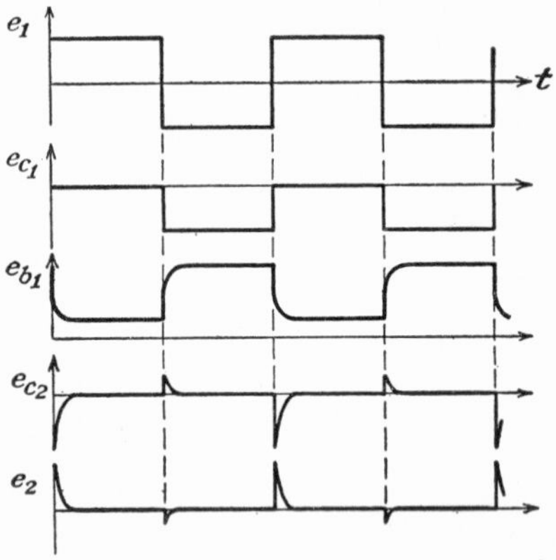

The circuit of Fig. 7-19 illustrates a practical application of an RC differentiator as a peaker circuit. The general character of the waveshapes at several points in the circuit is illustrated in Fig. 7-20. Care must be exercised in analyzing the operation of such a circuit to avoid error, since the grids of $T1$ and $T2$ may be subject to extremes of excitation, to cause either grid conduction or plate cut-off. It is to be noted that the grid-cathode resistance r_c, when the grid is conducting, is low and is of the order of 1,000 ohms. When a tube is conducting, the average tube resistance (beam resistance r_b, given as the ratio e_b/i_b) is low. When the tube is cut off, the grid-cathode resistance may be taken as infinite; and the beam resistance is also infinite. Thus for the circuit of Fig. 7-19, the

Fig. 7-20. The waveshapes at several points in the circuit of Fig. 7-19.

equivalent circuit of the differentiator portion of the circuit during the time that $T1$ is cut off has the form shown in Fig. 7-21.   The equivalent circuit during the time that $T1$ is conducting is shown in Fig. 7-22.

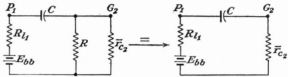

FIG. 21. The equivalent circuit of Fig. 7-19 during the time that $T1$ is cut off.

7-3. D-C Restoration and Clamping.   Suppose that an unsymmetrical waveform is passed through a capacitor or a transformer.   The average ordinate of the output waveform must assume a zero potential, since neither the capacitor nor the transformer will pass a d-c current.   If the input waveform did contain a d-c component, this component would be lost in its passage through either of these elements.

Examples of waveforms which must remain unsymmetrical are readily found.   Two examples are the saw-tooth potential for use with an electrostatic cathode-ray tube and the saw-tooth current for use with an electromagnetic cathode-ray tube.   In both cases, the appropriate waveform

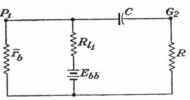

FIG. 7-22. The equivalent circuit of Fig. 7-19 during the time that $T1$ is conducting.

is used to deflect the cathode-ray beam according to a known function of time, and, in many applications, a linear function of time is sought.   The effect of removing the d-c component from the saw-tooth potential or from the saw-tooth current is to displace the trace of the beam on the face of the cathode-ray tube.   The effect on the waveform when the d-c component is removed is illustrated in Fig. 7-23.

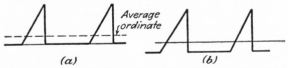

FIG. 7-23. (a) A saw-tooth deflecting potential.   (b) The saw-tooth potential after passing through an element without a conductive path.

It is possible to return the trace on the face of the cathode-ray tube to its desired position after passage through a capacitor or transformer by applying a bias potential which is equal to the average ordinate displacement.   This is equivalent to restoring to the wave the d-c component which was eliminated.   This method, referred to as *d-c restoration*, is acceptable if an invariable waveform is employed.   If some dimension of the wave is changed, such as its amplitude or the duration of the potential rise, the average value will change and the amount of d-c restoration that is required will be different.

An example of the situation here being discussed is to be found in radar equipment, the indicating system of which may permit four different sweep speeds (or, alternatively, four different range scales). To have the trace on the cathode-ray tube start at a fixed point on the

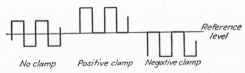

Fig. 7-24. A potential variation with respect to a definite reference potential.

screen, irrespective of the range scale being used, will require the switching of four different potentials which have been carefully adjusted for the range scale being used. Such systems have been used satisfactorily, but have been generally supplanted by electronic circuits.

Simple electronic circuits exist which will hold either amplitude extreme of a waveform to a given level of potential. Such circuits are known as *keyed restorer*, or *clamping*, circuits and are divided into two classes, *continuously acting* and *synchronized* clamps.

The continuously acting diode and grid clamping circuits clamp either amplitude extreme once each cycle and allow the waveform to extend in only one direction from the reference potential. Figure 7-24 illustrates the effect of such clamps. One type of synchronized clamp maintains the output potential at a fixed invariable level until a synchronizing pulse is applied, when the output potential is allowed to follow the input. At the end of the synchronizing pulse, the output potential is returned immediately to the reference level. The general action is illustrated in

Fig. 7-25. A synchronized clamp that introduces a d-c reference level.

Fig. 7-25. In a type of synchronized clamp that is extensively used in television receivers, the output potential is reset during the synchronizing period to a fixed reference level, and the clamp is then opened to allow the output to follow the input for a fixed period of time before the level is again reset.

7-4. Rectangular-waveform Analysis. The discussion in Sec. 7-3 indicates that, upon passing a periodic waveform through a capacitor, the d-c component of potential will be lost in the output. It is of some interest to examine the process analytically, since the transient character of the response of an RC network to a rectangular waveform is important in this and in subsequent work.

Suppose that the applied potential to the network of Fig. 7-26a has the form illustrated in Fig. 7-26b.   The network might be the equivalent circuit of an RC-coupled amplifier or any comparable type of circuit.   It is desired to examine the form of the output potential e_2, subject to the condition that the capacitor C is initially uncharged.

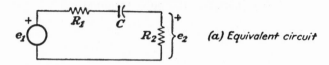

(a) Equivalent circuit

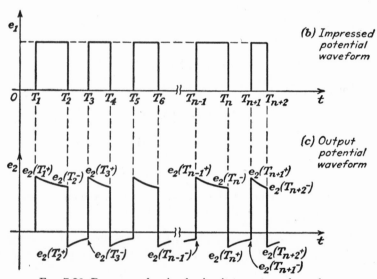

FIG. 7-26. Response of a simple circuit to rectangular pulses.

Under the specified condition that the capacitor is initially uncharged, the potential e_2 is zero in the range $0 < t < T_1$.   At the time $t = (T_1+)$, the applied potential changes instantaneously to E.   Since the capacitor potential cannot change instantaneously, the full potential E divides between R_1 and R_2.   Then at $t = (T_1+)$,

$$e_2(T_1+) = \frac{R_2}{R_1 + R_2} E = mE \tag{7-6}$$

where $m = R_2/(R_1 + R_2)$.   In the time interval $(T_1+) < t < (T_2-)$, the capacitor begins to charge, and the potential $e_2(t)$ varies according to the exponential relation

$$e_2(t) = mEe^{-(t-T_1)/(R_1+R_2)C} \tag{7-7}$$

which may be written as

$$e_2(t) = mEe^{-(t-T_1)/\tau} \qquad (7\text{-}8)$$

where

$$\tau = (R_1 + R_2)C \qquad (7\text{-}9)$$

At the time $t = (T_2+)$, just after the pulse terminates,

$$e_2(T_2+) = e_2(T_2-) - mE \qquad (7\text{-}10)$$

which becomes, by Eq. (7-6),

$$e_2(T_2+) = e_2(T_2-) - e_2(T_1+) \qquad (7\text{-}11)$$

During the time interval $(T_2+) < t < (T_3-)$, $e_2(t)$ decays exponentially according to the simple decay law

$$e_2(t) = e_2(T_2+)e^{-(t-T_2)/\tau} \qquad (7\text{-}12)$$

At the time $t = (T_3-)$,

$$e_2(T_3-) = e_2(T_2+)e^{-(T_3-T_2)/\tau} \qquad (7\text{-}13)$$

At the time $t = (T_3+)$, the impressed potential increases by E, and so

$$e_2(T_3+) = e_2(T_3-) + mE \qquad (7\text{-}14)$$

Now extend the sequence to the nth interval, with n even. The potentials in the neighborhood of the nth interval are:

At $t = (T_n-)$: $e_2(T_n-) = e_2(T_{n-1}+)e^{-(T_n-T_{n-1})/\tau}$ (7-15)
At $t = (T_n+)$: $e_2(T_n+) = e_2(T_n-) - mE$ (7-16)
At $t = (T_{n+1}-)$: $e_2(T_{n+1}-) = e_2(T_n+)e^{-(T_{n+1}-T_n)/\tau}$ (7-17)
At $t = (T_{n+1}+)$: $e_2(T_{n+1}+) = e(T_{n+1}-) + mE$ (7-18)
At $t = (T_{n+2}-)$: $e_2(T_{n+2}-) = e_2(T_{n+1}+)e^{-(T_{n+2}-T_{n+1})/\tau}$ (7-19)

These expressions allow the output waveform to be deduced for any time subsequent to closing the switch and may be sketched quickly.

The special case of recurrent identical waveform is often of particular interest. Now we may write

$$\begin{aligned} T_n - T_{n-1} &= T_a \\ T_{n+1} - T_n &= T_0 \end{aligned} \qquad (7\text{-}20)$$

Equations (7-15) to (7-19) may be combined for this case, as follows:

$$\begin{aligned} e_2(T_{n+2}-) &= [e_2(T_{n+1}-) + mE]e^{-T_a/\tau} \\ &= [mE + e_2(T_n+)e^{-T_0/\tau}]e^{-T_a/\tau} \\ e_2(T_{n+2}-) &= \{mE + [e_2(T_n-) - mE]e^{-T_0/\tau}\}e^{-T_a/\tau} \qquad (7\text{-}21) \end{aligned}$$

This is the complete period recurrence relationship. The general nth term is obtained by the proper extension of this expression. The result is

$$e_2(T_n-) = mE(e^{-T_a/\tau} - e^{-(T_a+T_0)/\tau} + e^{-(2T_a+T_0)/\tau} - e^{-(2T_a+2T_0)\tau} + \cdots$$
$$+ \cdots - e^{-\left[\left(\frac{n}{2}-1\right)T_a+\left(\frac{n}{2}-2\right)T_0\right]/\tau} + e^{-\left[\frac{n}{2}T_a+\left(\frac{n}{2}-1\right)T_0\right]/\tau}) \quad (7\text{-}22)$$

This expression is of value in determining the time required for a circuit to reach equilibrium after the application of such a periodic rectangular potential. Equilibrium exists when each cycle is identical with the

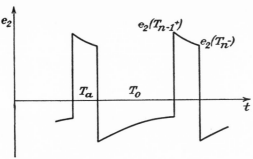

FIG. 7-27. The response of a simple RC circuit to a recurrent rectangular waveform.

preceding cycle. Mathematically this occurs as $n \to \infty$, but practically it occurs when $t \gg \tau$. Under steady-state conditions

$$e_2(T_{n+2}-) = e_2(T_n-)$$
or
$$e_2(T_{n+1}+) = e_2(T_{n-1}+)$$

From Eq. (7-21), when this condition exists,

$$e_2(T_n-) = mE \frac{(1 - e^{-T_0/\tau})e^{-T_a/\tau}}{1 - e^{-(T_2+T_0)/\tau}} \quad \text{for } t \gg \tau \quad (7\text{-}23)$$

This expression, together with Eqs. (7-15) and (7-16), permits the complete output waveform to be plotted (see Fig. 7-27).

7-5. Continuously Acting Clamps. *a. Diode Clamp.* The simplest type of clamping circuit utilizes a diode in a simple RC circuit, as illustrated in Fig. 7-28. The action of this circuit depends on the fact that when the cathode of the diode is made negative with respect to the anode, electrons flow and the circuit acts as if a low resistance had been connected across the terminals. When the cathode is positive with respect to the anode, no electrons flow and there is, in effect, a high resistance across the terminals. The "closed" impedance is usually between 300 and 3,000 ohms for most diode and triode clamps, and the "open" impedance is several megohms. Clearly, the diode acts as a switch across resistor R, although, at best, the diode is an imperfect switch, actually, with a small nonlinear resistance in the closed position and a high, though finite, resistance in the open position.

To examine the operation of the positive clamping circuit in greater detail, suppose that the waveform of Fig. 7-29a is applied to the input of the circuit of Fig. 7-28. The resulting output waveform is shown in Fig. 7-29b. During the time interval from A to B, the input potential is zero, and the output potential is likewise zero. At the point B, the

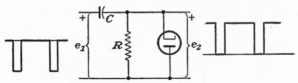

FIG. 7-28. A positive clamping circuit.

input potential drops suddenly to -100 volts, to the point C. Since the capacitor cannot change its charge instantaneously, the potential across R also drops suddenly to -100 volts. But the cathode of the diode is now 100 volts negative with respect to the anode, and the tube will conduct heavily, charging the capacitor very rapidly. The charging-time constant is CR', where R' is the parallel combination of R and r_b of the diode, and owing to the small value of r_b is essentially Cr_b. Charging of the capacitor continues until the capacitor potential becomes equal to the applied potential. At this time, the output potential has returned to zero, and the diode becomes nonconducting. Moreover, during the interval until D is reached, the output potential remains at zero potential.

At point D the input potential changes back to zero, a 100-volt change in the positive direction. This rise appears across R. Now, however, the capacitor discharges slowly through R, as the diode is

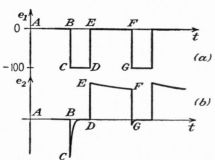

FIG. 7-29. The applied negative potential to a diode clamp, and the corresponding clamped output.

nonconducting, and R is usually a high resistance. The potential across R decays slowly, with the time constant RC, until point F is reached, when the input potential drops to -100 volts. Instantaneously the output across R falls to a value that is 100 volts below its value at the instant that point F is reached. The diode conducts, quickly reduces the output to zero, and returns the charge on the capacitor. Note that no portion of the waveform is lost after the first cycle.

If the situation is as illustrated in Fig. 7-30 for a negative clamping circuit, the corresponding output waveform for an applied positive gate potential will be of the form shown in Fig. 7-31.

It is of interest to examine the operation of the diode clamp analytically. This may be done by extending the analysis of Sec. 7-4. In the interest of greater generality, the circuit to be analyzed is that given in Fig. 7-32. For convenience, the diode is assumed to possess an infinite resistance in the back, or open, direction. In the forward, or closed,

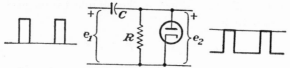

FIG. 7-30. A negative clamping circuit.

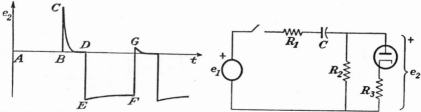

FIG. 7-31. The output waveform from a negative clamping circuit for an applied positive gate pulse.

FIG. 7-32. The diode clamping circuit to be analyzed in detail.

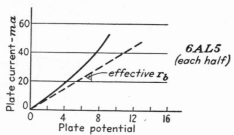

FIG. 7-33. Typical diode characteristic. (Effective diode resistance for slightly positive potentials is approximately 300 ohms.)

direction the resistance is r_b, the beam resistance of the diode. This is a nonlinear function of the applied potential. It will be chosen as the reciprocal of the slope of the tangent to the diode characteristic at the origin. The characteristic of a typical diode is given in Fig. 7-33. Also, the circuit parameters are chosen such that $R_2 \gg R_3'$, where $R_3' = R_3 + r_b$ when the diode conducts.

It is supposed that the potential applied to the circuit consists of a recurring rectangular-pulse waveform as illustrated in Fig. 7-34. The input waveform is given in Fig. 7-34a; the output waveform has the form given in Fig. 7-34b.

The same sequence is followed in the analysis as in Sec. 7-4, by examining conditions just prior to and just after a change in the input potential. The results become, when $t = (T_1+)$,

$$e_2(T_1+) = \frac{R_3'}{R_1 + R_3'} E \tag{7-24}$$

During the interval (T_1+) to (T_2-), the capacitor is charging, and the output potential falls according to the simple exponential law. The result at (T_2-) is then

$$e_2(T_2-) = e_2(T_1+)e^{-T_a/\tau_a} \tag{7-25}$$

where $\tau_a = (R_1 + R_3')C$, since with the diode conducting the parallel

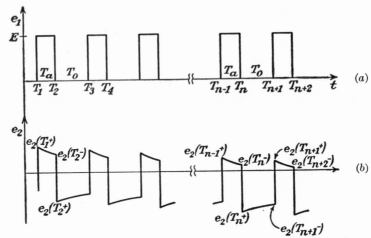

Fig. 7-34. The impressed and output waveforms of a simple diode clamp.

combination of R_2 and R_3' ($= R_3 + r_b$) is nearly R_3', since R_2 is chosen greater than R_3'.

At $t = (T_2+)$ the input changes by an amount $-E$. Now, however, a two-step process operates, namely, (1) for the period when the diode conducts, and (2) for the time when the diode ceases to conduct. In particular, the change in input potential to reduce the potential across the diode circuit to zero, when conduction ceases, is $\dfrac{R_1 + R_3'}{R_3'} e_2(T_2-)$.

As a result

$$e_2(T_2+) = \frac{R_2}{R_1 + R_2}\left[\frac{R_1 + R_3'}{R_3'} e_2(T_2-) - E\right]$$

$$e_2(T_2+) = n\left[\frac{e_2(T_2-)}{m} - E\right] \tag{7-26}$$

where $n = R_2/(R_1 + R_2)$ and $m = R_3'/(R_1 + R_3')$. During the next part of the cycle

$$e_2(T_3-) = e_2(T_2+)e^{-T_0/\tau_0} \tag{7-27}$$

where $\tau_0 = (R_1 + R_2)C$, since, with the diode open, only R_1 and R_2 are in the circuit.

To find the potential $e_2(T_3+)$ when the input changes by an amount $+E$, a two-step process again becomes effective, (1) the change in potential until the potential across the diode becomes zero, with no diode conduction, and (2) the influence of the conducting diode for potentials above this value. It is obvious that:

1. Until the potential reaches zero, the change across the input is $e_2(T_3-)/n$.

2. During the remainder of the potential swing, the available potential at the input is $E - e_2(T_3-)/n$.

Hence, with the diode conducting, the output potential reaches the value

$$e_2(T_3+) = m\left[E - \frac{e_2(T_3-)}{n} \right] \tag{7-28}$$

The process may now be generalized to the neighborhood of $t = T_n$. From the diagram,

$$e_2(T_n-) = e_2(T_{n-1}+)e^{-T_a/\tau_a} \tag{7-29}$$

As in the foregoing, when the applied potential falls to zero

$$e_2(T_n+) = n\left[\frac{e_2(T_n-)}{m} - E \right] \tag{7-30}$$

During the next period, the variation is exponential, and

$$e_2(T_{n+1}-) = e_2(T_n+)e^{-T_0/\tau_0} \tag{7-31}$$

With the application of the potential E to the input,

$$e_2(T_{n+1}+) = m\left[E + \frac{e_2(T_{n+1}-)}{n} \right] \tag{7-32}$$

This covers the complete cycle of operation, the next step being

$$e_2(T_{n+2}-) = e_2(T_{n+1}+)e^{-T_a/\tau_a} \tag{7-33}$$

which corresponds to Eq. (7-29) for the start of the previous cycle of potential.

The condition for equilibrium or steady-state operation of the circuit occurs for $t \gg \tau_a + \tau_0$, and when each cycle of operation yields potentials which are identical with those of the preceding cycle. Thus under steady-state operation $e_2(T_n-) = e_2(T_{n+2}-)$. To find this value, combine the above to get

$$e_2(T_{n+2}-) = m \left[E + \frac{e_2(T_{n+1}-)}{n} \right] e^{-T_a/\tau_a}$$

$$= m \left[E + \frac{1}{n} e_2(T_n+)e^{-T_0/\tau_0} \right] e^{-T_a/\tau_a}$$

$$e_2(T_{n+2}-) = m \left\{ E + \left[\frac{1}{m} e_2(T_n-) - E \right] e^{-T_0/\tau_0} \right\} e^{-T_a/\tau_a} \qquad (7\text{-}34)$$

Under equilibrium conditions, therefore, with $e_2(T_{n+2}-) = e_2(T_n-)$,

$$e_2(T_n-) = m \frac{E(1 - e^{-T_0/\tau_0})e^{-T_a/\tau_a}}{1 - e^{-(T_0/\tau_0 + T_a/\tau_a)}} \qquad (7\text{-}35)$$

This expression is examined in the light of Fig. 7-34, which shows the form of $e_2(t)$ as a function of time. Clearly, the action of this negative clamping circuit is to displace the entire waveform below the reference axis. Also, under optimum conditions there would be no potential in the positive sense. Desirably, therefore, $e_2(T_n-)$ should be zero, with $e_2(T_{n-1}+)$ very small. The criteria are specified. By Eq. (7-35), for $e_2(T_n-)$ to be nearly zero,

$\tau_0 \gg T_0$, which requires $(R_1 + R_2)C$ to be large
$\tau_a \gg T_a$, which requires $(R_1 + R_3')C$ to be small

By comparison of these conditions, it is seen that the clamping action is best when R_2 is made much larger than R_3' and when R_1 and R_3' are both as low as possible. The most important criteria for good clamping action are that $(R_1 + R_2)C$ be large compared with T_0 and that $R_1 + R_2$ be large compared with $R_1 + R_3'$.

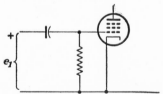

FIG. 7-35. A grid clamping circuit.

b. *Grid Clamping.* The function of clamping may be performed at the grid of a triode, since, with the grid made positive with respect to the cathode, an electron current flows and the effective cathode-grid resistance is very low. Also, when the grid is made negative with respect to the cathode, no grid current flows, and the circuit is essentially open. Hence the grid of a triode or a multielectrode tube, when connected according to the circuit of Fig. 7-35, will act as the plate of a diode and produce the same clamping action as the diode. In fact, the open and closed impedances of the grid clamp are roughly comparable with those of the diode.

c. *Clamping above or below Ground Potential.* It is not necessary that a clamping circuit tie one extremity of the input signal to zero potential. The reference potential can be made almost any desired value by introducing the necessary fixed reference potential. In the circuit of Fig. 7-36, clamping is established with reference to the fixed potential E.

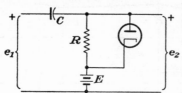

Fig. 7-36. Clamping circuit that establishes the reference potential E volts.

The operation of a simple clamp and also the effects of the clamp impedance are made more evident by a specific example.

Example 1. The circuit and the applied potential waveform are illustrated in the accompanying sketch. Assume that the effective grid-cathode resistance during grid conduction is 1,000 ohms.

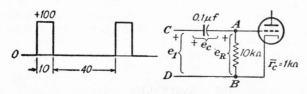

a. Estimate the reading of a d-c voltmeter which draws negligible current when connected between points C and A in the circuit in the sketch.

b. What would the voltmeter read when connected between C and D?

c. What would the voltmeter read when connected between A and B?

Solution. The equivalent circuits during the charging and discharging periods are shown in the accompanying diagrams.

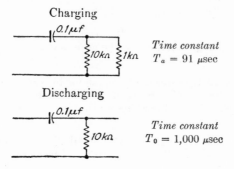

The potential differences at various points in the circuit are illustrated in the accompanying figure. These sketches show the potential variations across the

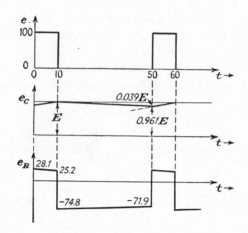

capacitor and across the grid resistor after steady-state conditions have been reached.

The potential across the capacitor at the end of the charging cycle (10 μsec) is denoted as E. During the discharge portion of the cycle, the capacitor potential falls from the value E to the value $E(e^{-40/1,000}) = 0.961E$. During the charge portion of the cycle, the potential across the capacitor increases from $0.961E$ to E according to the charging curve $(100 - 0.961E)(1 - e^{-10/61})$. For an equilibrium condition to be established, it is required that the potential lost during discharge equal the potential gained during charge; hence

$$(100 - 0.961E)0.104 = 0.039E$$

or

$$E = 74.8 \text{ volts}$$

a. $E_{CA} = \overline{e_C} = 0.98 \times 74.8 = 73.3$ volts

b. $E_{CD} = 100 \times \dfrac{10}{40 + 10} = 20$ volts

c. $E_{AB} = \overline{e_R} = \dfrac{\frac{1}{2}(28.1 + 25.2) 10 - \frac{1}{2}(74.8 + 71.9) 40}{50} = -53.3$ volts

Hence $E_{CD} = E_{CA} + E_{AB}$ is verified to the accuracy used.

Example 2. Repeat the foregoing example for the case where the circuit constants are changed to read $C = 0.001$ μf, $R = 10^6$ ohms.

Solution. The charging and discharging circuits, with the corresponding time constants, are

Charging: $T_a = 1,000 \times 0.001 \times 10^{-6} = 1$ μsec
Discharging: $T_0 = 10^6 \times 10^{-9} = 1,000$ μsec

The important waveforms are illustrated in the accompanying figure.

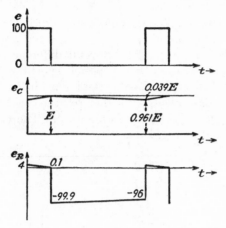

A comparison of the above examples shows that, the lower the clamp impedance relative to the circuit impedance, the "tighter" the clamp becomes. In particular, if a zero-impedance clamp were possible, then perfect clamping would result.

7-6. Switched Clamps. It is sometimes necessary to open or to close a clamp at intervals which may or may not be directly related to the signals. If the clamp can conduct in only one direction when closed, it is called a *one-way*, or *single-sided*, clamp. If the clamp can conduct in both directions when closed, it is a *two-way*, or *double-sided*, clamp.

Switched Clamps—Single-sided. The clamping circuits discussed in Sec. 7-5 are essentially single-sided, and if provision is made to cause the diodes or triodes that produce the clamping action to turn off during a certain prescribed period, the clamp then becomes a switched single-sided clamp. The modification that is necessary in order to convert the

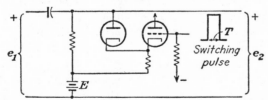

Fig. 7-37. A switched diode clamp that is open for a time T.

biased clamp of Fig. 7-36 into a switched clamp is illustrated in Fig. 7-37. Here the diode is switched out of the circuit by the application of a square pulse for a time T to the grid of the cathode follower. Clearly, for the switching to operate, the amplitude of the signal at the cathode of the cathode follower must exceed the bias potential E. The other clamping circuits can be modified in generally similar ways.

A somewhat comparable circuit that utilizes a triode is given in Fig. 7-38.   In this circuit the clamping is done through the beam resistance of the tube, but since the clamp impedance is rather large, the clamp is correspondingly quite "loose."

Switched Clamps—Double-sided.   Several different types of switched double-sided clamps exist.   One type of synchronized clamp is so arranged that the output may follow the input during the time that the synchronizing pulse is applied, but is then returned to the reference potential when the synchronizing pulse is removed.   The elements of such a circuit are illustrated in Fig. 7-39.

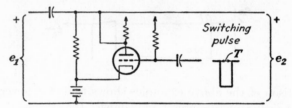

FIG. 7-38. A one-way clamp using a single triode.

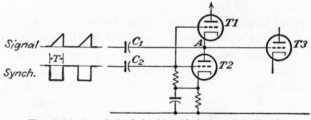

FIG. 7-39. A switched double-sided clamping circuit.

Suppose that the synchronizing pulse is applied as a negative rectangular gate which drives $T1$ and $T2$ beyond cutoff for the desired length of time.   With tubes $T1$ and $T2$ cut off, the grid of $T3$ is free to follow any changes in the input-potential amplitude.   Since capacitor C_1 has no discharge path, the potential is transferred to the grid of $T3$, which then follows this potential variation.   At the end of the synchronizing period, tubes $T1$ and $T2$ again conduct, and the grid potential of $T3$ is returned to the reference potential determined by $T1$ and $T2$ in series.

If for any reason a signal appears on the grid of $T3$ without a synchronizing potential on the clamping triodes, the effect of $T1$ and $T2$ is to prevent the grid potential on $T3$ from changing.   This self-compensating effect arises because a slight increase in the potential at the point A causes $T2$ to conduct more current, which reflects itself as an increase in the bias of $T1$.   This tends to reduce the current through $T1$, which thus counteracts the impressed potential.   In a similar manner, if the signal tends to decrease the current through $T2$, the grid bias of $T1$ decreases, with a resulting increase in current. Hence, so long as $T1$ and $T2$ conduct, the potential at the grid of $T3$ is held constant and no input signal will reflect itself as a variation in the output of $T3$.

This clamping circuit operates quite satisfactorily and is used for many applications. However, owing to the existence of interelectrode and distributed capacitances between the synchronizing and the signal line, a slight dimple might appear on the signal, somewhat as illustrated in Fig. 7-40, owing to the interaction of the synchronizing pulse on the signal line. This effect is quite tolerable in some applications but is objectionable in

No coupling   With interaction

Fig. 7-40. The effect on the output signal of the synchronizing pulse acting through the interelectrode and distributed capacitances to the signal line.

television circuits, where such an extraneous signal might affect the actual signal pattern. This effect is overcome by using two synchronizing pulses of opposite polarity in appropriate circuits.

A clamping circuit of importance in television practice[1] provides for establishing an arbitrary reference potential at fixed and regular intervals on some chosen circuit element in the picture amplifier. The clamping is applied during the period that the television picture is blanked during the retrace period. A diagram of such a clamping circuit is given in Fig. 7-41.

The reference potential is that which exists at the mid-point of R_1. This may be deduced as follows: During the keying-pulse intervals, both diodes conduct, and both terminals of R_1 are at nearly the same potential. Because of this conduction, the equal coupling capacitors C_2 and C_3 are oppositely charged. During the intervals when the diodes are not conducting, a current flows in R_1, thus discharging these capacitors. Since both the circuit and the keying signals are balanced, the diodes always reach the same potential during the pulse intervals, this potential being that at the mid-point of R_1 during the intervals between pulses. The time constant $C_2R_1 = C_3R_1$ is made large compared with the period of the pulses, so that the current in R_1 is small and the charges on C_2 and C_3 remain substantially constant.

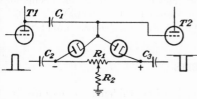

Fig. 7-41. A double-sided switched clamp.

If R_1 is connected as shown, the reference potential may be shifted with respect to ground. However, if the circuit is seriously unbalanced, some difficulty may be experienced in maintaining the pulse shape. To minimize this, the resistor R_2 may be inserted in the ground connection. The current through this resistor is very small, and even with large R_2 there is no serious disturbance of the reference potential.

The coupling capacitor C_1 must charge through the clamp circuit, in the absence of grid current in $T2$. During the open-circuit intervals in the clamp circuit, the charge on C_1 cannot change. Consequently the l-f response of the coupling circuit between $T1$ and $T2$ is not seriously affected.

A clamping circuit that is essentially self-balancing is illustrated in Fig. 7-42. If it is assumed that the four diodes are identical, then upon

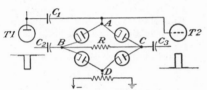

the application of the keying pulses the points A and D are at the same potential.

Both the foregoing clamping circuits require that the keying pulses be larger than the amplitude of the picture signal at the point where the clamp operates. Otherwise con-

Fig. 7-42. A self-balancing clamp circuit.

duction from the signal line through the clamp may occur and thus affect the level. Usually the amplitude of the keying pulses is made about twice the amplitude of the picture signal.

REFERENCES

1. Roe, J. H., *Proc. IRE*, **12**, 1532 (1947).
2. As general references, consult:
   "Principles of Radar," 3d ed., Massachusetts Institute of Technology Radar School Staff, McGraw-Hill Book Company, Inc., New York, 1952.
   "Radar Electronic Fundamentals," *War Dept. Tech. Manual* TM11-455.

PROBLEMS

General Note: The solution of many of the following problems may require direct reference to a tube manual for additional tube information.

7-1. The double-diode limiting circuit of Fig. 7-5 is used to clip a sinewave input $100 \sin 5,000t$. In the circuit, $R = 100$ kilohms, and $E_1 = E_2 = 5$ volts. 6H6 tubes are used.

   a. Plot the output potential e_2 as a function of time.

   b. Suppose that the output e_2 is amplified to a 200-volt peak-peak potential and is passed through a second identical clipper. Plot the output as a function of time. Indicate the total rise time on the diagram.

7-2. Sketch the waveform at the output of the diode clipping circuit shown.

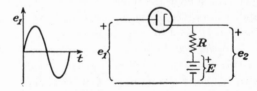

7-3. Consider the circuit in the accompanying figures. Determine the wave-shapes at the several points indicated, and sketch these in the manner shown.

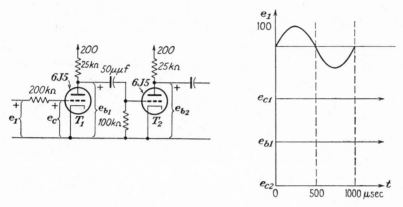

Neglect interelectrode and wiring capacitances. Assume $r_c = 500$ ohms when grid current is drawn.

7-4. A two-series diode clipping circuit is illustrated. Determine the clipping characteristic (a plot of e_2 vs. e_1) for this circuit, assuming ideal diodes.

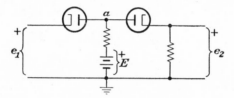

7-5. Consider the cathode-follower clipping circuit shown in the accompanying figure. Prepare a plot of output vs. input potential amplitudes.

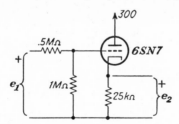

7-6. Write an expression for the output potential as a function of time after closing the switch (see the figure for this problem).

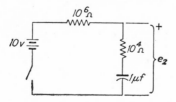

7-7. The interelectrode and wiring capacitances will affect the shape of the output waveform for a given input waveform. Refer to the circuit in the accompanying diagram.

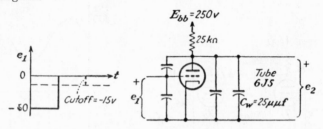

a. Draw the equivalent circuit of this amplifier when the tube is conducting; when the tube is nonconducting.

b. Determine the output waveshape for the designated input wave.

7-8. Repeat Prob. 7-7 when the circuit is modified as shown in the accompanying figure.

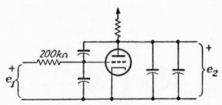

7-9. A saw-tooth potential is applied to the circuit shown in the accompanying diagram. Calculate and sketch the output potential during one complete period.

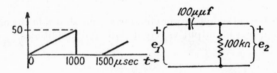

7-10. The input potential to a given amplifier is as shown (see figure).

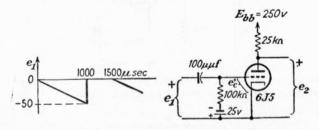

a. Calculate and sketch e_c during one complete period. Neglect tube and wiring capacitances.

b. Calculate and sketch the output potential during the period.

7-11. A biased diode clamping circuit (see Fig. 7-36) is modified as shown. Discuss the effects of the modification.

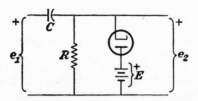

7-12. A recurring pulse series is applied through a series diode to the network shown. Assume that the resistance of the diode is R_1 during the pulse and is infinite in the reverse direction. Obtain an expression for the reading E_2 of an

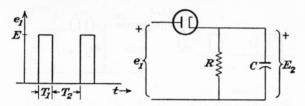

average-reading voltmeter of infinite input impedance under steady-state conditions.

7-13. A circuit which has been called a diode-pump integrating circuit is illustrated.

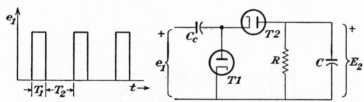

a. Find an approximate expression for the reading of an average-reading voltmeter across the output capacitor C.

b. Discuss whether the duration of the input pulse is critical, provided the coupling capacitor C_c becomes fully charged before the end of the pulse. If the effective internal resistance of the pulse source is R_s, what relation between R_sC_c and T_1 must be met in order that the conditions discussed be fulfilled?

7-14. Given the circuit shown in the diagram. The generator has negligible internal resistance and produces 100-volt rectangular pulses of 2 μsec duration.

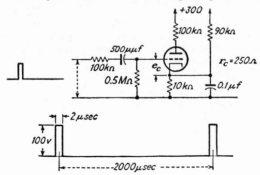

a. Draw a simplified equivalent circuit for the generator and its load during the 2-μsec pulse interval.

b. Draw the simplified equivalent circuit for the generator and its load during the interval between the pulses.

c. From the equivalent circuits, determine the principal function of the 500-$\mu\mu$f capacitor? Is any appreciable signal bias developed? If so, how much?

d. Sketch the grid potential e_c approximately to scale.

7-15. Refer to the circuit in the figure.

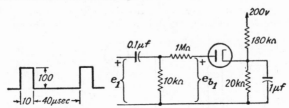

a. What is the maximum value of e_{b1}?

b. What is the approximate value of the potential across the 0.1-μf capacitor?

c. Sketch the waveform e_{b1}.

7-16. Given the circuit shown in the figure. The input to the circuit is a

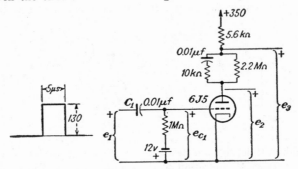

series of rectangular pulses having the amplitude and duration shown, with a pulse recurrence frequency of 60 per second. Choose the following values:

$$r_c = 500 \text{ ohms when grid exceeds } +10 \text{ volts}$$
$$r_b = 1,000 \text{ ohms when grid exceeds } +10 \text{ volts}$$
$$e_{c1} \text{ at beginning of pulse } = -27.5 \text{ volts}$$

a. Draw the equivalent circuit for the charging of C_1 during each pulse, and determine the potential across C_1 at the end of the pulse.

b. Determine the grid potential e_{c1} at the end of the pulse.

c. Sketch the potential across C_1 and e_{c1}.

d. Calculate the average d-c value of e_{c1}.

e. Calculate and sketch the potential e_2.

f. Calculate and sketch the potential e_3.

CHAPTER 8

OSCILLATORS

The effects of feedback in amplifiers were examined in Chap. 5. It is there shown that positive feedback is to be avoided in an amplifier if stability is to be achieved. On the other hand, if the circuit is provided with a sufficient amount of regenerative feedback, the vacuum-tube circuit will serve as a generator of periodically varying waves. This output may be sinusoidal, with a high degree of purity of waveform; it may be an essentially square wave, hence being of high harmonic content; or it may be periodically recurring, though of general nonsinusoidal shape.

A large variety of feedback circuits which differ considerably in detail are available for the production of self-sustained oscillations. These possess certain features which are common to all. In each case a feedback circuit exists through which is fed back into the input circuit a certain fraction of the output and in such a phase and of such an amplitude that self-excitation results. In the usual class of tube, the feedback from the output to the input circuit is accomplished externally to the tube by means of coupling networks. In certain special types of tubes, e.g., a klystron of the reflex type and a magnetron of the running-wave type, the feedback is accomplished through the electron beam itself. Nevertheless even these can be represented by equivalent circuits which have features that are common to all feedback oscillators.

Conventional self-excited oscillators for the production of sinusoidal waves ordinarily operate as class C devices, the essential nonlinearity of the operation ultimately providing the amplitude limit of the oscillations which are produced. Class A oscillators which incorporate amplitude-controlling schemes are also possible and find extensive use in certain applications. Another class of oscillators, known as relaxation oscillators, operate over such wide amplitude limits that the tube is cut off over a substantial portion of the cycle. Conventional oscillator considerations are no longer applicable in this latter case, as the operation is of a recurring transient character rather than one in which there is energy transfer from output to input circuits during an appreciable portion of the cycle.

It is not intended to discuss the theory of oscillators in full detail, since our interests are here confined to a class of oscillators which yield

227

waveforms which are very nearly sinusoidal in character. A more extensive treatment of oscillators is readily available.[1] A linear theory will here be assumed. The transient-type oscillators will receive detailed treatment below.

8-1. Conditions for Self-excitation. To ascertain the conditions that must be fulfilled for oscillations to be sustained in a vacuum-tube circuit, refer to Fig. 8-1. The circuit is supposed to be open initially at the point A, as shown. If a potential e_1 is impressed on the input terminals of the vacuum-tube circuit, without regard for the source of this poten-

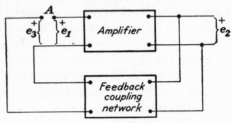

Fig. 8-1. A vacuum-tube circuit with coupling between the output and the input circuits.

tial, the output potential with the feedback network connected will be e_2, as shown. Also, a potential e_3 will appear across the output terminals of the feedback coupling network. If it should happen that the circuits are such that the feedback potential e_3 is identically equal to the impressed potential e_1, the points A could be closed and the system would continue to operate, producing an output without an external source of excitation.

The requirement that $e_3 = e_1$ states that the instantaneous potentials must be equal at all times, no restriction being imposed on the waveform. In fact, it is not necessary that the amplifier preserve the waveform of the potential e_1 as it is transmitted through the amplifier. The requirement is very stringent, however, that the potential e_3, when it emerges from the feedback coupling loop, must be restored to the original e_1. Consequently the waveform which is available from such a circuit, and its frequency, will be precisely that required for the fundamental condition $e_1 = e_3$ to be fulfilled.

As indicated above, the present interest is in oscillators which operate under nearly linear conditions, so that the output is essentially sinusoidal. In this case, the general requirement $e_1 = e_3$ now may be written $E_1 = E_3$, where this condition now requires that the amplitude, phase, and frequency of E_1 and E_3 be identical. If K denotes the gain of the amplifier and β is the feedback factor of the feedback coupling network, then

$$E_2 = KE_1$$

and also

$$E_3 = \beta E_2$$

Consequently for oscillations it is required that

$$E_3 = \beta E_2 = K\beta E_1$$

from which it follows that

$$K\beta = 1 \qquad\qquad (8\text{-}1)$$

This relationship implies the same criterion for oscillation as the condition $E_1 = E_3$.

From Eq. (8-1) it is possible to state the following principle, which relates to the amplitudes of E_1 and E_3, namely:

An oscillator will not function if, at the oscillator frequency, the magnitude of the product of the gain of the amplifier and the feedback factor of the feedback network is less than unity.

A relationship is also possible concerning the phase shift in the system. Note that in general the amplifier and the feedback coupling network will include reactive elements, so that the phase shift introduced when a signal is transmitted through the system will vary with the frequency. It is now noted that

A sinusoidal oscillator will operate at that frequency for which the total phase change as a signal proceeds around the complete loop is either zero or an integral multiple of 2π.

It is conceivable that more than one frequency might exist which would fulfill the prescribed phase requirement. Under such circumstances the oscillator might operate simultaneously at the several frequencies which satisfy the phase condition. Of course, if the amplitude condition is not simultaneously fulfilled, then oscillations will not take place, even if the phase condition is satisfied.

It is of some interest to examine the effect of having the magnitude of $|K\beta|$ greater than unity, the requirement for sustained oscillations. Clearly, if the input signal is larger than the required minimum, the output will also be larger, with the result that E_3 would increase. This in turn would cause E_1 to be larger, with an inevitable chain effect, resulting in a continually increasing amplitude. Such an increase in the amplitude can continue only so long as it is not limited by the onset of a nonlinear operation in the vacuum tubes associated with the amplifier, a nonlinearity which actually increases with increased oscillation amplitude.

The condition $|K\beta| = 1$ is the minimum case for oscillation and provides no margin for changes which might occur either in the tubes or in the circuit components of the oscillator. Ordinarily practical considerations dictate that $|K\beta|$ be slightly larger than unity, in order to allow for the incidental variations in the tube and circuit parameters. A factor of safety of about 5 per cent is adequate under most circumstances. On the basis of the foregoing practical considerations, it is required that

In every practical oscillator $|K\beta|$ is slightly greater than unity; the amplitude of oscillation is limited by the nonlinearities which occur with increasing amplitude.

8-2. Frequency Stability. Vacuum-tube oscillators will suffer changes in frequency with variations in any operating characteristic that involves either the tube or the circuit parameters. For example, a change in temperature may cause a change in the inductance and capacitance of the tank elements; it may also cause a change in the grid-cathode and plate-cathode interelectrode capacitances. A change in plate potential will result in changes in the interelectrode capacitances. A change in the coupled load to the output causes a change in the shunt loading, with a consequent change in frequency. Although these factors have been neglected in the foregoing discussions, they do play a part in determining the frequency, since they will contribute to a variation of the tube or circuit constants of the coupling network.

A relationship is possible which serves as a guide in estimating the relative frequency stability of an oscillator, the comparative frequency stability of several oscillators, or the influence on the frequency of factors which have only a slight effect on the frequency of the oscillator.

The desired relationship is found from Eq. (8-1), the condition for oscillation. When oscillations exist, the amplitude $|K\beta|$ and the total circuit phase θ must have such values as to fulfill the criterion, as discussed in Sec. 8-1. Suppose that the phase shift through the tube does not vary appreciably with frequency, for very small changes in frequency. This is a generally valid assumption. Then any variation in frequency must be accompanied by a change in the phase of the β network which is such that the total phase of the circuit remains substantially constant; otherwise, oscillations will cease. The rate of the variation of phase with frequency $d\theta/d\omega$ is evidently related to the frequency stability of the system. In fact, the frequency stability S_f is defined by the relation

$$S_f = \omega_0 \frac{d\theta}{d\omega} \equiv \frac{d\theta}{d\omega/\omega_0} \qquad (8-2)$$

where ω_0 is the mean frequency of the oscillator. This shows that, the larger the value of S_f, the more stable is the system. In the limit as S_f becomes infinite, the oscillator is completely frequency-stable.

As an indication of the significance of this stability criterion, suppose that a variation occurs in some elements of the circuit other than the β network, which is supposed to control the frequency of the system. If the requisite phase condition specified by Eq. (8-1) were initially satisfied at the particular frequency of oscillation, then when the change in the element occurs, the circuital phase condition will, in general, no longer be satisfied. As a result, the frequency of the oscillator will shift until the circuital phase condition is satisfied once again. If the β network produces a very large phase shift for a small frequency change, i.e., if S_f is large, then the required frequency shift to restore the circuital phase condition will be very small.

A number of corrective measures may be taken in order to improve the stability of an oscillator. This would include the careful choice of inductor and capacitor, either with negligible temperature coefficients or with such temperature variation that a change in one parameter is counteracted by an opposite change in the other. Any changes that might result from changes in the plate potential can be overcome by the use of adequately regulated sources.

The effect of changes in the load impedance on the frequency may be eliminated by using an amplifier to isolate the load from the oscillator. This system is called a *master-oscillator power-amplifier* system and is usually abbreviated MOPA.

A number[1] of other methods exist for improving the frequency stability of oscillators. These include the use of compensating reactances to effect virtual isolation of the tank circuit from the remainder of the oscillator; the use of a crystal for controlling the frequency; the use of an amplitude-sensitive feedback stabilization loop. Some considerations of these matters will be given below.

8-3. Tuned - plate Oscillator.
The tuned-plate oscillator is one in which an antiresonant circuit is connected directly in the plate circuit of the vacuum tube, the grid excitation being supplied by inductive coupling to the plate circuit.

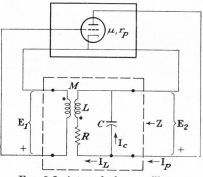

FIG. 8-2. A tuned-plate oscillator.

The complete circuit, drawn in the manner of Fig. 8-1, except for battery supplies, has the form illustrated in Fig. 8-2. An analysis will be made of this oscillator circuit.

For simplicity, it will be assumed that the grid current is negligible. The grid excitation is then simply

$$\mathbf{E}_1 = -j\omega M \mathbf{I}_L = \mathbf{Z}_M \mathbf{I}_L \tag{8-3}$$

The plate load impedance is

$$Z = \frac{Z_L Z_C}{Z_L + Z_C}$$

$$(8\text{-}4)$$

where $Z_L = R + j\omega L$ $Z_C = \dfrac{1}{j\omega C}$

The amplifier gain **K** is then

$$\mathbf{K} = \frac{-\mu Z}{r_p + Z}$$

$$(8\text{-}5)$$

The transfer function of the feedback network β is deduced as follows: Since

$$E_1 = \beta E_2$$

$$\beta = \frac{E_1}{E_2} = \frac{Z_M I_L}{I_p Z}$$

But since $I_L Z_L = I_C Z_C$ and $I_p = I_L + I_C$,

$$\beta = \frac{I_L Z_M}{(I_L + I_C)Z} = \frac{I_L Z_M}{\left(I_L + I_L \dfrac{Z_L}{Z_C}\right) Z}$$

from which

$$\beta = \frac{Z_M Z_C}{Z(Z_C + Z_L)}$$

$$(8\text{-}6)$$

The conditional equation for sustained oscillations may then be written as

$$\mathbf{K}\beta = 1 = \frac{-\mu Z}{r_p + Z} \frac{Z_M Z_C}{Z(Z_C + Z_L)}$$

$$(8\text{-}7)$$

Expand this to the form

$$(r_p + Z)(Z_C + Z_L) + \mu Z_M Z_C = 0$$

or

$$r_p(Z_C + Z_L) + Z_L Z_C + \mu Z_M Z_C = 0$$

or

$$-g_m Z_M Z_C = Z_C + Z_L + \frac{Z_L Z_C}{r_p}$$

$$(8\text{-}8)$$

Combine with the known forms for the various **Z**'s in this expression to get

$$g_m \frac{M}{C} = R + j\left(\omega L - \frac{1}{\omega C}\right) - j\frac{R}{\omega C r_p} + \frac{L}{C r_p}$$

$$(8\text{-}9)$$

Now equate real and imaginary parts. This gives

$$\omega L - \frac{1}{\omega C} - \frac{R}{\omega C r_p} = 0 \qquad \text{phase condition}$$

$$g_m \frac{M}{C} = R + \frac{L}{C r_p} \qquad \text{amplitude condition}$$

$$(8\text{-}10)$$

The first of these yields

$$\omega^2 = \frac{1}{LC}\left(1 + \frac{R}{r_p}\right)$$ (8-11)

If the quantity ω_0 is defined by the relation

$$\omega_0 \equiv \frac{1}{\sqrt{LC}}$$

then Eq. (8-11) becomes

$$\omega = \omega_0 \sqrt{1 + \frac{R}{r_p}}$$ (8-12)

This equation shows that the frequency of oscillation will be approximately the resonant frequency of the circuit, the factor involving the ratio R/r_p being small. However, the frequency of oscillation will always be slightly higher than the resonant value. Clearly, the tube plays only a minor part in determining the frequency of oscillation, the external circuit elements exercising the main control. In fact, the influence of the tube on the frequency becomes less as the shunt resistance of the antiresonant circuit increases or, correspondingly, as the series resistance in the tank decreases. If circuits of very low dissipation are provided, the oscillator has a very high degree of stability.

The second of Eqs. (8-10) yields the value

$$M = \frac{CRr_p + L}{\mu}$$

which is the amplitude condition which is equivalent to $|K\beta| = 1$.

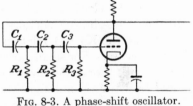

FIG. 8-3. A phase-shift oscillator.

8-4. Phase-shift Oscillator.[2] It is not necessary that an oscillator include an LC antiresonant circuit in the coupling network. A simple one-tube oscillator is possible which incorporates RC networks alone to provide the requisite phase change in traversing the closed loop. The circuit is illustrated in Fig. 8-3.

The operation of the circuit may best be understood by considering that each L section, which consists of a C and R combination, shifts the phase by 60 deg at the frequency ω. This explanation assumes that there is no loading by one RC combination on the others and that there is no loading by the coupling network on the plate load resistance. The use of three such sections will shift the phase of the output by a total of 180 deg relative to the input, and this, together with the 180-deg shift by the tube, will provide the 2π shift for successful operation. Under these assumptions, it follows that

$$\tan \theta = \sqrt{3} = \frac{1}{\omega RC}$$ (8-13)

or

$$\omega = \frac{1}{\sqrt{3}\,RC} \qquad (8\text{-}14)$$

A more exact calculation, under the assumption that the amplifier loading by the phase-shifting network may be neglected, yields the relation

$$\omega = \frac{1}{\sqrt{6}\,RC} \qquad (8\text{-}15)$$

It would be possible, of course, to obtain the required 180-deg phase shift with more than three sections, but there is no particular advantage in doing so.

As might be surmised, there is an appreciable attenuation in potential in progressing through the network. At the frequency of oscillation, it is found that $\beta = \frac{1}{29}$. Consequently, for oscillations to be possible, i.e., to fulfill the condition $|K\beta| = 1$, the amplifier must possess a gain of at least 29. Consequently, either a high-μ triode or a pentode must be employed in such a circuit.

The frequency of the oscillator may be varied by changing the value of any of the elements in the feedback network. However, care in the change of the element is important; otherwise, the impedance looking into the phase-shifting network, and its phase, may change to such an extent that the $K\beta = 1$ relation may no longer be satisfied and oscillations will cease. For small variations in frequency, a single element may be changed. For wide variations in frequency, the three capacitances should be varied simultaneously. The three resistances could also be varied simultaneously, but this will cause a serious change in impedance, with a consequent effect on the amplifier gain and so the possibility of discontinued oscillation. It is quite possible to remove the restriction that the values of all R and of all C be equal. Such a change will complicate the matter of securing variable-frequency operation.

8-5. Resistance - Capacitance Oscillators. A form of coupling network that has been used extensively in relatively l-f oscilla-

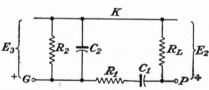

FIG. 8-4. An RC coupling network for an oscillator.

tors is given in Fig. 8-4. The phase shift through such a network as this is a fairly sensitive function of the frequency, and such RC oscillators are quite stable. However, such a simple network will not provide a large phase shift between the input and output terminals, and it is necessary to incorporate a second vacuum tube in the circuit in order to provide an addi-

tional 180-deg phase shift. The circuit, when drawn in the manner of
the previous circuits, is that shown in
Fig. 8-5.

This circuit may be analyzed in a direct
manner. Refer to Fig. 8-6, which shows
the complete coupling network, in which
the amplifier is replaced by a "box" which
provides a gain K_N and a phase shift of
180 deg. An inspection of this diagram
shows that

$$E_1 = K_N E_2'$$

This may be written in the form

$$E_1 = K_N I Z_g$$

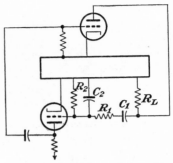

Fig. 8-5. An RC coupled oscillator.

if it is assumed that the input impedance to the amplifier is very high.

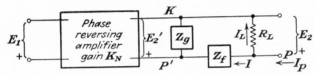

Fig. 8-6. The complete coupling circuit of the RC oscillator.

The transfer impedance of the network becomes

$$Z_T = \frac{E_1}{I_p} = \frac{K_N I Z_g}{I_L + I}$$

But as

$$I(Z_g + Z_f) = I_L R_L$$

then

$$Z_T = \frac{K_N I Z_g}{I \dfrac{Z_g + Z_f}{R_L} + I} = \frac{K_N Z_g R_L}{Z_g + Z_f + R_L} \qquad (8\text{-}16)$$

Also, it is noted that the impedance looking into the feedback network is

$$Z = \frac{R_L(Z_g + Z_f)}{Z_g + Z_f + R_L} \qquad (8\text{-}17)$$

The feedback factor β of the network is

$$\beta = \frac{E_1}{E_2} = \frac{I_p Z_T}{I_p Z} = \frac{K_N Z_g}{Z_g + Z_f} \qquad (8\text{-}18)$$

Also, the gain of the amplifier is K_a,

$$K_a = \frac{-\mu Z}{r_p + Z} \qquad (8\text{-}19)$$

The conditional equation for oscillations, $\mathbf{K}_a\beta = 1$, becomes

$$\mathbf{K}_a\beta = 1 = \frac{-\mu Z}{r_p + Z}\frac{Z_T}{Z} = \frac{-\mu Z_T}{r_p + Z} \tag{8-20}$$

Combining with the known forms for Z and Z_T gives

$$-\frac{\mu \mathbf{K}_N Z_g R_L}{r_p(Z_g + Z_f + R_L) + R_L(Z_g + Z_f)} = 1 \tag{8-21}$$

from which it follows that

$$-\mu \mathbf{K}_N R_L = \frac{r_p(Z_g + Z_f + R_L) + R_L(Z_g + Z_f)}{Z_g} \tag{8-22}$$

By including in this expression the known values of Z_g and Z_f, namely,

$$Z_g = \frac{-j(R_2/\omega C_2)}{R_2 - j(1/\omega C_2)} \qquad Z_f = R_1 - j\frac{1}{\omega C_1} \tag{8-23}$$

and equating real and imaginary terms, two expressions result. They are

$$-\mu \mathbf{K}_N R_2 R_L = \left(R_1 + R_2 + \frac{R_2 C_2}{C_1}\right)(r_p + R_L) + r_p R_L$$

$$\frac{R_L}{r_p}\left(R_1 R_2 - \frac{1}{\omega^2 C_1 C_2}\right) + (R_1 + R_L)R_2 - \frac{1}{\omega^2 C_1 C_2} = 0 \tag{8-24}$$

The first of these expressions yields for the required gain of the amplifier in the coupling network

$$-\mathbf{K}_N = \frac{1}{\mu R_2 R_L}\left[r_p R_L + \left(R_1 + R_2 + \frac{R_2 C_2}{C_1}\right)(r_p + R_L)\right] \tag{8-25}$$

The second yields for the frequency

$$\omega^2 = \frac{1}{C_1 C_2\left(R_1 R_2 + \dfrac{R_2 R_L}{1 + R_L/r_p}\right)} \tag{8-26}$$

Ordinarily $R_1 = R_2 = R$, $C_1 = C_2 = C$, and $R > R_L$, whence

$$-\mathbf{K}_N = \frac{r_p R_L + 3(r_p + R_L)R}{\mu R_L R} \doteq \frac{3}{g_m}\left(\frac{1}{r_p} + \frac{1}{R_L}\right) \tag{8-27}$$

and

$$\omega^2 = \frac{1}{C^2\left(R^2 + \dfrac{R R_L}{1 + R_L/r_p}\right)} \doteq \frac{1}{C^2 R^2} \tag{8-28}$$

It will be observed from Eq. (8-27) that the coupling amplifier which is part of the network must indeed provide phase reversal, as indicated in Fig. 8-6. Moreover, for the values of r_p and R_L which would ordinarily be used, the magnitude of the gain of this coupling amplifier might be of the order of unity or less. What is implied by Eq. (8-27) is that the phase shift through the passive elements of the coupling network, composed of $C_1 R_1$ in series and $C_2 R_2$ in parallel, is 0 deg, and the amplifier circuit is required in order to provide the necessary additional 180 deg. From purely practical considerations, since the amplifier $\mathbf{K}_N$ would normally provide a gain considerably in excess of that required, negative feedback is ordinarily included in both vacuum-tube circuits, both to reduce the gain and also to improve the waveform. The manner of

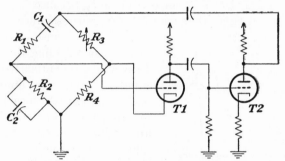

FIG. 8-7. The basic Wien bridge oscillator.

achieving feedback is illustrated in Fig. 8-7. Because of the form of the network, this RC oscillator is known as a Wien bridge oscillator.

The modification shown introduces certain significant consequences into the operation of the circuit. In particular, for a given R_4 and tube $T1$, if R_3 is adjusted so that the bridge is balanced, the grid-cathode potential is zero. That is, the Wien bridge output (in this case, chosen as the grid-cathode potential) is zero at the balance point but is different from zero for all frequencies in the neighborhood of balance. Clearly, there will be no feedback at the balance point, and the system will not oscillate. Note that for the bridge itself (neglecting the loading of R_4 by tube $T1$), the conditions for balance and balance frequency are

$$\frac{R_3}{R_4} = \frac{R_1}{R_2} + \frac{C_2}{C_1} \qquad \omega_0^2 = \frac{1}{R_1 R_2 C_1 C_2}$$

which become, for $R_1 = R_2 = R$, $C_1 = C_2 = C$, as chosen above,

$$\frac{R_3}{R_4} = 2 \qquad \omega_0 = \frac{1}{RC}$$

Thus, for these conditions, the circuit is a frequency-selective feedback rejection amplifier. For the circuit to act as an oscillator, the ratio R_3/R_4 must be chosen greater than 2.

Continuous variation of frequency of this oscillator is accomplished by varying simultaneously the two capacitances C_1 and C_2, these being variable air capacitors. Changes in frequency range are accomplished by switching into the circuit different values for the two resistors R_1 and R_2. The use of variable resistances could, in principle, be used for the continuous control. If, however, tracking is important, the capacitors are to be preferred, as it is less difficult to build variable air capacitors to track accurately than to build resistances to track with the same precision.

Owing to the limitations imposed on variable air capacitors, to attain low frequencies requires that large resistances R be used. A practical limit exists to the size of R, in one instance because of blocking that might occur in $T1$ (note that one R is the grid resistance of this stage), and second because of the increasing problem of shielding the grid against stray 60-cps potentials from the power supply. A practical limit to the size of R is perhaps 10 megohms, so that low frequencies of the order of 10 cps are readily achieved. At the high frequencies, with the consequent reduction of R, the loading of the phase-inverting amplifier increases. Even if the loading does not stop the oscillations, it will affect the stability of amplitude of oscillations with change of frequency range.

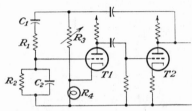

Fig. 8-8. Wien bridge oscillator.

A very ingenious modification of this circuit[3] which serves to stabilize the amplitude against range switching and against aging of tubes replaces R_4 by a tungsten-filament lamp, ordinarily a 115-volt 3-watt lamp. The revised circuit is given in Fig. 8-8. The effect of providing the tungsten-filament lamp, which possesses a positive temperature coefficient of resistance, is to provide a system which automatically changes the feedback factor β in such a direction as to keep **K** more nearly constant as the gain of $T1$ and $T2$ varies owing to loading or other variations in the circuit.

The current through the tungsten lamp R_4 consists of three components: (1) the d-c component through $T1$, which for class A operation is essentially constant; (2) the a-c component through $T1$ due to the a-c potential on the grid; (3) the a-c component of opposite phase through R_3 to the cathode. The resultant a-c current through R_4 is comparable with, and perhaps larger than, the d-c component, with the result that the value of the resistance of R_4 will be controlled to a very large extent by the amplitude of the oscillations. Note, of course, that for adequate control of the amplitude, the thermal time constant of the tungsten lamp must be large compared with the period of the oscillations; otherwise, an amplitude drift may occur.

8-6. Bridged-T and Twin-T Oscillators.[4] In addition to the Wien bridge which is incorporated into an oscillator circuit, the bridged-T and the twin-T networks may similarly be used. The characteristics of these networks are shown in Table 8-1.

TABLE 8-1

CHARACTERISTICS OF BRIDGED-T AND TWIN-T NETWORKS

Circuit	Condition for balance	Feedback factor
Bridged-T	$\omega_0^2 = \dfrac{1}{RrC_1C_2}$ $\qquad = \dfrac{C_1 + C_2}{LC_1C_2}$	$\dfrac{E_2}{E_1} \equiv \beta = \dfrac{1}{1 + j\dfrac{\omega/\omega_0}{1 - (\omega/\omega_0)^2}\dfrac{2}{Q}}$ $Q = \dfrac{\omega_0 L}{r}$
Twin-T	$\omega_0 = \dfrac{1}{nRC}$	$\beta = \dfrac{1}{1 + j\dfrac{\omega/\omega_0}{1 - (\omega/\omega_0)^2}\dfrac{2(n^2+1)}{n}}$

From the fact that the phase shift through the network is 0 deg at the condition of balance $\omega = \omega_0$, it might appear that the output of a single-tube circuit may be coupled directly to its input through the network and a normal phase-reversing amplifier, as in Fig. 8-5 for the Wien bridge oscillator. As with the Wien bridge oscillator, this is not possible because the feedback factor is zero at balance, so that the feedback potential, and in fact the input to the amplifier, is zero. That is, the system is operating essentially as a rejection circuit at the balance frequency, rather than as a band-pass circuit. To effect the necessary inversion and the proper freedom from loading, the circuit of Fig. 8-9 may be used. In this circuit, the inversion is derived from the resistor combination R_3R_4, tube $T2$ serving principally to provide a low-impedance driving source. That is, the cathode of tube $T1$ is always at a higher a-c potential than the grid.

An alternative circuit in which the necessary inversion is derived from $T2$ is given in Fig. 8-10.

It is possible to view the foregoing circuits as well as the Wien bridge circuit of Fig. 8-7 as circuits which provide two potentials to the input of tube $T1$, one of which is of such phase as to constitute regenerative feedback, and thereby increase the gain over that in the absence of feedback, while the other introduces degenerative feedback. The resultant

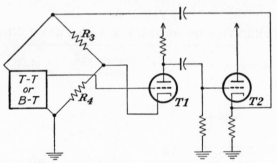

Fig. 8-9. The bridged-T and twin-T oscillator.

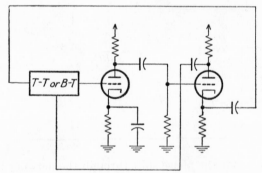

Fig. 8-10. Alternative bridged-T and twin-T oscillator circuit.

magnitudes of the two feedback potentials as a function of frequency are such that degeneration occurs at all frequencies except for a small range in the neighborhood of the frequency of oscillation. It is only at these frequencies that oscillation will occur.

From practical considerations, the Wien bridge oscillator is preferred over the other circuits, because of the ease of frequency control and variation, and because fewer variable circuit elements are required for control.

8-7. Negative-resistance Oscillators. One may interpret the foregoing analyses of feedback oscillators as a demonstration of the fact that it is possible to devise circuits containing vacuum tubes in which the power generated is sufficient to overcome the losses of the circuit and also to provide the power that is transferred to an external circuit. If the total loading or dissipation within the circuit is represented by a certain equivalent resistance in the plate circuit, then the tube may be represented as a negative resistance of such a magnitude as just to overcome the total dissipative terms. The oscillations in the circuit will then be sustained at the stable level required by the variations of the negative-resistance properties of the circuit.

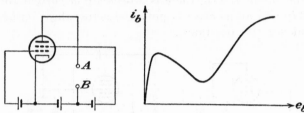

FIG. 8-11. A negative-resistance tetrode circuit, and the plate characteristics, showing the region of negative plate resistance.

If one is able to find a device that actually possesses a negative resistance, i.e., a device in which a positive increment of current through it is accompanied by a negative-potential increment across it, then this can be used to neutralize the positive resistance representing the total dissipation. Such negative-resistance devices do exist, the simple tetrode operating with a plate potential below that of the screen being a common example. The connections of such a device and the plate characteristics which show the region of negative plate resistance are shown in Fig. 8-11.

A circuit that exhibits an effective negative resistance and at the same time avoids the objectionable features of secondary emission is illustrated in Fig. 8-12. A pentode is operated with a plate potential that is lower than the

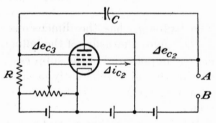

FIG. 8-12. A pentode circuit that exhibits a negative output resistance.

screen potential, and the suppressor grid is maintained slightly negative relative to the cathode. Since the plate is at a low positive potential, it does not exert much force on the electrons and under these conditions the suppressor grid repels most of the electrons that manage to get past the screen grid, with a resulting higher screen current.

If the suppressor potential is increased slightly, i.e., is made less negative, then there will be less repelling action by the suppressor and more plate current will flow at the expense of the screen current. The electrons that were previously being repelled by the suppressor and returned to the screen will now pass to the plate, with a consequent reduced screen current. Note that even if the screen potential is increased by the same potential as that applied to the suppressor grid the net effect is still a reduction of the screen-grid current. That is, if the screen current were to increase somewhat with the increase of screen potential, the decrease in screen current owing to the action of the suppressor grid is so much greater that the net effect is a reduction of the screen current. Therefore, with the circuit shown, there is a decrease of current through the terminals AB with an increase in potential across these terminals, with a consequent negative resistance.

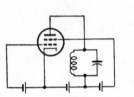 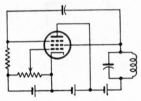

Fig. 8-13. A negative-resistance, or dynatron, and a negative-transconductance, or transitron, oscillator.

To analyze the circuit analytically,[5] it is assumed that the change in screen current is a linear function of the changes in the suppressor-grid and screen-grid potentials and also that the suppressor-grid current is negligible. That is, it is assumed that

$$\Delta i_{c2} = g_{32} \, \Delta e_{c3} - \frac{\Delta e_{c2}}{r_{g2}}$$

The factor g_{32} has the dimensions of a conductance and is such that $g_{32} \, \Delta e_{c3}$ gives a measure of the influence of a change in current i_{c2} due to a change in potential of the suppressor grid. Note from the foregoing discussion that g_{32} is inherently negative since a positive Δe_{c3} is accompanied by a negative Δi_{c2}. The factor r_{g2} is a measure of the change in i_{c2} due to a change in e_{c2}.

If it is assumed that g_{32} and r_{g2} remain constant over the range of operation, and by noting that with a large C and R a change in potential Δe_{c2} appears on the suppressor as a change Δe_{c3}, then

$$\Delta i_{c2} = \left(g_{32} + \frac{1}{r_{g2}} \right) \Delta e_{c2}$$

The input resistance between points A and B is then

$$r \equiv \frac{\Delta e_{c2}}{\Delta i_{c2}} = \frac{r_{g2}}{1 + g_{32}r_{g2}} \tag{8-29}$$

which is negative when

$$-g_{32}r_{g2} > 1$$

To examine the operation of the circuit of such negative resistances as part of an oscillator, suppose that a tank circuit is coupled to the terminals AB of the two circuits shown in Fig. 8-13. These circuits may be drawn in the manner of Fig. 8-1. Since the feedback potential is zero, the circuit simplifies to that shown in Fig. 8-14. This may be drawn as a simple coupled circuit, in the form illustrated in Fig. 8-15.

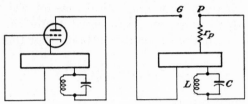

FIG. 8-14. The equivalent and simplified circuit of the negative-resistance oscillator.

To evaluate the characteristics of the circuit, apply Kirchhoff's law to the two-loop network. This yields

$$\left(r_p + \frac{1}{Cp}\right) i_1 - \frac{1}{Cp} i_2 = 0$$

$$-\frac{1}{Cp} i_1 + \left(R + Lp + \frac{1}{Cp}\right) i_2 = 0$$

(8-30)

To solve for i_2, the current through the inductance and load, the following differential equation must be evaluated:

$$\frac{d^2 i_2}{dt^2} + \left(\frac{R}{L} + \frac{1}{r_p C}\right) \frac{di_2}{dt} + \left(\frac{R + r_p}{r_p CL}\right) i_2 = 0 \qquad (8\text{-}31)$$

If it is assumed that r_p, which is inherently negative, remains substantially constant over the range of operation, this equation may be solved directly to give, for the oscillatory case,

$$i_2 = A e^{-\frac{1}{2}\left(\frac{R}{L} + \frac{1}{r_p C}\right)t} \sin (\omega t + \theta) \quad (8\text{-}32)$$

where A and θ are constants. The expression for i_1 has exactly the same form, although with different values for A and θ. The angular frequency of oscillation is

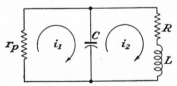

FIG. 8-15. The basic equivalent circuit of a negative-resistance oscillator.

$$\omega = \sqrt{\frac{R + r_p}{r_p LC} - \frac{1}{4}\left(\frac{R}{L} + \frac{1}{r_p C}\right)^2}$$

or

$$\omega = \sqrt{\frac{1}{LC} \frac{r_p + R}{r_p} - \frac{1}{4}\left(\frac{R}{L} + \frac{1}{r_p C}\right)^2} \qquad (8\text{-}33)$$

Under the assumed oscillatory conditions, the expression for i_2 indicates that the amplitude of the oscillations may decrease, remain constant, or increase, depending upon the exponential term in the expression. If the term $R/L + 1/r_pC$ is positive, then the oscillations which might have been started in any manner will ultimately fall to zero. If the quantity $R/L + 1/r_pC$ is negative, the oscillations will tend to increase in amplitude with time. For the critical case for which the quantity $R/L + 1/r_pC$ equals zero, the exponential factor is unity, and the amplitude of the oscillations remains constant. For this condition

$$r_p = - \frac{L}{RC} \tag{8-34}$$

and the corresponding frequency is

$$\omega = \sqrt{\frac{1}{LC}\left(1 + \frac{R}{r_p}\right)} = \sqrt{\frac{1}{LC}\left(1 - \frac{R^2C}{L}\right)} \tag{8-35}$$

Such negative-resistance oscillators are self-regulating in much the same manner as the normal feedback oscillators. Thus, owing to the variation of the negative-resistance characteristic of the tube circuit that is used, if the quantity $R/L + 1/r_pC$ were negative, thus allowing for continually increasing amplitude of oscillations, these oscillations would increase until the region of operation extended to the point where $r_p = -L/RC$, when the build-up condition would cease. These conditions are illustrated in Fig. 8-16. It should be noted from the diagram that even with an assumed sinusoidal output potential, and this is not a required condition, the output current will be nonsinusoidal.

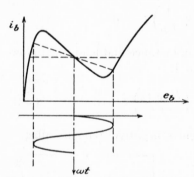

FIG. 8-16. The amplitude of oscillation increases until the value of r_p assumes the critical value L/RC.

8-8. Relaxation Oscillators. In addition to the feedback and negative-resistance oscillators that are discussed above, there is a class of oscillators that is known as *relaxation* oscillators. This type of oscillator, like the feedback oscillator, is provided with a feedback loop. However, in the case of the feedback oscillator, the amount of feedback is usually so adjusted that a substantially sinusoidal output potential results. In the relaxation circuits, the feedback potential is very large—so large, in fact, that the tube is driven beyond cutoff. The tube remains cut off for a time determined by the time constant of the elements in the grid circuit, after which the grid recovers control of the circuit. Because of this

ᵭperation, a seriously distorted output results.　But as such a distorted
ᵥave is rich in harmonics, it may be used as a harmonic source.　More
ᵭften, however, these devices provide waveshapes that possess direct
ᵢpplications.

Among the important relaxation oscillators are the multivibrator, a
ᵭevice that provides a sensibly square wave in the output, and the block-
ᵢng oscillator, a device that provides relatively narrow pulses.　The gen-
ᵭral character of the waveshapes at the output of these circuits is illus-
ᵗrated in Fig. 8-17.

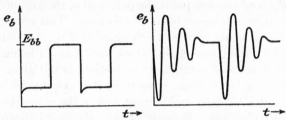

Fɪɢ. 8-17. The output-potential waveforms in the multivibrator and in the blocking
ᵭscillator.

Owing to the nonsinusoidal waveforms present in the circuit and the
ᶠact that cutoff exists for an appreciable portion of the cycle, the mathematical analysis of the general feedback circuit is no longer applicable to
a description of the operation of relaxation oscillators.　In fact, owing to
the cutoff that occurs, a substantially transient analysis must be made.
Details of the operation of several types of circuits will be given below.

8-9. Plate-coupled Multivibrator. The　multivibrator　was　first
described by Abraham and Bloch[6] in 1918.　The circuit is shown in
Fig. 8-18.　It will be observed
that this circuit is essentially that
of a simple two-stage resistance-
capacitance　coupled　amplifier,
with the output of the second
stage coupled through a capacitor
to the grid of the first tube.　Observe, in fact, that the circuit does
not differ too markedly from the
RC coupled oscillator illustrated

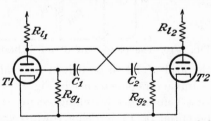

Fɪɢ. 8-18. A free-running plate-coupled
multivibrator.

in Fig. 8-5.　In this device any signal on the grid of the first stage will be
amplified by the two-stage RC amplifier, and the output signal is in phase
with the input signal on the grid of the first stage.　Because the output
of the second stage is of the proper polarity to reinforce the input signal,
positive feedback results and oscillations can take place.

The operation of the circuit is substantially the following: When the anode current in one of the tubes, say $T1$, is increasing because of a positive signal on the grid, a negative signal is being applied to the grid of the second tube $T2$. As a result, the current in $T2$ is reduced, and the output signal is positive. This positive signal, which is coupled back to $T1$, causes the grid of $T1$ to become more positive, thus increasing the anode current of $T1$ still further. This effect is cumulative—the current in $T1$ reaches a maximum, while the potential of the grid of $T2$ is driven so far negatively, almost instantaneously, that the current in $T2$ is cut off. With $T2$ still cut off, the charge on capacitor C_2 leaks away through the resistor R_{g2}, and at some point the potential of the grid of $T2$ becomes such that the tube will again begin to conduct. This results in a negative output signal being applied to the grid of $T1$. The current in $T1$ decreases, and a cumulative chain, which results in $T1$ being cut off and $T2$ reaching the state of maximum conduction, is initiated. Evidently there are two unstable limiting conditions that occur. In one of these $T1$ is cut off and $T2$ is fully conducting, and in the other the roles of $T1$ and $T2$ are interchanged. Because of this, the multivibrator has been called an *unstable* relaxation circuit.

8-10. Detailed Explanation of Operation.[7]　Consider the circuit from the instant when the cumulative action discussed above has just caused

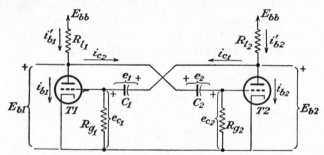

Fig. 8-19. The plate-coupled multivibrator, with potentials and currents labeled.

the grid of $T2$ to be driven beyond cutoff. The circuit of Fig. 8-18 is redrawn for convenience in Fig. 8-19 with potentials and currents labeled. Just before this switching occurs, tube $T2$ is conducting, and the grid potential of $T1$ is rising toward ground. The switching action occurs when the grid potential of $T1$ reaches the cutoff value E_{01}, a negative quantity. Thus just at the instant of switching, the potential across capacitor C_1 is $e_1(0-)$ and is given by

$$e_1(0-) = E_{b2} - E_{01} \qquad (8\text{-}36)$$

where E_{b2} is the potential across tube $T2$ when it is conducting.

When $T2$ is cut off, this tube is effectively removed from the action of the circuit and remains out of the circuit until its grid potential has recovered to the cutoff value E_{02}, when the tube will again begin to draw current.　During the cutoff period there will be no plate current through the plate resistor R_{l2}, and this plate will assume the potential of the B-supply source E_{bb}.　Hence, during the cutoff period of $T2$, the capacitor C_1 begins to charge toward E_{bb} from its initial value $e_1(0-) = e_1(0+)$. Since the charge on C_1 cannot change instantaneously, the sudden change in plate potential will appear on the grid of $T1$.　Thus $T1$ is caused to conduct strongly.　But as the grid of $T1$ becomes positive with respect to the cathode, grid current will flow.　Thus C_1 begins to charge toward

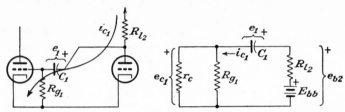

FIG. 8-20. The charging path, and the equivalent circuit for charging capacitor C_1.

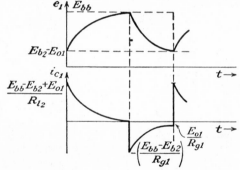

FIG. 8-21. The waveshapes of the current through and the potential across capacitor C_1 during its charging period.

E_{bb} through the path shown in Fig. 8-20.　In fact, since the resistance r_c of the internal grid-cathode path is smaller than the resistance R_{g1}, capacitor C_1 will charge mainly through this path.

　Since r_c of the internal grid-cathode path during conduction is small compared with R_{g1} and, in fact, is also small compared with R_{l2}, the charging time constant is approximately C_1R_{l2}.　During the charging process the potential e_1 across capacitor C_1 will vary between $E_{b2} - E_{01}$ and E_{bb}.　The potential and current variations have the forms illustrated in Fig. 8-21 and are governed approximately by the equations

$$e_1 \doteq E_{bb} - (E_{bb} - E_{b2} + E_{01})e^{-t/R_{l2}C_1} \tag{8-37}$$

and

$$i_{C1} \doteq \frac{E_{bb} - E_{b2} + E_{01}}{R_{l2}} e^{-t/R_{l2}C_1} \tag{8-38}$$

The process illustrated in Fig. 8-21 continues in the manner shown until the switching action occurs. At this time $T1$ stops conducting, and

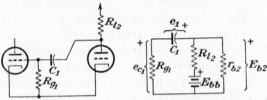

Fig. 8-22. The discharge path, and the equivalent circuit for the discharge of capacitor C_1.

$T2$ begins to conduct. The discharge path of C_1 and the equivalent electrical circuit are given in Fig. 8-22. At the instant that discharge of C_1 begins, the potential across C_1 is essentially E_{bb}. C_1 begins to discharge toward E_{b2} in the circuit shown. But in this circuit R_{l2} is shunted by r_{b2}, the beam resistance of the tube. Ordinarily r_{b2} is small compared with R_{g1}, and the controlling equations for the current and potential are approximately

$$e_1 \doteq E_{b2} + (E_{bb} - E_{b2})e^{-t/R_{g1}C_1} \tag{8-39}$$

and

$$i_{C1} \doteq -\frac{E_{bb} - E_{b2}}{R_{g1}} e^{-t/R_{g1}C_1} \tag{8-40}$$

Clearly, the current builds up toward zero until it reaches the value E_{01}/R_{g1}, at which time the potential on the grid of $T1$ is E_{01} and the cumulative action once again occurs. The cycle of operation is thus completed, and the circuit is ready to repeat its cycle.

The waveforms of the potentials and currents at various points of the circuit are given in Fig. 8-23. The corresponding results for the second tube are of the same form, but will be shifted T_1 sec along the time axis.

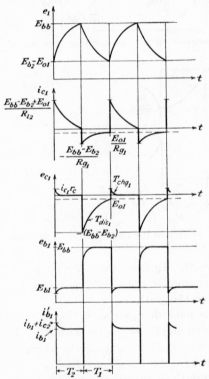

Fig. 8-23. The potential and current waveforms at various points in a symmetrical multivibrator.

8-11. Frequency of Oscillation. The period of oscillation of the multivibrator is readily found. It follows from Eq. (8-40), since $T1$ is off for the time required for e_{c1} to increase from $-(E_{bb} - E_{b2})$ to E_{01} along the exponential curve, that

$$E_{01} = -(E_{bb} - E_{b2})e^{-T_1/R_{g1}C_1}$$

from which

$$T_1 = R_{g1}C_1 \log_e \frac{E_{bb} - E_{b2}}{-E_{01}} \tag{8-41}$$

Similarly, for $T2$, the results are

$$T_2 = R_{g2}C_2 \log_e \frac{E_{bb} - E_{b1}}{-E_{02}} \tag{8-42}$$

The period of the complete oscillation, neglecting the switching time, is

$$T = T_1 + T_2 = R_{g1}C_1 \log_e \frac{E_{bb} - E_{b2}}{-E_{01}} + R_{g2}C_2 \log_e \frac{E_{bb} - E_{b1}}{-E_{02}} \tag{8-43}$$

If the two tubes have identical characteristics, then

$$E_{b1} = E_{b2} = E_b$$
$$E_{01} = E_{02} = E_0$$

and Eq. (8-43) becomes

$$T = (R_{g1}C_1 + R_{g2}C_2) \log_e \frac{E_{bb} - E_b}{-E_0} \tag{8-44}$$

If, also,

$$R_{g1} = R_{g2} = R_g \qquad C_1 = C_2 = C$$

Eq. (8-44) reduces to

$$T = 2R_gC \log_e \frac{E_{bb} - E_b}{-E_0} \tag{8-45}$$

The expressions given by Eqs. (8-43) to (8-45) apply to multivibrators having a low repetition frequency, since they do not take stray capacitances into account. At the higher repetition frequencies, the following more precise equation should be employed instead of Eq. (8-43):[8]

$$T = (C_1 + C_{kg1})R_{g1} \log_e \left(\frac{E_{bb} - E_{b2}}{-E_{01}} \frac{C_1}{C_1 + C_{kg1}} \right)$$
$$+ (C_2 + C_{kg2})R_{g2} \log_e \left(\frac{E_{bb} - E_{b1}}{-E_{02}} \frac{C_2}{C_2 + C_{kg2}} \right) \tag{8-46}$$

This expression is also subject to limitations and should not be used for extremely high repetition frequencies, except perhaps as an approximation.

The choice of the plate resistance R_l is important, since the quantity $E_{bb} - E_b = I_bR_l$. A value of R_l exists which yields optimum frequency stability. To deduce this value, consider the fractional change in the period of the system. From Eq. (8-45)

$$dT = \frac{2R_gC \, d(-E_0)}{-E_0}$$

from which it follows that

$$\frac{dT}{T} = \frac{d(-E_0)}{(-E_0) \log_e \dfrac{E_{bb} - E_b}{-E_0}} \tag{8-47}$$

This expression may be minimized by optimizing the denominator. When this is done, there results

$$E_{bb} - E_b = 2.71(-E_0)$$

Thus for optimum frequency stability, the value of R_l is so chosen that during conduction

$$R_l = \frac{E_{bb} - E_b}{I_b} = \frac{2.71(-E_0)}{I_b} \tag{8-48}$$

An approximate value for the period of oscillation of the multivibrator is frequently found in the literature. If one assumes that the period is that determined only by the time constants of the discharge circuits of C_1 and C_2 without regard for the potential levels between which the discharges occur, the period of the oscillation is approximately

$$T \doteq C_1 R_{g1} + C_2 R_{g2} \tag{8-49}$$

This result is in error, of course, and frequently an empirical constant is used to give the frequency of operation. The frequency is given by

$$f \doteq \frac{1}{N(C_1 R_{g1} + C_2 R_{g2})} \tag{8-50}$$

where N, the correction factor given in Eq. (8-50), is about 2 for frequency operation below 500 cps and rises to about 4 at 10,000 cps.

8-12. Biased Multivibrators.[8] If the time duration of the output wave of a multivibrator is important, switching of the nonconducting tube,

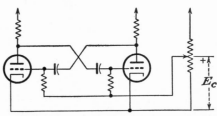

Fig. 8-24. A biased multivibrator to reduce the time jitter of the trailing edge.

which determines the trailing edge, is critical. Switching occurs when the exponential grid potential discharge curve intersects the tube cutoff curve. If this intersection is sharp, the time at which the trailing edge occurs is correspondingly well defined. If the intersection is gradual, the point of intersection will depend to a greater or lesser degree on the

variations of tube constants and potentials. To ensure a sharp intersection, it is usual to employ a positive bias on the tubes. Such a circuit is
illustrated in Fig. 8-24. The expression for the period of such a modified circuit becomes

$$T' = C_1 R_{g1} \log_e \frac{E_{bb} - E_{b2} + E_c}{-E_{01} + E_c} + C_2 R_{g2} \log_e \frac{E_{bb} - E_{b1} + E_c}{-E_{02} + E_c} \quad (8\text{-}51)$$

For normal operations it is found that the frequency of oscillation may
be varied over wide limits in an almost linear manner by controlling E_c.
The linearity between frequency of
oscillation and control potential E_c
can be improved by including resistors R_k in each cathode,[9] the
value of these being determined
experimentally.

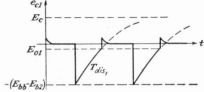

FIG. 8-25. Waveform of e_{c1} for the circuit of Fig. 8-24.

The effect of the application of
the positive bias is best illustrated
graphically, and Fig. 8-25 shows the
waveform e_{c1} on the grid of $T1$.
The equivalent circuits for the charging of C_1 and the discharging of C_2,
corresponding to those shown in Figs. 8-20 and 8-22, now become those
shown in Fig. 8-26.

If it is desired to operate the biased multivibrator at a fixed frequency,
E_c should be made as high as possible, e.g., equal to E_{bb}, for optimum fre-

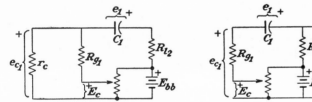

FIG. 8-26. Equivalent circuits for the charge and discharge of C_1 in Fig. 8-24.

quency stability. If the values of E_b and E_0 are negligible in comparison
with E_{bb}, the period then approximates to

$$T \doteq (C_1 R_{g1} + C_2 R_{g2}) \log_e 2 \quad (8\text{-}52)$$

If the positive bias is applied to a single tube only, as in the circuit of
Fig. 8-27, the expression for the period becomes

$$T = C_1 R_{g1} \log_e \frac{E_{bb} - E_{b2}}{-E_{01}} + C_2 R_{g2} \log_e \frac{2E_{bb} - E_{b1}}{E_{bb} - E_{02}} \quad (8\text{-}53)$$

This shows that the period has changed because the time required for the
grid recovery of $T2$ has been decreased, the recovery time for $T1$ remain-

ing unchanged. This means that the waveforms for the recovery of the two tubes are not of equal time duration, and an unsymmetrical or unbalanced condition results. Of course, an unsymmetrical waveform is

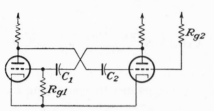

Fig. 8-27. Multivibrator with one grid returned to the plate-supply potential.

easily obtained with the previously discussed circuits by changing the grid-circuit time constants of one circuit and not of the other. However, one should not attempt to achieve a markedly unbalanced condition of time in the multivibrator, since, according to the above discussion, if the time constant C_2R_{g2} were made too different from C_1R_{g1}, the trailing edge of the long-time-constant tube might become unstable.

The waveform of e_{c2} of this circuit is given in Fig. 8-28. The equivalent circuits governing the charge and discharge of the capacitors are those of Fig. 8-26, with E_c in the discharge circuit replaced by E_{bb}.

8-13. Cathode-coupled Multivibrator. The circuit of a cathode-coupled multivibrator is given in Fig. 8-29. The operation of this circuit is somewhat different from the plate-coupled circuit of Fig. 8-18. To understand the action of

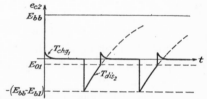

Fig. 8-28. Waveform of e_{c2} for the circuit of Fig. 8-27.

this circuit, suppose that it is initially without plate potential. There will be no charge on C, and the grids of both $T1$ and $T2$ will be at ground potential. When the supply potential is suddenly applied, both tubes will start to conduct and the plates of $T1$ and $T2$ will begin to fall in potential. But

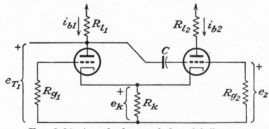

Fig. 8-29. A cathode-coupled multivibrator.

since the potential across C cannot change instantaneously, the drop in potential that takes place at the plate of $T1$ is coupled to the grid of $T2$, tending to cause $T2$ to cut off. This tendency is also accentuated by the tube currents which flow through the cathode resistor R_k, which raises the cathode potential of both tubes.   But, with the current i_{b2} tending to decrease, i_{b1} will increase, resulting in a larger negative potential to the grid of $T2$ and also a larger positive potential to the cathode of $T2$, and $T2$ will rapidly reach cutoff.

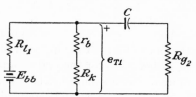

FIG. 8-30. The equivalent circuit for the discharge of C of Fig. 8-29.

$T2$ is held beyond cutoff during the time required for C to discharge along an exponential curve and reach the cutoff potential of the tube.   The equivalent circuit of the discharge is given in Fig. 8-30.   When this cutoff potential is reached, $T2$ will begin to conduct.   This current through R_k

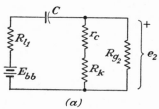
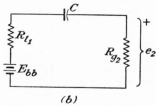

(a)   (b)

FIG. 8-31. The equivalent charging circuits of C (a) during the time that grid current is drawn, (b) for the remainder of the time interval.

will raise the cathode potential of $T1$, and the current i_{b1} will begin to decrease.   As a result, the plate potential of $T1$ will increase, resulting in a positive signal to the grid of $T2$, and the cumulative cycle will continue until $T1$ is cut off and $T2$ is conducting its maximum current.

The grid of $T2$ is driven highly positive, resulting in a large plate current, which causes the potential across R_k to rise quickly.   However, because grid current is drawn, the capacitor C charges relatively quickly for a time, until the potential e_2 and e_k are the same, and thereafter charging continues at a slower rate.   The equivalent charging circuits are shown in Fig. 8-31. As C charges, the bias on $T2$ decreases, causing i_{b2} to decrease. This in turn causes e_k to decrease.

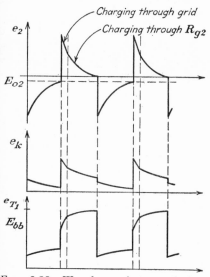

FIG. 8-32.   Waveforms in a cathode-coupled multivibrator.

The grid of $T1$ is held constant at ground potential so that this tube remains cut off as long as e_k is positive relative to ground by more than cutoff potential. When e_k drops to E_{01}, $T1$ begins to conduct and the cycle reverses.

The waveforms at several points in the circuit (see Fig. 8-32) illustrate the operation. A comparison of the waveform for e_{T1} in Fig. 8-32 with e_{b1} in Fig. 8-23 for the plate-coupled multivibrator shows the latter to be more nearly a square wave. As a result, the plate-coupled multivibrator is preferred, the cathode-coupled circuit seldom being used. Because of the lack of interest in the cathode-coupled circuit, and the fact that the analysis proves to be rather complex,* the mathematical analysis will not be given.

8-14. Pentodes in Multivibrator Circuits. One may use pentodes in a

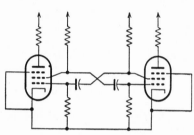

FIG. 8-33. An electron-coupled multivibrator.

multivibrator circuit, as illustrated in Fig. 8-33. It will be observed that the circuit is essentially a conventional plate-coupled multivibrator, the cathode, control grid, and screen grid serving as the triode for the switching action. Since the load resistors are connected to the anodes, which are shielded from the switching circuit by the suppressor grid, load changes will not materially affect the oscillatory circuit and the frequency is reasonably independent of the load.

8-15. Design Considerations. In addition to the choice of constants to yield the desired repetition frequency, a number of other factors must be considered in designing a multivibrator circuit. If the waveshape of the output is important, it is necessary to examine the factors which affect the steepness of the rapid shifts of potential. If a rapid rise of potential is desired, one may have to employ design factors that are common to the design of video amplifiers. Thus it is necessary to employ low values of plate resistance and to use tubes with low shunt capacitance. With reasonable care in the choice of these values, it is not difficult to design a multivibrator circuit which can reach its full rise of potential in 1 μsec, using low-current receiving types of tubes. If more rapid action is required, heavier-current tubes must be used. For example, the full rise may be obtained in 0.2 μsec, using a 6AG7 tube.

8-16. The Blocking Oscillator.[10] Suppose that the second stage of a free-running multivibrator is replaced by a transformer which is so connected that regenerative feedback results. Such a circuit has the properties that the tube can be made to conduct hard for a short period of

---

* A complete, though unpublished, analysis was worked out by W. R. LePage of the Department of Electrical Engineering, Syracuse University, in 1947.

time and then turn off for a relatively long interval before it again goes through its cycle. The circuit of such an oscillator is given in Fig. 8-34.

The operation of the circuit is substantially the following: Suppose that the grid is only slightly negative. The tube will conduct, and the potential of the anode will begin to fall. This changing potential, which appears across the transformer in the plate circuit, will be accompanied by a changing potential in the grid winding of the transformer. The phase of the transformer connection is such that the potential of the grid becomes positive, thus increasing the plate current. This is a regenerative action, which continues until the grid draws current, thus charging the capacitor C through r_c to a potential $\frac{1}{C} \int_0^\tau i_g \, dt$, where τ is the duration of the charging time, the current through R_g being assumed negligible. The charging ceases when the plate potential falls so low that the plate circuit can no longer drive the low impedance reflected from the grid circuit.

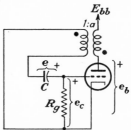

FIG. 8-34. A simple blocking oscillator.

At this time there is no longer any potential induced in the grid winding of the transformer, and the potential on C begins to discharge. The discharge of C causes the grid-cathode potential to decrease. This results in a decreasing plate current and hence a rising plate potential. The resulting potential in the grid winding causes the grid to go more negative, thus initiating the cumulative action that causes the tube to cut off. Now, however, with the tube cut off, the charge on the capacitor can leak off only through the grid resistor R_g, resulting in an exponential rise toward ground with a time constant approximately equal to $R_g C$. This rise continues until the grid potential reaches the cutoff potential of the tube, when the cycle will repeat itself.

The waveforms at various points in the circuit are shown in Fig. 8-35. This diagram shows oscillations of the waveforms after cutoff, which are superposed, in the case of e_c, on the exponential rise toward the normal zero bias. If such oscillations exist, and they would arise from the effective shunt capacitance which appears across the grid winding of the pulse transformer interacting with the winding inductance, they may be damped by connecting a resistor across the transformer winding. The resistance will ordinarily be determined experimentally to provide adequate damping without excessive loading.

The total repetition period of such a blocking oscillator is seen to be

$$T = \tau + R_g C \log_e \frac{E}{-E_0} \qquad (8\text{-}54)$$

where τ is the duration of the pulse and E is the potential to which the capacitor is charged during the pulse. However, because of the difficulty of calculating the potential E to which C is charged, this potential depending on the relation between C and the effective magnetizing inductance of

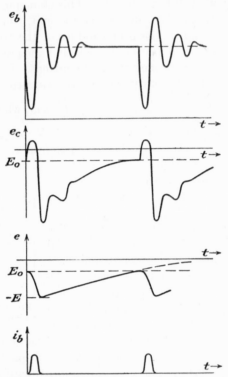

Fig. 8-35. The waveforms in a single-swing blocking oscillator.

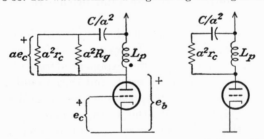

Fig. 8-36. A rough equivalent of the blocking oscillator during grid conduction, and its approximation with $R_g \gg r_c$.

the pulse transformer, this expression does not provide much useful information.

An approximate calculation is possible which gives a rough idea of the pulse duration. In this calculation, it will be assumed that the grid loading due to grid conduction acts continuously over the full half cycle. That is, a linear circuit is assumed. Also, the pulse duration will be taken as one-half cycle long. Under these assumptions, the circuit of Fig. 8-34 becomes, when referred to the plate circuit, that illustrated in Fig. 8-36. By straightforward circuit analysis, the resonant frequency is

$$f = \frac{a}{2\pi \sqrt{LC - a^2 r_c^2 C^2}}$$

whence, for the half cycle,

$$\tau = \frac{\pi \sqrt{LC - a^2 r_c^2 C'^2}}{a} \qquad (8\text{-}55)$$

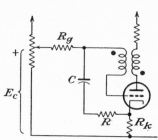

This shows that the length of the conducting period τ depends upon the capacitance C and upon the characteristics of the transformer.

FIG. 8-37. A biased blocking oscillator.

The transformer in the circuit may be connected in a number of ways. Thus, in addition to the connection of Fig. 8-34, the transformer windings can be in the grid and cathode lines and also in the plate and cathode lines (see Prob. 8-27).

Precisely the same considerations concerning the possibility of jitter of the trailing edge of the output pulse applies for the blocking oscillator as for the multivibrator, and the biased blocking oscillator achieves the same results in the same way as the biased multivibrator. Consequently, if the jitter is to be kept to a minimum, a biased blocking oscillator should be used. The diagram of such a circuit is given in Fig. 8-37. The recurrence period of this device will be given by the expression

$$T = \tau + RC \log_e \frac{E_c + E}{E_c - E_0} \qquad (8\text{-}56)$$

It is of interest to note from Eq. (8-55) for τ that, for a given transformer, C is the most important circuit element in determining τ, larger values of C being accompanied by longer pulses. For example, a certain transformer, when used in the circuit of Fig. 8-37, yielded pulses which could be varied from approximately 0.2 to 20 μsec by changing the size of the capacitance C.

Some measure of control of the amplitude is possible by controlling the plate supply potential. In the case when a pentode is used instead of a triode, with the cathode, control grid, and screen grid serving as the essential triode elements for the blocking action, the output being essentially electron-coupled to the plate, amplitude control is possible also by adjusting the negative potential to the suppressor grid.

8-17. Van der Pol Relaxation Oscillator. One of the earliest forms of single-tube relaxation oscillators was described by van der Pol in 1926.[11]

The circuit of such an oscillator is given in Fig. 8-38.   It consists of a tetrode in which the control grid and the screen grid are capacitively coupled, the control grid being maintained positive by means of a high resistance coupling to E_{bb}.   However, since these oscillators ordinarily incorporate a pentode rather than a tetrode, the pentode-type oscillator will be discussed here.

The circuit of the pentode-type relaxation oscillator is given in Fig. 8-39.   This circuit depends for its operation on the fact that a change of

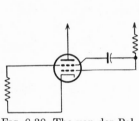

Fig. 8-38. The van der Pol oscillator.

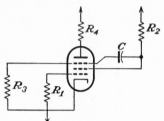

Fig. 8-39. A pentode van der Pol relaxation oscillator.

potential on the suppressor grid is accompanied by an amplified change of potential without phase reversal on the screen grid.   To see that this is so, consider for the moment that capacitor C is removed, and suppose that the tube is in a quiescent state.   The situation is then as illustrated in Fig. 8-40.   Suppose that a negative signal is applied to the suppressor grid of such amplitude that the anode current is interrupted.   As a result, the total space current will be collected by the screen grid, with a consequent decrease in screen potential, owing to the screen resistor.   In fact, if it is considered that the control-grid potential establishes the total space current, the effect of a signal on the suppressor grid is to control, in a nonlinear manner, the division of the space current between the anode and the screen grid, although a more positive suppressor grid results in a decreased screen current and hence a more positive screen-grid potential.   That is, the suppressor-signal and the screen-potential variations are in the same phase.   Thus, if the gain of the cir-

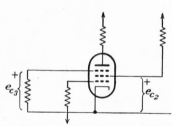

Fig. 8-40. Illustration of the principle of operation of the pentode type of van der Pol relaxation oscillator.

cuit is greater than unity and if feedback is arranged between the output circuit (the screen) and the input circuit (the suppressor), the device becomes an oscillator and is almost equivalent to a multivibrator.   It will be shown in Chap. 15 that transistor multivibrators are rather similar to the van der Pol relaxation oscillator.

Refer now to the circuit of Fig. 8-39, and suppose that, at the instant that the suppressor is positive, the anode is drawing current. As a result, he anode potential is falling, and the screen potential is rising, owing to he reduced screen current. The rising screen potential, which is coupled to the suppressor through the capacitor C, is accompanied by a rising suppressor-grid potential, since the capacitor potential cannot change instantaneously. This is a cumulative action that continues until the maximum current is drawn by the anode. When this condition is reached, a charging current immediately starts flowing into the capacitor through the combination of R_2 in parallel with the screen-cathode

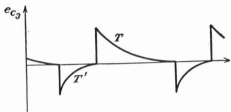

FIG. 8-41. Typical waveform of the suppressor potential in a pentode van der Pol relaxation oscillator.

path resistance and the combination of R_3 in parallel with the suppressor-cathode path resistance, assuming that a suppressor-grid current flows. As the potential across the capacitor rises, the suppressor potential falls. This results in a falling screen potential, and at a critical value the anode current begins to fall, with a resulting increase in screen current. This causes a cumulative effect which continues rapidly until the anode current is cut off and maximum current flows in the screen circuit. The capacitor charging current now flows through R_3 and the combination of R_2 in parallel with the screen-cathode path resistance, and the potential of the suppressor begins to rise. This brings the action to the point at which the considerations began, and the cycle repeats.

A typical waveform of the suppressor potential is given in Fig. 8-41. The wave is unsymmetrical because during one portion of the cycle the time constant T is given by $C\left(R_3 + \dfrac{R_2 r_2}{R_2 + r_2}\right)$, where r_2 is the average screen-cathode resistance; and during the second portion of the cycle the time constant T' is given by $C\left(\dfrac{R_2 r_3'}{R_3 + r_3'} + \dfrac{R_2 r_2'}{R_2 + r_2'}\right)$, where r_2' and r_3' are the average screen-cathode and the average suppressor-cathode resistances during this part of the cycle. Evidently, the larger that C and R_2 are made, the lower is the frequency of oscillation.

8-18. Synchronized Relaxation Oscillators. Synchronization in multivibrators may be of two general classes according to the character of the operation. The lightly synchronized multivibrator is free-running, and its frequency is "corrected" by the application of a synchronizing potential. The heavily synchronized multivibrator operates with one or both tubes so heavily biased that the circuit is inactive until a comparatively strong synchronizing or triggering potential is applied. Furthermore, the presence of the heavy bias causes the circuit to come to rest after it has passed through one complete cycle. Such circuits are frequently referred to as *gate, one-shot, monostable relaxation*, or *univibrator* circuits. Only the lightly synchronized multivibrators will be discussed here, Chap. 9 being devoted to a study of gate circuits, among others.

In the lightly synchronized multivibrator, the inherent poor frequency stability of the system is overcome by "driving" the multivibrator with a synchronizing potential. This forces the period of the multivibrator to be exactly the same period as the synchronizing frequency or a multiple or submultiple of it. The synchronizing waveform may be of almost any shape, although a pulse or a sine-wave potential is generally used.

Actually the discussion to follow applies for any of the free-running relaxation oscillators and is not confined to multivibrator circuits.

8-19. Synchronization by Positive Pulses. Figure 8-42 illustrates the effect of applying positive pulses to one grid of a free-running multivibrator. This diagram shows the conditions before synchronization occurs

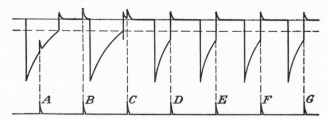

Fig. 8-42. Synchronizing a multivibrator with positive pulses.

and the transition stages until synchronization becomes complete. Note that the pulse A has no effect because it does not raise the grid recovery potential above the cutoff potential of the tube and that pulses B and C have no effect because they are applied to the grid of the conducting tube and grid clipping occurs. Pulse D is of sufficient amplitude to raise the grid above the cutoff potential, and as a result the tubes are switched as the current begins to flow in the tube that was formerly cut off.

Suppose that the frequency of the triggering pulses is considerably higher than the natural frequency of the multivibrator. The situation is then as illustrated in Fig. 8-43. Thus, if trigger A causes the multivibrator to switch, triggers B and C occur at times when the tube is conducting. Since the grid is already positive, these pulses have no effect on the conduction. Triggers D, E, F are applied to the nonconducting

tube, but they are not large enough to cause conduction.   Trigger G does
carry the grid potential above the cutoff point of the tube, and conduction
occurs.   In this example, every sixth pulse switches the multivibrator,
and hence the repetition frequency of the multivibrator is one-sixth of
the frequency of the triggering pulses.

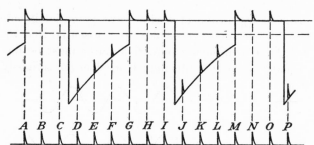

FIG. 8-43. Synchronization with pulses of higher frequency than the natural period
of the multivibrator.

In multivibrators, if accurate frequency division is desired, the division
per stage should be relatively low, say 10 or less.   If accurate division is
not required, a single stage may be used for a division of 100 or more.
Also, for best results, the peak of one pulse should rise above the base of
the next pulse on the grid recovery curve by about 20 per cent of its
height.

8-20. Sine-wave Synchronization.   The condition when a sine wave
is used for synchronization is not unlike that for synchronization by

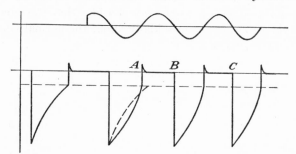

FIG. 8-44. Synchronization with sine-wave potential.

pulses, although the addition of a sine-wave synchronizing potential to
the grid recovery does change the grid-potential waveform, somewhat as
shown in Fig. 8-44.

The operation of the circuit is substantially the following: When $T1$ is
conducting during the time from A to B, grid limiting occurs and the
potential e_{c1} remains substantially constant.   When the synchronizing
potential falls below zero and starts to decrease the potential on the

grid, the multivibrator regenerative action causes $T1$ to cut off. As this occurs at the same point B, C, D, . . . in each cycle of the synchronizing potential, the multivibrator is forced to operate at the synchronizing frequency. Evidently, however, this action exists only when the synchronizing frequency is higher than the natural frequency of the multivibrator.

Synchronization by means of a sine-wave potential injected in the cathode circuit of one tube is possible. It is essential that the internal impedance of the synchronizing potential source must be low in order that the tube current through this impedance does not seriously alter the

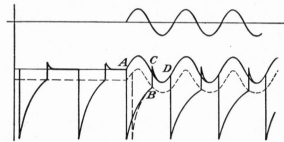

Fig. 8-45. Waveforms of a multivibrator synchronized by a sine wave in the cathode circuit.

shape of the wave. The operation of such a synchronized circuit is illustrated graphically in Fig. 8-45. If one supposes that the grid-ground potential is not affected by the presence of the sine-wave synchronizing potential but that the grid-cathode potential contains this sinusoidal component of potential, then one may consider that the effective cutoff potential of the tube varies sinusoidally about the normal value in phase with the synchronizing potential.

At the instant when the synchronizing potential is suddenly applied at point A, it is supposed that $T1$ is conducting. The synchronizing potential causes the cathode to rise, so that conduction of $T1$ is decreased. This leads to the regenerative action, and the tube is quickly cut off. This switching action will cause the tube to stop conducting at a time earlier than would be the case for the unsynchronized multivibrator. The potential e_{c1} will follow its normal exponential curve until it intersects the cutoff curve, which has the assumed sinusoidal form, and switching takes place at the point B. If it is assumed that during conduction the grid-cathode potential remains constant at some small positive value, which is given, in fact, by $i_g r_c$, the presence of added negative potential on the cathode will cause grid potential to follow the cathode potential and the potential follows the curve CD. When the cathode potential begins to rise, conduction in $T1$ is decreased and the regenerative action again takes place.

8-21. Synchronization of Blocking Oscillators. Blocking oscillators nay be synchronized with either sine waves or pulses applied to the grid, n much the same manner as for synchronizing multivibrators. For example, Fig. 8-46 illustrates the grid-potential waveform of a six-count livider. As for the multivibrator synchronization, the trigger heights should be such that the peak of one pulse rises above the base of the next pulse by about 20 per cent of its height. A smaller trigger might

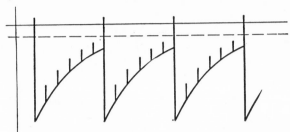

Fɪɢ. 8-46. A grid-potential waveform of a blocking oscillator synchronized with positive pulses.

allow the divider to fire unsynchronously between triggers. An excessively large trigger may introduce instability due to variations in trigger heights. Also, for accurate frequency division with a blocking oscillator, as for the multivibrator, the division per stage should be relatively low, also 10 or less.

REFERENCES

1. Seely, S., "Electron-tube Circuits," chap. 12, McGraw-Hill Book Company, Inc., New York, 1950.
2. Ginzton, E. L., and L. M. Hollingsworth, *Proc. IRE*, **29**, 43 (1941).
3. Terman, F. E., R. R. Buss, W. R. Hewlett, and F. C. Cahill, *Proc. IRE*, **24**, 649 (1939).
4. Sulzer, P. G., *Electronics*, **23**, 88 (September, 1950).
5. Herold, E. W., *Proc. IRE*, **23**, 1201 (1935).
6. Abraham, H., and E. Bloch, *Ministère guerre Pub.* 27 (April, 1918).
   Abraham, H., and E. Bloch, *Ann. Physik*, **12**, 237 (1919).
7. Vecchiacchi, F., *Alta frequenza*, **9**, 745 (1940).
8. Puckle, O. S., "Time Bases," 2d ed., John Wiley & Sons, Inc., New York, 1951.
9. Bertram, S., *Proc. IRE*, **36**, 277 (1948).
10. Benjamin, R., *J. IEE*, **93**, 1159 (1946).
    "Electron Circuits and Tubes," pp. 804–809, Cruft Laboratory, War Training Staff, McGraw-Hill Book Company, Inc., New York, 1947.
11. van der Pol, B., *Phil. Mag.*, **2**, 978 (1926).
12. As general references, see:
    Reich, H. J., "Theory and Application of Electron Tubes," 2d ed., McGraw-Hill Book Company, Inc., New York, 1944.
    Reintjes, J. F., and G. T. Coate, "Principles of Radar," 3d ed., Massachusetts Institute of Technology Radar School Staff, McGraw-Hill Book Company, Inc., New York, 1953.

Barkhausen, H., "Lehrbuch der Elektronenrohren," vol. III, S. Hirzel, Verlag, Leipzig, 1935.

Edson, W. A., "Vacuum Tube Oscillators," John Wiley & Sons, Inc., New York, 1953.

Von Tersch, L. W., and A. W. Swago, "Recurrent Electric Transients," Prentice-Hall, Inc., New York, 1953.

PROBLEMS

8-1. The circuits of the Hartley and the Colpitts oscillators are shown. Show

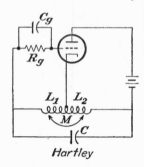

Hartley

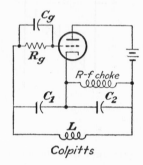

Colpitts

that the frequency of oscillation and the relation among the circuit parameters which specify the amplitude conditions are

Hartley:

$$\omega = \sqrt{\frac{1 + R_2/r_p}{C(L_1 + L_2 + 2M)}} \qquad g_m \doteq \frac{C(R_1 + R_2)(L_1 + L_2 + 2M)}{(L_1 + M)(L_2 + M)}$$

Colpitts:

$$\omega = \sqrt{\frac{1}{L}\left(\frac{1}{C_1} + \frac{1}{C_2} + \frac{R}{r_p C_2}\right)} \qquad g_m \doteq \frac{\mu R(C_1 + C_2)}{L(\mu - C_1/C_2)}$$

8-2. Two identical triodes are connected in a Franklin oscillator. Determine in terms of the circuit parameters:

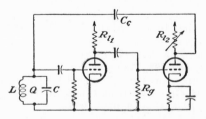

a. The expression for the critical value of the resistance R_{l2} at which oscillations will just begin.

b. The frequency of oscillation.

Assume that the power absorbed in the tuned circuit, which determines its Q, may be represented as that absorbed in a resistance in shunt with the inductance and capacitance.

8-3. Two identical triodes are connected in the oscillator circuit shown. Determine:

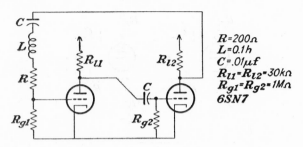

$$R=200\Omega$$
$$L=0.1h$$
$$C=.01\mu f$$
$$R_{l1}=R_{l2}=30k\Omega$$
$$R_{g1}=R_{g2}=1M\Omega$$
$$6SN7$$

a. Resonant frequency ω_0.

b. Minimum values of g_m, assuming that the tubes are being operated under identical conditions, for oscillations to be maintained.

8-4. Obtain an expression for the operating frequency of the cathode-coupled oscillator shown in the diagram.*

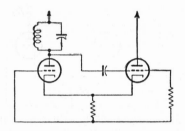

8-5. Refer to the tuned plate oscillator of Sec. 8-3. Neglect grid loading, and evaluate the frequency stability S_f at the value of ω_0 where $\theta = \pi/2$. Express the final results to show the dependence on the Q of the resonant circuit.

8-6. Deduce an expression for the frequency stability S_f of the phase-shift oscillator of Sec. 8-4.

8-7. Evaluate S_f at the resonant value of a twin-T oscillator. Neglect grid loading.

8-8. Consider the coupling network illustrated which is for use in a phase-shift oscillator.

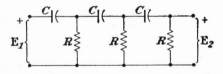

a. Derive an expression for the transfer function β of this network.

b. Determine the frequency ω_0 at which the total phase shift through the network is π.

c. Evaluate the expression of β at ω_0.

d. Determine the input or driving point impedance at $\omega = \omega_0$.

* M. G. Crosby, *Electronics*, **19**, 136 (May, 1946).

8-9. Consider the phase-shift oscillator given in the accompanying diagram.

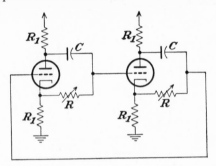

a. Evaluate the frequency of oscillation of this circuit.

b. Find the relationship among parameters for which the amplitude is independent of the frequency of oscillation.

8-10. A cathode-coupled Wien bridge oscillator is shown in the diagram

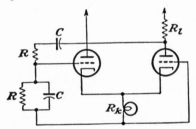

Determine the critical value of R_l at which oscillations will just start.

8-11. The Meacham bridge-stabilized oscillator* is illustrated.   Here R_4 is a

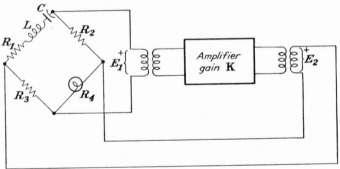

resistor, the resistance of which varies with the amplitude of oscillation, although the thermal capacity is sufficiently large so that the temperature remains substantially constant over the cycle of oscillation.

a. Suppose that the gain of the amplifier has the form $\mathbf{K} = K_0(1 + j\delta)$ in the immediate neighborhood of ω_0.   Derive an expression for S_f.

b. If $Q = 10^5$ of the resonant circuit (this is possible with a crystal), $K_0 = 100$, $\delta = 0.1$, calculate S_f.

* L. A. Meacham, *Proc. IRE*, **26**, 1278 (1938).

c. Calculate the frequency shift $\Delta f/f_0$ due to a 0.1-rad variation in the phase angle of the amplifier.

8-12. Piezoelectric crystals, which may be represented by an equivalent electrical circuit as shown in the accompanying diagram, where C_m represents the capacitance of the crystal and its mounting when it is not oscillating and the

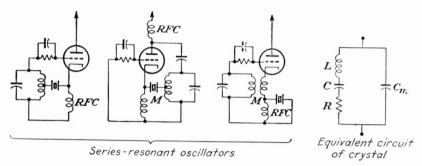

Series-resonant oscillators   Equivalent circuit of crystal

series combination L, C, and R represents the electrical equivalent of the vibrational characteristics of the material, may be used in so-called series resonant crystal-controlled oscillators.* Discuss the operating features of the oscillators illustrated.

8-13. Discuss the operation of the Pierce oscillator illustrated. Observe that the crystal is the only resonant element in the circuit.

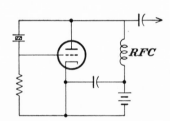

8-14. The plate characteristic of a type 24A tube connected as a tetrode is

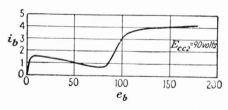

given in the figure. The d-c potential E_{bb} is adjusted to 45 volts. A parallel resonant circuit tuned to 1 Mc is used, with $C = 250\ \mu\mu f$.

a. Determine the minimum value of R for which oscillations will be sustained.

b. Plot the oscillation amplitude as a function of R.

c. Plot the current waveshape for maximum oscillation amplitude.

* F. Butler, *Wireless Engr.*, **23,** 157 (1946).

8-15. Discuss the operation of the negative-differential-transconductance

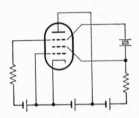
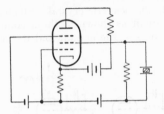

crystal-controlled oscillators* illustrated. Note that here, as for the Pierce oscillator, the crystal is the only resonant element in the circuit.

8-16. Discuss the operation of the transitron oscillators illustrated.

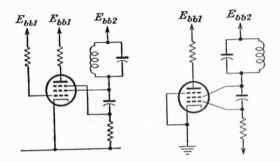

8-17. Consider the two-tube oscillator circuit shown. Show that for $R_l > r_p$ and $R_c + R_g > R_l$ the apparent resistance between terminals AB may be nega-

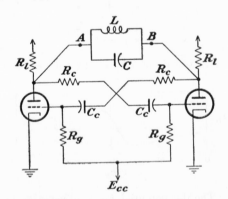

tive. (It will be noted that the circuit shown, with the tank circuit absent, is the simple plate-coupled multivibrator. In the case of the multivibrator the operation occurs over such extreme ranges that the analysis is a transient one, and not the class A operation of the circuit shown.)

---

* S. Bernstein, *Electronics*, **26**, 198 (February, 1953).

8-18. A modification* of the plate-coupled multivibrator is illustrated in the

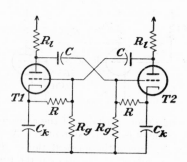

diagram.   Discuss the operation of this circuit, including sketches of the plate, grid, and cathode waveforms.

8-19. A modified† direct-coupled multivibrator is illustrated.   Describe its

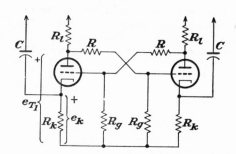

operation, including sketches of the plate and cathode waveforms.

8-20. Consider the biased multivibrator of Fig. 8-24, with $C_1 = C_2 = C$, $R_{g1} = R_{g2} = R_g$, and $R_{l1} = R_{l2} = R_l$.   Show that the frequency stability depends on the value of E_c.   Find the value which yields the optimum frequency stability. Assume $-E_0 < E_c$, and plot the variation of T as a function of $(E_{bb} - E_b)/E_c$. Show that the choice $E_c = E_{bb}$ yields nearly optimum results.

Note: In the following problems, if necessary, assume that r_c for each tube is 500 ohms.   If it is necessary to determine the value of r_b when $e_c = 0$, refer to the plate characteristics of the tube.   The cutoff grid potential of each tube may also be obtained from the plate characteristics.

8-21. Determine the frequency of oscillation of a plate-coupled multivibrator using 6J5 tubes for which

$$R_{g1} = R_{g2} = 500 \text{ kilohms} \qquad C_1 = C_2 = 0.01 \ \mu\text{f} \qquad R_{l1} = R_{l2} = 30 \text{ kilohms}$$
$$E_{bb} = 300 \text{ volts}$$

8-22. Repeat Prob. 8-21 when the grids are returned to a positive supply. Plot the frequency as E_{cc} is varied from 0 to E_{bb}.

---

* S. Chang and Yao-I Chu, *Electronic Eng.*, **24**, 270 (1952).
† S. Chang and Chu-I Chang, *Electronic Eng.*, **21**, 102 (1949).

8-23. Given the biased multivibrator shown in the diagram.

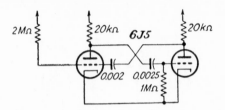

a. Calculate the discharge time constants of the capacitors.

b. Calculate the peak value of each grid potential. Assume the grid potential of the conducting tube to be zero in these calculations. $E_{bb} = 300$ volts.

c. Calculate the cutoff periods of each section of the tube.

d. Calculate the repetition frequency of the multivibrator.

8-24. Design a free-running balanced multivibrator to operate at 1,000 cps. Assume the following: $R_l = 10$ kilohms; $R_g = 500$ kilohms; 6J5 tubes; $E_{bb} = 200$ volts.

8-25. Design a free-running unbalanced multivibrator to operate at 5,000 cps, with one half cycle three times as long as the other. Use $R_g = 500$ kilohms, $R_l = 10$ kilohms, 6J5 tubes, and $E_{bb} = 250$ volts.

8-26. A pulse transformer having the following parameters:

$$\text{Primary inductance} = 5.5 \text{ mh}$$
$$\text{Primary resistance} = 17.2 \text{ ohms}$$
$$\text{Secondary resistance} = 38.7 \text{ ohms}$$
$$\text{Turns ratio} = 1:1.2$$

is used in the circuit shown. Estimate:

a. The time duration of the pulse.

b. The recurrence period of the blocking-oscillator circuit.

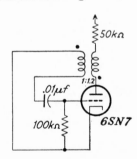

8-27. Sketch blocking-oscillator circuits with the transformer windings in:

a. Grid and cathode circuits.

b. Plate and cathode circuits.

Be sure to indicate the transformer-winding directions with appropriately placed dots.

8-28. Discuss the operation of the tetrode relaxation oscillator shown in the figure.*

* D. H. Black, *Elec. Commun.*, **18**, 50 (1939).

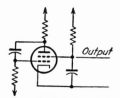

8-29. A balanced multivibrator is operated at 1,000 cps. The constants are those of Prob. 8-21 except for the values of C_1 and C_2. It is to be synchronized by injecting a positive pulse on the grid. What must be the amplitude of the synchronizing pulse if the frequency is 1,100 cps?

8-30. Repeat Prob. 8-29 if the pulse recurrence frequency is 5,600 cps.

8-31. Sketch a curve of the grid potential of one tube of a balanced multivibrator that is being synchronized by a sine-wave potential injected in the grid circuit. The synchronizing potential is in the frequency ratio of 5:1 with the multivibrator frequency.

8-32. Discuss the possibility of synchronizing a multivibrator with a positive pulse, the recurrence frequency of which is a submultiple of the free-running frequency of the multivibrator.

CHAPTER 9

HEAVILY BIASED RELAXATION CIRCUITS

There are two important classes of heavily biased relaxation circuits. One type is known as *gate, one-shot, monostable relaxation,* or *univibrator* circuits; the other general class is known as *trigger, bistable relaxation,* or *flip-flop* circuits. The gate circuit operates with one or both tubes so heavily biased that the circuit is inactive until a comparatively strong triggering or synchronizing potential is applied. This strong signal causes the circuit to change from its stable limiting condition to an unstable limiting state; and after a definite time interval that is determined by the circuit parameters, the circuit returns to the stable state, where it will remain until it is again triggered. The trigger, or flip-flop, circuit is quite like the gate circuit except that for fixed values of applied potential there are two stable conditions of equilibrium. The currents and potentials in such circuits can be made to change abruptly from one set of stable values to a second set of stable values, or back again, although independent disturbances are required for each switching action.

9-1. A-C Coupled Gate. Refer to the diagram of Fig. 9-1, which is essentially a multivibrator of the conventional plate-coupled type, but

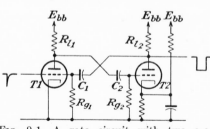

FIG. 9-1. A gate circuit with two a-c couplings.

with one tube biased to or beyond cutoff by the application of a fixed positive potential to the cathode of tube $T2$. In this circuit $T1$ is normally conducting, and $T2$ is normally cut off, thus requiring that the synchronizing or triggering pulse must be negative. Likewise, the duration of this negative trigger pulse should be less than the time of the unstable portion of the cycle. If it is required to operate the circuit with a positive trigger pulse, it should be applied to the grid of $T2$, although in this case the pulse amplitude must be larger than when it is applied to $T1$.

The analysis of such a circuit follows the same general reasoning as that used in analyzing the free-running multivibrator. The result of such an analysis leads to the following expression for the time duration of the output pulse:

$$T = C_1 R_{g1} \log_e \frac{E_{bb} - E_{b2}}{-E_{01}} \tag{9-1}$$

where the symbols have the same meaning as in Chap. 8.

An alternative circuit, but one which is normally triggered with a positive pulse, is given in Fig. 9-2. The time duration of the output square wave, in this case, is found to be

$$T = C_2 R_{g2} \log_e \frac{E_{bb} - E_{b1}}{-E_{02}} \tag{9-2}$$

Now a word about triggering and trigger pulses. The circuit of Fig. 9-1 may be triggered by the application of a positive pulse to the grid of tube $T2$, and the circuit of Fig. 9-2 may be triggered by the application of a negative pulse to the grid of tube $T2$. In both cases, however, the amplitude of the pulses may be different from those when triggering is done in the manner shown in the respective figures with pulses applied to the grids of tubes $T1$. Ordinarily the amplitudes are not very critical,

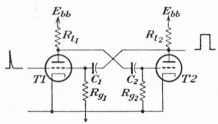

Fig. 9-2. A gate circuit that is roughly comparable with that of Fig. 9-1 except for the polarity of the triggering pulse.

nor need they be constant. However, when positive pulses are used, they must not be so large as to draw an appreciable grid current, since, with grid current, any input capacitors will be charged. At the end of the trigger pulse there will be an effective negative pulse due to the discharge of this capacitor. Consequently, if the input trigger is very narrow, these positive and negative pulses may counterbalance each other, and the circuit may not be actuated. Of course, the drawing of grid current can be avoided by using negative triggering pulses applied to the appropriate grid. This is not always desirable, however, and as will be shown (see, for example, Fig. 9-6), the effect of the triggering pulse will appear in the output gate. Reliable triggering is usually possible with a pulse that has a rapid rise time, say 0.1 μsec, and a gradual fall, so as to give a width of perhaps 1 μsec at the half amplitude value. The amplitude of the pulses will range from 20 to 50 volts.

If the pulse source must supply any appreciable current, then, owing to the effective output-terminal impedance of this source, the trigger waveshape may be affected adversely. Also, if this source effective output-terminal impedance is low, it may seriously load the gate circuit. It is possible to avoid both these difficulties by feeding the trigger pulses through diodes, in the manner illustrated in Fig. 9-3. The diode may be of the vacuum-tube type, such as the 6H6 or 6AL5, or it may be a germanium crystal diode. With the arrangement shown, the pulse must be negative, as indicated. For a positive-pulse triggered circuit, the diode would be reversed. For example, to operate the circuit shown with positive pulses, the diode would be reversed and would be connected to the plate of tube $T2$.

To understand the action of the diode, refer to Fig. 9-3. Tube $T1$ is normally off, and $T2$ is on. The potential of the plate relative to the cathode of the diode $T3$ is zero when $T1$ is off and is negative when $T1$ is on, by the potential drop across R_{l1}. Hence the diode will conduct only when a negative potential is applied to the cathode. Ordinarily, therefore, except upon the application of a triggering pulse, the diode is

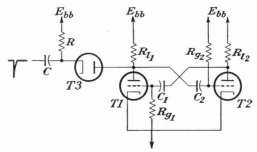

FIG. 9-3. The use of a diode as a trigger-source decoupler.

nonconducting, and the trigger driving circuit is essentially disconnected from the gate circuit. This is not completely the case, of course, because of the diode capacitances—that from plate to cathode, and that from plate to ground. These may be very small, however, so that the loading is only very slight. The application of a negative trigger of magnitude less than the IR drop in the plate resistor R_{l1} will cause $T2$ to cut off and $T1$ to fire. As soon as $T1$ fires, the plate potential e_{b1} falls and will disconnect the diode from the circuit.

The shape of the triggering pulse is not very critical, nor are the pulse duration and trailing slope important. It is still desirable to have the front edge of the trigger have a fast rise time, but because the trigger source is disconnected when e_{b1} falls by an amount equal to the pulse amplitude, the duration and trailing slope are unimportant. In fact, even if the pulse has a positive overshoot, this cannot get through the diode to cause any spurious firing.

The input time constant RC is not critical, although it must be small compared with the recurrence period of the triggering pulses. During the operation, the input time constant varies from the value determined by C and a resultant resistance comprising R paralleled by the series combination of the diode resistance and R_{l1}, with this group shunted by

C_2 and R_{g2} in series, and when $T1$ is on, the time constant returns to RC. Since such switching action occurs in a microsecond or less, the potential change on the capacitor C will be small. Capacitor C will recharge through R. Hence with RC small compared with the recurrence period of the pulses, the recharging will be complete before the next trigger, and the operation will proceed without complications due to any change in potential of C.

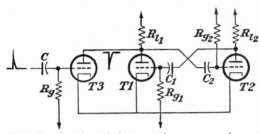

Fig. 9-4. The use of a triode as a trigger-source decoupler.

Triodes may be used for coupling the trigger to $T1$, in the manner illustrated in Fig. 9-4. In this case the input triode $T3$ and $T1$ comprise a common plate mixing arrangement. $T3$ is nominally beyond cutoff, and the application of a positive trigger to the grid provides an amplified negative trigger at the plate. The operation is otherwise the same as for the diode. Of course any trigger overshoots to the normally cutoff $T3$ are ineffective. The use of the triode circuit also provides sharpening of the input pulse, due to the amplification.

9-2. D-C Coupled Gate. The circuit of a d-c coupled gate is given in Fig. 9-5. It will be noted that this circuit is only a slight rearrangement of the circuit of Fig. 9-2. In this circuit, tube $T2$ is biased at or beyond cutoff by the application of a negative potential to the grid. This fixed bias is obtained from the potential divider comprising R_{l1}, R, and R_{g2}, which is connected between E_{bb} and E_{cc}. Also, in order to ensure that $T1$ is normally in the conducting stage, R_{g1}, which

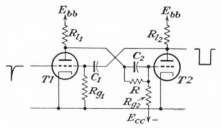

Fig. 9-5. A d-c coupled gate.

is shown connected to ground, may be connected to E_{bb}.

The capacitor C_2, which might appear to be unnecessary at first glance, actually serves a twofold purpose. It serves to decrease the switching time from $T1$ to $T2$, and also it serves to increase the reliability of operation of the circuit. To examine this matter, it is necessary to consider the effects of the several interelectrode tube capacitances. The tube capacitance C_{gk} in $T2$ tends to prevent the grid-cathode potential from changing rapidly. The capacitance C_{gp} which couples the grid with the plate of the tube tends to cause the grid potential to vary in a direction to oppose the effective switching from $T1$ to $T2$. The capacitance C_{kp} tends to prevent the plate potential from changing.

The effects of the interelectrode capacitances may be viewed in another way. The input capacitance of $T2$, which for a triode depends on the gain of the tube acting as an amplifier, would ordinarily be of the order of 50 $\mu\mu$f. This capacitance, plus distributed and wiring capacitances, may amount to perhaps 60 $\mu\mu$f. Since R_{g2} is of the order of a megohm, the grid time constant is of the order of 50 to 100 μsec. Consequently a 1-μsec pulse may be too short to effect switching. This difficulty is overcome by shunting R with C_2. If C_2 is chosen to make the time constant $RC_2 = R_{g2}C_{i2}$, where C_{i2} is the total effective input capacitance to tube $T2$, then the grid potential of $T2$ instantly follows the plate potential of $T1$. The circuit operates satisfactorily if this equality is not satisfied exactly.

The choice of C_2 should not be too large; otherwise a large overshoot in potential at G_2 may occur. This factor arises for the following reason: Consider the potential-divider action of the coupling resistor R and the grid resistor R_{g2}. The steady-state change in grid potential is $R_{g2}/(R + R_{g2})$ of the change in the plate potential of $T1$, and this ratio is normally about one-half. If C_2 is large compared with C_{i2}, the full $T1$ plate potential change will initially appear across G_2 and there will then be an exponential decay toward the steady-state change, which is approximately half this value. This large potential may drive G_2 positive, with the flow of grid current. This may cause the potential of C_2 to change appreciably, and the resultant potential may not decay completely before the next triggering pulse appears. In this case, reliable operation will not prevail. That is, too large a value of C_2 may limit the resolving time (the minimum time between successive triggering pulses) of the circuit. Ordinarily C_2 is chosen in the range from 50 to 100 $\mu\mu$f.

The waveforms of the potentials at various points in the circuit serve to clarify the operation of the circuit. These are given in Fig. 9-6.

The time duration of the gate from the d-c gate circuit illustrated is given by

$$T = C_1 R_{g1} \log_e \frac{E_{bb} - E_{b2}}{-E_{01}} \qquad (9\text{-}3)$$

If the grid of $T1$ is returned to E_{bb} in the manner shown in Fig. 8-27 to decrease jitter of the trailing edge, the time duration of the gate becomes

$$T = C_1 R_{g1} \log_e \frac{2E_{bb} - E_{b2}}{E_{bb} - E_{01}} \qquad (9\text{-}4)$$

There is some interest in examining the choice of C_1, for a specified tube, power supply, and gate duration. That is, with E_{bb}, E_{b2}, E_{01}, and T specified, the product $C_1 R_{g1}$ is specified, but the individual choice of C_1 and R_{g1} is not determined. To obtain some useful ideas, consider the case when it is desired to generate gates which have a time duration as wide as possible for the specified interval between triggering pulses.

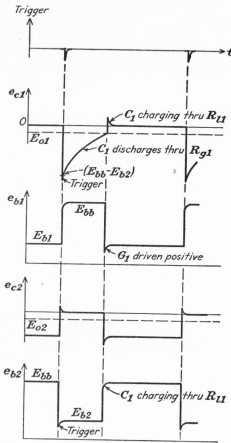

FIG. 9-6. The grid and plate potentials of the d-c coupled gate.

Refer now to the last diagram of Fig. 9-6. C_1 must recharge through R_{l1} before the next triggering pulse; otherwise it is not fully recharged, and e_{b2} does not reach the value E_{bb}. Consequently the numerator of the fractions in Eqs. (9-3) and (9-4) will no longer be constant, and the gate width will vary from pulse to pulse. There will be successive changes, owing to different charging times, and a group of pulses of varying widths will occur, which would probably then repeat. The limit to C_1 will then be specified by the practical requirements that R_{g1} must not be so large that leakage currents and the possibility of pickup become important.

9-3. The Cathode-coupled Gate. The cathode-coupled gate is essentially the cathode-coupled multivibrator which is so arranged that one tube is normally biased beyond cutoff. A comparison of the circuit of Fig. 9-7 with that of Fig. 8-29

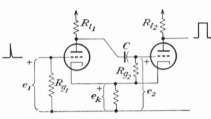

Fig. 9-7. A cathode-coupled gate.

shows that these are almost the same, except that R_{g2} in the circuit of Fig. 9-7 is connected from the grid to the cathode of $T2$ instead of from grid to ground. In this circuit, $T1$ will be nonconducting, and $T2$ will normally be in the conducting state. Consequently a positive triggering pulse applied to the grid of $T1$ is required in order to activate the circuit.

As ordinarily used, the grid of $T1$ is returned to a positive potential, rather than to ground. With this change, it is found that the pulse width t is directly proportional to the d-c potential E to a high degree of accuracy over a wide range of variation of this d-c potential. Such

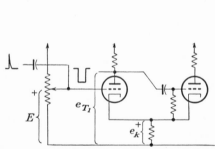

Fig. 9-8. A cathode-coupled gate with the grid of $T1$ tied to a positive bias E.

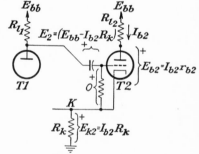

Fig. 9-9. The quiescent conditions in the cathode-coupled gate circuit when $T2$ conducts.

a modified circuit is illustrated in Fig. 9-8. A detailed analysis of the operation of this circuit follows.

The d-c bias potential E is kept low enough so that tube $T2$ is nominally conducting and $T1$ is off. The quiescent conditions before the trigger is injected are shown in Fig. 9-9. The current through this tube is given by the relation

$$I_{b2} = \frac{E_{bb}}{R_{l2} + r_{b2} + R_k} \tag{9-5}$$

and the cathode-ground potential E_{k2} is then simply

$$E_{k2} = I_{b2}R_k \tag{9-6}$$

Consequently, the potential across the capacitor, assuming that the grid-cathode potential of $T2$ during conduction is zero, is

$$E_2 = E_{bb} - E_{k2} \tag{9-7}$$

When the circuit is triggered, $T1$ conducts and $T2$ is turned off. The quiescent conditions are those shown in Fig. 9-10. The current through $T1$ is given by the relation

$$I_{b1} = \frac{E_{bb}}{R_{l1} + r_{b1} + R_k} \tag{9-8}$$

and the cathode-ground potential E_{k1} is

$$E_{k1} = I_{b1}R_k \tag{9-9}$$

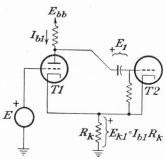

Fig. 9-10. The quiescent conditions in the cathode-coupled gate circuit when $T1$ is conducting.

Clearly, when the circuit is triggered, the plate of tube $T1$ falls from E_{bb} to $E_{bb} - I_{b1}R_{l1}$ and the point K changes from E_{k2} to E_{k1}. Because of this, the potential across the capacitor C will change from the value given in Eq. (9-7) to the value

$$E_1 = E_{bb} - I_{b1}R_{l1} - E_{k1} = E_{T1} - E_{k1} = E_{b1} \tag{9-10}$$

The capacitor potential changes by an amount

$$\Delta E = E_2 - E_1 = E_{bb} - E_{T1} - E_{k2} + E_{k1} \tag{9-11}$$

Of this, the fraction E_{c2} initially appears across the grid of $T2$, where

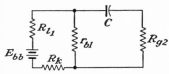

$$E_{c2} = (E_{bb} - E_{T1} - E_{k2} + E_{k1}) \frac{R_{g2}}{R' + R_{g2}} \tag{9-12}$$

Fig. 9-11. The discharge circuit of the capacitor C.

and where R' is the parallel combination of r_{b1} and $R_{l1} + R_k$. The potential will then approach zero along an exponential curve, and $T2$ will again begin to conduct when $e_{c2} = E_{02}$ in the circuit of Fig. 9-11. This occurs at the time when

$$-E_{02} = E_{c2}e^{-T/CR_{g2}} \tag{9-13}$$

approximately. This expression assumes that R_{g2} is large compared with the parallel combination of r_{b1} and $R_{l1} + R_k$. Solving for the time T yields

$$T = CR_{g2} \log_e \left(\frac{E_{bb} - E_{T1} - E_{k2} + E_{k1}}{-E_{02}} \frac{R_{g2}}{R' + R_{g2}} \right)$$

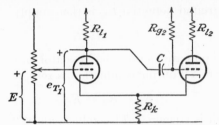

FIG. 9-12. A cathode-coupled linear delay circuit.

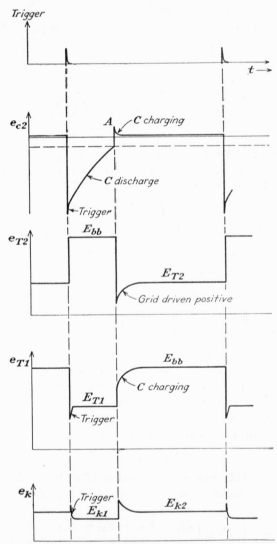

FIG. 9-13. The waveshapes in the cathode-coupled linear delay gate.

which is given with good approximation by

$$T \doteq CR_{g2} \log_e \frac{E_{bb} - E_{b1} - E_{k2}}{-E_{02}} \tag{9-14}$$

To reduce the jitter in the trailing edge of the pulse, and also to permit somewhat greater control of pulse width with d-c bias potential, the grid of $T2$ is returned to the plate supply potential through a large grid resistor, as illustrated.   Because of this change, the analysis given above must be modified.   Such an analysis leads to the following expression for the discharge time of the capacitor and hence for the width of the gate:

$$T \doteq CR_{g2} \log_e \frac{2E_{bb} - E_{T1} - E_{k2}}{E_{bb} - E_{k1} - E_{02}} \tag{9-15}$$

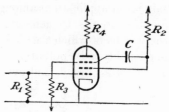

FIG. 9-14. A pentode gate circuit.

Sketches of the important waveshapes of the circuit are given in Fig. 9-13.   This circuit will receive further consideration in Sec. 9-6.

9-4. Pentode Gate Circuits.   The van der Pol relaxation oscillator shown in Fig. 8-39 may be converted into a gate circuit by applying a negative bias to the suppressor grid or by reducing the value of the resistance R_2.   As already discussed in Sec. 8-14, the principle of the circuit is essentially the same as that of the two-tube multivibrator, except that

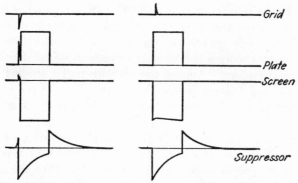

FIG. 9-15. The waveforms of a pentode gate when triggered with negative and with positive pulses.

the necessary amplification without phase reversal is obtained in a single tube.   A circuit of this pentode gate is given in Fig. 9-14.   Such a gate circuit may be triggered either by positive or by negative pulses, the general character of the waveforms at various points in the circuit being those illustrated in Fig. 9-15.

Another form of pentode gate circuit is illustrated in Fig. 9-16.[1]   In the quiescent condition the tube $T1$ draws grid current, and the plate

potential is at a value E_b.   The application of a negative triggering pulse
to the input will cause the tube to cut off, the time of cutoff being controlled by C_1, R_2, and E_{bb}.   During the triggering pulse, the capacitor C_1
is discharged through $T2$, and recharging takes place through R_2, since,
at the end of the pulse, $T2$ will be cut off.   The grid and plate waveforms are somewhat as illustrated in
Fig. 9-17.

9-5. Linear Delay Circuits.   Certain radar applications among others
require circuits to generate pulses,
the widths of which are directly proportional to a d-c potential, to a high
degree of accuracy, and over a wide

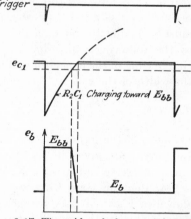

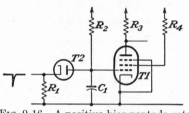

Fig. 9-16. A positive-bias pentode gate circuit.

Fig. 9-17. The grid and plate waveforms in the pentode gate circuit of Fig. 9-16.

range of variation of this d-c potential.   Such a circuit as this will
make possible the generation of a marker or triggering pulse at an accurately known instant after it is initiated.   Although a tremendous man-
power effort has been devoted to the investigation of circuits to fulfill
these requirements, only a few circuits have been found which are even
moderately satisfactory.   Among the circuits to be studied which do
possess the desired characteristics are (a) the linear delay gate circuit,
(b) the sanatron, (c) the phantastron, and (d) the linear-sweep delay
circuit.

The linear delay gate circuit is the cathode-coupled gate circuit of
Fig. 9-12, which will be shown to yield a gate width or time duration
which is directly proportional to the d-c potential E to the grid of $T1$.
In the other three circuits, a comparison is made between the specified
d-c potential and a point of equal potential on a linear saw-tooth potential wave.   At the time of potential agreement, a rapidly acting chain of
events is initiated to produce a pulse.   Consequently, these circuits
include a linear saw-tooth generator, a potential comparator, and a
pulse-generating circuit.   The manner of achieving these results is different in each case.

9-6. The Linear Delay Gate Circuit.   The essential element of the
linear delay gate circuit is the cathode-coupled gate circuit of Fig. 9-12.

To see that the time duration of the gate is directly proportional to the bias potential E, Eq. (9-15) is examined in some detail.*

First it is noted from the tube characteristics of a typical triode, say the 6SN7, that the plate current can be related to the plate and grid potentials by an equation of the form

$$I_b = \frac{1}{k}(E_b + \mu E_c) \tag{9-16}$$

where E_b is the plate-cathode potential and E_c is the grid-cathode potential. That is, except in the region of very small currents, the linear set of curves is a fair representation of the normal space-charge curves of the tube. It follows from this expression that

$$E_b = k I_b - \mu E_c \tag{9-17}$$

Also, it follows from Fig. 9-12 that

$$E_b + I_b(R_{l1} + R_k) = E_{bb} \tag{9-18}$$

By combining Eqs. (9-17) and (9-18) there results

$$I_b = \frac{E_{bb} + \mu E_c}{R_{l1} + R_k + k} \tag{9-19}$$

Also from the figure

$$E = E_c + I_b R_k \tag{9-20}$$

It then follows from Eqs. (9-19) and (9-20) that

$$I_b = \frac{E_{bb} + \mu E}{R_{l1} + (\mu + 1)R_k + k} \tag{9-21}$$

These expressions are combined with Eq. (9-15) to yield

$$T = CR_{g2} \log_e \frac{E_{bb} + I_b R_{l1} - E_{k2}}{E_{bb} - I_b R_k - E_{02}}$$

$$T = CR_{g2} \log_e \frac{[R_{l1} + (\mu + 1)R_k + k](E_{bb} - E_{k2}) + R_{l1}E_{bb} + \mu E R_{l1}}{[R_{l1} + (\mu + 1)R_k + k](E_{bb} - E_{02}) - R_k E_{bb} - \mu E R_k} \tag{9-22}$$

This may be written in the form

$$T = CR_{g2} \log_e \frac{a + bE}{c - dE} \tag{9-23}$$

where

$$
\begin{aligned}
a &= [R_{l1} + (\mu + 1)R_k + k](E_{bb} - E_{k2}) + R_{l1}E_{bb} \\
b &= \mu R_{l1} \\
c &= [R_{l1} + (\mu + 1)R_k + k](E_{bb} - E_{02}) - R_k E_{bb} \\
d &= \mu R_k
\end{aligned} \tag{9-24}
$$

* A somewhat similar analysis was given by K. Clegg, *Proc. IRE*, **38**, 655 (1950).

Now expand Eq. (9-23) to the form

$$T = CR_{g2} \left[\log_e \frac{a}{c} + \log_e \left(1 + \frac{b}{a} E \right) - \log_e \left(1 - \frac{d}{c} E \right) \right] \quad (9\text{-}25)$$

But over the range for which

$$\frac{b}{a} E < 1 \qquad \frac{d}{c} E < 1 \qquad\qquad (9\text{-}26)$$

the logarithm may be expanded and only the first term in the expansion retained. The expression for T then becomes

$$T \doteq CR_{g2} \left(\log_e \frac{a}{c} + \frac{b}{a} E + \frac{d}{c} E \right)$$

or finally

$$T \doteq CR_{g2} \left[\log_e \frac{a}{c} + \left(\frac{b}{a} + \frac{d}{c} \right) E \right] \qquad\qquad (9\text{-}27)$$

which indicates the linear variation of T with E. The change of period with changes in d-c reference potential, i.e., the slope of the curve, is simply

$$\frac{dT}{dE} = CR_{g2} \left(\frac{b}{a} + \frac{d}{c} \right) \qquad\qquad (9\text{-}28)$$

It is of interest to examine the allowable range of variation of E. Consider first the maximum allowable value of E. For gate operation, $T1$ must be off when $T2$ is on. However, if E is too large, this will not be true and the circuit will act as a multivibrator, and not as a gate circuit. The limiting value of E is given by the requirement that

$$E_{c1} = E - I_2 R_k \leqq E_{01}$$

or

$$E_{max} = I_2 R_k + E_{01} \qquad\qquad (9\text{-}29)$$

The minimum value of E is obtained directly from Eq. (9-23) and is that value for which the argument of the logarithm is unity. This occurs when

$$a + bE = c - dE$$

or

$$E_{min} = \frac{c - a}{b + d} \qquad\qquad (9\text{-}30)$$

For values of E less than this, the circuit cannot be triggered.

The normal range of variation of E, as dictated by Eqs. (9-29) and (9-30) is not very great, so that the gate width is dictated largely by the product CR_{g2}. The choice of the parameters C and R_{g2} is dictated in the present case by the same reasoning that was given in conjunction with the choice of C and R_g in the circuit of Fig. 9-5, with the general choice of C as small as possible with a not unreasonably large value of R_{g2}.

A circuit that was used extensively at the MIT Radiation Laboratory for producing a marker pulse is illustrated in Fig. 9-18. This circuit yields an output pulse the delay of which is directly proportional to the d-c potential applied to the grid of $T1$ within ± 0.25 per cent over the range from about 8 to 150 μsec. It must be emphasized that the parts

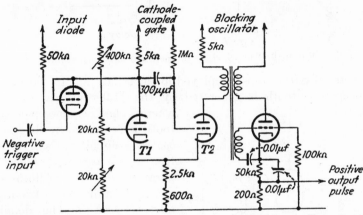

Fig. 9-18. A linear delay gate circuit which triggers a blocking oscillator to produce sharp pulses.

must be specially selected to achieve special ends. For example, the two resistors in the cathode of the cathode-coupled gate were by different manufacturers and provided compensating effects as the temperature varied. Other characteristics of this circuit will be given below.

9-7. The Sanatron Delay Circuit.[1] The sanatron delay circuit is one of a variety of linear delay systems which have been designed around the so-called *Miller integrating*, or *Miller run-down*, circuit, which is used to generate a highly linear saw-tooth potential waveform. The details of other linear delay systems will be discussed in later sections. For purposes of clarifying the need for the circuits to be discussed in this and in the following sections, the principle of operation of the sanatron will be graphically portrayed. The details of the circuit operation are given in Fig. 9-26.

As already mentioned, the sanatron operates on the basis of comparing a specified d-c reference with a point of equal potential on a linear saw-tooth potential and measuring the time interval between the inception of the linear saw tooth and the point at which potential equality occurs. The important principles are displayed graphically in Fig. 9-19.

In fact, this diagram also portrays the principles of operation of the so-called *linear-sweep delay circuit*, although the details of this system

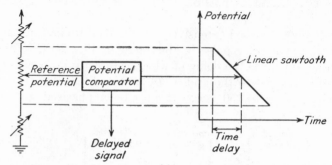

Fig. 9-19. The principles of operation of the sanatron.

differ markedly from those employed in the sanatron. In the sanatron, the linear saw tooth is generated by the Miller integrating circuit,

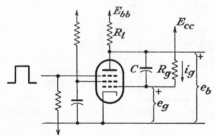

Fig. 9-20. The basic Miller integrating circuit.

whereas the linear-sweep delay saw tooth is generated by the so-called *bootstrap* circuit. Also, the sanatron uses a cathode-coupled comparator, whereas the linear-sweep delay uses a diode or a triode pickoff comparator. The details of these circuits will be examined below.

The Miller integrating circuit is illustrated in Fig. 9-20. The important operating feature of this circuit is that the potential of the plate e_b will fall linearly with time when the plate is made conducting by apply-

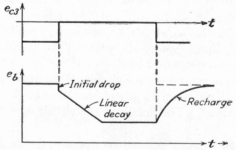

Fig. 9-21. The suppressor and plate potentials of the Miller integrating circuit of Fig. 9-20.

ing a positive gate to the suppressor, which is normally biased beyond cutoff. The general character of the output is illustrated in Fig. 9-21.

Before examining the circuit analytically, a qualitative discussion is desirable. Note that, before the arrival of the gate to the suppressor grid, the control grid is very near the cathode potential, owing to the fact that the grid draws current. Also, the plate current is cut off because of the bias of the suppressor. Immediately after the arrival of the gate pulse, the plate potential falls. The grid potential is likewise lowered, since the falling plate potential is applied to the grid through capacitor C. The grid potential continues to fall until a point near grid cutoff is reached. At this juncture, the true Miller charging condition sets in, and the linear decay of the plate potential begins. That is, the plate waveform includes an initial drop of 5 to 10 volts which is followed by a linearly falling potential.

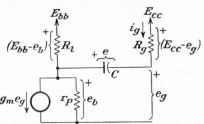

Fig. 9-22. The equivalent circuit of the Miller integrator when the pentode is rendered conducting by the application of a potential to the suppressor.

To examine the action of the circuit analytically, it is noted that when the positive gate is applied to the suppressor grid, which thereby permits the plate to draw current, a current generator is effectively switched into the circuit between the plate and ground. The equivalent circuit when plate conduction occurs is essentially that shown in Fig. 9-22. It follows from this diagram that

$$Y_l(E_{bb} - e_b) + Y_g(E_{cc} - e_g) = g_m e_g + Y_p e_b \tag{9-31}$$

Also note that

$$e_b = e + e_g \tag{9-32}$$

and

$$e_b = -\frac{1}{Cp} i_g + e_g \tag{9-33}$$

where p denotes the usual operational form for the operator d/dt. Note that Eq. (9-33) may be written as

$$e_b = -\frac{1}{Cp} Y_g(E_{cc} - e_g) + e_g$$

so that

$$Cpe_b = (Cp + Y_g)e_g - Y_g E_{cc} \tag{9-34}$$

Combine this with Eq. (9-31) to get

$$(Y_l + Y_p + g_m + Y_g)Cpe_b + Y_g(Y_l + Y_p)e_b = Y_g(Y_l E_{bb} - g_m E_{cc}) \tag{9-35}$$

This may be written in the operational form

$$(p + a)e_b = A$$

where

$$a = \frac{Y_g(Y_l + Y_p)}{(Y_l + Y_p + g_m + Y_g)C} \qquad (9\text{-}36)$$

$$A = \frac{Y_g(Y_l E_{bb} - g_m E_{cc})}{(Y_l + Y_p + g_m + Y_g)C}$$

This is the controlling differential equation that relates the variation of the plate potential with time for the specified circuit parameters.

The general solution of this differential equation is the expression

$$e_b(t) = \frac{A}{a} + \left[e_b(0+) - \frac{A}{a} \right] e^{-at} \qquad (9\text{-}37)$$

where $e_b(0+)$ is the value of the potential e_b just after the tube begins to conduct. An approximate value for this is possible from considerations of Eq. (9-32) by noting that just after switching

$$e_b(0+) = e(0+) + e_g(0+)$$

Also, making use of the fact that

$$e_b = K e_g$$

then

$$e_b(0+) = \frac{e(0+)}{1 - K}$$

Moreover, the potential across the capacitor C does not change during the switching operation. But before switching the plate is at E_{bb}, under the assumption that the grid is practically at ground potential and that the plate current of the tube is cut off. Then

$$e_b(0+) = \frac{E_{bb}}{1 - K} \qquad (9\text{-}38)$$

where the gain is approximately

$$K = -g_m R_l'$$

where

$$R_l' = \frac{R_l r_p}{R_l + r_p} \qquad (9\text{-}39)$$

Equation (9-37) is then given by

$$e_b(t) = \frac{Y_l E_{bb} - g_m E_{cc}}{Y_l + Y_p} + \left(\frac{E_{bb}}{1 - K} - \frac{Y_l E_{bb} - g_m E_{cc}}{Y_l + Y_p} \right) e^{-\frac{Y_g(Y_l + Y_p)}{(Y_g + Y_l + Y_p + g_m)C}t} \qquad (9\text{-}40)$$

Ordinarily E_{cc} is chosen equal to E_{bb}. In this case

$$e_b(t) = E_{bb} \left[\frac{Y_l - g_m}{Y_l + Y_p} + \left(\frac{1}{1 - K} - \frac{Y_l - g_m}{Y_l + Y_p} \right) e^{-\frac{Y_g(Y_l + Y_p)}{(Y_g + Y_l + Y_p + g_m)C}t} \right] \qquad (9\text{-}41)$$

For the usual circuit parameters, $Y_p \doteq Y_l \doteq Y_g \sim 10^{-6}$ mho,

$$e_b(t) = E_{bb}\left[-g_m R_l' + \left(\frac{1}{1-K} + g_m R_l'\right) e^{-\frac{1}{1+g_m R_l'}\frac{t}{R_g C}}\right]$$

or finally

$$e_b(t) = E_{bb}\left[K + \left(\frac{1}{1-K} - K\right) e^{-\frac{t}{(1-K)R_g C}}\right] \qquad (9\text{-}42)$$

For the usual conditions of operation, this expression may be expanded and only the lower-order terms retained. This yields

$$e_b(t) = E_{bb}\left\{ K + \left(\frac{1}{1-K} - K\right)\left[1 - \frac{t}{(1-K)R_g C} + \cdots \right]\right\}$$

which may be written in the form

$$e_b(t) \doteq E_{bb}\left(\frac{1}{1-K} - \frac{t}{R_g C}\right) \qquad (9\text{-}43)$$

A plot of this expression indicates a small initial step of amplitude $E_{bb}/(1-K)$ followed by an exponential decay, which over the range of operation is practically a linear fall in potential. Some measure of the linearity is possible by examining the ratio of the second-order to the first-order term in the above expansion. The percentage deviation from the linear is approximately

$$\% \text{ deviation} = \frac{\tfrac{1}{2}[t/(1-K)R_g C]^2}{t/(1-K)R_g C} \times 100 = 50\,\frac{1}{(1-K)R_g C}\,t \qquad (9\text{-}44)$$

For a circuit for which the linear time is to extend for 100 μsec, typical parameters are $R_g = 3$ megohms, $C = 100$ $\mu\mu$f, and $K \doteq 200$. The deviation becomes

$$50\,\frac{t}{(1-K)R_g C} = \frac{100 \times 10^{-6} \times 50}{3 \times 10^6 \times 100 \times 10^{-12} \times 200} \doteq 0.1\%$$

Although Eq. (9-43) indicates the presence of a small initial potential drop in the plate potential at the onset of plate conduction, the extent of the drop normally exceeds that indicated by the equations. The explanation is to be found in the contribution to the initial plate current by charging currents which appear due to charging the tube and wiring capacitances. In fact, it is these capacitances which cause a gradual change between the initial drop and the linear potential decay, instead of the sharp break predicted by Eq. (9-43).

At the end of the plate conduction period, when the pulse to the suppressor is removed, so that the pentode plate current is again reduced to zero, the capacitor begins to recharge to the potential E_{bb} with a time constant which is $R_l C$, approximately.

If the circuit is modified as illustrated in Fig. 9-23, a control is possible to the upper and lower potential limits between which the linear saw tooth traverses. In this circuit, if the potential of the plate is higher than E_1, the diode $T2$ will conduct. In this way the plate of $T1$ is tied to E_1. Likewise, when the plate potential is falling with the application of the gate to the suppressor grid of $T1$, diode $T3$ will be nonconducting until the plate potential falls to E_2, when the diode $T3$ will fix the lower potential of the plate fall to E_2.

The linear saw-tooth wave from the Miller integrating circuit is then used in a potential comparator circuit. In this circuit a comparison is effected between the potential, and hence the corresponding setting of a potentiometer, with that of any desired position on the linear saw tooth.

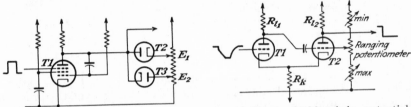

FIG. 9-23. A Miller integrator with controlled limits.

FIG. 9-24. A double-triode potential-comparator circuit.

The output, which appears as the movable edge of the gate, is directly proportional to the potential on the linear potentiometer, and hence to the position of the potentiometer shaft. A double-triode *potential comparator* circuit is illustrated in Fig. 9-24. Note that the saw-tooth potential from the Miller integrator is fed directly to the grid of one tube, the second tube being connected to the movable arm of the linear potentiometer.

The circuit resembles the cathode-coupled gate, and its operation depends on two cumulative actions taking place when certain conditions are realized. Suppose that the potential at the slider of the ranging potentiometer is about $\frac{1}{2}E_{bb}$. At the instant that the Miller integrator is activated by the application of the positive gate to the suppressor grid, the potential of the grid of $T1$ will be E_{bb}, the potential of the grid of $T2$ will be $\frac{1}{2}E_{bb}$, and $T1$ will be conducting. This state of the comparator circuit continues while the grid potential of $T1$ falls with the saw tooth, until it approaches the potential of the grid of $T2$. The circuit now becomes unstable, and a flip action takes place, with $T1$ becoming nonconducting and $T2$ beginning to conduct. Clearly, as the potential of the slider is reduced, the flip action takes place at an increasingly delayed time after the start of the initial event. The time delay between them will be proportional to the angular position of the shaft of the ranging potentiometer. The corresponding action which returns the circuit to its initial state takes place at the equivalent potential on the exponential rise when the Miller circuit capacitor is recharging.

The amplitudes of the potential steps that appear at the anodes of $T1$ and $T2$ depend on the amount of current that is transferred from $T1$ to $T2$ at the instant of the flip action. This current depends on the setting of the potentiometer slider, but the variation may be reduced considerably by returning the cathode resistor to a negative supply. The two adjustable resistors at each end of the ranging potentiometer are to permit the potential across the ranging potentiometer to be adjusted during calibration.

A second form of potential comparator, known as the *Multiar*, is illustrated in Fig. 9-25. The circuit resembles the positive-bias gate circuit

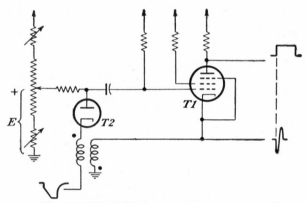

Fig. 9-25. The Multiar potential comparator.

of Fig. 9-16, which is combined with a blocking-oscillator circuit. Tube $T1$ is normally on, owing to the positive grid bias. The application of the saw-tooth potential through the blocking-oscillator transformer and the pick-off diode $T2$ has no effect until the applied potential falls to the potential E. At this point the diode begins to conduct, and the falling potential is applied to the grid of $T1$. The tube current begins to fall, thereby starting a regenerative cycle which proceeds to cut off very rapidly because of the blocking-oscillator effect of the transformer. Clearly, as the potential E of the slider is reduced, the regenerative flip action occurs lower on the saw-tooth potential, and hence at a longer delay from the start of the saw tooth. The circuit is returned to its quiescent state on the rising part of the saw-tooth charging circuit. However, the blocking-oscillator pulse does not appear in the output because of the decoupling action of the diode $T2$.

The complete sanatron system incorporates a pentode gate circuit for producing the positive gate for starting the integrator, the Miller integrator circuit, and the potential comparator circuit. A circuit diagram is given in Fig. 9-26. The significant waveforms at several points in this circuit are given in Fig. 9-27.

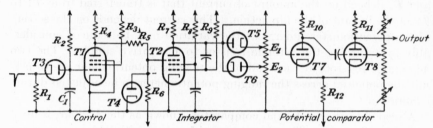

Fig. 9-26. The complete sanatron delay circuit.

9-8. The Phantastron. The phantastron is a transitron circuit arrangement which combines the Miller integrator and the trigger properties of the sanatron in a single tube. The Miller effect improves the linearity, while the transitron portion of the circuit provides the feedback required to permit the capacitor to recharge at the end of the linear portion of the run-down. The schematic diagram is given in Fig. 9-28, and the significant waveforms at several points in the circuit are given in Fig. 9-29. Owing to the mutual effects that exist during the course of its operation, the phantastron in the form shown is somewhat inferior to

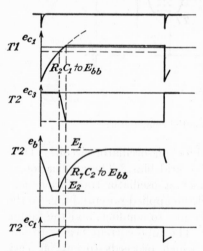

Fig. 9-27. The potential waveforms at various points of the sanatron.

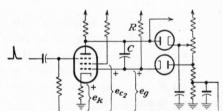

Fig. 9-28. The phantastron delay circuit.

the sanatron. It was for this reason that during World War II the British, who devised both circuits, preferred the sanatron.

The American version of the phantastron is designed around the 6SA7 heptode, which, owing to the mutual shielding between significant elements, proves to be entirely satisfactory. One version of the circuit is given in Fig. 9-30.

A second variation of the basic circuit is given in Fig. 9-31. This circuit employs a cathode follower to restore the 6SA7 to the quiescent state quickly by helping to restore the plate potential to the starting condition at the end of the operating period. The circuit of Fig. 9-31 with appropriate parameters yields an output pulse, the delay of which is directly proportional to the d-c potential applied to the control diode within ± 0.1 per cent over the range from about 8 to 150 μsec. Several of the important waveforms in this circuit are given in Fig. 9-32.

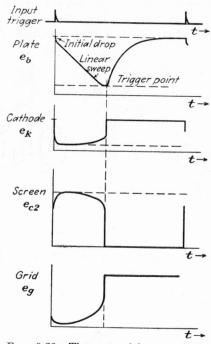

FIG. 9-29. The potentials at various points of the phantastron.

9-9. The Linear-sweep Delay Circuit. The linear-sweep delay circuit operates on the same principles as the sanatron, as illustrated in Fig. 9-19, except that the linear saw tooth is a rising one rather than a falling one. The linear saw tooth is generated in this system by means of a so-called "bootstrap" circuit, which incorporates feedback for improving the linearity of the sweep potential. A potential comparator, consisting of a pick-off diode and high-gain amplifier is used to determine the point on the saw-tooth potential at which a potential comparison is effected between a known potential and the corresponding point on the saw tooth.

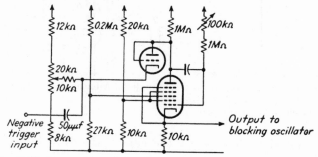

FIG. 9-30. One version of the phantastron built around the 6SA7.

The essential elements of the linear sweep generator may be discussed by reference to the circuit of Fig. 9-33. In this circuit, $T1$ is normally conducting, and the potential across the capacitor is E_{b1}. With $T2$ absent and with the application of a negative gate to the grid of $T1$, the capacitor will begin to charge from E_{b1} toward E_{bb} along an exponential curve, with a time constant $(R_1 + R_2)C$. With $T2$ connected as

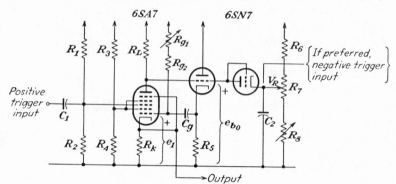

Fig. 9-31. A second version of the phantastron delay circuit.

shown and with the application of the negative gate to cut $T1$ off, then, as the potential across the capacitor increases, the feedback through the cathode follower $T2$ which is applied to the circuit through which the capacitor charges will cause the point A to increase. In effect, therefore, the capacitor, instead of charging to a constant potential E_{bb}, charges toward a continually increasing potential. As a result, instead of the charging curve being exponential, it is very nearly linear, the extent of the linearity

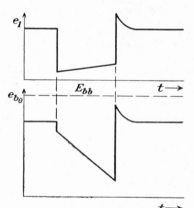

Fig. 9-32. Important potential waveforms at two points of the phantastron with cathode follower and pickoff diode.

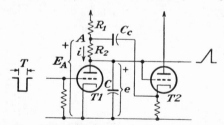

Fig. 9-33. A linear saw-tooth generator.

being determined by how nearly the gain of the cathode follower is to unity.

An analytic description of the operation of the saw-tooth generator is readily possible. To analyze the circuit operation, assume that C_c, the coupling capacitor from the cathode of the cathode follower to point A, is sufficiently large so that no change in potential occurs across it during the course of operation. Now, as the potential e across the charging capacitor changes, this potential is applied to the grid of the cathode follower. The varying component of potential to the grid of the cathode follower is $e - E_{b1}$, since the potential across the capacitor C just prior to the application of the negative gate to the grid of $T1$ is E_{b1}, the potential drop across the tube $T1$ under quiescent conditions. Thus when $T1$ is cut off, the complete charging equation is given by

$$\left(R_2 + \frac{1}{Cp}\right) i = E_A + K(e - E_{b1})$$

the effective output-terminal impedance of the cathode follower being considered zero. This is rewritten as

$$R_2 i + \frac{1 - K}{Cp} i = E_A - KE_{b1} \tag{9-45}$$

The complete solution of this equation has the form

$$i = \frac{E_A - KE_{b1}}{R_2} e^{\frac{-(1-K)}{R_2C}t} \tag{9-46}$$

To find the expression for the potential e, use is made of the fact that

$$e = \frac{1}{Cp} i = \frac{E_A - KE_{b1}}{R_2C} \int e^{\frac{-(1-K)}{R_2C}t} \, dt \tag{9-47}$$

which becomes, since $e = E_{b1}$ when $t = 0$,

$$e = E_{b1} + \frac{E_A - KE_{b1}}{1 - K} - \frac{E_A - KE_{b1}}{1 - K} e^{\frac{-(1-K)}{R_2C}t}$$

or finally

$$e - E_{b1} = \frac{E_A - KE_{b1}}{1 - K} (1 - e^{-(1-K)t/R_2C}) \tag{9-48}$$

This result may be interpreted to show that the effective potential toward which the capacitor is charging is $(E_A - KE_{b1})/(1 - K)$. But since K for the cathode follower is nearly unity, then the effective potential of the charging source is very large and approaches infinity. Moreover, since the effective time constant is very small, the capacitor charges linearly. In fact, the actual charging proceeds approximately according to

$$e - E_{b1} = \frac{E_A - KE_{b1}}{1 - K} \frac{1 - K}{R_2C} t$$

or

$$e - E_{b1} = \frac{E_A - KE_{b1}}{R_2C} t \tag{9-49}$$

Sketches of the significant potentials as functions of time are given in Fig. 9-34. As in Eq. (9-44), the deviation from linearity is readily obtained. It follows that

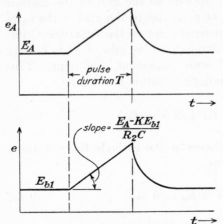

$$\text{Per cent deviation} = 50\,\frac{1-K}{R_2C}\,t$$

$$(9\text{-}50)$$

A complete circuit of the linear-sweep delay is shown in Fig. 9-35. In this circuit, $T1$ and $T2$ are connected as a simple cathode-coupled gate, the negative square wave thus generated being applied to the grid of $T3$. The time duration of this square wave is the maximum length of the delay desired. This negative square wave is applied to the linear saw-tooth circuit, comprising $T3$ and $T6$. $T4$

Fig. 9-34. The potentials in the "bootstrap" sweep generator.

helps restore the sweep quickly to the quiescent condition. A more complete discussion of its operation is found in Sec. 10-6. The 2-kilohm resistor to ground causes a rapid rise at the beginning of the saw tooth, making

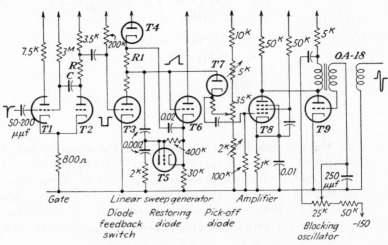

Fig. 9-35. A 150-μsec linear-sweep delay circuit.

it a trapezoidal wave. This is necessary in order to make the sweep start rapidly enough to overcome circuit capacitances. Often this resistor may be omitted. The 400-kilohm resistor and $T5$ are placed in the circuit as an additional sweep correction to produce linearity. A discussion of the peration of this action is also found in Sec. 10-6.   T7 is called the *pick-off* liode because it begins to conduct at a point on the sweep determined by he selection of its cathode potential with the adjustment of the 35-kilohm potentiometer.   This is essentially the potential comparator in the circuit. When $T7$ begins to conduct, its output is amplified by $T8$, whose plate utput triggers $T9$, the blocking oscillator tube.

Table 9-1 shows a comparison of the features of the cathode-coupled linear delay gate circuit (Fig. 9-12), the phantastron circuit (Fig. 9-31), and the linear-sweep delay circuit (Fig. 9-35).   The percentage change in range indicated is the maximum change at any point in the cycle.

TABLE 9-1*

COMPARISON OF THREE DELAY CIRCUITS FOR 150 μSEC
MAXIMUM DURATION

Subject	Linear delay gate	Phantastron	Linear sweep
Duration vs. potential...	0.25% from about 8 to 150 μsec	0.1% from 8 to 150 μsec	0.1% from 5 to 150 μsec
10% change in E_{bb} about 250 volts	±0.5% change in time duration	∓0.15% change in duration	±0.15% change in duration
Temp coefficient (% change in duration per °C)...............	−0.005%/°C	−0.002%/°C	±0.003%/°C
Number of tube envelopes..............	2½	3	5
Max over-all sensitivity to all tubes..........	±10% change	±5%	±1%

* Taken from *MIT Radiation Lab. Rept.* T-18.

9-10. Trigger, or Flip-flop, Circuits.   The trigger, flip-flop, or bistable circuit is not unlike the gate circuit except that, for fixed values of applied potential, there are two stable conditions of equilibrium.   The currents and potentials in such a circuit can be made to change abruptly from one set of stable values to a second set of stable values, or back again, although independent disturbances are required for each switching action.

Refer to the circuit of Fig. 9-36, which was first discussed by Eccles and Jordan in 1919.[2]   Observe that this circuit is like the multivibrator, although direct coupling exists between the plate of $T1$ and the grid of $T2$ and between the plate of $T2$ and the grid of $T1$.   Further, the grids are normally maintained negative by the potential divider and the negative C-supply potential.

Suppose that $T1$ is conducting and $T2$ is cut off.   The d-c potentials on the grids of the tubes are then, respectively, approximately zero on $T1$, owing to grid clipping, and $E_{cc} + \dfrac{R_{g2}}{R_2 + R_{g2}} (-E_{cc} + E_{b1})$ on $T2$. These

must be such that e_{c1} is slightly positive and e_{c2} is negative. If now a positive signal is applied to both grids simultaneously, there will be no appreciable action in $T1$ but $T2$ will begin to conduct. This will reduce the grid potential on $T1$, which reduces the tube current, setting off a regenerative action that continues until $T1$ ceases to conduct and $T2$ is

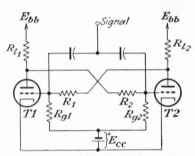

FIG. 9-36. The Eccles-Jordan trigger circuit.

fully conducting. The transfer is effected in precisely the same manner as that discussed for other multivibrator circuits. The circuit will remain in this new stable condition until another positive pulse is applied.

Negative trigger pulses may also be used to effect the switching. In this case the negative trigger acts on the conducting tube, causing a sudden decrease in the plate current and a corresponding rise in the plate potential. This rise is passed to the tube that is cut off, resulting in a flow of current in its plate circuit, which initiates the switching action. As a matter of fact, any mixture of positive and negative triggers may be present, and each trigger will operate the circuit regardless of polarity. Moreover, the amplitude of the pulses need not be constant, the only requirement being that they be sufficient to cause switching. Pulse heights should not be too large; otherwise grid current may result, with consequent charging of input capacitors, with delayed response due to their time constants.

A practical form of the trigger circuit is illustrated in Fig. 9-37. Note the use of capacitors C_1 and C_2 across the coupling resistors R_1 and R_2. These are used to overcome the effects of the presence of the tube capacitances and also to increase the reliability of operation, precisely as for the

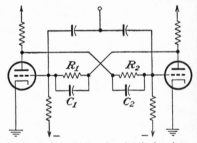

FIG. 9-37. A "scale-of-2" circuit.

action of the capacitor in the d-c coupled gate circuit of Fig. 9-5. Since two pulses are required to cause the circuit to complete its cycle, viz., for each tube to pass from the nonconducting state to the conducting state and then back again, the output from a differentiating circuit connected to either plate will consist of a series of positive and negative pulses, the rate of each being one-half that of the triggering group.

Thus, if either the positive or the negative output pulses are selected, there will be one-half as many as the primary triggering source.   This accounts for the name, *scale-of-2* circuit.   Circuits of this type are used very extensively in scaling down the number of pulses produced in nuclear-physics reactions.   Ordinarily such scaling circuits are connected in cascade to produce scale-of-4, scale-of-8, scale-of-16, etc., outputs.   This permits a high-speed pulse source to be measured on a low-speed mechanical recorder.   In nuclear-physics and cosmic-ray applications the pulses are not uniformly spaced in time.   The circuits will function properly provided that the pulses are not too close together. The *resolution* time of an average scaler, i.e., the minimum time between

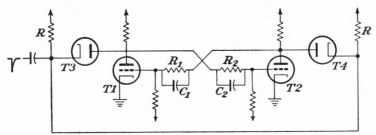

Fig. 9-38. The use of diodes for triggering pulse injection to a trigger circuit.

successive triggering pulses for accurate counting, is of the order of 5 μsec.

A circuit of the Eccles-Jordan type may be used to form gates, one edge of which is controlled by one circuit, the other edge of which is controlled by a second circuit.   In this case, the grids are fed from separate sources, one source switching the circuit on, the other switching it off.

Precisely this technique may be used to measure the time interval between two events.   The two events must be converted into triggering pulses by appropriate means, which might be mechanical, electrical, magnetic, etc.   One trigger is applied to one grid, and the second pulse is applied to the other grid.   The output from one plate is used to control the starting, the output from the second plate controls the subsequent stopping of an integrating device, such as the charging of a capacitor.   The use of a linear charging circuit will yield a capacitor potential which is proportional to the time interval between the triggering pulses.

The problems attendant on triggering the trigger circuit from a source of pulses are precisely those discussed in Sec. 9-1, and the techniques used for pulse injection are the extension of those used before, except that now the pulses must be applied simultaneously to both tubes.   A circuit provided with diode injection is given in Fig. 9-38.   The operation here illustrated requires a negative triggering pulse.   Suppose that $T1$ is on and $T2$ is off.   The application of the negative pulse of amplitude less than IR_l, the drop across the plate-load resistor, will not affect the nonconducting state of $T3$. However, the pulse will pass through $T4$ to the grid of $T1$ and reduce the current in $T1$. This will set off the cumulative action which will continue until $T2$ is conducting and $T1$ is off. The next pulse will be blocked by $T4$ but will pass through $T3$ to the grid of $T2$ to effect the firing of $T2$.

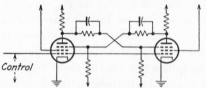

Control

FIG. 9-39. Eccles-Jordan type of trigger circuit using pentodes.

A number of variants of this basic circuit have been published. Reich[3] replaced the triodes by pentodes. In this case the grids are free for the application of the initiating signals, the suppressor grids serving the same function as the triode grids. The circuit is shown in Fig. 9-39. Here the application of a positive potential to the control grid of the nonconducting tube cannot cause conduction to begin, owing to the high negative potential on the suppressor grid, which prevents plate current from flowing. The application of a negative potential to the control grid of the conducting tube reduces its current and triggers the circuit. If a short-duration negative pulse is applied to the control grids of both tubes simultaneously, both tubes will be cut off. However, the coupling capacitors cause the suppressor of the tube which was conducting to be more

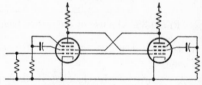

FIG. 9-40. An alternative form of trigger circuit using pentodes.

negative than that of the other tube, and as a result the current transfers to the second tube at the end of the triggering pulse. The capacitances should be such that the time taken for them to charge or to discharge from one equilibrium value of potential to the other values is large compared with the duration of the triggering pulse but small compared with the time between successive pulses.

An alternative circuit that operates satisfactorily was suggested by Regener.[4] The circuit is shown in Fig. 9-40.

A cathode-coupled scale-of-2 circuit was suggested by Scal.[5] The circuit is shown in Fig. 9-41. It will be

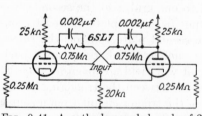

FIG. 9-41. A cathode-coupled scale-of-2 circuit.

observed that this circuit bears the same relation to the cathode-coupled multivibrator that the circuit of Fig. 9-37 bears to the plate-coupled multivibrator.

9-11. Single-tube Pentode Trigger Circuit. It was first pointed out by Reich[3] that, by replacing the coupling capacitor between the screen and the suppressor grids of the pentode relaxation oscillator of Fig. 9-39 with a resistor, the result is a trigger circuit. This circuit is illustrated in Fig. 9-42.

A physical explanation of the operation of the circuit is possible. Suppose that the tube is initially in such a state that the current to the plate is zero when the current to the screen is a maximum. If the resistances R and R_3 and the suppressor bias are properly chosen, the suppressor potential is sufficiently low to maintain no plate current and the tube remains in the zero-plate-current state.

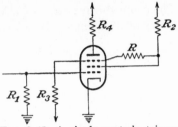

Suppose now that a positive triggering pulse is applied to the control grid which is sufficiently positive to cause

FIG. 9-42. A single-pentode trigger circuit.

plate current to exist. As a result, the screen current will begin to decrease, and the screen and also the suppressor potentials will begin to rise. This causes the plate potential to tend to increase, resulting in a cumulative action which continues until the plate current attains its maximum possible value. At this point, the screen is almost at E_{bb}, the suppressor potential is slightly positive owing to the suppressor grid current when the potential is positive, and the plate continues to draw current. The tube thus remains in the conducting state.

To turn the tube off will require the application of a second positive triggering pulse. With an increase of tube current, the screen will collect more electrons, lowering the screen potential. This lowers the suppressor potential, which then begins to control the anode current. With a decreased anode current, the screen current increases, and the cumulative action begins, which ends when the anode current is zero.

9-12. Scaling Circuits. Scaling circuits may be constructed by forming a cascaded group of scale-of-2 circuits,[6] the results being scale-of-4, scale-of-8, scale-of-16, scale-of-32, scale-of-64 circuits, or, in general, a count of 2^n for n stages. Circuits which include feedback are possible to yield scale-of-5,[7] scale-of-6,[8] scale-of-10 circuits,[9] and others. These scalers use the basic trigger circuit but provide for forced resetting at a specified count.

To examine[10] in a general way the effect of feedback in cascaded trigger pairs, consider the system illustrated in Fig. 9-43. This system may be extended to any similar form, as desired. As illustrated, the outputs of the respective stages are denoted N_1, N_2, N_3, and N_4, with N_{in} denoting the number of input pulses. The input to the pair designated $P1$ is written directly as $N_{in} + N_3$. The output of $P1$ is

$$N_1 = \tfrac{1}{2}(N_{in} + N_3)$$

Similarly

$$N_2 = \tfrac{1}{2}(N_1 + N_4)$$
$$N_3 = \tfrac{1}{2}(N_2 + N_4)$$
$$N_4 = \tfrac{1}{2}N_3$$

The count-down ratio is N_{in}/N_4 and may be obtained by solving the fore-going relationships. By writing the equations as

$$2N_1 - N_3 = N_{in}$$
$$N_1 - 2N_2 + N_4 = 0$$
$$N_2 - 2N_3 + N_4 = 0$$
$$N_3 - 2N_4 = 0$$

from which, by determinantal methods,

$$N_4 = \frac{\begin{vmatrix} 2 & 0 & -1 & N_{in} \\ 1 & -2 & 0 & 0 \\ 0 & 1 & -2 & 0 \\ 0 & 0 & 1 & 0 \end{vmatrix}}{\begin{vmatrix} 2 & 0 & -1 & 0 \\ 1 & -2 & 0 & 1 \\ 0 & 1 & -2 & 1 \\ 0 & 0 & 1 & -2 \end{vmatrix}} = \frac{N_{in}}{8}$$

the count-down ratio becomes, for this case,

$$\text{Count-down ratio} = \frac{N_{in}}{N_4} = 8 \tag{9-51}$$

If in the circuit of Fig. 9-43 the feedback line marked N_3 is removed, it can be shown by the foregoing methods that the count-down ratio is 10.

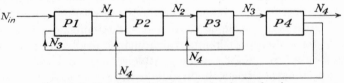

Fig. 9-43. Feedback in a four-stage triggered pair.

This is a desirable choice, since a decade scaler system results. It should be noted that this is not the only choice that yields a scale-of-10 circuit. For example, by omitting the N_4 line to $P2$, by providing $P2$-$P3$ and $P4$-$P2$ feedback lines, or by providing $P3$-$P1$ and $P3$-$P2$ feedback lines, scale-of-10 circuits result. From practical considerations some of these possibilities must be avoided, owing to the complexity that results when an attempt is made to construct the circuit.

A circuit which fits the mathematical description for a feedback line from $P2$ to $P3$ is given in Fig. 9-44. In this circuit the grids of $T4$ and $T6$ are at a high potential, that is, $T4$ and $T6$ are conducting when $T8$ fires, so that the second and third trigger pairs are fired again by the firing of $T8$.

To note the character of the operation, suppose that at the outset tubes $T2$, $T4$, $T6$, $T8$ are conducting. With the application of a series of pulses to the input, ordinary binary operation takes place until the sixteenth

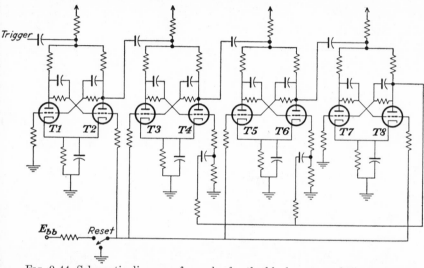

FIG. 9-44. Schematic diagram of a scaler for the block system of Fig. 9-43.

pulse. At this time $T8$ is turned off, and the positive pulse from the output of $T8$ triggers the second and third pairs again. Thus after the sixteenth pulse the system is in the same state as it was after the sixth pulse. The continued application of pulses to the input causes the system to operate between state 6 and state 16, with 1 output pulse for each 10 applied to the input. The reset arrangement can produce any initial state between 1 and 16, the arrangement shown providing a reset to state 6, thereby providing truly decade operation. The system operation is shown graphically in Fig. 9-45, which gives the waveforms at the input and the plate of $T2$, $T4$, $T6$, $T8$.

It must be noted that not all circuits may satisfy the requisite conditions for the above analysis to apply, although circuits may be devised which operate properly, say as a scale-of-10 circuit. One such circuit is illustrated[9] in Fig. 9-46.

A circuit[11] has been described which utilizes no direct feedback to effect switching.   Instead, an electronically switched gate is used to reset the counter at the appropriate point in the counting sequence.   This circuit is so arranged that the eighth pulse flips the third binary pair in the usual way.   This in turn flips a gate control binary which gates an amplifier. The gated amplifier feeds the tenth pulse to the gate control binary, resetting the decade and producing the output pulse.

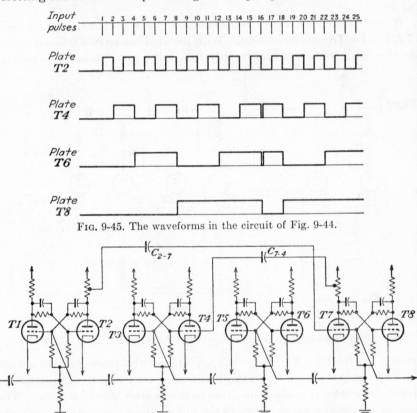

Fig. 9-45. The waveforms in the circuit of Fig. 9-44.

Fig. 9-46. A decade scaler consisting of a conventional trigger circuit with forced recycling at the count of 10.

Ring counter circuits have also been devised to allow a count-down operation.   A block diagram showing the general features of a ring system, which is capable of operating with as many as 50 stages, is given in Fig. 9-47.   The pulses are fed continuously into all stages, which are some form of a trigger pair.   Suppose that the circuit is such that the first pulse causes the left tube of pair $P1$ to conduct, all other left stages being in the nonconducting state.   When $P1$ is switched, this causes the left of $P2$ to conduct.   The next pulse will affect only $P2$, causing the output from this pair to switch $P3$.   In this way, each input pulse causes the next pair in line to conduct. Thus the switched pair progresses successively down the string of stages, each pair producing a count-down of 1. The output is taken from the end of the string, the stage which returns the system to the original state. Clearly, any desired count-down ratio is possible, simply by incorporating the requisite number of pairs in the ring.

The pulse from each preceding stage which serves to flip a given stage over from its normal state will arrive at the stage almost simultaneously

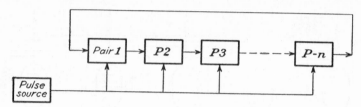

FIG. 9-47. Block diagram of a conventional ring counter.

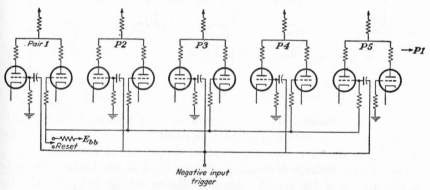

FIG. 9-48. The essentials of a closed ring counter system.

with the regular input pulse which tends to keep the stage in its normal state. If the regular input pulses are short enough and if the time constants of the stages are long enough, then the flipping-action pulse may be delayed until the regular input pulse has passed, and satisfactory operation is possible.

The essential features of a five-trigger-pair ring circuit is given[10] in Fig. 9-48, although the feedback networks, the coupling systems, and the cathode circuits are omitted. Suppose that the reset causes the right-hand tube of all but the last stage to conduct. The first negative input pulse triggers $P5$ only, since all other grids are negative. The output from this pair simultaneously triggers the next stage (pair 1 in this case), the remainder of the system remaining stable and unchanged. The next negative trigger will affect only $P1$, which, when it switches, will cause $P2$ to trigger, etc., with a progressing of the pulse from one pair to the next.

The output would normally be taken from the right-hand tube of $P5$ in the present case.

A form of scale-of-5 pentode circuit which produces a succession of pulse progressions by means of grid-potential control by switching is given in Fig. 9-49.[7]

Coincidence techniques have also been employed as a means of achieving desired count-down circuits.[12] These circuits will not be discussed, however.

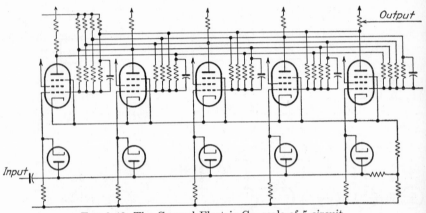

Fig. 9-49. The General Electric Co. scale-of-5 circuit.

9-13. Pulse Generators. It is ordinarily not possible to distinguish between a narrow gate and a pulse, particularly since the two may be generated in the same manner. A sharp distinction is hardly necessary, but one might perhaps distinguish between them on the basis of the ultimate purpose of the signal. Another distinguishing feature might be based on the time duration of the signal. There are, however, certain methods available for generating very narrow pulses with reasonably sharp rise and fall which are not suitable for generating wider gates. It is not always necessary that the pulse be rectangular, although certain applications require such a pulse. Several methods for generating such narrow rectangular pulses will be considered. These methods fall into two general classes. In one, tube circuits are employed, and these may be gas-filled or vacuum tubes, with provision for damping to keep the pulse narrow and rectangular. In another type, artificial transmission or pulse-forming lines are used to control the duration of the pulse and also to effect a rectangular shape.

A simple circuit for generating pulses incorporates an oscillatory circuit between the plate and cathode of a thyratron. Such a circuit is given in Fig. 9-50. It is the function of the oscillatory circuit when shock-excited to cause the plate potential to fall below that required to maintain the

ischarge of the thyratron, once it has been fired. The pulses so gen-
rated are not rectangular in shape but are acceptable for some types of
ervice.

Simple *RLC* ringing or pulse circuits using hard tubes are also possible.
uch a circuit which incorporates the tank circuit in the cathode circuit is
llustrated in Fig. 9-51. The out-
ut from this circuit in the absence
f the damping diode *T*2 is a train
f damped oscillations which ter-
ninates rapidly at the end of the
nput pulse, owing to the damping
f the beam resistance of *T*1. The
se of the damping diode removes
lmost all but the first half cycle.
n many cases the diode may be

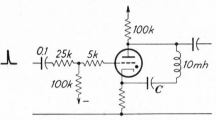

FIG. 9-50. A thyratron pulse generator
with an oscillatory extinguishing circuit.

eplaced by a resistor of a resistance which is chosen to produce nearly
ritical damping when the tube is cut off.

A comparable *RLC* peaker with the tuned circuit in the plate lead is
llustrated in Fig. 9-52. Here, as in the foregoing circuit, a damping

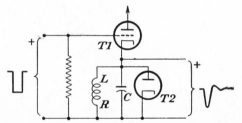

FIG. 9-51. A simple ringing pulse-generator circuit.

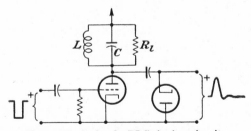

FIG. 9-52. A simple *RLC* ringing circuit.

esistance which is chosen to damp critically the tuned circuit, or a damp-
ng diode, will yield a single pulse instead of a limited group of oscillations.

Figure 9-53 shows a circuit for generating narrow rectangular pulses
ranging from less than 1 μsec duration to perhaps 10 or 20 μsec duration.
n this circuit an 884 thyratron with its ionization time of approximately

10^{-8} sec is used to generate the pulse, the trailing edge of which is controlled by a second thyratron. The output pulse from such a circuit has relatively sharp sides.

Suppose that the 884 has been triggered by the application of a positive triggering pulse to the grid. This causes the 884 to conduct, and the potential that appears across the 0.001-μf capacitor from plate to ground, less the drop in the 884, appears across the cathode resistor, capacitor, and the 2050 clipper thyratron. Note that the 200-kilohm plate resistor and the 1-megohm cathode resistor are so large that a continuous discharge through the 884 cannot be sustained and that the energy of the pulse must be supplied from the 0.001-μf capacitor. Clearly, for different

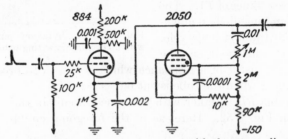

FIG. 9-53. A thyratron pulse generator with thyratron clipper.

pulse lengths, different capacitance plate-ground capacitors will be required.

Once the 884 has been fired, the potential on the plate of the 2050 increases to some positive value, and if the energy in the pulse is small compared with that on the plate capacitor, the 2050 plate potential remains relatively constant. Owing to the RC circuits between the plate and the control grid and the grid and the cathode of the 2050, there will be a time delay before the grid-cathode potential increases from the normally nonconducting value of -15 volts, determined by the potential divider between the -150-volt source and ground, to the approximately zero potential required for the tube to fire. The time duration is controlled by the adjustable 1-megohm resistor in the circuit. Once the 2050 fires, the cathode of the 884 is effectively short-circuited to ground thus terminating the output pulse. Of course, the 2050 continues to conduct until enough of the charge has leaked off the capacitor in the 884 circuit for the potential across the 2050 to fall below that required for maintaining the discharge.

A hard-tube circuit for the generation of pulses of short duration[13] is illustrated in Fig. 9-54. This is essentially a cathode-coupled trigger circuit which is controlled by a phantastron delay. In this circuit, $T1$ is normally on, $T2$ is off, and no plate conduction exists in $T3$, although the suppressor grid is conducting. With the application of a negative triggering pulse, $T1$ goes off, causing the suppressor potential of $T3$ to rise, with a consequent plate conduction and the inception of the Miller action in $T3$, with its linearizing influence on the plate-potential decay. The increasing plate current results in a decreasing screen current and a rising screen potential. The rising screen potential, which appears on the grid of $T2$, maintains $T2$ in the conducting state. This situation remains

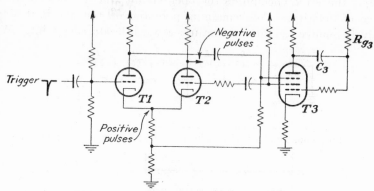

Fig. 9-54. A hard-tube short-pulse generator.

until the regenerative action in $T3$ ceases, and this is dictated by the Miller circuit time constant and the suppressor-circuit time constant. When the flyback sequence occurs, $T2$ is turned off and the circuit is back in its original state. By the proper choice of parameters, pulses in the range from 0.7 to 12.8 μsec, with good rise and fall times, have been generated.

The use of a blocking oscillator which is biased normally off, and which is triggered as desired, will yield pulses which are often suitable for some services. Such a circuit, which provides for an adjustable pulse width, is given in Fig. 9-55. This type of circuit is incorporated in the linear-sweep delay circuit given in Fig. 9-35.

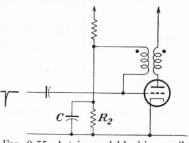

Fig. 9-55. A triggered blocking oscillator for pulse generation.

9-14. Line-controlled Pulse Generators. The use of artificial transmission lines in the formation of short rectangular pulses has become widespread in recent years. The basic circuit is shown in Fig. 9-56. The line is considered to consist of a sufficient number of sections so that it closely approximates a continuous transmission line. One end of the line is open-circuited; a resistance R_0 equal to the characteristic impedance of the line $Z_0 = \sqrt{L/C}$ is connected across the other end. The line is initially charged by means of the battery, and hence all capacitors are charged to full battery potential. When the switch is closed, one half of the battery potential appears across the terminating resistance R_0 and the remaining half of the potential traverses the line as a potential wave. The wave front is delayed $T = \sqrt{LC}$ sec for each section through which it passes. As it progresses down the line, the potential wave removes one-half of the potential present across the line. When it reaches the end of the line, the wave encounters the open circuit and is reflected without change of polarity. The remaining potential on the line is then progressively removed as the wave returns toward the starting point. When

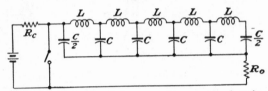

Fig. 9-56. The basic circuit incorporating a pulse-forming line.

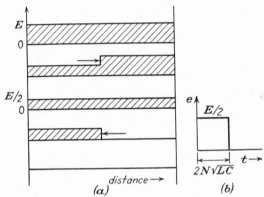

Fig. 9-57. (a) The traveling potential wave on an open-circuited transmission line that is originally charged and is being discharged. (b) The waveshape across R_0 as a function of time.

the wave front reaches the starting point, it cancels the potential across the resistance R_0 and the entire system comes to rest. In traversing the line forward and backward, the occupied time is

$$T = 2N \sqrt{LC} \quad \text{sec} \qquad (9\text{-}52$$

where N is the number of sections.

The sequence of events is illustrated in the block diagram of Fig. 9-57 which shows the potential distribution on the line at various times during the existence of the running wave. As a result of the sequence of actions a potential pulse appears across the resistor R_0. When the switch is closed, the potential instantaneously assumes a value equal to one-half of the applied potential. This potential persists until the potential wave has traversed the line and returned to R_0, and it thereupon drops to zero suddenly.

The circuit provides a very simple method of forming a rectangular pulse of controllable length, provided that the pulse length is short enough to be obtained in an artificial line of practical dimensions.   The practical

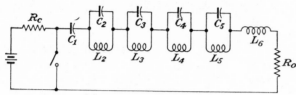

Fig. 9-58. The general characteristics of a pulse-forming circuit employing a Guillemin line.

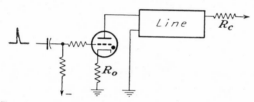

Fig. 9-59. A line-controlled thyratron pulse generator.

difficulty that might be encountered in such a pulse-forming circuit is the number of sections required to approximate a continuous transmission line.   Each section introduces a small deviation in the flat top of the pulse.   If the top is to be essentially flat, a large number of sections should be used.

The Guillemin line is a network which simulates the section of a transmission line which is open-circuited at the far end.   A circuit of this line is given in Fig. 9-58.   This network is a closer approximation to the continuous transmission line than a simple line of an equal number of sections.   Several typical line-controlled pulse circuits are given below.

Figure 9-59 is essentially the circuit of Fig. 9-50, except that the pulse

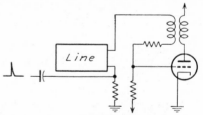

Fig. 9-60. A line-controlled blocking oscillator.

duration is controlled by the "length" of the line in the plate circuit, the thyratron being extinguished when the plate potential falls to zero.

In the circuit of Fig. 9-60 a line is added to the grid circuit of a blocking oscillator to control the duration of the pulse.   In this circuit the triggering pulse is applied to the artificial line and is followed immediately thereafter by the beginning of the rectangular wave.   The potential wave traverses to the open end of the line and then is reflected back without change of sign. When the wave front reaches the input end, the positive grid potential is removed from the line, reducing the input potential to zero. This causes the grid-cathode potential to be driven below cutoff, thus yielding a sharp pulse in the output of the circuit.

A delay line may also be used as the cathode impedance in an amplifier tube, as shown in Fig. 9-61. The operation of this circuit is essentially the following: The sharp rise at the beginning of the applied gate to the grid is accompanied by a corresponding sharp increase in the plate current. This causes a cathode-ground potential wave, which then proceeds down the transmission line, which is essentially open-circuited, as the terminating resistance R_k is made much higher than the characteristic impedance of the line. R_k serves only to complete the d-c path from cathode to ground. The potential wave is reflected from the open end and retraces its path back along the line. This reflected potential at the input end adds to the applied potential to cause the cathode-ground potential to reach a value of nearly twice the initial potential. This increase in the cathode-ground potential is enough to cause the tube to cut off, thus terminating the pulse.

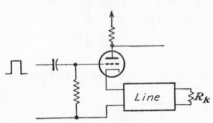

Fig. 9-61. A pulse generator with the line in the cathode circuit.

REFERENCES

1. Williams, F. C., and N. F. Moody, *J. IEE*, **39**, 1188 (1946).
2. Eccles, W. H., and F. W. Jordan, *Radio Rev.*, **1**, 143 (1919).
3. Reich, H. J., *Rev. Sci. Instr.*, **9**, 222 (1938).
4. Regener, V. H., *Rev. Sci. Instr.*, **17**, 180 (1946).
5. Scal, R. K. F., *Electronics*, **20**, 150 (September, 1947).
6. Sharpless, T. K., *Electronics*, **21**, 122 (March, 1948).
7. General Electric Co., Decade Scaling Unit, Type YYZ-1.
8. Langberg, E. L., *Rev. Sci. Instr.*, **18**, 796 (1947).
9. Potter, J. T., *Electronics*, **17**, 110 (June, 1944).
10. Von Tersch, L. W., and A. W. Swago, "Recurrent Electrical Transients," p. 306, Prentice-Hall, Inc., New York, 1953.
11. Kemp, E. L., *Electronics*, **26**, 145 (February, 1953).
12. Parshad, R., and A. Sagar, *Rev. Sci. Instr.*, **24**, 542 (1953).
13. Levell, D. A., *Electronic Eng.*, **24**, 507 (1952).
14. As a general reference, see:
    Chance, B., *et al.*, "Waveforms," Massachusetts Institute of Technology, Radiation Laboratory Series, vol. 19, McGraw-Hill Book Company, Inc., New York, 1949.

PROBLEMS

9-1. A 6SN7 tube is to be used to produce a positive rectangular gate of 108 μsec duration. The pulse repetition frequency is 400 per second. The gate is driven by a negative trigger pulse, and the positive gate is to begin at the time that the trigger is applied.

a. Draw the circuit for such a gate. Indicate on the circuit the terminals to which the negative trigger is applied, the terminals from which the gate is taken, and the circuit elements which determine the length of the gate.

b. One grid should be returned to B+, and the other to ground. Give reasons.

c. Calculate the coupling capacitor connected to the grid of tube $T1$. Use the following data:

	Section 1 Grid to B+	Section 2 Grid to ground
E_{bb}	300 volts	300 volts
R_g	0.5 megohm	1 megohm
R_l	20 kilohms	30 kilohms
μ	20	20
Static r_c	500 ohms	500 ohms
Static r_b when $e_c = 0$	10 kilohms	10 kilohms

9-2. Refer to the following circuit. Prove that if $R_1C_1 = R_2C_2$ there is attenuation but no distortion. (A somewhat similar circuit will be found of importance for current sources; see Prob. 11-7.)

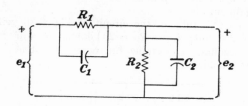

9-3. *a.* A gate circuit using a 6SN7 tube in the circuit of Fig. 9-5 is triggered at 1,000 per second. Specify the parameters to yield a gate having a duration of 650 μsec and 200 volts high.

b. Repeat (*a*) if the gate width is to be 950 μsec long.

9-4. *a.* Calculate the recharging time constant of the capacitor C in the cathode-coupled delay gate.

b. To what value does e_{c2} jump when the circuit recovers, i.e., what is the value of e_{c2} at point A of Fig. 9-13?

9-5. Carry out the analysis that leads to Eq. 9-15 for the duration of the gate of Fig. 9-12.

9-6. The circuit shown in the diagram is to be designed to give a pulse output

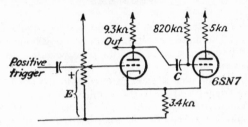

of 100 μsec width. Assume the following:

$$\text{6SN7 tube; } E_{bb} = 250 \text{ volts}$$
$$r_c = 1 \text{ kilohm when } e_c = 0 \text{ or positive}$$
$$r_b = 10 \text{ kilohms when } e_c = 0 \text{ or positive}$$
$$E_0 = -10 \text{ volts}$$
$$\text{Trigger prf} = 400 \text{ cps}$$

a. For operation under these conditions, what limits are imposed on the values that E might assume?

b. Calculate the value of the coupling capacitor C.

9-7. The circuit of Fig. 9-18 uses a 6SN7 tube and is supplied from a 300-volt regulated power supply. Suppose that the bias potential E can be varied over the limits from 20 to 65 volts.

a. Are the approximations in Eqs. (9-26) satisfied over this potential range?

b. Calculate the duration of the gate at each limiting value. The plate current is related to the tube potentials by the approximate expression

$$i_b = 9.1 \times 10^{-5}(e_b + 20e_c) \qquad \text{amp} \pm 10\%$$

9-8. Derive an expression for the recharge of the capacitor in the Miller integrator of Fig. 9-20 when the suppressor pulse is removed and the plate current of the pentode is again cut off.

9-9. Consider a 6SN7 tube in the circuit of Fig. 9-36, with the following parameters: $E_{bb} = 250$ volts; $R_{l1} = R_{l2} = 20$ kilohms; $R_1 = R_2 = 1$ megohm; and $R_{g1} = R_{g2} = 1$ megohm. Determine the range of potentials for which the following tabulation holds:

$T1$	$T2$	E_{cc}
Full on	Full on	
Full on	Part on	
Full on	Cut off	
Part on	Cut off	
Cut off	Cut off	

9-10. Consider the basic Eccles trigger circuit of Fig. 9-36. Suppose $R_{l1} = R_{l2} = 15$ kilohms; $R_1 = R_2 = 400$ kilohms; $R_{g1} = R_{g2} = 0.5$ megohm; $E_{bb} = 300$ volts; $E_{cc} = -75$ volts. Calculate the tube currents when the system is in one of its stable states.

9-11. Suppose that E_{bb} = 250 volts in the circuit of Fig. 9-41.   Calculate the tube currents when the system is in one of its stable states.

9-12. Specify the parameters of the trigger circuit of Fig. 9-41 using a 6SN7 tube to yield a 100-volt swing.   Assume E_{bb} = 250 volts; cutoff grid at −25 volts; full on at zero grid volts.

9-13. The Schmitt trigger circuit* is illustrated.   Discuss the operation of this

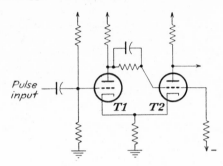

circuit, with consideration of (a) choice of circuit parameters, (b) polarity of triggering pulses.

9-14. Estimate the minimum value of C that is required in Fig. 9-50 in order that the thyratron cuts off at the peak of the pulse.   Choose the sustaining potential of the thyratron at 16 volts.   For a capacitance twice this minimum value, estimate the duration of the first pulse.   Choose E_{bb} = 250 volts.

9-15. *a.* The circuit illustrated incorporates a pentode which is nominally biased

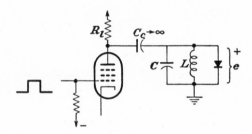

beyond cutoff.   The input to the grid or the suppressor turns the tube on.   Show that the output has the form†

$$e = \frac{2IRMe^{-Mt}\sin{(N-M^2)t}}{\sqrt{N-M^2}}$$

where $M = \frac{1}{2}CR$; $N = 1/LC$, R = parallel combination of r_p and R_l, and that the time for a half cycle is $t_0 = \pi/2\sqrt{N-M^2}$.

b. Show that the peak potential of the output is

$$e_{\text{peak}} = \frac{I}{(L/C)^2}e^{-\pi/4Q}$$

* O. H. Schmitt, *J. Sci. Instr.*, **15**, 24 (1938).
† L. Reiffel, *Rev. Sci. Instr.*, **22**, 215 (1951).

9-16. The variable resistance of the pulse circuit of Fig. 9-53 is set at 0.5 megohm. Estimate the duration of the pulse generated by the circuit. Choose $E_{bb} = 300$ volts.

9-17. The circuit shown may be used to produce pulses of different pulse

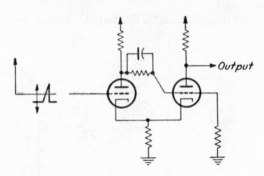

lengths. Discuss the operation of the circuit, with specific consideration to the front edge and back edge of the output pulse.

9-18. It is required to design a circuit which will provide the several outputs as shown on the accompanying time diagram.

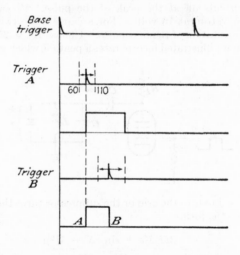

a. Draw a block diagram of a circuit that will satisfy the requirements.

b. Show the complete circuit diagram. Do not evaluate the circuit elements to be used.

All times are given in microseconds.

9-19. The fundamental problem in the design of a tuned pulse-forming network is to determine a network composed of but few circuit elements which will respond with a closely rectangular wave of current when excited with a unit voltage. Show that the rectangular wave may be represented by a Fourier series, the first five terms of which have the form

$$f(t) = a_1 \sin \omega t + a_3 \sin 3\omega t + a_5 \sin 5\omega t + a_7 \sin 7\omega t + a_9 \sin 9\omega t$$

Calculate the values of the coefficients a_n.   Plot the resulting curve represented by these results, and compare with the results for which

$$a_1 = 1.2575 \qquad a_3 = 0.3725 \qquad a_5 = 0.1735$$
$$a_7 = 0.08315 \qquad a_9 = 0.02777$$

9-20. The diagram for this problem shows the actual circuit of the pulse-

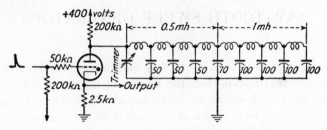

forming stage of a pulse modulator.   Calculate the width and amplitude of the generated pulse.

CHAPTER 10

SAW-TOOTH SWEEP GENERATORS

The function of the sweep circuit in a cathode-ray tube is to cause the luminous spot that results from the impact of the electron beam on the fluorescent screen phosphor to move across the screen with a known velocity, whether it be constant or whether it be varying in some definite way with respect to time (see Chap. 1 for an analytical discussion of the mechanics of electron-beam deflection). The proper selection of the form of the sweep is most important, since otherwise a relatively simple investigation may prove to be almost impossible. If, for example, it is desired to examine the shape of a periodically recurring wave, a sweep circuit that is proportional to the time would normally be desired. Such a linear sweep might not be appropriate in some application where a sweep that is proportional to some other quantity might be indicated.

The problems which arise in producing sweep circuits for electrostatic cathode-ray tubes are quite different from those which arise in producing the sweep circuits for electromagnetic-type tubes. This chapter will consider the problems which arise in the generation of sweeps for electrostatic-type tubes; the following chapter will consider the problems arising in the generation of magnetic and other sweeps.

10-1. Simple Saw-tooth Sweep. One of the most common sweep requirements is for a repetitive trace along a straight line. Owing to the

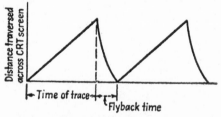

Fig. 10-1. A simple saw-tooth sweep.

dimensional limitations of the cathode-ray tube screen, the waveform required to produce it is of the saw-tooth form, as shown in Fig. 10-1. The waveform illustrated is the ideal, since it varies linearly with time, but, following standard practice, no attempt is made to linearize the flyback portion of the wave. With the waveform shown, the electron spot

318

moves across the tube face with a uniform velocity and with a speed depending upon the slope of the curve. The spot is caused to return to the starting point very rapidly, and ordinarily it is not seen, or, at worst, its brilliancy is much reduced over that of the writing portion of the cycle.

The ideal saw tooth illustrated is not easily obtained by direct means, and various methods have been employed to linearize or to compensate nonlinear waves. The details of such circuits will be examined below.

10-2. Capacitive Sweep Circuits. Many of the more common circuits employ the changing potential across a capacitor upon the application of a constant source of potential across a series resistor and capacitor combination. These circuits usually employ separate charging and discharging circuits in order that the retrace or flyback time may be made much shorter than the writing time. Ordinarily the charging circuit is permitted to function continuously, the rapid discharge being accomplished by a rapidly acting switching circuit. The basic form of such a circuit is shown in Fig. 10-2.

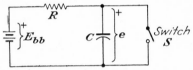

Fig. 10-2. The elements of a switching circuit for producing a saw-tooth wave.

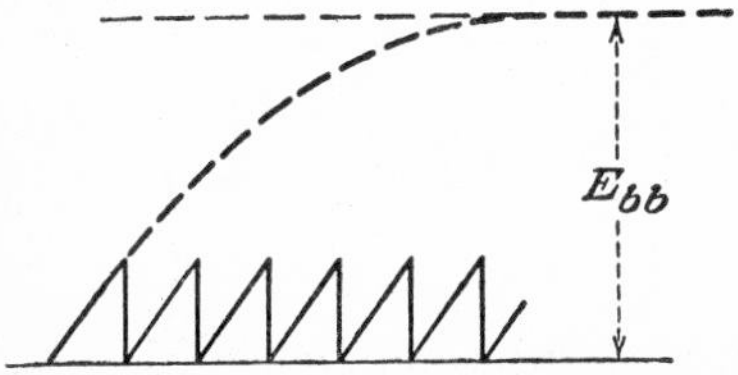

The potential across the capacitor in the circuit shown follows the form

$$e = E_{bb}(1 - e^{-t/RC}) \qquad (10\text{-}1)$$

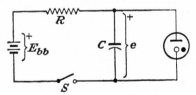

Fig. 10-3. Achieving a linear saw tooth from an RC circuit.

where E_{bb} is the potential applied to the RC combination, t is the time in seconds, C is the capacitance in farads, and R is the resistance in ohms. For a short time after the application of the potential E_{bb}, the potential increase across the capacitor will be reasonably linear with time. For example, for a time equal to one-fifth the time constant of the circuit, the potential increase will be linear within about 10 per cent. If the switching is properly timed, a reasonably satisfactory wave, of the form illustrated in Fig. 10-3, is possible.

One of the earliest and probably one of the simplest capacitive saw-tooth generators utilizes a glow-discharge tube as the switch in the circuit of Fig. 10-2. The circuit of this saw-tooth generator is given in Fig. 10-4. Suppose that the capacitor is initially uncharged when the

Fig. 10-4. A saw-tooth generator using a glow-discharge tube.

switch S is closed. The potential across the capacitor will increase according to Eq. (10-1). When e_c equals the breakdown potential of the glow tube E_d, charge will flow through the tube from the capacitor. This discharge is accompanied by a rapidly falling capacitor potential. When the potential across the capacitor falls below the extinction potential E_e of the glow tube, the discharge ceases. The discharge current is high since it is limited only by the resistance and inductance of the leads that connect the capacitor to the glow tube, and the discharge time is very small.

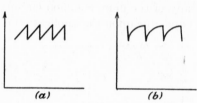

(a)   (b)

FIG. 10-5. The waveshape of the output in a simple glow-tube sweep generator. Curve a is for a supply potential of 600 volts; curve b is for a supply potential of 135 volts. The amplitude of oscillation is the same in both cases.

Once the tube becomes extinguished, the capacitor immediately begins to recharge. When the potential across the capacitor again reaches the discharge E_d, the tube will again break down and conduction will continue until the capacitor potential again falls to E_e, when the process repeats itself. This process is periodic and results in oscillations that have a period T equal to the time required for the capacitor to charge from the potential E_e to E_d and then discharge to E_e. The expression governing the process is found from Eq. (10-1) to be

$$T = RC \log_e \frac{E_{bb} - E_e}{E_{bb} - E_d} \tag{10-2}$$

The amplitude of the oscillation equals the potential difference $E_d - E_e$. Such simple glow-tube circuits may be used for frequencies of 1 cycle every few minutes to frequencies well up in the a-f range.

The waveshape of the resulting saw tooth is dependent upon the magnitude of the supply source E_{bb}. The use of a VR-90, for which E_d equals approximately 120 volts and for which E_e equals 85 volts approximately, and a 600-volt supply yield a wave that is approximately triangular, as shown in Fig. 10-5a. The same circuit when used on a 135-volt supply yields the curved waveform of Fig. 10-5b.

10-3. Thyratron Sweep Generators. Two obvious shortcomings of the simple glow-tube sweep generator are (1) that high potentials must be used in order to obtain relatively linear saw-tooth waves and (2) that the amplitude of the output wave is relatively small. The use of a thyratron as a switch allows reasonable flexibility in control of the period of oscillation and also in the amplitude of the saw-tooth wave so generated. The circuit of a potential saw-tooth generator employing an 884 thyratron in such a relaxation circuit is given in Fig. 10-6. In this circuit R_g is a protective resistor in the grid circuit, and R' is a protective current-limiting resistor in the plate circuit. R' is made as small as possible consistent with the tube-current rating in order that the capacitor may discharge very quickly through the tube.

To understand the operation of the circuit, reference must be made to the critical grid curve of the thyratron, which is given in Fig. 10-7. Suppose that the battery potentials are set at $E_{cc} = 20$ and $E_{bb} = 250$ volts. Also suppose that

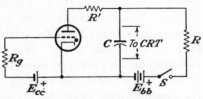

FIG. 10-6. A saw-tooth generator employing a thyratron.

the capacitor is initially uncharged. After the switch S is closed, the potential across the capacitor will increase exponentially according to Eq. (10-1). This charging process will continue until the potential

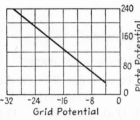

FIG. 10-7. Typical critical grid characteristic of an 884 argon-filled thyratron.

across the capacitor reaches approximately 160 volts. At this time the tube will break down. Charge will leak off the capacitor very rapidly, and the tube will stop conducting when the cathode-anode potential falls below about 16 volts, the arc-maintaining potential of the tube. The capacitor will again begin to charge through the local RC circuit, and the entire process will repeat itself. The period of oscillation can be adjusted by varying R, C, or the potential E_{cc} or E_{bb}. Certain of these results are made evident from an inspection of Fig. 10-8.

The oscillations of a gas-tube generator are not very stable in frequency. The thyratron oscillator can be synchronized with a given fre-

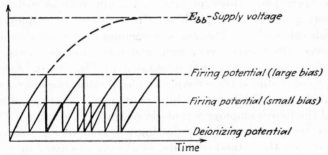

FIG. 10-8. The change of amplitude and frequency of a thyratron saw-tooth generator by change of grid bias.

quency by injecting a small potential of the desired frequency into the grid, in precisely the same way as synchronization is achieved for a multivibrator or blocking oscillator (see Chap. 8). The entire synchronization process is illustrated in Fig. 10-9. The normal action of the circuit in the absence of any synchronizing signal is shown in Fig. 10-8 and is shown dotted in Fig. 10-9. Firing will normally occur at the points A, C, etc. Now suppose that the natural period of the circuit is adjusted to be slightly larger than the period of the synchronizing signal, assumed to be a sinusoidal wave. The effect of this sinusoidal synchronizing potential on the grid is to cause the firing potential of the circuit to vary in accordance with this varying grid potential. At some time during the synchronizing cycle the firing potential will be low (below the zero

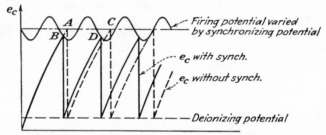

Fig. 10-9. Synchronizing a thyratron saw-tooth generator with a sine wave.

synchronizing potential level), and the tube will fire at point B. On the next cycle the circuit is fired at point D. When the steady-state firing sequence is reached, the situation is essentially that illustrated. The period, or time per cycle, is thus reduced from AC to BD, and the circuit is now synchronized, or locked, to the frequency of the injected potential. The circuit may be synchronized to a submultiple or a multiple of the synchronizing frequency.

10-4. Free-running Vacuum-tube Circuits. The thyratron of the previous section may be replaced by a vacuum tube with substantially the same operation. However, since a vacuum tube as such is neither self-triggering nor self-extinguishing, circuits must be employed which accomplish this action. The use of a vacuum-tube relaxation-oscillator circuit serves the purpose very well, and such circuits are used extensively. Four such circuits are illustrated in Fig. 10-10. One circuit employs a conventional plate-coupled multivibrator; one employs a cathode-coupled multivibrator; the third employs a blocking-oscillator circuit; and the fourth employs a pentode relaxation oscillator. These circuits may be synchronized by injecting a synchronizing potential into the grid or into the cathode circuits, as already discussed in connection with the several oscillator circuits. Hence all the properties of the gas-tube relaxation circuits are also possessed by the vacuum-tube circuits. In addition, the hard-tube circuits will operate at higher frequencies than the gas-tube circuits.

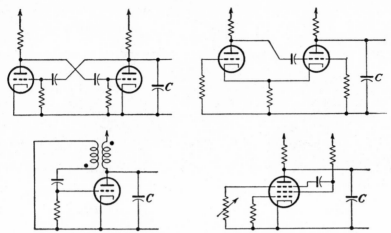

FIG. 10-10. Free-running vacuum-tube sweep generators.

10-5. Triggered Sweep Circuits.   The use of a vacuum tube as a switch allows very accurate timing of the start of the sweep potential, since there is substantially no delay between the application of a signal on the grid and the consequent effect in the plate circuit.   In particular, refer to the circuit of Fig. 10-11.   In this circuit, the grid is so biased that the tube is conducting when no negative square wave is applied to the grid.   The potential across the capacitor is E_1, which may be equal to E_b, if the time is sufficient for the capacitor to discharge to its minimum value.   With the application of the negative gate, the tube ceases to

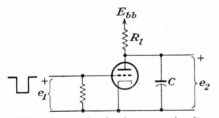

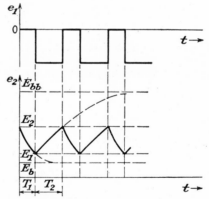

FIG. 10-11. A hard-tube sweep circuit.

FIG. 10-12. The input and output potential waveforms in the circuit of Fig. 10-11.

conduct, and the potential across C begins to increase toward E_{bb} through the plate-load resistor R_l and may reach the potential E_2 during this charging period.   The situation is illustrated in Fig. 10-12.

Suppose that the charge-discharge cycle takes place between the limits E_1 and E_2, as illustrated.   During the charge period, the equivalent circuit is that shown in Fig. 10-13a. Figure 10-13b gives the equivalent circuit during the discharge period. For the situation illustrated in Fig.

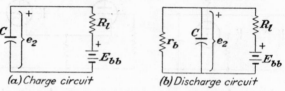

(a) Charge circuit   (b) Discharge circuit

Fig. 10-13. Equivalent circuits of Fig. 10-11 during the charge and discharge periods.

10-12, the potential variation during the charging period is governed by the equation

$$\text{For } t \text{ over period } T_2: \quad e_2 = E_{bb} - (E_{bb} - E_1)e^{-t/R_l C} \qquad (10\text{-}3)$$

During the discharge time, the governing equation is

$$\text{For } t \text{ over period } T_1: \quad e_2 = E_2 e^{-t/r_b C} \qquad \text{for } r_b \ll R_l \qquad (10\text{-}4)$$

These expressions may be used to evaluate E_1 and E_2. The results are obtained as follows: From Eq. (10-3),

$$E_2 = E_{bb} - (E_{bb} - E_1)e^{-T_2/R_l C} \qquad (10\text{-}5)$$

and, from Eq. (10-4),

$$E_1 = E_2 e^{-T_1/r_b C} \qquad (10\text{-}6)$$

Solve these equations simultaneously, thus:

$$E_2 = E_{bb} - (E_{bb} - E_2 e^{-T_1/r_b C})e^{-T_2/R_l C}$$

from which

$$E_2 = \frac{E_{bb}(1 - e^{-T_2/R_l C})}{1 - e^{-(T_1/r_b C + T_2/R_l C)}} \qquad (10\text{-}7)$$

and

$$E_1 = \frac{E_{bb}(1 - e^{-T_2/R_l C})e^{-T_1/r_b C}}{1 - e^{-(T_1/r_b C + T_2/R_l C)}} \qquad (10\text{-}8)$$

It is desirable that the switch tube resistance be as low as possible, perhaps even driving the grid positive to achieve a low value of r_b. Also, the switching time should be long enough to allow E_1 to fall to its minimum possible value E_b. This provides the maximum possible charging potential. As already noted, the charging is substantially linear only if a small part of the charging potential excursion is utilized.

If the tube is normally biased negatively so that there is no plate current and the charge and discharge periods are sufficiently long, then upon the application of a positive gate, the potential across the capacitor will fall from the value E_{bb} to the value determined by the drop across the tube E_b and the drop across the resistor R_{l2}, if one is used to limit the current through the tube. The generator circuit is given in Fig. 10-14, and the general character of the discharge curves is illustrated in Fig. 10-15.

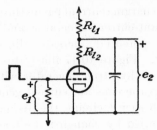

FIG. 10-14. A negatively biased saw-tooth generator.

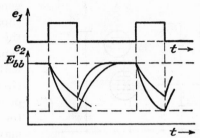

FIG. 10-15. The output-potential waveform from the sweep generator of Fig. 10-14.

10-6. Linearizing Saw-tooth Waves. When a linear-sweep potential is necessary, the most direct recourse is to employ a high potential toward which the capacitor is to charge and then to use only the lower portion of the charging curve. An alternative and somewhat more satisfactory method is to replace the charging resistor by a pentode or other constant-current generator and charge the capacitor through this. For the majority of cases, the degree of linearity obtainable with such a constant-current generator is usually sufficient. Other methods of linearizing saw-tooth generators do exist, and these generally employ one or another of the following methods of obtaining the desired compensation: (*a*) the inverse curvature of a vacuum-tube characteristic, (*b*) an auxiliary time-constant circuit, (*c*) feedback methods. Each of these methods will be considered below.

1. *Charging to a High Potential.* As already pointed out, the use of a fraction of the charging curve will yield a substantially linear potential increase, particularly if the capacitor is charging to a high potential. It is not necessary that a high d-c potential source be available, and the circuit of Fig.

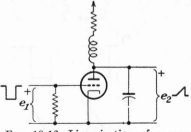

FIG. 10-16. Linearization of a sawtooth wave by using a high-charging potential, obtained by interrupting the current in a large inductor.

10-16 illustrates the method of generating a high potential by interrupting the current in a large choke (of the order of 500 henrys). Such circuits have long flyback times and are limited to circuits having a small duty cycle (the ratio of the duration of the sweep to the sweep recurrence period).

2. *Use of Constant-current Generators.* The use of a constant-current generator in place of the ordinary charging resistor allows a very satisfactory linear saw-tooth potential to be generated. With such a device, the capacitor charging current passes through the constant-current generator, and the capacitor potential increases linearly with time. Figure 10-17 illustrates the circuit of a thyratron generator with a pentode as the constant-current generator. With such a circuit, the frequency may be varied by changing the bias of the pentode, since this controls the tube current and hence the charging rate of the capacitor.

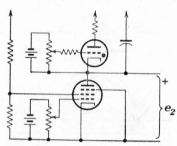

FIG. 10-17. A thyratron saw-tooth generator with a pentode charging circuit.

The circuits of Fig. 10-18 show the connections and the waveforms expected from a vacuum-tube circuit employing pentode charging. For a circuit that incorporates a triode as a constant-current generator see the figure of Prob. 10-7.

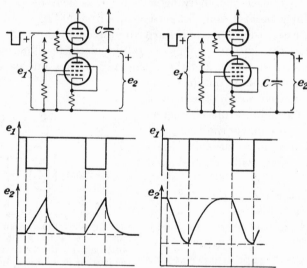

FIG. 10-18. Positive and negative linear saw-tooth generators employing pentode constant-current generators for linearization.

A slightly modified circuit provides pentode charging with adjustable feedback. In this way, any curvature that might still remain in the saw tooth can be compensated by controlling the feedback. This circuit is illustrated in Fig. 10-19.

3. *Linearization by Means of Inverse Curvature.* These methods compensate to a certain degree for the curvature of the charging characteristic by inserting a device having a similar but inverse characteristic. An arrangement which is often adopted is to amplify the potential across the capacitor by means of a tube in such a way that the curvature of the tube characteristic is employed as a linearizing means. It is fortunate in this respect that the curvature of a part of the transfer curve of the

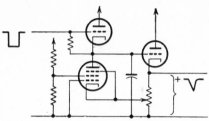

FIG. 10-19. A saw-tooth generator incorporating pentode charging with adjustable feedback.

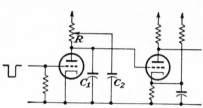

FIG. 10-20. A circuit for linearizing a saw tooth by employing the curved characteristic of a vacuum-tube amplifier.

tube approximates the inverse of an exponential characteristic. Such a circuit is illustrated in Fig. 10-20. In this circuit the output potential is amplified by a second tube which is operated with such a bias that the nonlinear operation compensates the nonlinear input. The added capacitor C_2 is to maintain the anode potential reasonably constant during the discharge period of C_1.

4. *Linearization by Means of an Auxiliary Time-constant Circuit.* A simple method that yields fairly satisfactory results modifies the exponential waveform across the capacitor by the addition of an integrating circuit.[1] The essentials of the circuit are illustrated in Fig. 10-21. In this circuit, the charging capacitor consists of two parts C_1 and C_2 in series. These are charged together, through the resistor R_1, and discharge through the tube.

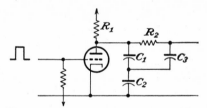

FIG. 10-21. A circuit that employs an integrating network in the output to linearize the saw-tooth wave.

Assume that the capacitors C_1 and C_2 have just been charged. The potential across capacitor C_3 will be less than that across C_1, as C_3 charges through R_2. The potential of C_3 depends on the time constant C_3R_2 and the length of time that C_3 is charging through R_2, and, for sufficiently long times, the potential across C_3 will approach that across C_1. When the gate is applied to the grid of the tube, C_1 and C_2 begin to discharge, while the potential across C_3 falls more slowly owing to the large time constant C_3R_2. At the end of the gate period C_1 and C_2 have been considerably discharged, although, owing to the long time constant, C_3 will still retain a considerable charge. C_1 and C_2 now start to charge once more.   Capacitor C_1 receives charge from two sources, the B+ supply through R_1 and from C_3 through R_2. C_3 supplies charge to C_1 until the potentials are equalized, and C_3 charges thereafter from C_1. The potential variation across C_1 and C_2 is exponential, while that across C_3 is approximately parabolic.   If C_2 and C_3 are properly chosen, the output is approximately linear.

5. *Linearization by Means of Feedback.*   Feedback may be used for improving the linearity of the output of a saw-tooth generator.   Recall that the potential e_2 across the capacitor in the simple saw-tooth circuit

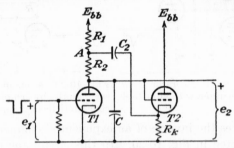

FIG. 10-22. A linear saw-tooth generator employing a cathode follower for feedback, often called the "bootstrap" circuit.

of Fig. 10-11 is exponential because the charging current decreases owing to the reduction in the difference between E_{bb} and e_2 with time.   The exponential variation can be compensated by introducing a potential in the charging circuit to counterbalance the increasing potential across the capacitor.   A circuit that accomplishes this result is illustrated in Fig. 10-22.   This is the bootstrap circuit which was examined in considerable detail in Sec. 9-9 as part of the linear-sweep delay circuit.

As already discussed, $T1$ in this circuit is normally conducting, and the potential across the capacitor is E_{b1}.   With $T2$ absent and with the application of a negative gate to the grid of $T1$, the capacitor will begin to charge from E_{b1} toward E_{bb} along an exponential curve, with a time constant $(R_1 + R_2)C$.   With $T2$ connected as shown, and with the application of the negative gate to cut $T1$ off, as the potential e_2 increases, the potential at R_k also increases, and if the gain of the cathode follower is unity, the two potentials are exactly equal.   Consequently, by the application of the output of the cathode follower into the circuit in such a way that the potential across the capacitor is just balanced by the cathode-follower output, i.e., the potential e_A increases directly with increases in e_2, then the effective potential across R_2 remains constant, with a resultant linear saw-tooth output.   The capacitance of C_2 is made sufficiently large so that the potential across it remains substantially constant under normal operation.   Clearly, when the potential e_A exceeds E_{bb}, the capacitor C_2 will begin to discharge and a loss of linearity of the saw tooth will result, since e_A will no longer be equal to e_2, owing to the change in potential across C_2.

This effect can be largely overcome by replacing resistor R_1 by a diode, as shown in Fig. 10-23. Before the application of the negative gate, both $T1$ and $T3$ are conducting, and e_A is thereby established. With $T1$ cut off, the potential e_2 begins to rise linearly with time, as above. Now when the potential e_A exceeds E_{bb}, the diode $T3$ will cut off and effectively decouple the circuit from the B+ supply, thereby eliminating the

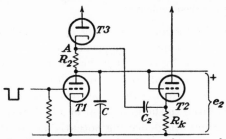

Fig. 10-23. The use of a diode in the plate circuit to reduce any d-c shift and to maintain the feedback gain.

loading on C_2 and permitting the linear variation to extend above E_{bb}. Of course, the charge on C_2 now serves to maintain the charging potential of C, but C_2 is sufficiently large so that only a small change in potential occurs across it during the operating period. With the presence of $T3$, a second advantage occurs during the recycling period. Although C discharges rapidly through $T1$, C_2 would normally recharge through R_1 and, owing to the requirement that the potential across C_2 must remain substantially constant during operation, the discharge and also the recharge time constant must be large. With $T3$ available, which closes to give a low impedance during recycling, C_2 will recharge rapidly.

As discussed, the extent to which the resulting saw tooth is linear depends upon how closely the gain of the cathode follower approaches unity. Of course, if amplification is provided before applying the output across the capacitor C to the grid of the cathode follower, it is then possible to get almost any degree of compensation. Such a circuit would have the form illustrated in Fig. 10-24.

It is a disadvantage of the above circuits that the grid of the cathode follower is driven negatively during the flyback period. Because of the various stray capacitances across the output circuit, these will tend to delay the fall of the cathode potential, and the cathode follower may momentarily cut off, with a consequent poor flyback. For those applications in which the duty cycle is small, the results with the circuit of Fig. 10-23 are highly satisfactory.

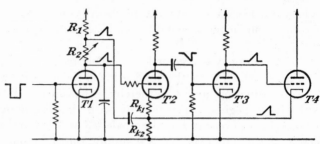

FIG. 10-24. A linear saw-tooth generator with amplification before the application of feedback through a cathode follower.

10-7. Push-pull Deflection. By tying one of each pair of deflecting plates in a cathode-ray tube to the second anode, the total number of external leads is reduced by two. On the other hand, when this is done, both defocusing and trapezium distortion will result.[2] Consequently, in those cases where these effects cannot be tolerated, it is necessary to connect the anode potential to the mid-point of a high resistance across each pair of plates and apply the deflecting potential across the plates. Using the connection illustrated in Fig. 10-25 provides the opportunity for using push-pull deflection. This is particularly desirable since a number of advantages are gained. These are improved linearity of the trace, improved deflection sensitivity, and avoiding the need for clamping circuits.

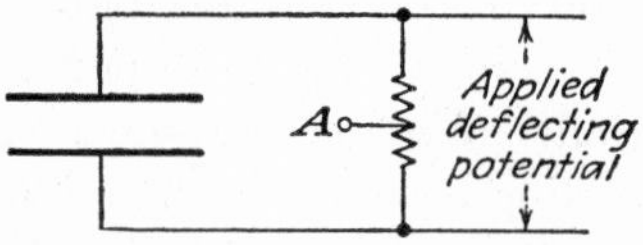

Actually, the use of push-pull deflection with one of the pair of deflecting plates being connected directly to the saw-tooth generator, the other being fed from an inverting amplifier of unity gain, results in a sacrifice in linearity and in flyback speed. However, it is possible to arrange the circuit so that the distortion introduced by the tube approximately cancels out the effect of an exponential curvature in the waveform of the saw tooth. It is essential that the gain of the amplifier remain unity—otherwise, some distortion will result, but this is not difficult to achieve if the amplifier is provided with negative feedback.

FIG. 10-25. The connection to the deflecting plates in a cathode-ray tube to reduce defocusing and trapezium distortion.

The improved deflection sensitivity results because the instantaneous deflecting potential difference with push-pull deflection is twice what it is with a single-sided, or unbalanced, deflection.

Clamping circuits are unnecessary because the average ordinate of one wave is equal and opposite to that of the other wave, and the effects are in such a direction as to cancel each other.

Five important methods of obtaining push-pull deflection potentials from a single input wave are available. These are:

1. A single-tube phase-reversing stage which may or may not provide more than unity gain. This may be subdivided into:

a. Those circuits in which the input saw-tooth waveform is sensibly linear and the tube distortion is arranged to be a minimum.

b. Those circuits in which the input waveform is exponential and the amplifier characteristic is employed also for compensation of the input curvature.

2. A single-tube paraphase amplifier.

3. A two-tube paraphase amplifier which has been modified to handle the peculiarities of a saw-tooth waveform. This may be subdivided into:

a. A standard form of push-pull amplifier.

b. A cathode-coupled paraphase amplifier.

4. Split saw tooths.

5. The use of two equivalent saw tooths operating in phase opposition.

It is not possible to state which of these methods is the most satisfactory, since each possesses certain merits. For most purposes, type 2, the single-tube paraphase circuit, where no amplification is required, and type 3b, the cathode-coupled paraphase amplifier, where amplification is required in addition to the provision of a push-pull output, will ordinarily provide satisfactory results. The use of types 4 and 5 usually permits deflection potentials with a minimum of distortion.

Single-tube Phase-reversing Amplifier. Any vacuum tube used as a conventional plate-coupled amplifier provides an output potential that is opposite in polarity to the input potential. However, since the gain of such a stage is ordinarily greater than unity, some means must be found to reduce the amplification. One common method of reducing the gain is to introduce sufficient negative feedback; the anode follower, discussed in Sec. 5-10, would be suitable for this service. However, it is quite likely that the phase difference between input and output potentials might differ slightly, particularly at the higher frequencies, where stray capacitances become important.

A second way to reduce the gain of the simple amplifier circuit to unity is to use a potential divider in the input circuit to reduce the amplitude of the grid signal by an amount equal to the gain of the amplifier. If the waveform which is to be inverted contains many harmonics, special care must be taken to compensate the potential divider for the shunting effect of the stray capacitances associated with it.

Single-tube Paraphase Amplifier. A combination of amplifier and phase inverter to provide a push-pull output from a single input wave is known as a *phase splitter*, or *paraphase amplifier*. A single-tube paraphase amplifier in which the plate load resistance is divided equally between the plate and cathode circuits is the simplest form of paraphase

amplifier and was examined in Sec. 5-4. The circuit of this amplifier is
redrawn for convenience in Fig. 10-26.

An important feature of this circuit is to be noted. This arises from
the presence of stray capacitances between the cathode and ground. If
a positive sweep potential is applied to the grid, the stray capacitances
will charge slowly during the trace. When the grid is brought down
sharply at the end of the trace, the tube
current decreases and the capacitance
must discharge through the cathode resistance, a relatively long time-constant circuit. If, on the other hand, a negative saw
tooth is applied to the grid, the cathode-
ground capacitance will charge slowly and
during the retrace time the tube current
will be large. As a result the cathode
potential is enabled to change rapidly,
and the flyback is not impaired.

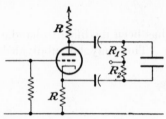

Fig. 10-26. A single-tube paraphase amplifier.

Another feature of this circuit is important. An analysis of this circuit is given in Sec. 5-4, the output potentials and the effective internal
impedances being given by Eqs. (5-43) and (5-44), which are rewritten
here for convenience:

From plate: $E_2 = \dfrac{-\mu R}{r_p + (\mu + 2)R} E_1$ $Z_{tf} = r_p + (\mu + 1)R$

From cathode: $E_2 = \dfrac{\mu R}{r_p + (\mu + 2)R} E_1$ $Z_{tf} = \dfrac{R + r_p}{\mu + 1}$

It is observed from these that although the output potentials are equal
in magnitude and in phase opposi-
tion, the effective internal impedances are quite different, being high
for the output from the plate, and
being low for the output from the
cathode. As a result, for h-f response, the total stray capacitances
associated with the tube and the
capacitance of the deflecting plates
must be equalized. If this is not
done, the flyback potential may overshoot the start of the trace.

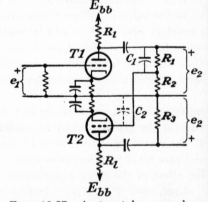

Fig. 10-27. A two-tube paraphase
amplifier.

Two-tube Paraphase Amplifiers.
In the two-tube paraphase amplifier,
one tube is used as a conventional
amplifier, and a second tube is used as a phase-inverter amplifier. Figure
10-27 illustrates such a circuit. The resistors R_1 and R_2 comprise a poten-

ial divider across the output of a conventional amplifier, the ratio of the
resistances being chosen so that the gain from the anode of $T1$ to the anode
of $T2$ is unity.　Often a capacitor C_1 is used, as shown, to compensate
for the effects of the input capacitance of $T2$.　C_1 is chosen to make
$R_1C_1 = R_2C_2$, where C_2 is the input capacitance of $T2$, for reasons discussed
in Prob. 9-2.　Also the operating conditions of the tubes are carefully
chosen to allow the curvature of the characteristic of $T2$ to compensate for
the curvature of $T1$.　Thus the output potentials relative to ground are
both slightly distorted to provide a comparatively undistorted potential

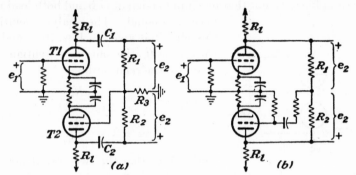

FIG. 10-28. Two forms of floating paraphase amplifiers.

difference between the output terminals.　This method is difficult to apply
in practice because the adjustments necessary to reduce distortion to a
minimum are critical.

　A second form of two-tube paraphase amplifier employs the differential
potential between the outputs of two tubes as the input signal to the
phase-inverter section.　This circuit, which is also referred to as the
floating paraphase amplifier, is illustrated in two versions in Fig. 10-28.

　In the circuit of Fig. 10-28a tube $T1$ is an amplifier to increase the
amplitude of the applied waveform.　The cathode resistors R_k, if not
by-passed, will provide some degeneration, which will help to reduce distortion.　The output from $T1$ is coupled through C_1 to R_1 and R_3, both
of which have the same value as R_2.　The potential which appears across
R_3 is applied to the grid of $T2$.　The output of $T2$ is passed through C_2
and is applied across R_2 and R_3.　Thus half the output of both $T1$ and
$T2$ appears across R_3.　Since these potentials are of opposite polarity,
the resultant potential across R_3 is the difference between these two.
The output of $T1$ is larger than the output of $T2$, and in order that this
difference should be kept as small as possible, pentodes are used, so as
to take advantage of their high amplification.

　The feature of the circuit of Fig. 10-28b is that the difference between
the output potentials is taken care of in the choice of the resistors R_1

and R_2 so that the output potentials have the same amplitude. To do this requires that the following condition be satisfied,

$$\frac{R_2}{R_1} \doteq \frac{K-1}{K+1} \tag{10-9}$$

where K is the gain of the stage.

Cathode-coupled Paraphase Amplifier. The cathode-coupled paraphase amplifier is illustrated in Fig. 10-29. By comparing this circuit with that of Fig. 6-1, it will be noted that it is essentially the cathode-coupled difference amplifier, except that one input signal $e_2 = 0$ and both load resistances are equal. The analytic solution of this circuit is given in Eqs. (6-8) and (6-9) with $e_2 = 0$, the output potentials being given by the relationships

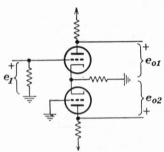

$$e_{01} = \frac{-\mu R_l}{2(r_p + R_l)} e_1$$
$$e_{02} = \frac{+\mu R_l}{2(r_p + R_l)} e_1 \tag{10-10}$$

These show that the two output potentials are of equal magnitude but of opposite polarity, as required.

Fig. 10-29. A cathode-coupled paraphase amplifier.

The attractive features of this circuit as an acceptable solution to the paraphase problem for push-pull deflection are the following:

1. Low distortion and relatively small value of grid current when overloaded.

2. Freedom from any tendency to self-oscillation.

3. Permits d-c connections at the input and output.

4. Permits providing shift, astigmatism correction, and balance controls.

5. Permits sweep expansion.

Figure 10-30 shows a circuit in which a cathode-coupled paraphase amplifier is arranged to provide sweep expansion and other controls.

Split Saw Tooths. It is sometimes desirable to avoid the necessity for amplification and phase inversion by generating a saw-tooth waveform having sufficient amplitude to allow half the output potential to be applied to each deflecting plate. The principle involved is indicated in Fig. 10-31a. Here the two charging resistors have a capacitor between them, although one might equally well use two equal charging capacitors with the charging resistor between them. The output provides equal potentials of opposite phase. The discharging device is indicated by the switch S. Figure 10-31b shows a practical circuit for obtaining a split saw tooth from two capacitors and one charging device.

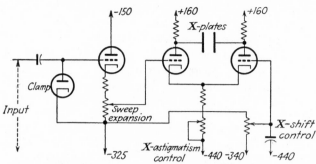

Fig. 10-30. A cathode-coupled paraphase amplifier with sweep expansion.

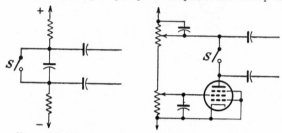

Fig. 10-31. A split saw-tooth generator. (*a*) Employs a single capacitor and two resistors. (*b*) Employs two capacitors and one charging device.

Saw Tooths in Phase Opposition. In Fig. 10-32 is shown a circuit which comprises two saw-tooth generators, one of which is connected in the reverse sense to the other. In this circuit a single discharging device may be employed, but the plate supply would be larger than would be necessary if separate discharging devices are employed. The resistors R_1 and R_2 may be replaced by con-stant-current devices. The switch S which represents the discharging de-vice is used to bring the capacitors to the same potential. Since R_1 and R_2 are equal, this potential is half that of the plate source. When the switch S is opened, one plate is driven in the positive direction and the other plate is driven in the negative direction.

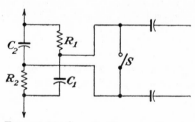

Fig. 10-32. Saw tooths operating in push-pull.

The circuit of Fig. 10-33 is one in which the elements are so arranged as to provide a push-pull output in which the whole of the available sup-ply potential may be made to appear across each of the capacitors C_1 and C_2. In this circuit the two thyratrons $T1$ and $T2$ are connected across the capacitors C_1 and C_2, respectively, and the bias potentials applied to their grids are determined by the adjustment of the resistors R_{k1} and R_{k2}. The potentials across these resistors remain constant.

When the capacitors C_1 and C_2 are being charged, the potential of the anode of $T2$ remains fixed, while those of the cathode and grid rapidly become more negative with respect to the anode. Since the grids of the two thyratrons are joined together through C_3 and the discharge current of C_3 passes through R_{g1}, the grid-cathode bias of $T1$ is greater than that due to the potential drop across R_1. For this reason R_1 must be adjusted

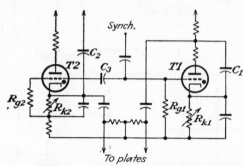

FIG. 10-33. Two thyratron saw-tooth generators operating in push-pull.

to provide a smaller bias potential than is the case with R_2, since otherwise there will be a time lag between striking of $T1$ and $T2$. The object is to obtain simultaneous striking, and this is best achieved by making the potentials at the two grids equal at the instant immediately prior to striking by accurate adjustment of R_1.

REFERENCES

1. Hawkins, G. F., *Wireless World*, **5**, 425 (1939).
2. Millman, J., and S. Seely, "Electronics," 1st ed., sec. 3-10, McGraw-Hill Book Company, Inc., New York, 1941.
   DuMont, A. B., *Electronics*, **8**, 16 (January, 1935).
   Fleming-Williams, B. C., *Wireless Engr.*, **17**, 61 (1940).
   As a general reference, see:
   Puckle, O. S., "Time Bases," 2d ed., John Wiley & Sons, Inc., New York, 1951.

PROBLEMS

10-1. An 884 thyratron is used in the saw-tooth generator of Fig. 10-6. The parameters are adjusted to be

$$E_{bb} = 300 \text{ volts} \qquad E_{cc} = -20 \text{ volts} \qquad C = 0.003 \ \mu\text{f} \qquad R = 10^6 \text{ ohms}$$

a. Calculate the frequency of oscillation.
b. Calculate the peak amplitude of the generated waves.
c. Plot the waveshape of the generated waves. Assume that the flyback time is zero.

10-2. Design a thyratron relaxation saw-tooth generator to yield a substantially linear saw tooth having a peak amplitude of 25 volts, with a recurrence frequency of 1,000 cps. Specify reasonable values of E_{bb}, E_{cc}, R, and C, and give reasons for your choice.

10-3. A circuit of a transitron sweep generator* is illustrated. (This should

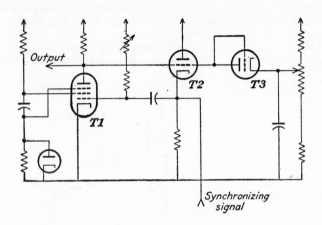

be compared with Prob. 8-16 and the phantastron of Fig. 9-31.) Discuss the operation of this circuit, with particular reference to the purpose of each tube $T1$, $T2$, $T3$.

10-4. Derive an equation for the potential across capacitor C in the circuit of Fig. 10-11:

a. During the time that the gate is applied.

b. After the gating period.

c. Sketch these results.

10-5. The output from a simple RC sweep generator is applied to the input of

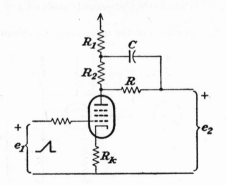

the amplifier circuit shown.† With $e_1 = E(1 - e^{-t/T})$, and with $R_2/R_1 = CR/T$, find the expression for the output potential.

---

* O. C. Wells, *Electronic Eng.*, **24**, 407 (1952).

† A. W. Keen, *Electronic Eng.*, **21**, 195 (1949).

10-6. The parameters in the simple sweep circuit of Fig. 10-11 are the following for tube 6SN7:

$$R_l = 75 \text{ kilohms} \qquad C = 0.005 \ \mu f \qquad E_{bb} = 300 \text{ volts} \qquad prf = 1,000 \text{ cps}$$

The input negative gate has an amplitude of 50 volts, and a duration of 150 μsec
  a. Calculate and plot curves of the form illustrated in Fig. 10-12.
  b. Repeat a for $R_l = 50$ kilohms.

10-7. Tube $T1$ in the circuit shown draws 10 ma at zero bias.   The diode has an equivalent beam resistance of 300 ohms when conducting.   Plot the waveform

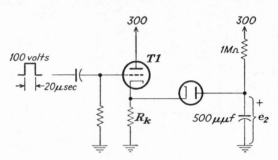

e_2 for the input waveshape shown.   The cutoff potential of $T1$ is -20 volts and $g_m = 2400$ μmhos.

10-8. Set up and solve the differential equation that controls:
  a. The charge to capacitor C of Fig. 10-18a when the negative cutoff gate is applied.
  b. The discharge of capacitor C at the end of the gate period.

10-9. The circuit of Fig. 10-18b is to be used in a saw-tooth generator circuit The triode is a 6J5, and the pentode is a 6SJ7.   A linear saw tooth with a 100-volt excursion is required, the duration of which is 250 μsec.   The recurrence frequency is 1,000 cps.   The available plate-supply source $E_{bb} = 300$ volts.   Specify all elements of the circuit.

10-10. Compare the operation of the accompanying circuit with Fig. 10-20.

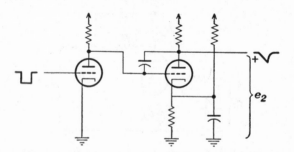

10-11. a. Find expressions for the potential across C during the charge and discharge portions of the cycle of the circuit in the figure for this problem. Assume that the beam resistance of $T2$ is r_b when the tube conducts and is infinite when the gate is applied.

b. Plot the results of part *a.*

c. On this same curve sheet, plot the results of Prob. 10-4, assuming the same value of C and that $R_l = R_1$.

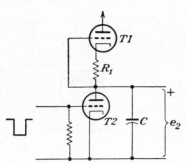

10-12. Derive an expression for the output potential from the circuit of Fig. 10-21 when a positive pulse is applied to the grid. The tube is normally biased beyond cutoff. What should be the relation among the circuit elements for an approximately linear output?

10-13. The circuit shown in the diagram is essentially the feedback circuit of Fig. 10-22. Discuss the advantages of this arrangement over that of Fig. 10-22.

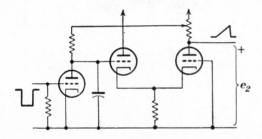

10-14. If the circuit of Fig. 10-22 is modified as shown in the accompanying

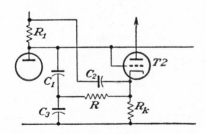

diagram, and assuming that the cathode of $T2$ rises linearly at a constant rate K_1, show that the potential appearing across C_3 during the saw tooth is given by

$$e_3 = K_1 t + K_1 R C_3 e^{-(t/RC_3 + 1)}$$

Neglect the effect of charging C_2 from the main source.

10-15. Discuss the operation of the accompanying circuit, developed by Puckle.

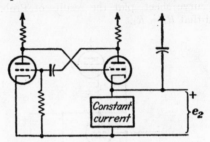

10-16. Discuss the operation of the self-balancing phase inverter shown in the accompanying figure.

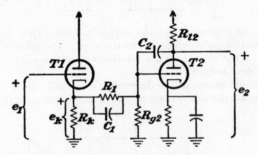

a. Determine the choice of the capacitor ratio C_1/C_2.

b. Ascertain the change in e_2 by a 10 per cent change in μ_2.

CHAPTER 11

SPECIAL SWEEP GENERATORS

It is shown in Sec. 1-27 that the deflection of the electron beam in an electromagnetically deflected cathode-ray tube is proportional to the strength of the deflecting field. The field strength is proportional to the current passing through the deflecting coil, if saturation is avoided. Consequently, if it is desired to deflect the electron beam linearly with time, the current through the deflecting coil must be varied linearly with time. When the end of the sweep is reached, the electron beam must be returned to its starting point quickly. It will be seen below that achieving a linear saw-tooth current through a deflecting coil (a series RL circuit) is a more difficult task than that of generating a linear saw-tooth potential.

There are four general methods in use for obtaining a linear saw-tooth current through a deflecting yoke. They make use of (1) the initial portion of the exponential change of current through the yoke when a step potential is impressed on the series RL circuit, (2) the initial change of current in an inductance during an oscillation when the current in a parallel RLC circuit is varied suddenly, (3) the increase of current in an inductance due to the application of a trapezoidal potential of properly chosen dimensions, and (4) the use of feedback to provide for linearization of the saw tooth. Each of these methods will be examined below.

11-1. Exponential Rise of Current. The basic circuit of the sweep generator for producing an exponential current through an inductance is given in Fig. 11-1. In this circuit it is supposed that the deflecting-yoke circuit is initially relaxed. When the switch S is closed, the current will begin to rise exponentially according to the equation

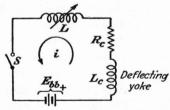

Fig. 11-1. A simple circuit for producing a saw-tooth current.

$$i = \frac{E_{bb}}{R_c} \left(1 - e^{-R_c t/(L+L_c)} \right) \tag{11-1}$$

341

The initial rate of rise of current is given by

$$\frac{di(0+)}{dt} = \frac{E_{bb}}{L + L_c} \qquad (11\text{-}2)$$

and hence the sweep speed may be varied by adjusting the magnitude of the inductance in the circuit.

To return the sweep to the initial condition, the switch S is opened. When this is done, however, the current tends to oscillate owing to the oscillatory circuit consisting of the yoke inductance and the distributed capacitance of the yoke. In order to damp out these oscillations, it is sometimes necessary to connect a resistor or a damping diode across the deflecting yoke.

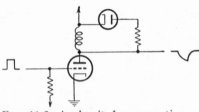

FIG. 11-2. A circuit for generating a sweep current by impressing a rectangular pulse on an RL circuit.

An electronic circuit that is based on these principles is illustrated in Fig. 11-2. In this circuit, the tube is normally biased beyond cutoff, and no current is flowing in the deflecting-coil circuit. At the time that the sweep is to be produced, a positive gating pulse is applied to the grid of the tube. The purpose of the re-sistor and diode that are connected across the deflection coil is to damp out the oscillations that are excited at the end of the sweep. The diode serves to disconnect the damping resistor during the rise of current. When the driver tube is cut off at the end of the positive pulse, a reversal of potential across the inductance results, which will make the diode conduct and permit current to flow through the damping resistor.

11-2. Initial Part of Oscillation. When the current in a circuit consisting of a coil shunted by a capacitor is interrupted, an oscillatory current is produced in the tuned circuit. The first part of the first cycle of the oscillation of the current is reasonably linear and may be used as a sweep current. The elements of the circuit are illustrated in Fig. 11-3.

The shape of the current in the coil is somewhat as illustrated in Fig. 11-4. The rate of change of current in the interval from a to b depends upon the resonant frequency of the deflecting-coil inductance and the shunt capacitance, and the amplitude of the initial current. Of course, if different values of shunt capacitance are used, different resonant frequencies result, whence the sweep speeds (considering the region from a to b to be the effective portion of the sweep) may be varied. Likewise, the amplitude of the oscillation will depend upon the magnitude of the d-c current in the coil before it is interrupted.

A sweep circuit that employs such an oscillatory circuit is given in Fig. 11-5.   In this circuit the deflecting coil is coupled to the plate circuit of a current-amplifier stage by means of a large capacitor C.   The inductances L_1 and L_2 are very large and serve to isolate the oscillatory current from the zero-position d-c restoring circuit and the plate supply

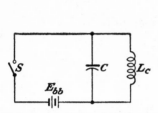

FIG. 11-3. A circuit for obtaining an oscillating current in a deflecting coil.

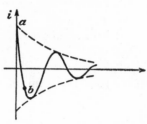

FIG. 11-4. The current in the deflecting coil in the circuit of Fig. 11-3.

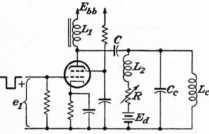

FIG. 11-5. An oscillatory sweep-current circuit with arrangements for adjusting the zero position of the sweep.

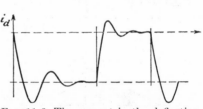

FIG. 11-6. The current in the deflecting-coil circuit when a pulse is applied to the grid of the current tube in Fig. 11-5.

E_{bb} and thus confine the current to the deflecting-yoke circuit.   However, the bias battery E_d sends a steady current through resistor R, inductor L_2, and the deflecting coil for the purpose of centering the spot.

In this circuit the application of the pulse to the amplifier tube causes the current in the deflecting-coil circuit to decrease and oscillate about one level, and the removal of the pulse causes the current to oscillate about the d-c value determined by the local circuit containing E_d.   The shape of the curve is somewhat as illustrated in Fig. 11-6.   The second oscillation is damped more rapidly than the first because the beam resistance of the tube is in parallel with the circuit during this portion of the cycle.

11-3. Linear Current by Trapezoidal Potential.   Both of the foregoing methods for obtaining a linear-sweep current utilize a small essentially linear portion of a nonlinear function.   It is possible to find a potential waveform which, when applied to the inductive circuit of the deflecting coil, will yield a current that is linear with time. Specifically, if a linear current is required in a circuit comprising a series inductance and resistance, then since

$$i = kt \qquad (11\text{-}3)$$

and

$$e = L\frac{di}{dt} + Ri \qquad (11\text{-}4)$$

the required terminal potential is readily seen to be

$$e = Lk + Rkt \qquad (11\text{-}5)$$

The waves have the form illustrated in Fig. 11-7.

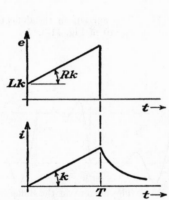

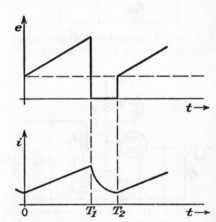

Fig. 11-7. The potential required to produce a saw-tooth current in an inductive circuit.

Fig. 11-8. The potential and current waveforms in an inductive circuit.

If at the end of a time T the input potential waveform immediately falls to zero, as illustrated, then the circuit potential and current become

$$e(t) = 0$$
$$i(t) = kTe^{-Rt/L} \qquad (11\text{-}6)$$

In general, when the applied potential waveform is recurrent, which is the usual situation, an initial current may exist in the circuit when the input potential is again applied. The situation is then of the form illustrated in Fig. 11-8. The equations of the current may be shown to have the form

$$i(t) = kt + i(0+)e^{-Rt/L} \qquad 0 < t < T_1$$

and

$$i(t) = i(T_1)e^{-Rt/L} \qquad T_1 < t < T_2 \qquad (11\text{-}7)$$

so that

$$i(0+) = i(T_2) = i(T_1)e^{-RT_2/L} \qquad (11\text{-}8)$$

The current at the end of the interval T_1 is

$$i(T_1) = kT_1 + i(T_2)e^{-RT_1/L} \qquad (11\text{-}9)$$

Combining the above gives

$$
\begin{aligned}
i(t) &= kt + i(T_1)e^{-R(t+T_2)/L} & 0 < t < T_1 \\
i(t) &= i(T_1)e^{-Rt/L} & T_1 < t < T_2
\end{aligned}
\qquad (11\text{-}10)
$$

To find the end points $i(T_1)$ and $i(T_2)$ requires the simultaneous solution of Eqs. (11-8) and (11-9), and, with these known, the entire waveform may be plotted according to Eqs. (11-10).

It is of importance to note that if the impressed potential waveform is altered by increasing the height of the step, so that e is now given by

$$e = i(0+)R + Lk + Rkt \qquad (11\text{-}11)$$

then the resultant current is of the form

$$i(t) = i(0+) + kt \qquad (11\text{-}12)$$

This shows that current linearity may be obtained, despite the presence of an initial current, simply by increasing the amplitude of the initial step by a sufficient amount.

A circuit which is capable of developing a trapezoidal potential waveform is shown in Fig. 11-9. The switch S that is connected across R_c and C permits the capacitor to be charged and discharged.

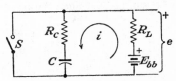

FIG. 11-9. A circuit for generating a trapezoidal wave.

When the switch is opened, the current in this circuit increases according to the relation

$$i = \frac{E_{bb}}{R_L + R_c} e^{-t/(R_L+R_c)C} \qquad (11\text{-}13)$$

if the initial charge on the capacitor is zero. The output potential of the circuit is

$$e = E_{bb} - iR_L$$

or

$$e = E_{bb} - \frac{E_{bb}R_L}{R_L + R_c} e^{-t/(R_L+R_c)C} \qquad (11\text{-}14)$$

The slope of the potential wave is

$$\frac{de}{dt} = \frac{E_{bb}R_L}{(R_L + R_c)^2 C} e^{-t/(R_L+R_c)C} \qquad (11\text{-}15)$$

At the initial time, $t = (0+)$,

$$\frac{de(0+)}{dt} = E_{bb} \frac{R_L}{(R_L + R_c)^2 C}$$

and

$$e(0+) = E_{bb} \frac{R_c}{R_L + R_c}$$

(11-16)

The jump/slope ratio is given by

$$\frac{\text{Jump}}{\text{Slope}} = \frac{R_L + R_c}{R_L R_c} C$$

(11-17)

If the time constant $(R_L + R_c)C$ is large compared with the sweep time T, so that only a reasonably linear portion of the exponential curve is

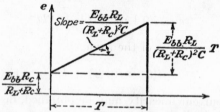

FIG. 11-10. Trapezoidal potential and the relation to the circuit constants.

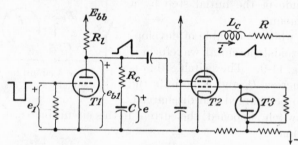

FIG. 11-11. A circuit for generating a saw-tooth current wave for electromagnetic deflection.

used, the output potential will be a sufficiently good trapezoidal potential wave having the properties shown in Fig. 11-10.

An electronic circuit that incorporates the foregoing features for producing a linear saw-tooth current through the deflecting coil is given in Fig. 11-11. It will be observed that tube $T1$ serves as the switch of Fig. 11-9, the output trapezoidal wave being applied to the grid of a current-amplifier tube $T2$. A biased clamp $T3$ is used to set the reference level.

It is possible to derive an approximate expression for the trapezoidal potential that is generated in the driver circuit that includes $T1$. If $E(0+)$ denotes the potential across the capacitor when the negative gate is applied to the grid of $T1$, then the plate potential $E_{b1}(0+)$ immediately jumps to

$$E_{b1}(0+) = \frac{R_c}{R_c + R_l}[E_{bb} - E(0+)] + E(0+) \qquad (11\text{-}18)$$

as is evident from an inspection of Fig. 11-12, the equivalent circuit during the charging cycle. The current during the charging cycle is

$$i(t) = \frac{E_{bb} - E_{b1}(0+)}{R_l} e^{-t/(R_c+R_l)C} \qquad (11\text{-}19)$$

Since, at any time,

$$e_{b1}(t) = E_{bb} - i(t)R_l \qquad (11\text{-}20)$$

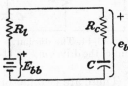

then

$$e_{b1}(t) = E_{bb} - [E_{bb} - E_{b1}(0+)]e^{-t/(R_c+R_l)C} \qquad (11\text{-}21)$$

FIG. 11-12. The equivalent charging circuit of the driver of Fig. 11-11.

and at the end of the charging period

$$e_{b1}(T) = E_{bb} - [E_{bb} - E_{b1}(0+)]e^{-T/(R_c+R_l)C} \qquad (11\text{-}22)$$

A sketch showing the variations expressed analytically by these relations is given in Fig. 11-13.

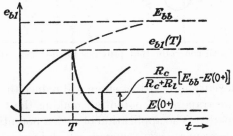

FIG. 11-13. The plate-potential trapezoidal wave of tube $T1$ in the circuit of Fig. 11-11.

It is of interest to examine the inital jump/slope ratio. This is found to be

$$\frac{\text{Jump}}{\text{Slope}} = \frac{\dfrac{R_c}{R_c + R_l}[E_{bb} - E_{b1}(0+)]}{[E_{bb} - E(0+)]/(R_c + R_l)C} = R_cC\,\frac{E_{bb} - E_{b1}(0+)}{E_{bb} - E(0+)} \qquad (11\text{-}23)$$

By comparing this with the jump/slope ratio given by Eq. (11-17), it is seen that the results obtained by using the vacuum-tube circuit are not precisely those required to produce a linearly rising saw-tooth current in the plate circuit of $T2$. To make possible the linear saw tooth requires that the two ratios be equal. Such equality is approximated by choosing R_l much greater than R_c. With this done, the slope of the sweep current, which is dictated by the slope of the trapezoidal wave, may be controlled by adjusting E_{bb} or R_l, without affecting the linearity of the current rise.

During the discharge time, the capacitor C discharges in the equivalent circuit given in Fig. 11-14. Ordinarily it is desired that C discharge as rapidly as possible so that $E(0+)$ is small. The exact equations for the discharge are obtained by analyzing Fig.

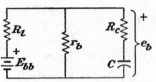

Fig. 11-14. The discharge circuit of the driver in Fig. 11-11.

11-14. This is left as a problem for the student (see Prob. 11-3).

A variation of the circuit of Fig. 11-11 that does not require a clamp is shown in Fig. 11-15. This circuit requires a separate adjustment for each sweep speed, if multiple sweep speeds are provided.

There are two factors which tend to influence adversely the considerations given above, viz., the distributed capacitance of the coil, and the capacitance of the circuit wiring. Since the potential across a capacitor in a series RC circuit cannot change suddenly, the distributed capacitance

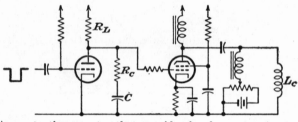

Fig. 11-15. A saw-tooth generator that provides for d-c restoration by means of a separate circuit.

at the input to the current or driver stage will reduce the steepness of the initial jump of the trapezoidal potential, making the trapezoid tend to approach a saw tooth. The application of such a potential to the RL circuit through the current tube is a current which increases slowly at first, as shown in Fig. 11-16, and gradually becomes linear with time. Frequently one applies a sharp spike at the beginning of the sweep to help overcome this effect. Such a wave has the form shown in Fig. 11-17.

The effect of the distributed capacitance of the deflecting-coil circuit, which may be considered to appear as a capacitance across the coil, is to produce an oscillatory circuit. The rapid change of current passing through the coil at the time of the return trace will ordinarily shock-excite the coil into oscillation. But since it is necessary to provide some means of dissipating the energy in the electromagnetic field of the coil so that the current can fall to zero in a short time, a re-

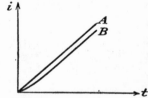

Fig. 11-16. The effect of distributed capacitance in retarding the start of a sweep current.

sistor is often connected in parallel with the deflecting coil. This resistor serves to damp the oscillations produced by the shock excitation. The complete curve is generally of the form illustrated in Fig. 11-18.

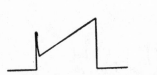

Fig. 11-17. The use of a narrow spike to aid in starting a linear-sweep current.

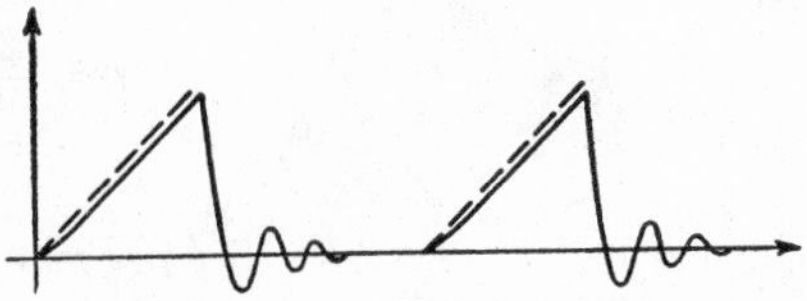

Fig. 11-18. The waveform of the current in the deflecting coil.

11-4. Feedback Circuits. The sweep-current circuits discussed in the foregoing sections have been used extensively for magnetic sweep-current generation, although present-day methods generally incorporate feedback in the circuit as a means for linearizing the current wave. The use of feedback serves several desirable ends. First, a significant cause of nonlinearity in the sweep current, especially if the sweep duration is long enough so that the effects of distributed capacitances are unimportant, is the nonlinear characteristics of the current-amplifier tube. Such nonlinear effects are greatly reduced by incorporating negative feedback in the circuit. Second, the input to the feedback amplifier is a linear

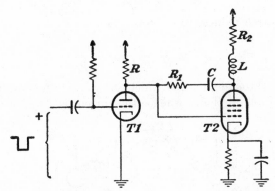

Fig. 11-19. A feedback-type current saw-tooth generator.

potential saw tooth in order to produce the linear current saw tooth. In effect, therefore, with the proper feedback, the application of a linear potential saw tooth to the grid of the current tube results in the generation within the amplifier of a trapezoidal potential waveform of correct proportions to produce the linear current saw tooth in the deflecting yoke.

A form of feedback-type current-saw-tooth generator is illustrated in Fig. 11-19. The successful operation of this circuit requires that the gain of $T2$ be high, and also that R be high. In this case, when the input negative gate is applied, there is applied a step function of current, as shown in the equivalent circuit of Fig. 11-20. The shunting effect of the plate resistance of $T2$ is neglected. An analysis of this network follows.

From the diagram, it follows that the operational response of the network is

$$i = \frac{E_{bb}}{R} - g_m e_g \qquad (11\text{-}24)$$

and

$$(R_2 + Lp)i = e_g - \left(R_1 + \frac{1}{Cp}\right)\frac{E_{bb}}{R} \qquad (11\text{-}25)$$

Combine these equations to the form

$$[(g_m R_2 + 1) + g_m Lp]i = \left[(g_m R_1 + 1) + \frac{g_m}{Cp}\right]\frac{E_{bb}}{R} \qquad (11\text{-}26)$$

This equation is written as

$$g_m L\left(\frac{g_m R_2 + 1}{g_m L} + p\right)i = \frac{g_m}{CR}\left(\frac{g_m R_1 + 1}{g_m}C + \frac{1}{p}\right)E_{bb} \qquad (11\text{-}27)$$

Note, however, that if the parameters are so chosen that

$$\frac{g_m R_2 + 1}{g_m L} = \frac{g_m}{(g_m R_1 + 1)C} \qquad (11\text{-}28)$$

then the equation reduces to the form

$$i = \frac{g_m}{RC}\frac{1}{g_m R_2 + 1}\frac{E_{bb}}{p} \qquad (11\text{-}29)$$

This is an operational equation which shows that the current is proportional to the integral of E_{bb}, whence the current is a linear saw tooth.

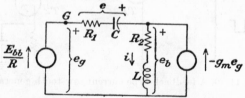

Fig. 11-20. The equivalent circuit upon the application of the negative gate.

Refer to Eq. (11-28). For the case for which $g_m R_2 > 1$ and $g_m R_1 > 1$, the relation among the parameters reduces to

$$\frac{R_2}{L} \doteq \frac{1}{R_1 C} \qquad \text{for } g_m \text{ large} \qquad (11\text{-}30)$$

as the required condition for a linear saw-tooth current.

The circuit above is applicable to linear-saw-tooth-current generation when the effects of distributed capacitances are unimportant. This is the same limitation that exists in most circuits already considered, and a truly linear saw tooth is not possible.

Somewhat more elaborate feedback circuits permit correction of current saw-tooth nonlinearities. Consider the circuit of the feedback sweep amplifier shown in Fig. 11-21. Note that the input is a linear potential saw-tooth wave. The input saw tooth to this amplifier may be generated by a simple *RC* sweep generator, since only a small input signal is required, and for most purposes the resulting linearity in using a small portion of

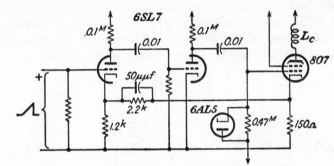

Fɪɢ. 11-21. A feedback sweep-current amplifier.

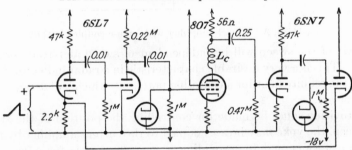

Fɪɢ. 11-22. An improved version of the amplifier of Fig. 11-21.

the exponential wave is adequate. This input is passed through two potential-amplifying stages and is then applied to the grid of the current-amplifier tube. A comparison is now effected between the input potential waveshape and the output current waveshape. If the total current through the current tube differs from a linear variation, there will be a difference in potential between the cathode of the input stage and an appropriately chosen sample of the output current stage. Owing to the feedback between the output and the input stages, the effective signal will vary in a manner to yield a linear current in the output. Note in the figure that the grid of the output stage is d-c restored to a value beyond cutoff.

An improved circuit is shown in Fig. 11-22. In this improved circuit, the sampled output current is amplified before being fed back to the input.

There are two features of the above circuits that should be discussed. In the first circuit, the sampling of the output current is done by means of the potential drop across the cathode resistor. Evidently, therefore, it is the total current that is being sampled, and not the current through the deflecting yoke. Of course, if the fraction of the total current through the deflecting yoke remains constant as the current increases, then there will be no error resulting from this manner of sampling. The circuit of Fig. 11-22 does sample the current in the deflecting yoke.

A second feature is one which is important in certain types of application. It will be noted from Figs. 11-21 and 11-22 that the deflecting yoke is in the plate lead of the current-amplifier tube. Likewise, with the clamping tube that is provided, the position of the cathode-ray beam at

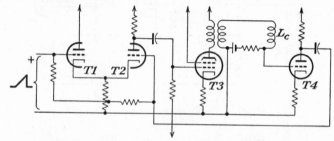

Fig. 11-23. A feedback amplifier with an a-c coupled output.

the start of the sweep will be independent of sweep amplitude or sweep speed. This is a very desirable characteristic in a radar indicator, since it avoids the requirement for a centering potential, which will depend on the sweep speed.

If provision must be made for controlling the position of the start of the sweep, the yoke may be a-c coupled to the current amplifier by means of a transformer and by providing a separate source for effecting the desired displacements. The elements of a circuit that permits this type of operation are given in Fig. 11-23. In this circuit the current in the deflecting yoke is sampled, amplified, and combined with the input saw tooth in a difference amplifier. The amplifier tends to apply to the output circuit the difference waveform between the output current wave and the input potential. The action is to reduce this difference to a negligible amount, if the gain is sufficiently high. If the single stage $T4$ is not sufficient to provide the required output, additional amplification can be provided either between $T2$ and $T3$ or between $T4$ and $T2$.

It is possible to use potential-feedback techniques for effecting linearization of the saw-tooth current. This requires only that a potential waveform which is proportional to the sawtooth current be made available. This is readily accomplished by means of a simple network (see Prob. 11-6).

11-5. Circular-sweep Generator. In certain applications it is found desirable to employ other than a linear sweep of the cathode-ray beam across the face of the tube. In some instances the beam may be deflected across the tube face according to some prescribed function of time, not necessarily linear. In other cases the cathode-ray beam may be caused to describe a circular path, a spiral path, a rotating radial path, or, in fact, any of a wide variety of paths. Several such sweep generators will be studied.

An elliptical or circular sweep of the electron beam can be readily accomplished by making use of the fact that the application of sinusoidal potentials which differ in time phase by 90 deg to the two sets of deflecting plates of the cathode-ray tube which are 90 deg apart in space will generate an ellipse, if the vertical deflection is different from the horizontal deflection, or will generate a circle, if the two deflections are the same. The amplitude of the potentials must be slightly

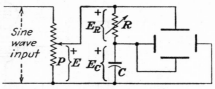

Fig. 11-24. Phase-shifting circuit for producing an elliptical or circular trace.

different in general in generating a circular sweep in order to take into account the different deflection sensitivities of the deflecting plates, owing to their different distances from the screen.

The simplest circuit for obtaining the necessary two potentials which are 90 deg apart in time phase is illustrated in Fig. 11-24. The circle diagram of this circuit is given in Fig. 11-25, and it will be seen that, for

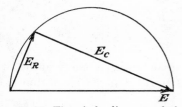

Fig. 11-25. The circle diagram of the phase-shifting network of Fig. 11-24.

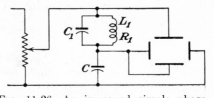

Fig. 11-26. An improved simple phase-shifting circuit.

a fixed value of C, the degree of ellipticity, which depends upon the relative potential across R and C, is controlled by controlling the value of R. The potentiometer P controls the amplitude of the sine-wave potential that is applied to the phase-shifting circuit. If this potential is large, the potentials across both R and C will also be large. Consequently, the circle traced on the screen will be of large diameter.

If the source of potential for the sweep generator contains appreciable harmonics, the trace cannot be made circular. A modification of the circuit of Fig. 11-24 is possible which will avoid most of the errors arising from this cause.   It consists in replacing the resistance of the circuit by a parallel circuit that is tuned to the frequency of the supply source.   The circuit then has the form illustrated in Fig. 11-26.   At the supply frequency, the impedance of the parallel circuit is equivalent to a pure resistance of value L_1/C_1R_1, where R_1 is the effective resistance of the inductor.   With this circuit, the parallel branch impedance is capacitive for the harmonic frequencies, and so the variation of this impedance with frequency is substantially the same as that for the capacitor C, with the

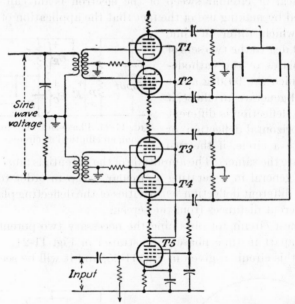

FIG. 11-27. A circular-sweep generator circuit.

result that the amplitudes of the harmonic potentials applied to the two deflector plates are substantially reduced and the circularity of the trace is not seriously impaired.

The main advantages from the use of a circular trace are the ease of generation, the increase in the length of trace possible on a given cathode-ray tube face, and the avoidance of flyback.   A disadvantage is that such sweeps are ordinarily used with tubes which require the presence of a central electrode to which the signal is applied in order to obtain a radial deflection of the trace.   However, it will be shown that the use of such special tubes is not required since it is possible to obtain a radial deflection without the use of the central electrode.

The disadvantage of these generators is that the omission of push-pull sweep deflection results in trapezium distortion unless the tube is specially designed to reduce this.   The effect of the distortion is readily avoided through the use of the somewhat more elaborate circuit illustrated in Fig. 11-27. This circuit, which is based on the same principles as above, provides a greater flexibility.

In this circuit the values of C and R are chosen so that a circular sweep will be generated at the frequency of the applied potential. Push-pull deflection is provided in order to reduce trapezium distortion. The gain of the four amplifier tubes is controlled by the potential on the screen grids, which is controlled by the potential at the plate of $T5$, a quantity that is set by the setting of the bias potentiometer in the grid circuit of this tube.

If no signal is applied to the grid of $T5$, the potential at its plate will be constant and a circle will be generated. However, if a signal is applied to the grid of $T5$, the potential at the plate will be changed in accordance with the shape of the input signal, assuming that there is no distortion. This will cause the diameter of the circle to change in accordance with the applied signal, whence the signal is made to appear on the beam. Such a pattern may have the form illustrated in Fig. 11-28a.

To obtain the spiral trace illustrated in Fig. 11-28b, it is necessary only to apply a saw tooth to the input of T5, the frequency of which is a sub-multiple of the frequency of the applied sine wave. In particular, suppose that the applied sine-wave potential is 1,000 cps and that a saw-tooth potential of 200 cps is applied to the grid of $T5$. The gain of the amplifier tubes will be varied

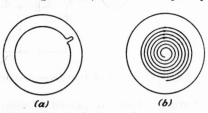

(a)   *(b)*

Fig. 11-28. A circular and a spiral trace possible with the circuit of Fig. 11-27.

continuously during the 5 cycles of the sine wave. As the gain increases from zero to the maximum, the spot rotates on a circle of ever-increasing radius, returning to the center during the flyback period of the saw tooth. If the saw tooth is not a submultiple of the sine wave, the spiral will revolve.

By substituting current-amplifier tubes for the potential-amplifier tubes in the push-pull circuit and replacing the electrostatic deflecting system by an electromagnetic deflecting yoke, the foregoing discussion is valid for the electromagnetic type of tube.

11-6. Rotating Radial Sweep. A radial linear sweep which can be rotated with uniform angular velocity is extensively used in radar applications. Such an indicating system is known as a plan position indicator (PPI) since, in its operation, the rotation is synchronized with the scanning of the radar system, the resulting display being in effect a plan view of the scanned area. A number of methods have been used to generate such a display.

A direct method for producing the plan-position-indicator sweep incorporates the magnetic deflecting yoke which produces the nominal linear deflection in a mechanical assembly which can be rotated physically.   The physical rotation of the mechanical assembly can be synchronized with the primary driving source either by means of rigid mechanical couplings or by means of a servomechanism, a device which permits accurate follow-up of driven and driver systems by purely electrical interconnection.

A second method that has been extensively used utilizes a so-called *two-phase selsyn transformer*, or *resolver*.   Such a device consists of two stator

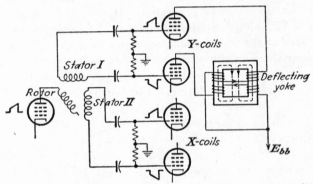

Fig. 11-29. A selsyn transformer circuit for producing a rotating radial sweep.

windings which are placed at right angles to each other and which are excited from a single-phase movable rotor.   The application of, say, a trapezoidal potential waveform (which would theoretically provide a linear-sweep current) to the primary will yield two output potentials which are in time phase but the amplitudes of which vary, respectively, as the sine and cosine of the angle of the rotor or primary with respect to the secondary windings.   These outputs when amplified and applied to two deflecting coils at right angles to each other will produce a display of the type here considered.   That this is so follows readily from the fact that the horizontal and vertical magnetic fields are proportional to

$$B_x = \phi(t) \cos \varphi$$
$$B_y = \phi(t) \sin \varphi$$

from which it follows that

$$B = \sqrt{B_x^2 + B_y^2} = \phi(t)$$

That is, the resulting field, and hence the deflection, at any angle φ is constant in amplitude and of the form to produce a linear saw-tooth current wave. Of course, the requirement imposed on the selsyn transformer is that it faithfully reproduce in the output circuit the waveshape of the input wave. The main elements of such a circuit are given in Fig. 11-29.

REFERENCES

1. As general references, see:
   Puckle, O. S., "Time Bases," 2d ed., John Wiley & Sons, Inc., New York, 1951.
   Soller, J. T., M. A. Starr, and G. E. Valley, Jr., "Cathode Ray Tube Displays," Massachusetts Institute of Technology Radiation Laboratory Series, vol. 22, McGraw-Hill Book Company, Inc., New York, 1948.

PROBLEMS

11-1. The deflecting yoke of a magnetic cathode-ray tube has an inductance of 8.9 mh and a resistance of 15 ohms. It is connected in the circuit of Fig. 11-3. The initial current in the coil is 80 ma when S is opened. Calculate and plot the current through the coil when $C = 0.01$, 0.1, and 1 μf, respectively. Estimate the range over which a linear current within 5 per cent exists.

11-2. The deflecting yoke of Prob. 11-1 is connected in the circuit of Fig. 11-11. Tube $T1$ is a 6J5, $T2$ is a 6V6, $E_{bb} = 300$ volts. The clamp sets the grid bias of $T2$ at -50 volts. If the current wave through the yoke is to vary linearly from 0 to 80 ma in 60 μsec.

a. Specify the trapezoidal wave that must be applied to the grid of $T2$.

b. Specify a set of constants of the circuit of $T1$ to yield such a trapezoidal wave.

11-3. Deduce the equations for the discharge cycle of the circuit of Fig. 11-14.

11-4. The essentials of a current sweep generator are illustrated.*

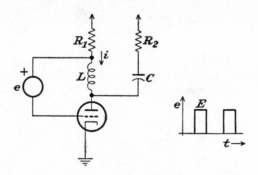

a. Derive an expression for the current i through L, assuming that the tube parameters are constant over the operating range and that the grid impedance is high, so that no current is delivered by the source e.

b. What choice of time constants yields optimum linearity?

* W. T. Cocking, *Wireless Engr.*, **28**, 165 (1951).

11-5. Repeat Prob. 11-4 when the circuit is connected as shown.

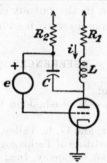

11-6. The essentials of a feedback linearizing saw-tooth current generator*
are illustrated.   Deduce an expression for the current i_1, with the application of
the input gate.

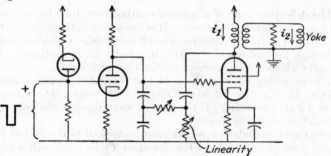

11-7. Show that the output potential e_2 in the circuit shown is proportional
to the coil current i, when $R_1C = L_c/R$ and R_1 is very large.

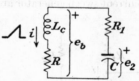

11-8. The elements of a feedback current saw-tooth generator,† which is
essentially a shunt-fed version of the circuit discussed in Sec. 11-4, are illustrated
in the accompanying figure.   Show analytically that the current in the coil has a

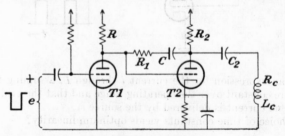

---

* C. H. Banthorpe, *Electronic Eng.*, **22**, 339 (1950).
† A. B. Starks-Field. *Electronic Eng.*, **25**, 192 (1953).

saw-tooth current waveform for a square-wave potential input, when the parameters are chosen such that

$$R_1 C = \frac{L_c}{R_c} \quad \text{for } g_m R_2 \gg 1 \text{ and } X_{C_2} \ll Z_{\text{coil}}$$

11-9. Sketch a circuit for producing a linear saw-tooth current which incorporates the network of Prob. 11-7 in a potential feedback circuit.

CHAPTER 12

RECTIFIERS

Any electrical device which has a high resistance to current in one direction and a low resistance to current in the opposite direction possesses the ability to convert an a-c current into a current which contains a d-c component in addition to a-c components. An ideal rectifier would be one with zero resistance in the forward direction and with an infinite resistance in the reverse direction. A number of devices possess non-linear characteristics, among which are high-vacuum thermionic diodes, gas-filled and vapor-filled thermionic diodes, pool-cathode mercury arcs, and certain crystals.

The important rectifiers for power purposes fall into two general groups, depending on their inherent characteristics. The vacuum tube

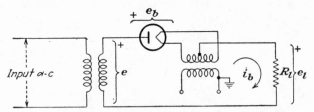

Fig. 12-1. A simple half-wave rectifier circuit.

rectifier possesses an infinite resistance on the inverse cycle, as the tube will not conduct when the plate is negative with respect to the cathode. On the forward, or conducting, portion of the cycle, the vacuum diode is characterized by an almost constant and low value of resistance. The gas or vapor rectifiers also possess an infinite resistance on the inverse cycle, but as discussed in Sec. 1-25, they are characterized by a substantially constant tube drop during conduction. Owing to these differences, the resulting operation in a circuit is slightly different. A detailed discussion is included below.

12-1. Single-phase Half-wave Vacuum Rectifier. The basic circuit for half-wave rectification is shown in Fig. 12-1. It is assumed that the load is a pure resistance. Also, it is supposed that the power transformer is ideal, with negligible resistance and leakage reactance.

An application of Kirchhoff's potential law to the load circuit yields

$$e = e_b + i_b R_l \qquad (12\text{-}1)$$

where e is the instantaneous value of the applied potential, e_b is the instantaneous potential across the diode when the instantaneous current is i_b, and R_l is the load resistance. This one equation is not sufficient for the determination of the two unknown quantities i_b and e_b that appear in the expression. Here, as for triodes and multielectrode tubes, a second relation is contained in the static plate characteristic of the tube. Consequently a solution is effected by drawing the load line on the plate characteristic.

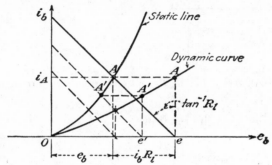

Fig. 12-2. The static and dynamic characteristics of a rectifier.

There is one significant difference between the solution of the diode as a rectifier and that for the other tubes as amplifiers. With the rectifier, an a-c source supplies the power to the circuit. A vacuum tube as an amplifier converts direct current from the plate supply into alternating current.

The dynamic characteristic of the rectifier circuit is obtained in a somewhat different manner from the corresponding curve for an amplifier. The procedure is illustrated in Fig. 12-2. For an applied potential e, the current is the intersection of the load line with the static characteristic, say point A. That is, for the particular circuit, the application of the potential e results in a current i_A. This is one point on the dynamic curve and is drawn vertically above e in the diagram. The slope of the load line does not vary, although the intersection with the e_b axis varies with e. Thus, when the applied potential has the value e', the corresponding current is $i_{A'}$. The resulting curve so generated is the dynamic characteristic.

If the static characteristic of the tube were linear, the dynamic characteristic would also be linear. Note from the construction, however, that there is considerably less curvature in the dynamic curve than there is in the static characteristic. It will be assumed in what follows that the dynamic curve is linear.

To find the waveshape of the current in the output circuit, the procedure followed is that illustrated in Fig. 12-3. This procedure is very much like that used to find the waveshape in a general amplifier circuit; in fact, the situation here is quite like that of a class B amplifier, except that cutoff of the tube exists at zero input.

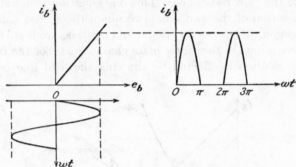

FIG. 12-3. The method of obtaining the output-current waveform from the dynamic characteristic.

If it is assumed that the relation

$$e_b = i_b r_p \tag{12-2}$$

is valid during conduction, and this supposes that the static characteristic is linear, then from Eq. (12-1) it follows that

$$e = e_b + i_b R_l = i_b(r_p + R_l) = E_m \sin \omega t \tag{12-3}$$

or

$$i_b = \frac{E_m}{R_l + r_p} \sin \omega t = I_m \sin \omega t \qquad \text{when } 0 \leq \omega t \leq \pi$$

$$i_b = 0 \qquad \text{when } \pi \leq \omega t \leq 2\pi \tag{12-4}$$

where

$$I_m = \frac{E_m}{R_l + r_p}$$

The d-c power supplied to the load is defined as the product of the reading of a d-c ammeter in the load circuit and a d-c voltmeter across the load. Thus

$$P_{\text{d-c}} \equiv E_{\text{d-c}} I_{\text{d-c}} \tag{12-5}$$

Clearly, the reading of the d-c ammeter is represented by

$$I_{\text{d-c}} = \frac{1}{2\pi} \int_0^{2\pi} i_b \, d\alpha = \frac{1}{2\pi} \int_0^{\pi} I_m \sin \alpha \, d\alpha = \frac{I_m}{\pi} \tag{12-6}$$

and so

$$P_{\text{d-c}} = I_{\text{d-c}}^2 R_l = \left(\frac{1}{\pi}\right)^2 \frac{E_m^2 R_l}{(r_p + R_l)^2} \tag{12-7}$$

The power supplied to the circuit from the a-c source, and this is the power that would be read by a wattmeter with its current coil in the line and with the potential coil across the source, is given by the integral

$$P_i = \frac{1}{2\pi} \int_0^{2\pi} e i_b \, d\alpha \tag{12-8}$$

This becomes, by Eqs. (12-2) and (12-3),

$$P_i = \frac{1}{2\pi} \int_0^{2\pi} i_b^2 (r_p + R_l) \, d\alpha \tag{12-9}$$

which may be written in the form

$$P_i = I_{\text{rms}}^2 (r_p + R_l) \tag{12-10}$$

where the rms current has the value

$$I_{\text{rms}} = \sqrt{\frac{1}{2\pi} \int_0^{2\pi} i_b^2 \, d\alpha} = \sqrt{\frac{1}{2\pi} \int_0^{\pi} I_m^2 \sin^2 \alpha \, d\alpha} = \frac{I_m}{2} \tag{12-11}$$

The efficiency of rectification is defined by the relation

$$\eta_r = \frac{P_{\text{d-c}}}{P_i} \times 100\% = \frac{I_{\text{d-c}}^2 R_l}{I_{\text{rms}}^2 (r_p + R_l)} \times 100\%$$

which becomes

$$\eta_r = \left(\frac{I_{\text{d-c}}}{I_{\text{rms}}} \right)^2 \frac{100}{1 + r_p/R_l} \tag{12-12}$$

By combining this with Eqs. (12-6) and (12-11), there results

$$\eta_r = \left(\frac{I_m/\pi}{I_m/2} \right)^2 \frac{100}{1 + r_p/R_l} = \frac{40.6}{1 + r_p/R_l} \quad \% \tag{12-13}$$

This indicates that the theoretical maximum efficiency of the single-phase half-wave rectifier is 40.6 per cent. But it may be shown that maximum power output occurs when $R_l = r_p$, with a corresponding theoretical plate-circuit efficiency of 20.3 per cent.

There are several features of such a rectifier circuit that warrant special attention. Refer to Fig. 12-1, which shows the complete wiring diagram of the rectifier. On the inverse cycle, i.e., on that part of the cycle during which the tube is not conducting, the maximum potential across the rectifier tube is equal to the transformer maximum value. That is, the peak inverse potential across the tube is equal to the transformer maximum value.

Note also from the diagram that with the negative terminal of the output connected to ground the full transformer potential exists between the primary and the secondary windings of the filament heating transformer.

This requires that the transformer insulation must be adequate to withstand this potential without rupture. Evidently if the positive terminal is grounded, then the transformer need not have a high insulation strength.

12-2. Ripple Factor. Although it is the object of a rectifier to convert a-c into d-c current, the simple circuit considered does not achieve this. Nor, in fact, do any of the more complicated rectifier circuits, either single-phase or polyphase, accomplish this exactly. What is achieved is a unidirectional current, periodically fluctuating components still remaining in the output. Filters are ordinarily used in rectifier systems in order to help decrease these fluctuating components, and these will receive detailed consideration in Chap. 13. A measure of the fluctuating components is given by the ripple factor r, which is defined as

$$r = \frac{\text{rms value of a-c components of wave}}{\text{avg or d-c value of wave}}$$

and which may be written as

$$r = \frac{I'_{\text{rms}}}{I_{\text{d-c}}} = \frac{E'_{\text{rms}}}{E_{\text{d-c}}} \tag{12-14}$$

where I'_{rms} and E'_{rms} denote the rms values of the a-c components only.

An analytical expression for the ripple factor is readily possible. It is noted that the instantaneous a-c component of the current is given by

$$i' = i - I_{\text{d-c}}$$

But by definition

$$I'_{\text{rms}} = \sqrt{\frac{1}{2\pi} \int_0^{2\pi} (i - I_{\text{d-c}})^2 \, d\alpha} = \sqrt{\frac{1}{2\pi} \int_0^{2\pi} (i^2 - 2iI_{\text{d-c}} + I_{\text{d-c}}^2) \, d\alpha}$$

This expression is readily interpreted. The first term of the integrand when evaluated yields the square of the rms value of the total wave I_{rms}^2. The second term yields

$$\frac{1}{2\pi} \int_0^{2\pi} 2iI_{\text{d-c}} \, d\alpha = 2I_{\text{d-c}}^2$$

The rms ripple current then becomes

$$I'_{\text{rms}} = \sqrt{I_{\text{rms}}^2 - 2I_{\text{d-c}}^2 + I_{\text{d-c}}^2} = \sqrt{I_{\text{rms}}^2 - I_{\text{d-c}}^2}$$

By combining these results with Eq. (12-13)

$$r = \frac{\sqrt{I_{\text{rms}}^2 - I_{\text{d-c}}^2}}{I_{\text{d-c}}} = \sqrt{\left(\frac{I_{\text{rms}}}{I_{\text{d-c}}}\right)^2 - 1} \tag{12-15}$$

This expression is independent of the current waveshape and applies in general, since the development was not confined to a particular waveshape.   In the case of the half-wave single-phase rectifier the ratio

$$\frac{I_{\text{rms}}}{I_{\text{d-c}}} = \frac{I_m/2}{I_m/\pi} = \frac{\pi}{2} = 1.57$$

and hence

$$r = \sqrt{1.57^2 - 1} = 1.21 \tag{12-16}$$

This shows that the rms value of the ripple potential exceeds the d-c potential of the output.   This merely tends to show that a single-phase

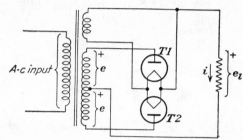

Fig. 12-4. Schematic wiring diagram of a single-phase full-wave rectifier.

half-wave rectifier without filter is a relatively poor device for converting a-c into d-c potential.

12-3. Single-phase Full-wave Rectifier.   The circuit of the single-phase full-wave rectifier, given in Fig. 12-4, is seen to bear some resemblance to a push-pull circuit.   Actually the circuit comprises two half-wave circuits which are so connected that conduction takes place through one tube during one half of the total power cycle and through the other tube during the second half of the power cycle.   The output current through the load has the form illustrated in Fig 12-5, where the portions of the wave marked 1 flow through tube $T1$ and the portions of the wave marked 2 flow through tube $T2$.

The d-c and rms values of the load current are found from Eqs. (12-6) and (12-11) to be

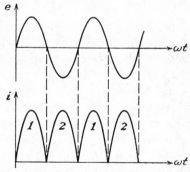

Fig. 12-5. The transformer potential and output load current in a single-phase full-wave rectifier.

$$I_{\text{d-c}} = \frac{2I_m}{\pi}$$

$$I_{\text{rms}} = \frac{I_m}{\sqrt{2}} \tag{12-17}$$

where I_m is the peak value of the current wave. The d-c output power is then

$$P_{\text{d-c}} = I_{\text{d-c}}^2 R_l = \left(\frac{2}{\pi}\right)^2 \frac{E_m^2 R_l}{(r_p + R_l)^2} \qquad (12\text{-}18)$$

By comparing this expression with Eq. (12-7) it is seen that the power delivered to the load is higher by a factor of 4 in the full-wave case. However, the power depends on the circuit parameters in the same way as for the half-wave circuit.

The input power from the a-c source is readily found to have the same form as Eq. (12-10), viz.,

$$P_i = I_{\text{rms}}^2 (r_p + R_l) \qquad (12\text{-}19)$$

The efficiency of rectification is

$$\eta_r = \frac{81.2}{1 + r_p/R_l} \quad \% \qquad (12\text{-}20)$$

This expressions shows a theoretical maximum that is twice that of the half-wave rectifier.

The ripple factor is readily found when it is noted that

$$\frac{I_{\text{rms}}}{I_{\text{d-c}}} = \frac{I_m/\sqrt{2}}{2I_m/\pi} = 1.11$$

From Eq. (12-15),

$$r = \sqrt{1.11^2 - 1} = 0.482 \qquad (12\text{-}21)$$

Thus the ripple factor has dropped from 1.21 in the half-wave rectifier to 0.482 in the present case. What has been accomplished in the full-wave rectifier, therefore, is that the rectification process has become more efficient, with a higher percentage of the power supplied to the circuit being converted into the desired d-c power, and with a consequent smaller fraction remaining in a-c form, which, while producing heating of the load, does not contribute to the desired d-c power.

A study of Fig. 12-4 indicates that when one tube is conducting, say $T1$, then tube $T2$ is in the nonconducting state. Except for the tube drop $i_b r_p$ in $T1$, the peak inverse potential across $T2$ is $2E_m$, or twice the transformer maximum potential measured to the mid-point, or the full transformer potential. The potential stress between windings of the filament transformer is seen to be the full d-c potential, if the negative is grounded, and is sensibly zero, if the positive is grounded.

12-4. Circuits with Gas Diodes. Gas diodes may be used in the half-wave and full-wave circuits discussed above. Owing to their different plate characteristics, the results are somewhat different. For these tubes a sensibly constant potential appears across the tube when the tube is conducting, but conduction does not begin until the applied potential exceeds the breakdown potential of the tube. The tube will consequently conduct for less than 180 deg in each cycle. The situation is illustrated in Fig. 12-6.

The equation of the potential across the load during conduction is obtained by applying Kirchhoff's law to the plate circuit,

$$e_l = i_b R_l = E_m \sin \alpha - E_0 \tag{12-22}$$

and the corresponding expression for the current is

$$i_b = \frac{E_m \sin \alpha - E_0}{R_l} \tag{12-23}$$

where E_0 is the constant tube drop during conduction.

The d-c plate current is found by taking the average value of the instantaneous current and is

$$I_{\text{d-c}} = \frac{1}{2\pi} \int_{\alpha_1}^{\alpha_2} \frac{E_m \sin \alpha - E_0}{R_l} d\alpha \tag{12-24}$$

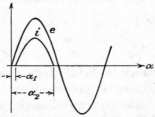

where α_1 is the angle at which the tube fires and α_2 is the angle at which conduction ceases. Ordinarily the applied plate potential is much larger than E_0, and the angles α_1 and $\pi - \alpha_2$ are very nearly zero. Consequently the limits on the integral of Eq. (12-24) may be changed to 0 and π without appreciable error in the result. When this is done and the integral is evaluated, it is found that

Fig. 12-6. The applied potential and the current waveshape in a half-wave rectifier circuit using a gas diode.

$$I_{\text{d-c}} = \frac{E_m}{\pi R_l} - \frac{E_0}{2R_l} = \frac{E_m}{\pi R_l} \left(1 - \frac{\pi}{2} \frac{E_0}{E_m} \right) \tag{12-25}$$

The load potential $E_{\text{d-c}}$ may be written as

$$E_{\text{d-c}} = \frac{E_m}{\pi} \left(1 - \frac{\pi}{2} \frac{E_0}{E_m} \right) \tag{12-26}$$

This equation does not contain the load current. This means, of course, that $E_{\text{d-c}}$ is independent of the load current, with consequent perfect regulation.

To calculate the efficiency of rectification, it is necessary to calculate the input power to the plate circuit. This is given by

$$P_i = \frac{1}{2\pi} \int_0^{\pi} e i_b \, d\alpha = \frac{1}{2\pi} \int_0^{\pi} E_m \sin \alpha \, \frac{E_m \sin \alpha - E_0}{R_l} \, d\alpha$$

where the limits are again taken as 0 and π. This expression reduces to

$$P_i = \frac{E_m^2}{4R_l}\left(1 - \frac{4}{\pi}\frac{E_0}{E_m}\right) \tag{12-27}$$

The efficiency of rectification is then

$$\eta_r = \frac{P_{\text{d-c}}}{P_i} = \frac{4}{\pi^2}\frac{\left(1 - \frac{\pi}{2}\frac{E_0}{E_m}\right)^2}{1 - \frac{4}{\pi}\frac{E_0}{E_m}} \tag{12-28}$$

which may be reduced to the form

$$\eta_r = 40.6\left(1 - 1.87\frac{E_0}{E_m}\right)\quad\% \tag{12-29}$$

Note that this value is independent of the load current or load resistance. To the same approximation, namely, $E_m \gg E_0$, the ripple factor is given by

$$r = 1.21\left(1 + 0.5\frac{E_0}{E_m}\right) \tag{12-30}$$

which is slightly higher than the value with the vacuum diode. This increased ripple results because the tube conduction is less than 180 deg.

The corresponding properties of the full-wave circuit with gas tubes will follow a completely parallel development and yield results that bear the same relation to the vacuum-tube case that the foregoing results do to the corresponding half-wave vacuum-rectifier case.

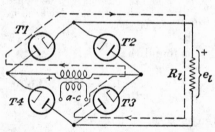

Fig. 12-7. Single-phase full-wave bridge rectifier circuit.

12-5. Miscellaneous Single-phase Rectifier Circuits. A variety of other rectifier circuits exist which find widespread use. Among these are bridge rectifier circuits, potential-doubling circuits, and potential-multiplying circuits. The bridge circuit finds extensive use both as a power rectifier and also as the rectifying system in rectifier-type a-c meters. The rectifiers for power use utilize thermionic diodes of both the vacuum and gas varieties, whereas those for instrument use are usually of the copper oxide or crystal types.

To examine the operation of the bridge circuit, refer to Fig. 12-7. It is observed that two tubes conduct simultaneously during one half of the cycle and the other two tubes conduct during the second half of the cycle.

The conduction paths and directions are such that the resulting current through the load is substantially that shown in Fig. 12-5.

The primary features of the bridge circuit are the following: The currents drawn in both the primary and secondary of the plate-supply transformer are sinusoidal. This permits a smaller transformer to be used for a given output power than is necessary for the same power with the single-phase full-wave circuit of the two-tube type.* Also, the transformer need not have a center tap. Since each tube has only transformer potential across it on the inverse cycle, the bridge circuit is suitable for high-potential applications. However, the transformers supplying the heaters of the tubes must be properly insulated for the high potential.

A rectifier meter is essentially a bridge-rectifier system which utilizes copper oxide elements. The potential to be measured is applied through a multiplier resistance to two corners of the bridge, a d-c milliammeter being used as an indicating instrument across the other two corners. But as the d-c milliammeter reads average values of current, the scale of the meter is calibrated to give rms values of sinusoidal waves by applying a sinusoidal potential to the input terminals. The indication on such an instrument is not correct for input signals that contain appreciable harmonics.

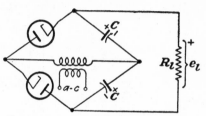

Fig. 12-8. A full-wave potential-doubling circuit.

A common potential-doubling circuit is shown in Fig. 12-8. The output[1] from such a circuit is approximately equal to twice the transformer maximum potential. It operates by alternately charging each of the two capacitors to the transformer peak potential E_m, current being continually drained from the capacitors through the load. This circuit is characterized by poor regulation unless very large capacitors are used. The peak inverse potential is twice the transformer peak potential. If ordinary rectifiers are used, two separate filament sources are required. If a relatively low potential system is built, and these are used extensively in a-c/d-c radio sets, special tubes such as 25Z5 are available. These tubes are provided with separate indirectly heated cathodes. The cathodes in these tubes are well insulated from the heaters, which are connected in series internally.

The regulation of the potential doubler can be improved, particularly at the higher loads, by employing a bridge doubler rectifier,[2] which is illustrated in Fig. 12-9. The feature of this rectifier circuit is that at

---

* For a discussion of *transformer utilization factor*, see J. Millman and S. Seely, "Electronics," 2d ed., chap. 14, McGraw-Hill Book Company, Inc., New York, 1951.

light loads the output potential is approximately twice the transformer peak potential. However, the potential will never fall below the output of the bridge circuit at any load, nor will the ripple factor exceed that of

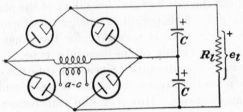

FIG. 12-9. A bridge doubler rectifier.

the bridge circuit, viz., $r = 0.482$. Most other features of this circuit are like those in the normal bridge circuit, such as the peak inverse potential to which each tube is subjected, and the heater-cathode insulation problems.

An alternative potential-doubling circuit[3] is shown in Fig. 12-10. The output potential from this circuit, like that from Fig. 12-8, is approximately equal to twice the transformer maximum potential. It operates by charging capacitor C_1 during one half cycle through tube $T1$ to the trans-

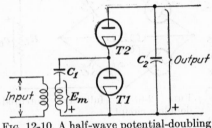

FIG. 12-10. A half-wave potential-doubling circuit.

former peak potential E_m and during the next half cycle charges C_2 through tube $T2$ to the potential determined by that across C_1 and the transformer in series, the peak being approximately $2E_m$. The peak inverse potential across each tube is twice the transformer peak potential.

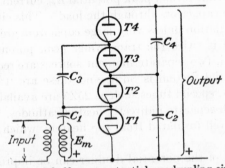

FIG. 12-11. A half-wave potential-quadrupling circuit.

This circuit may be extended to a quadrupler by adding two tubes and two capacitors, as shown in Fig. 12-11. It may be extended to provide n-fold multiplication, odd or even.

12-6. Controlled Rectifiers. It is sometimes necessary to provide a control on the amount of the rectified current in a rectifier. Such controlled currents are required in motor speed control, in certain electric welding operations, in lighting-control installations in theaters, in torque controls of various types, and in a variety of industrial control applications. Such control of the output of a rectifier may be accomplished by controlling the potential of the power transformer feeding the rectifier, or this might, in some cases, be controlled by inserting a controlling resistor in the output circuit. The first method may require expensive control equipment, and the second would be characterized by poor efficiency. The development of thyratrons, ignitrons, and excitrons, the latter two being single-anode pool tanks, has made control a direct and relatively

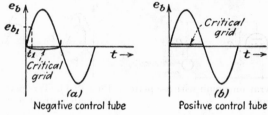

(a) Negative control tube   *(b)* Positive control tube

FIG. 12-12. The grid-control curve for an applied sinusoidal plate potential to a thyratron.

inexpensive process. The basic analyses are common to the three types of tubes, and no loss of generality is incurred by confining our attention to thyratrons.

In the discussion in Sec. 1-27 it was indicated that the complete electrostatic shielding of the cathode by the massive grid structure in the thyratron (and also in the excitron) provides a means for controlling the initiation of the arc in the tube by controlling the grid potential. Thus since the arc is extinguished once each cycle on each negative half cycle, provided that the arc is initiated regularly, control is possible if the point in each half cycle at which the arc is initiated can be controlled. Such regular control is possible, thus providing a control on the average rectified current.

In order to analyze the action of a thyratron in a controlled circuit, use is made of the critical grid breakdown characteristic of Fig. 1-34. As indicated in Sec. 1-27, a knowledge of this single curve is sufficient to predict the behavior of the thyratron in the control circuit. This curve gives the minimum grid potential required for conduction to occur for each value of plate potential. Thus if a sinusoidal plate potential is applied to the tube, the potential on the grid that is required just to permit conduction at each point in the cycle is found from the critical grid curve. The conditions are illustrated in Fig. 12-12. On this diagram, corresponding to any time t_1 in the positive half cycle, the plate potentia is e_{b1}. The corresponding critical grid potential is obtained directly from the critical grid breakdown characteristic and is shown in the figure This means that, unless the grid potential is more positive than that given by e_{cg} at the particular instant, conduction will not take place. O course, once conduction begins at any point in the cycle, the grid loses control of the arc and cannot again control until the arc is extinguished.

Suppose that the circuit is so arranged that the grid potential exceeds the critical grid breakdown value at some angle, say φ. Conduction will start at this point in the cycle. But the potential drop across the tube during conduction of the thyratron, like that in any gas arc discharge remains substantially constant at a low value E_0 that is independent of

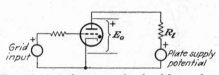

FIG. 12-13. A thyratron circuit with a-c plate and grid excitation.

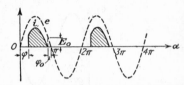

FIG. 12-14. The plate potential and the plate current in a thyratron.

the current. Consequently the current in the plate circuit of the tube is readily found. Refer to Fig. 12-13, which gives the schematic diagram of a thyratron circuit, and to Fig. 12-14, which shows the potential and current waveshapes in the thyratron.

If the tube drop after conduction has begun is E_0, then the current in the plate load of resistance R_l during the conducting portion of the cycle is

$$i_b = \frac{E_m \sin \alpha - E_0}{R_l} \tag{12-31}$$

where E_m is the maximum value of the applied potential. Clearly, the current is zero until conduction takes place, after which it assumes the value dictated by Eq. (12-31). The current follows the form of Eq (12-31) until the supply potential e falls below E_0 at the phase $\pi - \varphi_0$ The current remains zero until the phase φ is again reached in the next cycle.

The average rectified current, i.e., the value read on a d-c ammeter, is given by the expression

$$I_{\text{d-c}} = \frac{1}{2\pi} \int_{\varphi}^{\pi - \varphi_0} i_b \, d\alpha$$

$$= \frac{E_m}{2\pi R_l} \int_{\varphi}^{\pi - \varphi_0} \left(\sin \alpha - \frac{E_0}{E_m} \right) d\alpha$$

which integrates to

$$I_{\text{d-c}} = \frac{E_m}{2\pi R_l} \left[\cos \varphi + \cos \varphi_0 - \frac{E_0}{E_m} (\pi - \varphi_0 - \varphi) \right] \qquad (12\text{-}32)$$

where $\alpha = \omega t$, and where φ_0 is defined by the relation

$$E_0 = E_m \sin \varphi_0 \qquad (12\text{-}33)$$

If the ratio E_0/E_m is very small, then φ_0 may be taken as zero. Equation (12-32) reduces under this condition to the form

$$I_{\text{d-c}} \doteq \frac{E_m}{2\pi R_l} (1 + \cos \varphi) \qquad (12\text{-}34)$$

The limits of variation of the angle are from 0 to π.

It is clear from this analysis that the average rectified current can be controlled by varying the position in the cycle at which the grid potential exceeds the critical grid starting value. The maximum current is obtained when the arc is initiated at the beginning of each cycle. The minimum current is obtained when the arc is not initiated, and

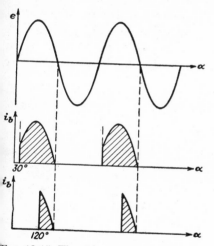

FIG. 12-15. The character of the conduction in a thyratron for various angles of initiation of the arc.

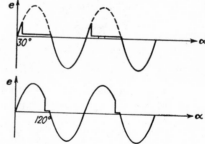

FIG. 12-16. The potential across the thyratron for various current-conduction periods.

this would occur if initiation were adjusted to occur at the end of each cycle. Sketches showing the character of the results are given in Fig. 12-15.

The potential across the thyratron throughout the cycle will vary in the manner illustrated in Fig. 12-16. During the portion of the cycle when the tube is not conducting current, the full applied potential appears across the tube. During the portion of the cycle when the tube is conducting, the drop across the tube is E_0, which is assumed constant and independent of the tube current.

The reading of a d-c voltmeter placed across the tube will be

$$E_{\text{d-c}} = \frac{1}{2\pi} \int_0^{2\pi} e_b \, d\alpha$$

This integral is written as

$$E_{\text{d-c}} = \frac{1}{2\pi} \left(\int_0^{\varphi} E_m \sin \alpha \, d\alpha + \int_{\varphi}^{\pi - \varphi_0} E_0 \, d\alpha + \int_{\pi - \varphi_0}^{2\pi} E_m \sin \alpha \, d\alpha \right)$$

This integrates to

$$E_{\text{d-c}} = \frac{E_0}{2\pi} (\pi - \varphi_0 - \varphi) - \frac{E_m}{2\pi} (\cos \varphi + \cos \varphi_0) \qquad (12\text{-}35)$$

If the peak transformer potential $E_m \gg E_0$, this equation reduces to

$$E_{\text{d-c}} \doteq - \frac{E_m}{2\pi} (1 + \cos \varphi) \qquad (12\text{-}36)$$

The appearance of the negative sign merely means that the cathode is more positive than the plate for most of the cycle. It is to be emphasized that the d-c voltmeter does not read the value E_0 when an a-c potential is applied to the tube but will read E_0 if a d-c potential is applied.

The readings of d-c and a-c indicating instruments may be calculated in somewhat similar ways. For example, the reading of an a-c ammeter in the plate lead will be

$$I_{\text{rms}} = \sqrt{\frac{1}{2\pi} \int_0^{2\pi} i_b^2 \, d\alpha}$$

which is

$$I_{\text{rms}} = \sqrt{\frac{1}{2\pi} \int_{\varphi}^{\pi - \varphi_0} \left(\frac{E_m \sin \alpha - E_0}{R_l} \right)^2 d\alpha} \qquad (12\text{-}37)$$

This integration is readily effected. Similarly, the reading of a watt-meter to indicate the total power supplied to the plate circuit is

$$P = \frac{1}{2\pi} \int_0^{2\pi} e i_b \, d\alpha$$

which is

$$P = \frac{1}{2\pi} \int_{\varphi}^{\pi - \varphi_0} E_m \sin \alpha \, \frac{E_m \sin \alpha - E_0}{R_l} \, d\alpha \qquad (12\text{-}38)$$

This integration is also readily effected. In particular, it is essential to set up the basic expression for any quantity before proceeding in its evaluation.

12-7. Phase-shift Control. In the phase-shift method of control, the conduction point of the cycle is controlled by controlling the phase angle between the plate and grid potentials. The situation is illustrated in Fig. 12-17. In this figure, the grid-cathode potential e_c lags the plate cathode potential e_b by the angle θ. Note from the figure that the grid potential equals the critical grid breakdown potential at the angle φ and conduction begins at this point in the cycle. The arc is extinguished when the plate potential falls below the value to maintain conduction.

If the applied grid potential is large compared with the critical grid potential at the point of conduction, the angles φ and θ are approximately the same. Also, it may be assumed under these conditions that the critical grid curve coincides with the zero-potential axis. Also, if $E_m \gg E_0$, then Eq. (12-34) will give the dependence of d-c load current on the phase angle for all values of φ for which the grid potential lags

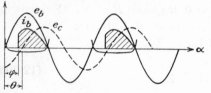

FIG. 12-17. Phase-shift control of a thyratron.

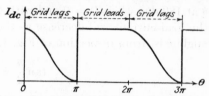

FIG. 12-18. The average load current as a function of phase angle between the grid and plate potentials.

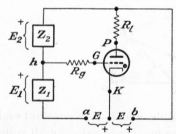

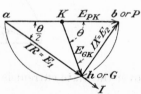

FIG. 12-19. A simple phase-shifting network and the potential circle diagram.

behind the plate potential. When the grid potential leads the plate potential by any angle, conduction will occur very nearly at the beginning of each cycle, with full rectification. A sketch showing these results is given in Fig. 12-18. The curve possesses a discontinuity at the 180-deg position, since for an angle slightly larger than 180 deg the plate current is at its full value, whereas for an angle slightly less than 180 deg the plate current is zero.

For those cases where a small plate potential or a small grid potential is used, the foregoing simplifications are not valid. However, the analysis follows the same general form, due account being taken of the difference between φ and θ and of the angles $\pi - \varphi_0$ and π.

Circuits for achieving the phase-shift control in a single-phase system are readily analyzed. A common circuit and the potential sinor diagram that applies to this circuit are given in Fig. 12-19. The phase between

the grid and the plate potentials is controlled by means of the two impedances Z_1 and Z_2. It should be noted that the potential circle diagram in
Fig. 12-19 has been drawn under the assumption that

$$Z_1 = R \text{ (a resistance)} \qquad Z_2 = j\omega L \text{ (an inductance)}$$

Also, the potential circle diagram applies only during the periods before
conduction begins in each cycle. Before conduction begins, there is no
current in the load R_l, and points b and P are the same. From the results
of the potential circle diagram, it is clear that the phase θ between the
plate and grid potentials can be varied over the range from 0 to 180 deg
by varying the control resistance R in the phase-shifting network, with
θ at 180 deg when $R = 0$ and with θ at 0 deg when $R = \infty$. Evidently,
the load current will decrease as the resistance R decreases. The phase
angle θ is, from inspection of Fig. 12-19,

$$\tan \frac{\theta}{2} = \frac{E_2}{E_1} = \frac{Z_2}{Z_1} \tag{12-39}$$

If the control impedances Z_1 and Z_2 are interchanged, then the sinor
diagram that results has the form given in the accompanying diagram,
which shows that E_{gk} leads the potential E_{pk}. Then, from Fig. 12-18, no

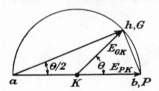

control over the plate current is possible, and I_{d-c} is a constant and equal
to its maximum value for all values of θ.
The use of R and C as control impedances is possible and is generally preferred
over the use of R and L. With an RC
phase-shifting circuit, control is possible
for $Z_1 = -jX_C$, $Z_2 = R$ but is not possible for $Z_1 = R$, $Z_2 = -jX_C$.

12-8. D-C Bias Control. The magnitude of the d-c or average rectified current of a thyratron may be controlled by
applying a d-c bias to the grid of the tube

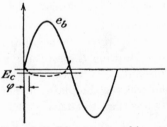

Fig. 12-20. Direct-current bias control of a thyratron.

and controlling its magnitude. The plate supply must be an a-c potential.
The situation is best understood by reference to Fig. 12-20.

The tube will conduct at the point where E_0 intersects the critical grid
curve, the angle φ in the diagram. Clearly, if the negative grid potential
is too large to intersect the critical grid curve, no conduction will be pos-

sible. The optimum bias is that for which the grid-potential line is
tangent to the critical grid curve, and the tube conducts for one-half of the

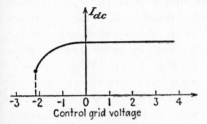

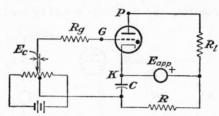

Fig. 12-21. The average plate current in
a thyratron as a function of the d-c grid-
bias potential.

Fig. 12-22. A circuit for bias phase control
of a thyratron.

cycle. For less negative bias, the conduction angle φ is less than 90 deg.
Control is evidently possible over the range from full conduction to half
conduction. The results of Fig. 12-21
show the character of the control.

12-9. Bias Phase Control. The
combination of d-c and a-c potentials
as a bias yields bias phase control. A
circuit for such control is given in
Fig. 12-22. The network comprising
R and C serves to introduce an a-c
potential of fixed phase with respect
to the plate potential.

Suppose, for convenience, that
$R = X_C$. The a-c grid potential will
then lag the plate potential by 45
deg. The amplitude of the a-c grid
potential is 0.707 that of the plate
potential. Suppose also that the
critical grid potential coincides with
the zero axis. The general features
of the operation of this control are
illustrated in Fig. 12-23. The conditions corresponding to three different
values of E_C are illustrated. In the
first, E_C is positive; in the second, E_C
is zero; in the third, E_C is negative.
For the circuit shown, the minimum

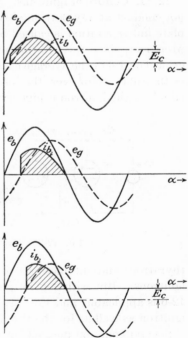

Fig. 12-23. Bias phase control, showing current variations for three different values of d-c component E_C.

rectified current occurs when E_C is negative and equal to E_{gm}. Conduction begins at 135 deg in the cycle and continues until the end of the
cycle. If the d-c bias is made more negative than this, no conduction

is possible. It is evident from the diagrams that conduction will begin at the start of the cycle when the d-c bias equals 0.707 times E_{gm}.

12-10. On-Off Control. A variety of circuits exist which permit on-off control. Such circuits would be used when it is desired to use a thyratron as an arcless switch or contactor. A circuit for on-off control is given in Fig. 12-24. With switch S open, no conduction occurs since E_{cc} is so adjusted that it is more negative than the maximum negative critical grid value. When the switch S is closed, the grid is tied to the cathode and approximately maximum rectified current is delivered. The resistance R serves to prevent short circuiting of the battery source E_{cc} when S is closed.

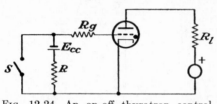

Fig. 12-24. An on-off thyratron control circuit.

12-11. Control of Ignitrons. As discussed in Sec. 1-29, the ignitron will not conduct at any portion of the cycle of an applied a-c potential to the plate unless ignition is caused by applying a potential to the igniter rod. Moreover, since this ignition pulse may be applied at any point in the cycle, control of the average current is afforded by controlling the ignition of the tube. However, the instantaneous power required by the igniter circuit of the ignitron is higher than that required by the grid circuit of a

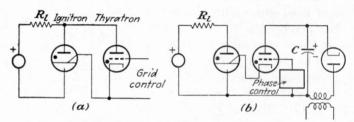

Fig. 12-25. Several ignitron control circuits.

thyratron, and the methods of thyratron control are not applicable to ignitrons. But with control accomplished the general discussion of Sec. 12-6 is applicable, and Eqs. (12-31) to (12-38) express the results for the ignitron as well as for the thyratron.

Several common methods of establishing the point of ignition in each cycle of an ignitron are illustrated in Fig. 12-25. These methods utilize thyratrons for the control of the ignitron. In the first of these diagrams, the ignitron current passes through the load resistor, whereas, in the second, the igniter-rod current does not pass through the load.

Refer to Fig. 12-25b, and suppose that the thyratron is not conducting. In this circuit the capacitor C will be charged to the peak value of the transformer potential through the rectifier. If the thyratron grid potential is adjusted to permit conduction, the capacitor charge will pass through the thyratron and igniter-rod circuits, and the ignitron will conduct provided that the ignitron anode potential is sufficiently positive to maintain the discharge. The current surge through the ignitron-rod circuit will quickly discharge the capacitor, the thyratron anode potential will fall below that to maintain the arc, and the thyratron igniter-rod circuit current will fall to zero. The capacitor will be recharged through the diode rectifier circuit in time to control the ignition point in the next cycle.

REFERENCES

1. For an analysis of the operation, see D. L., Waidelich, *Proc. IRE*, **29**, 554 (1941).
2. Corbyn, D. B., *Electronic Eng.*, **24**, 418 (1952).
3. Cockroft, J. D., and E. T. S. Walton, *Proc. Roy. Soc. (London)*, **136**, 619 (1932).
   Waidelich, D. L., *Proc. IRE*, **30**, 534 (1942).
   Mitchell, R. G., *Wireless Engr.*, **22**, 474 (1945).

PROBLEMS

12-1. A type 5U4G is connected in a half-wave circuit to supply power to a 1,500-ohm load from a 350-volt rms source of potential.

a. On a plate characteristic of the tube, plot the load line, and from this find the dynamic curve.

b. Obtain a plot of the output-current waveshape for a sinusoidal applied potential.

c. Estimate the value of the plate resistance r_p from the static characteristic at four different values of current (50, 100, 150, 200 ma). Use the average of these as the r_p of the tube.

d. Plot on the curve in part b the value obtained from Eq. (12-4), and compare.

12-2. The two sections of a 6X5 diode are connected in parallel and supply power to a 5,000-ohm load from a 325-volt rms source of potential. The effective plate resistance of the parallel combination of diodes is approximately 125 ohms. Calculate the following:

a. The d-c load current.

b. The a-c current (rms).

c. The reading of a d-c voltmeter placed across the diode terminals.

d. The total input power to the plate circuit.

e. The efficiency of rectification.

f. The regulation from no load to the given load.

g. The ripple factor.

12-3. Suppose that a 6X5 tube supplies power to a 5,000-ohm load from a 325-0-325 transformer. Repeat Prob. 12-2 under these conditions.

12-4. Show that the input power to a rectifier using gas diodes may be expressed in the form

$$P_i = I_{rms}^2 R_l + E_0 I_{d-c}$$

12-5. A gas diode for which the breakdown and maintaining potential is taken to be 10 volts supplies power in a half-wave rectifier circuit to a 1,000-ohm load from a 325-volt rms source. Calculate the following:

a. The d-c current through the load.

b. The a-c (rms) current through the load.

c. The reading of a d-c voltmeter placed across the diode.

d. The reading of an rms a-c voltmeter across the diode.

e. The power input to the plate circuit.

f. The efficiency of rectification.

g. The ripple factor.

12-6. The peak inverse plate potential rating of a 2X2/879 half-wave high-vacuum rectifier is 12,500 volts. Calculate the maximum d-c potential possible to a load, without exceeding the peak inverse potential, when such tubes are used in:

a. A half-wave circuit.

b. A full-wave circuit.

c. A full-wave bridge circuit.

d. A full-wave potential-doubling circuit.

e. A half-wave potential-doubling circuit.

f. Specify in each case the insulation strength of each filament transformer when the positive terminal is grounded.

12-7. Analyze the operation of the potential-quadrupling circuit of Fig. 12-10. Calculate:

a. The maximum possible potential across each capacitor.

b. The peak inverse potential of each tube.

c. The required insulation strength of each filament transformer.

12-8. The arc drop in a certain thyratron is 12 volts. The tube supplies power to a 100-ohm resistor from a 330-volt rms supply. Calculate the reading of a d-c ammeter in the circuit when:

a. The grid and plate potentials are in phase.

b. The grid potential leads the plate potential by 60 deg.

c. The grid potential lags the plate potential by 60 deg.

Assume a zero critical grid potential for all values of plate potential.

12-9. The circuit of Fig. 12-19 is used to control the current in a load of 100 ohms. The potential E_{ab} = 330 volts rms, and the power frequency is 60 cps. A 1,000-ohm resistor and a 2-μf capacitor are available.

a. Draw a potential diagram that applies for the case where conduction occurs for less than the full half cycle.

b. Calculate the d-c current in the load.

c. Calculate the a-c power supplied by the line to the plate circuit.

12-10. The full-wave controlled rectifier for a certain application is shown in the accompanying diagram. The resistor in the phase-shift network is adjusted to 1,000 ohms.

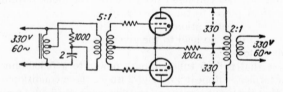

a. Draw a potential diagram that applies for the case where conduction continues for less than the full half cycle.

b. Calculate the d-c current in the load.

c. Calculate the a-c power supplied by the line to the plate circuit.

12-11. An FG-27A tube operates at a temperature of 50°C and supplies power to a 100-ohm load from an input potential source of 330 volts rms.

a. A d-c bias potential of −4 volts is applied.   Calculate the d-c plate current.

b. A 4-volt rms grid potential that lags the plate by 60 deg is applied.   Calculate the d-c plate current.

c. The two sources in parts *a* and *b* are connected in series.   Calculate the d-c plate current.

12-12. An ignitron is used in the circuit of Fig. 12-25*b*.   The phase of the control circuit of the thyratron is adjusted for conduction to begin 60 deg after the beginning of each cycle.   The tube drop during conduction is 20 volts.   If the applied potential is 330 volts rms and the load resistor is 20 ohms, calculate:

a. The d-c load current.

b. The a-c power to the load circuit.

c. The power dissipated in the tube.

d. The total power dissipated in the load.

CHAPTER 13

RECTIFIER FILTERS AND REGULATORS

It is usually the requirement of a power supply to provide a relatively ripple-free source of d-c potential from an a-c line. However, as seen in the last chapter, a rectifier actually provides an output which contains a-c components in addition to the d-c term that is desired, a measure of the a-c components being given by the ripple factor. It is customary to include a filter between the rectifier and the ouput to attenuate these ripple components. Often an electronic regulator is also included, if the potential output is to be substantially constant with load, or if the ripple must be small.

The analysis of the action of such rectifier filters is complicated by the fact that the rectifier as a driving source is nonlinear, thus requiring the solution of circuits with nonlinear elements. It is possible in most cases to make reasonable assumptions in order to effect an approximate engineering solution. Thus, the results obtained are only approximate.

13-1. The Harmonic Components in Rectifier Circuits. An analytic representation of the output of the single-phase half-wave rectifier is obtained in terms of a Fourier series expansion. This series representation has the form

$$i = b_0 + \sum_{k=1}^{\infty} b_k \cos k\alpha + \sum_{k=1}^{\infty} a_k \sin k\alpha \qquad (13\text{-}1)$$

where $\alpha = \omega t$ and where the coefficients that appear in the series are given by the integrals

$$b_0 = \frac{1}{2\pi} \int_0^{2\pi} i \, d\alpha$$

$$b_k = \frac{1}{\pi} \int_0^{2\pi} i \cos k\alpha \, d\alpha \qquad (13\text{-}2)$$

$$a_k = \frac{1}{\pi} \int_0^{2\pi} i \sin k\alpha \, d\alpha$$

It should be recalled that the constant term b_0 that appears in this Fourier series is the average or d-c value of the current.

The explicit expression for the current in a half-wave rectifier circuit, which is obtained by performing the indicated integrations using Eqs.

382

(12-4) over the two specified intervals, yields

$$i = I_m \left[\frac{1}{\pi} + \frac{1}{2} \sin \omega t - \frac{2}{\pi} \sum_{k=2,4,6,\ldots} \frac{\cos k\omega t}{(k+1)(k-1)} \right] \qquad (13\text{-}3)$$

where $I_m = E_m/(r_p + R_l)$ and E_m is the peak transformer potential. The lowest angular frequency that is present in this expression is that of the primary source. Also, except for this single term of frequency ω, all other terms that appear in the expression are even-harmonic terms.

The corresponding Fourier series representation of the output of the full-wave rectifier which is illustrated in Fig. 12-5 may be derived from Eq. (13-3). Thus, by recalling that the full-wave circuit comprises two half-wave circuits which are so arranged that one circuit is operating during the interval when the other is not operating, then clearly the currents are functionally related by the expression $i_2(\alpha) = i_1(\alpha + \pi)$. The total load current, which is $i = i_1 + i_2$, then attains the form

$$i = I_m \left[\frac{2}{\pi} - \frac{4}{\pi} \sum_{k=2,4,6,\ldots} \frac{\cos k\omega t}{(k+1)(k-1)} \right] \qquad (13\text{-}4)$$

where $I_m = E_m/(R_l + r_p)$, E_m being the maximum value of the transformer potential measured to the center tap.

A comparison of Eqs. (13-3) and (13-4) indicates that the fundamental angular-frequency term has been eliminated in the full-wave circuit, the lowest harmonic term in the output being 2ω, a second-harmonic term. This will be found to offer a distinct advantage in filtering.

The Fourier series representation of the half-wave and full-wave circuits using gas diodes can be obtained in the same way as above, although the form will be more complex. This is so because conduction begins at some small angle φ_0 and ceases at the angle $\pi - \varphi_0$, when it is assumed that the breakdown and the extinction potentials are equal. But since these angles are usually small under normal operating conditions, it will be assumed that Eqs. (13-3) and (13-4) are applicable for circuits with vacuum or gas diodes. The Fourier series representation of the output of a controlled rectifier is also possible, although the result is quite complex. However, such controlled rectifiers are ordinarily used in services in which the ripple is not of major concern, and, as a result, no detailed analysis will be undertaken. Some results will be given below covering these rectifiers, however.

13-2. Inductor Filters. The operation of an inductor filter depends on the inherent property of an inductor to oppose any change of current that may tend to take place through it. That is, the inductor stores energy in its magnetic field when the current is above its average value and releases energy when the current falls below this value. Consequently any sudden changes in current that might otherwise take place in the circuit will be smoothed out by the action of the inductor.

In particular, suppose that an inductor is connected in series with the load in a single-phase half-wave circuit, as illustrated in Fig. 13-1. For simplicity, suppose that the tube and choke resistances are negligible.

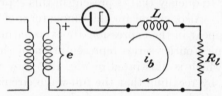

Fig. 13-1. Half-wave rectifier circuit with choke filter.

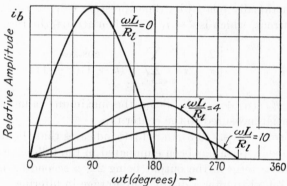

Fig. 13-2. The effect of changing inductance on the waveform of the current in a half-wave rectifier with inductor filter. The load R_l is assumed constant.

Then the controlling differential equation for the current in the circuit during the time of current conduction is

$$L \frac{di_b}{dt} + R_l i_b = E_m \sin \omega t \qquad (13\text{-}5)$$

A solution of this differential equation may be effected. This solution is complicated by the fact that current continues over only a portion of the cycle. The general character of the solution is shown graphically in Fig. 13-2, in which is shown the effect of changing the inductance on the waveform of the current. Since a simple inductance choke is seldom used with a half-wave circuit, further details of the analysis will not be given.

Suppose that an inductor filter is applied to the output of a full-wave rectifier. The circuit and a sketch of the output-current waveshape are given in Fig. 13-3. Since no cutout occurs in the current, the analysis assumes a different form from that for the half-wave case. Now, instead of considering the circuit differential equation, as in Eq. (13-5), and adjusting the initial conditions to fulfill the required physical conditions, an approximate solution is effected. It is supposed that the equation of the potential that is applied to the filter is given by Eq. (13-4). Moreover, it is noted that the amplitudes of the a-c terms beyond the first, and this is of second-harmonic frequency, are small compared with that of the first term. In particular, the fourth-harmonic frequency term is only 20 per cent of the second-harmonic term. Furthermore, the impedance of the inductor increases with frequency, and better filtering action exists for the higher-harmonic terms. Consequently it is assumed that all higher-order terms may be neglected.

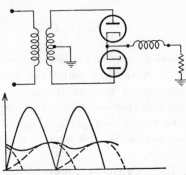

In accordance with the discussion, it is supposed that the input potential to the filter and load has the approximate form

FIG. 13-3. Full-wave rectifier circuit with inductor filter, and the waveshape of the load current.

$$e = \frac{2E_m}{\pi} - \frac{4E_m}{3\pi} \cos 2\omega t \quad (13\text{-}6)$$

The corresponding load current is, in accordance with a-c circuit theory,

$$i_l = \frac{2E_m}{\pi R_l} - \frac{4E_m}{3\pi} \frac{\cos (2\omega t - \psi)}{\sqrt{R_l^2 + 4\omega^2 L^2}} \quad (13\text{-}7)$$

where

$$\tan \psi = \frac{2\omega L}{R_l} \quad (13\text{-}8)$$

The ripple factor, defined in Eq. (12-14), becomes

$$r = \frac{(4E_m/3\pi)(1/\sqrt{R_l^2 + 4\omega^2 L^2})}{2E_m/\pi R_l} = \frac{2R_l}{3\sqrt{2}} \frac{1}{\sqrt{R_l^2 + 4\omega^2 L^2}}$$

which may be expressed in the form

$$r = \frac{2}{3\sqrt{2}} \frac{1}{\sqrt{1 + (4\omega^2 L^2/R_l^2)}} \quad (13\text{-}9)$$

If the ratio $\omega L/R_l$ is large, this reduces to

$$r = \frac{1}{3\sqrt{2}} \frac{R_l}{\omega L} \quad (13\text{-}10)$$

This expression shows that the filtering improves with decreased load resistance or, correspondingly, with increased load current. At no load,

$R_l = \infty$, and the filtering is poorest, with $r = 2/3 \sqrt{2} = 0.47$. This is also the result which applies when no choke is included in the circuit. [Compare with result with Eq. (12-21), which gives 0.482. The difference arises from the terms in the Fourier series that have been neglected.] The expression also shows that large inductances are accompanied by decreased ripple.

The d-c output potential is given by

$$E_{\text{d-c}} = I_{\text{d-c}}R_l = \frac{2E_m}{\pi} = 0.637E_m = 0.90E_{\text{rms}} \qquad (13\text{-}11)$$

where E_{rms} is the transformer secondary potential measured to the center tap. Note that under the assumptions made, viz., negligible power-transformer leakage reactance, transformer resistance, tube resistance, and inductor resistance, the output potential does not change with load, with consequent perfect regulation. Because the neglected effects are not negligible, the output potential actually decreases with increased current.

13-3. Capacitor Filter. Filtering is frequently effected by shunting the load with a capacitor. During the time that the rectifier output is increasing, the capacitor is charging to the rectifier output potential and energy is stored in the capacitor. During the time that the rectifier potential falls below that of the capacitor, the capacitor delivers energy to the load, thus maintaining the potential at a high level for a longer period than without the capacitor. The ripple is therefore considerably decreased. Clearly, the diode acts as a switch, permitting charge to flow into the capacitor when the rectifier potential exceeds the capacitor potential, and then acts to disconnect the power source when the potential falls below that of the capacitor.

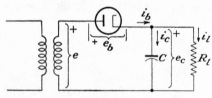

Fig. 13-4. A single-phase half-wave capacitor-filtered rectifier.

To examine the operation in some detail, refer to Fig. 13-4, which shows a diagram of the circuit. The tube current during the conducting portion of the cycle is

$$i_b = i_c + i_l \qquad (13\text{-}12)$$

where

$$i_l = \frac{e_l}{R_l} = \frac{e_c}{R_l} \qquad (13\text{-}13)$$

and where

$$i_c = \frac{dq_c}{dt} = C\frac{de_c}{dt} \qquad (13\text{-}14)$$

where q_c is the capacitor charge. The controlling differential equation of the charging current through the tube is then

$$i_b = \frac{e_c}{R_l} + C \frac{de_c}{dt} \qquad (13\text{-}15)$$

But the potential e_c during the time that the tube is conducting is simply the transformer potential, if the tube drop is neglected. Hence the capacitor potential during this portion of the cycle is sinusoidal and is

$$e_c = e = E_m \sin \omega t$$

The corresponding tube current is

$$i_b = \frac{E_m}{R_l} \sin \omega t + \omega C E_m \cos \omega t$$

This may be written in the equivalent form

$$i_b = E_m \sqrt{\omega^2 C^2 + \frac{1}{R_l^2}} \sin (\omega t + \psi) \qquad (13\text{-}16)$$

where

$$\psi = \tan^{-1} \omega C R_l \qquad (13\text{-}17)$$

A sketch of the current wave is illustrated in Fig. 13-5.

Equation (13-16) shows that the use of large capacitances, in order to improve the filtering, is accompanied by large tube currents. Therefore,

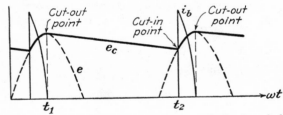

FIG. 13-5. The tube current and the load potential in a single-phase half-wave capacitor-filtered rectifier.

if a large capacitance is used for a given load in order to maintain the output potential more nearly constant, a very peaked current exists. In fact, for a certain required average current demand by the load, the tube-current pulse becomes more and more peaked as the capacitance is made larger. This imposes serious duty conditions on the tube, since the average current through the tube may be well within the tube rating and yet the large peak current may injure the cathode. Vacuum diodes would not be appreciably damaged by the high peak-current demands, since temperature-saturated currents may be drawn without seriously injuring the cathode. In the case of gas tubes, however, any attempt to draw higher than temperature-saturated current will usually be accompanied by severe positive-ion bombardment of the cathode, with consequent cathode disintegration. It is for this reason that large-capacitance input filters should not be used with rectifiers that employ gas diodes.

When the tube stops conducting, $i_b = 0$ and the controlling differential equation during the nonconducting portion of the cycle is, from Eq. (13-15),

$$C \frac{de_C}{dt} + \frac{e_C}{R_l} = 0 \tag{13-18}$$

The solution of this differential equation is

$$e_C = A e^{-t/R_l C} \tag{13-19}$$

This shows that the capacitor discharges exponentially through the load.

To determine the value of the constant A that appears in this expression, use is made of the fact that at the time $t = t_1$, the cutout time,

$$e_C = e = E_m \sin \omega t_1$$

Combining this result with Eq. (13-19) gives

$$A = E_m \sin \omega t_1 e^{t_1/R_l C} \tag{13-20}$$

and Eq. (13-19) becomes

$$e_C = E_m \sin \omega t_1 e^{-(t-t_1)/R_l C} \tag{13-21}$$

The quantity t_1 that appears in this expression is known, since at $t = t_1$ the tube current is zero. From Eq. (13-16) this requires

$$\sin(\omega t_1 + \psi) = 0$$

from which it follows that

$$\omega t_1 = \pi - \psi = \pi - \tan^{-1} \omega C R_l \tag{13-22}$$

If t_1 from Eq. (13-22) is substituted in Eq. (13-21), there results

$$e_C = E_m \sin \omega t_1 e^{-(\omega t + \psi - \pi)/\omega C R_l} \tag{13-23}$$

To find the "cutin" point, it is noted that e_C equals the impressed transformer potential e at this point. This requires

$$E_m \sin \omega t_2 = E_m \sin \omega t_1 e^{-(\omega t_2 - \psi - \pi)/\omega C R_l}$$

or

$$\sin \omega t_2 = \sin \omega t_1 e^{-(\omega t_2 - \psi - \pi)/\omega C R_l} \tag{13-24}$$

The evaluation of the cutin time t_2 cannot be solved explicitly, for this is a transcendental equation. Graphical methods can be used effectively in this evaluation. The results are given in Fig. 13-6. Included on this graph are a plot of Eq. (13-22) for the cutout angle and a plot of Eq. (13-24) for the cutin angle.

The foregoing analysis gives a complete specification of the operation of the capacitor filter, the current through the tube being given by Eqs. (13-16) and (13-17), the potential across the load resistor being given by

$$e_C = E_m \sin \omega t \qquad \text{for } \omega t_2 < \omega t < \omega t_1 \qquad (13\text{-}25a)$$

and by Eq. (13-23)

$$e_C = E_m \sin \omega t_1 e^{-(\omega t - \omega t_1)/\omega R_l C} \qquad \text{for } \omega t_1 < \omega t < 2\pi + \omega t_2 \qquad (13\text{-}25b)$$

With this information it is possible to evaluate the d-c output potential, the ripple factor, the peak tube current, etc. These quantities may then be plotted as functions of the parameters R_l, C, E_m. Such an analysis is quite involved, but it has been carried out,[1] and the results are given in graphical form.

13-4. Approximate Analysis of Capacitor Filters. It is expedient to make several reasonable approximations in order to obtain an approximate analysis of the behavior of the capacitor filter. Such an approximate analysis possesses the advantage that the important factors of the operation are simply related to the

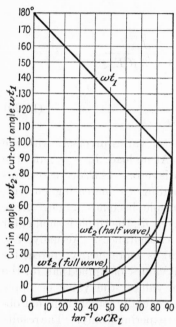

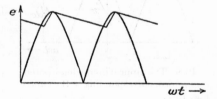

FIG. 13-6. Plot of cutin angle ωt_2 and cutout angle ωt_1 vs. circuit parameters for the capacitor filter.

FIG. 13-7. Oscillogram of the load potential in a single-phase full-wave capacitor filtered rectifier.

circuit parameters. Moreover, the results are sufficiently accurate for most engineering applications. The character of the approximation is made evident by an inspection of Fig. 13-7, which shows the trace of an oscillogram of the load potential in a single-phase full-wave capacitor-filtered rectifier. The potential curve may be approximated by two straight-line segments, as shown in Fig. 13-8. If the total capacitor discharge potential is denoted as E_r, then, from the diagram, the average value of the potential is

$$E_{\text{d-c}} = E_m - \frac{E_r}{2} \qquad (13\text{-}26)$$

Also, the rms value of the triangular ripple potential may be shown to be

$$E'_{rms} = \frac{E_r}{2\sqrt{3}} \qquad (13\text{-}27)$$

Also, if it is assumed that the capacitor discharge continues for the full half cycle at a constant rate which is equal to the average load current $I_{d\text{-}c}$, the fall in potential during this half cycle is E_r. That is, approximately

$$E_r = \frac{I_{d\text{-}c}}{2fC} \qquad (13\text{-}28)$$

The ripple factor is then given by

$$r = \frac{E'_{rms}}{E_{d\text{-}c}} = \frac{E_r}{2\sqrt{3}\,E_{d\text{-}c}} = \frac{I_{d\text{-}c}}{4\sqrt{3}\,fCE_{d\text{-}c}}$$

But since $E_{d\text{-}c} = I_{d\text{-}c}R_l$,

$$r = \frac{1}{4\sqrt{3}\,fCR_l} \qquad (13\text{-}29)$$

This expression shows that the ripple factor varies inversely with the load resistance and the filter capacitance. At no load, $R_l = \infty$, and the ripple is zero. As R_l decreases, corresponding to increasing current, the ripple becomes larger. Also, for given R_l, the ripple is smaller for large capacitances. Actually, Eq. (13-29) is more nearly correct for small values of ripple than for the larger values, the value of ripple being generally larger than that obtained experimentally. The results are adequate for most purposes.

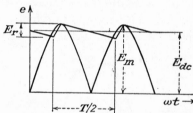

Fig. 13-8. The approximate load-potential waveform corresponding to the curves of Fig. 13-7.

The regulation curve is obtained by combining Eqs. (13-26) and (13-28). This yields

$$E_{d\text{-}c} = E_m - \frac{I_{d\text{-}c}}{4fC} \qquad (13\text{-}30)$$

This expression represents a linear fall in potential with d-c output current. Also, it shows that the simple capacitor filter will possess poor regulation unless the capacitance C is large.

Now refer to the circuit of Fig. 13-4 to ascertain the peak inverse potential across the tube. It is seen to be twice the transformer peak potential. For the full-wave case, the peak inverse potential is also twice the transformer maximum potential, as measured from the mid-point to either end, or the full transformer potential. Thus the presence of the capacitor increases the peak inverse potential in the half-wave circuit from E_m to $2E_m$ but does not affect the peak inverse potential in the full-wave circuit.

13-5. L-section Filter. An L-section filter consists of a series inductor and a shunt capacitor, as shown in Fig. 13-9. This filter is so arranged that the inductor offers a high impedance to the harmonic terms, and the capacitor shunts the load, so as to bypass the harmonic currents. The resulting ripple is markedly reduced over that of the relatively simple filters of Secs. 13-2 and 13-3.

The ripple factor is readily approximated by taking for the potential applied to the input terminals of the filter the first two terms in the Fourier series representation of the output potential of the rectifier, viz.,

$$e = \frac{2E_m}{\pi} - \frac{4E_m}{3\pi} \cos 2\omega t \qquad (13\text{-}31)$$

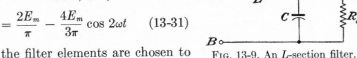

Fig. 13-9. An L-section filter.

But since the filter elements are chosen to provide a high series impedance and a very low shunting impedance, certain plausible approximations may be made. Thus, since the choke impedance is high compared with the effective parallel impedance of the capacitor and load resistor, the net impedance between terminals AB is approximately X_L and the a-c current through the circuit is

$$I'_{\text{rms}} \doteq \frac{4E_m}{3\sqrt{2}\,\pi} \frac{1}{X_L} = \frac{\sqrt{2}}{3} E_{\text{d-c}} \frac{1}{X_L} \qquad (13\text{-}32)$$

Likewise, since the a-c impedance of the capacitor is small compared with R_l, it may be assumed that all the a-c current passes through the capacitor and none through the resistor. The a-c potential across the load (the ripple potential) is the potential across the capacitor and is

$$E'_{\text{rms}} \doteq \frac{\sqrt{2}}{3} E_{\text{d-c}} \frac{X_C}{X_L} \qquad (13\text{-}33)$$

The ripple factor is then given by

$$r = \frac{\sqrt{2}}{3} \frac{X_C}{X_L} = \frac{\sqrt{2}}{3} \frac{1}{2\omega C} \frac{1}{2\omega L} \qquad (13\text{-}34)$$

which may be written, at 60 cps, with L in henrys and C in microfarads,

$$r = \frac{0.830}{LC} \qquad (13\text{-}35)$$

It should be noted that the effect of combining the decreasing ripple of the inductor filter and the increasing ripple of the simple capacitor filter for increasing loads is a constant ripple circuit, independent of load.

The above analysis assumes that no current cutout exists at any time of the cycle. If it did, the analysis would follow along the lines of Sec. 13-3 and Eq. (13-31) for the potential would not apply. But since with no inductance in the filter cutout will occur, whereas with sufficient inductance there will be no cutout, it would be expected that there would be some minimum inductance for a given current below which cutout would

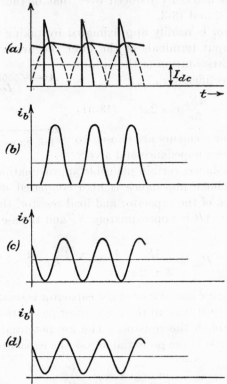

Fig. 13-10. The tube-current waveform in the full-wave rectifier with an L-section filter, when (a) $L = 0$, (b) $L < L_c$, (c) $L = L_c$, (d) $L > L_c$, for constant I_{d-c}.

occur, although for larger values than this critical value the conduction would continue for the full cycle. The situation is best illustrated graphically. Figure 13-10 shows the expected tube current for various amounts of series inductance L.

If the rectifier is to pass current throughout the entire cycle, the peak current delivered must not exceed the d-c component. But the d-c value is E_{d-c}/R_l. Also, the peak a-c current is $(2E_{d-c}/3)(1/X_L)$. Hence for current flow during the full cycle it is necessary that

$$\frac{E_{d-c}}{R_l} \geq \frac{2E_{d-c}}{3} \frac{1}{X_L}$$

or

$$X_L \geq \frac{2R_l}{3} \qquad (13\text{-}36)$$

from which the value for the critical inductance is found to be

$$L_c = \frac{2R_l}{3\omega}$$

which has the value

$$L_c = \frac{R_l}{1,130} \qquad (13\text{-}37)$$

for a 60-cps power frequency, where R_l is in ohms and L_c is in henrys. However, owing to the approximations that have been made in this analysis, it is advisable for conservative design to use a larger value of L_c than that given in Eq. (13-37). A good practical figure is to choose the denominator as 1,000 instead of 1,130.

The effect of the cutout is illustrated in Fig. 13-11, which shows a regulation curve of the system, for constant R_l and varying series inductance. Clearly, when the series inductance is zero, the filter is of the simple capacitance type and the output potential is approximately E_m. With increasing inductance, the potential falls, until at $L = L_c$ the output potential is that corresponding to the simple L filter with no cutout, or $0.637E_m$. For values of L greater than L_c, there is no change in potential, except for the effects of the resistances of the various elements of the circuit.

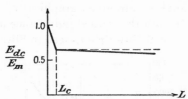

Fig. 13-11. The regulation curve of a rectifier with L-section filter as a function of series inductance, for constant output current

It is not possible to satisfy the conditions of Eq. (13-37) for all values of load, since at no load this would require an infinite inductance. However, when good potential regulation is desired, it is customary to use a bleeder resistance across the load so as to maintain the conditions of Eq. (13-37) even if this represents a power loss.

A more efficient method than using a high bleeder current, with its attendant power dissipation, is to make use of the fact that the inductance of an iron-core reactor depends, among other things, on the amount of d-c current in the winding. Chokes for which the inductance is high at low values of d-c current and which decrease markedly with increased d-c currents are called "swinging" chokes. The swinging choke is provided with a closed iron core, whereas the core of the inductor which is to possess a more nearly constant inductance is provided with a narrow air gap. A typical curve for such a reactor is illustrated in Fig. 13-12. The advantage of such a choke is that for high R_l, and therefore low d-c current, the inductance is high. As a result, the conditional equation (13-37) is satisfied over a wider range of R_l. Clearly, however, when a swinging choke is used, the ripple factor is no longer independent of the load.

The above analysis for the critical inductance of the L-type filter applies for the full-wave rectifier for which conduction continues for 180 deg in each cycle. Consequently the results so obtained are not applicable when an L-section filter is used with a controlled rectifier. The analysis for a full-wave controlled rectifier is considerably more complicated than that above, owing to the fact that the amplitude of the harmonics in the Fourier series representation of the output depends on the delay angles, and these are of such amplitude that they cannot be neglected in the analysis. The results of such an analysis are given graphically[2] in Fig. 13-13. The curves give a measure of both the critical inductance and the output potential.

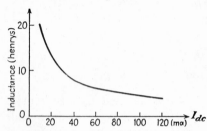

FIG. 13-12. The inductance of a swinging choke as a function of the d-c current through it.

13-6. Multiple L-section Filters. If it is desired to limit the ripple to a value that is less than that possible with a single L-section filter using commercially available elements, two or more L-section filters may be connected in cascade, as shown in Fig. 13-14. An approximate solution is possible by following the methods of

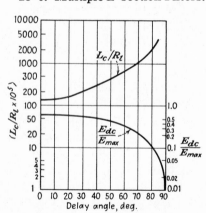

FIG. 13-13. Critical inductance and d-c output potential as a function of the delay angle in a full-wave controlled rectifier.

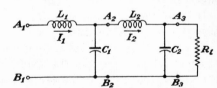

FIG. 13-14. A two-unit L-section filter.

Sec. 13-5. It is assumed, therefore, that the choke impedances are much larger than the reactances of the capacitors. Also, it is assumed that the reactance of the last capacitor is small compared with the resistance of the load. Under these assumptions, the impedance between A_3 and B_3 is X_{C2}.

The impedance between A_2 and B_2 is X_{C1}, and the impedance between A_1 and B_1 is X_{L1}, approximately.

The a-c current I_1 is approximately

$$I_1 = \frac{\sqrt{2}}{3} E_{\text{d-c}} \frac{1}{X_{L1}}$$

The a-c potential across C_1 is approximately

$$E_{A_2 B_2} = I_1 X_{C1}$$

The a-c current I_2 is approximately

$$I_2 = \frac{E_{A_2 B_2}}{X_{L2}}$$

The a-c potential across the load is approximately

$$I_2 X_{C2} = I_1 X_{C2} \frac{X_{C1}}{X_{L1}} = \frac{\sqrt{2}}{3} E_{\text{d-c}} \frac{X_{C1}}{X_{L1}} \frac{X_{C2}}{X_{L2}}$$

The ripple factor is given by the expression

$$r = \frac{\sqrt{2}}{3} \frac{X_{C1}}{X_{L1}} \frac{X_{C2}}{X_{L2}} \tag{13-38}$$

A comparison of this expression with Eq. (13-34) indicates the generalization that should be made in obtaining an expression for the ripple factor of a cascaded filter of n sections. The expression would have the form

$$r = \frac{\sqrt{2}}{3} \frac{X_{C1}}{X_{L1}} \frac{X_{C2}}{X_{L2}} \cdots \frac{X_{Cn}}{X_{Ln}} \tag{13-39}$$

If the sections are all similar, then Eq. (13-39) becomes

$$r = \frac{\sqrt{2}}{3} \left(\frac{X_C}{X_L}\right)^n = \frac{\sqrt{2}}{3} \frac{1}{(16\pi^2 f^2 LC)^n} \tag{13-40}$$

where f is the source frequency. It follows from this that the required LC product for a specified ripple factor r at a 60-cps source frequency is given by

$$LC = 1.76 \left(\frac{0.471}{r}\right)^{1/n} \tag{13-41}$$

Note also that, to the approximation that the impedance between A_2 and B_2 is simply X_{C1}, the critical inductance is given by Eq. (13-37), as for the single-section unit.

13-7. Π-section Filter. The use of a Π-section filter provides an output potential that approaches the peak value of the a-c potential of the source, the ripple components being very small. Such a filter is illustrated in Fig. 13-15. Although such filters do provide a higher d-c output potential than is possible with an L-section filter, the tube currents are peaked and the regulation is generally poor, these results being common with the simple capacitor filter.

A study of the oscilloscope patterns at various points of such a filter

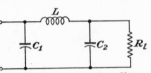

FIG. 13-15. A II-section filter.

shows that the action can be understood by considering the inductor and the second capacitor as an L-section filter that acts on the triangular output potential wave from the first capacitor. The output potential is then approximately that from the input capacitor, the ripple contained in this output being reduced by the L-section filter. That is, the ripple factor of the II-section filter is given approximately by

$$r_\pi = r_c r_L \qquad (13\text{-}42)$$

where r_C is given by Eq. (13-29) and r_L is given by Eq. (13-34). This becomes

$$r_\pi = 0.855 \frac{X_{c1} X_{c2}}{X_L R_l} \qquad (13\text{-}43)$$

with all reactances calculated at the second-harmonic frequency. For a 60-cps power source, this is

$$r_\pi = \frac{2 \times 10^3}{C_1 C_2 L R_l} \qquad (13\text{-}44)$$

with the capacitances in microfarads, the inductance in henrys, and the resistance in ohms. This result is only approximate, since it assumes in effect that the ripple output from the capacitor filter is sinusoidal rather than triangular.

A somewhat more accurate evaluation of the ripple factor, due to Arguimbau,[3] is possible. The technique employed is similar to that used to evaluate the grid driving power of a class C amplifier. For the filter connected to a rectifier at the power frequency ω, the important ripple term is of second-harmonic frequency. Consequently, it is required to find the peak value of the second-harmonic current I'_{2m} to the input capacitor of the II filter. This is given by the Fourier component

$$I'_{2m} = \frac{1}{\pi} \int_0^{2\pi} i_b \cos 2\omega t \, d(\omega t) \qquad (13\text{-}45)$$

Now assume that the current pulse is significant only near the peak value of the cosine curve. Therefore, the cos $2\omega t$ factor appearing in the ntegral is replaced by unity, and approximately

$$\sqrt{2}\, I_2' \doteq \frac{1}{\pi} \int_0^{2\pi} i_b\, d(\omega t) = 2I_{\text{d-c}} \tag{13-46}$$

Hence, the upper limit of the rms second-harmonic potential is

$$E_2' = I_2' X_{C1} = \sqrt{2}\, I_{\text{d-c}} X_{C1} \tag{13-47}$$

But the potential E_2' is applied to the L section, so that, by the same logic as before, the output ripple is $E_2' X_{C2}/X_L$. Hence, the ripple factor is

$$r_\pi = \sqrt{2}\, \frac{I_{\text{d-c}} X_{C1} X_{C2}}{E_{\text{d-c}} X_L} = \sqrt{2}\, \frac{X_{C1}}{R_l} \frac{X_{C2}}{X_L} \tag{13-48}$$

where all reactances are calculated at the second-harmonic frequency. At 60-cps primary frequency, this reduces to

$$r_\pi = \frac{3.3 \times 10^3}{C_1 C_2 L R_l} \tag{13-49}$$

Note that here, as in the previous analysis, the effects of higher harmonics than the second have been neglected. This result is probably more accurate than that given in Eq. (13-44) owing to the more reasonable approximation in the analysis.

If the inductor of the Π-section filter is replaced by a resistor, a practice that is often used with low-current-drain power supplies, the ripple factor is given by Eq. (13-48) with X_L replaced by R. Thus

$$r_\pi = \sqrt{2}\, \frac{X_{C1} X_{C2}}{R R_l}$$

or

$$r_\pi = \frac{2.5 \times 10^6}{C_1 C_2 R R_l} \tag{13-50}$$

13-8. Glow-tube Regulator. The use of an electronic rectifier with an appropriate filter serves to provide a low-ripple source of d-c potential, the percentage of ripple present in the output depending upon the form of the filter that is used. Such rectifier systems, while generally satisfactory for many purposes, possess several shortcomings which may make them inadequate for certain services. The output potential depends critically upon the input potential to the rectifier, and a poorly regulated power system will be accompanied by a corresponding change in the output from the rectifier. Also, since the output impedance of the rectifier is usually quite high, the rectifier system will possess a poor regulation.

It is frequently necessary to construct a power supply the output potential of which is constant over wide ranges of input a-c potential, so as to provide a constant output potential source from a poorly regulated power line. Or it may be necessary to maintain a constant output potential for a varying output load. Electronic potential regulators provide such a control device and are extensively used for such service.

The simplest form of potential regulator makes use of the substantially constant potential characteristic of a glow tube. A glow tube is a cold-cathode discharge tube which is characterized by a fairly high tube drop and a low current-carrying capacity (see Sec. 1-25). The potential across

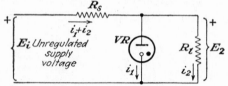

FIG. 13-16. Glow-tube potential regulator.

the tube over the operating range is fairly constant and independent of the current. When connected in the circuit shown in Fig. 13-16, the potential across the load will be a constant and equal to the tube drop of the glow tube, over a range of currents. Specifically, if a VR-150/30 is used, the potential across the load will be approximately 150 volts provided that the current through the tube does not exceed the rated 30 ma of the tube.

If a potential is desired that is higher than that of a single glow tube, several tubes may be connected in series. This will provide a constant

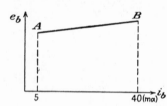

FIG. 13-17. A typical glow-tube volt-ampere characteristic.

potential source that is the sum of the tube drops of the tubes that are used. For example, the use of a VR-150 and a VR-105 in series will provide a constant 255-volt source. The supply potential must be greater than the breakdown potential of the tubes in order to make operation possible. The difference between the supply potential and the operating tube potential drop will appear across the stabilizing resistor R_s.

An analysis of such a circuit is readily possible[4] if use is made of the practical fact that over the range of operation the volt-ampere characteristic of the regulator tube is almost linear. A typical characteristic has the form shown in Fig. 13-17. This characteristic may be expressed by an equation of the form

$$e = ai_1 + b \qquad (13\text{-}51)$$

where

$$a = \frac{e_B - e_A}{i_B - i_A} \quad \text{and} \quad b = e_A - ai_A \qquad (13\text{-}52)$$

From the circuit diagram of Fig. 13-16 it is seen that

$$E_i = (i_1 + i_2)R_s + E_b \qquad (13\text{-}53)$$

Also,

$$E_b = E_2 = R_l i_2 = ai_1 + b \qquad (13\text{-}54)$$

from which it follows that

$$i_1 = \frac{E_2 - b}{a}$$

$$\qquad (13\text{-}55)$$

and

$$i_2 = \frac{E_2}{R_l}$$

Combining these equations yields

$$E_i = \left(\frac{E_2 - b}{a} + \frac{E_2}{R_l}\right) R_s + E_2$$

from which

$$E_2 = \frac{aR_l E_i + bR_l R_s}{R_l R_s + aR_s + aR_l} \qquad (13\text{-}56)$$

This is the expression for the regulated potential as a function of the supply potential and the circuit parameters.

The variation of the output potential as the input potential varies is of considerable importance.   The ratio dE_i/dE_2 is known as the stabilization ratio and is found to be

$$S = \frac{dE_i}{dE_2} = \frac{R_l(R_s + a) + aR_s}{aR_l} \qquad (13\text{-}57)$$

Combining this with the expression for E_2 gives

$$S = \frac{aE_i + bR_s}{aE_2} \qquad (13\text{-}58)$$

This equation shows that for perfect regulation, i.e., infinite stabilization ratio, the fraction dE_i/dE_2 should be infinite.   For best stabilization features, both E_2 and a should be small; and b, E_i, and R_s should be large. Using typical values with a VR-75 tube, one finds

$$E_i = 250 \text{ volts}$$

$R_l = \infty$	$R_s = 32.5$ kilohms	$\Delta E_i = 20$	$\Delta E_2 = 0.15$
$R_l = 3$ kilohms	$R_s = 5.85$ kilohms	$\Delta E_i = 20$	$\Delta E_2 = 0.60$

Such simple gas-tube regulators operate quite satisfactorily, but they are seriously limited in their usefulness because of their limited flexibility, both because of their fixed potential ratings and the relatively low current-carrying capacity.

13-9. Simple Vacuum-tube Regulator.   One may employ the variable beam-resistance characteristic of a vacuum tube to maintain the output potential from a power supply at a substantially constant level. The beam resistance, as previously defined, is $r_b = e_b/i_b$ and is quite different from the plate resistance r_p of the tube. The circuit of such a simple potential regulator is given in Fig. 13-18.

Assume that the potential across the load is at the desired value. Under this condition, the cathode is positive relative to ground by a potential E_2. The grid may be made positive relative to ground by a potential E_g which is less than E_2. The potentiometer R_2 is adjusted until the bias on the tube is such that the tube will pass the requisite load

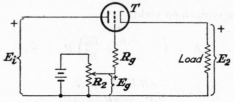

Fig. 13-18. A simple vacuum-tube potential regulator.

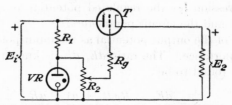

Fig. 13-19. A simple potential-regulator circuit.

current. With this bias, the resistance of T is established at the desired value to reduce the rectifier output to the desired load potential.

If the rectifier output potential increases for whatever reason, the potential at the cathode of T tends to increase. As E_2 increases, the bias on the tube increases and the effective beam resistance of the tube becomes greater. Consequently the potential drop across the tube becomes greater. If the circuit is properly designed, the increased potential across T is approximately equal to the increase of rectifier output potential and the rectifier output potential remains substantially constant.

The practical form of the circuit will replace the battery by a glow tube. Such a circuit is shown in Fig. 13-19.

The output potential from this regulator is not absolutely constant, since for an increased input to the circuit the potential at the cathode of T must rise slightly if the regulator is to function. However, if the characteristics of tube T are carefully chosen, the rise of load potential is not large.

It would be expected, of course, that vacuum tubes in which the beam resistance varied rapidly with small changes in bias would be most desirable for service in such regulators.   Tubes possessing such a characteristic could probably be designed if there were no alternative approach.   Actually such special tubes are not necessary, as it is quite possible to achieve the same ends by including a d-c amplifier in the circuit in such a way that slight changes in output potential are amplified before being applied degeneratively to T.   These circuits are used extensively, and a detailed analysis will be given below.

13-10. Electronic Potential Regulators—Basic Considerations.[5]   The design of electronically regulated power supplies has become fairly well standardized.   The elements of such a circuit are given in Fig. 13-20.

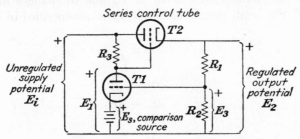

FIG. 13-20. A basic electronic regulator circuit.

As discussed above, the operation of the circuit is essentially the following: The source of unregulated potential from the rectifier and filter is applied across the input terminals of the regulator.   The unregulated d-c current is fed through the series control tube, now designated $T2$ in the diagram, to the output circuit.   The regulating action is obtained by comparing a fixed fraction of the output potential with a standard potential source, such as a battery or a VR gas tube.   Any difference between the two is applied degeneratively after amplification by a high-gain d-c amplifier to the control grid of the series current-control tube.   The correction may be made nearly perfect by using a d-c amplifier of sufficient gain.   If the current requirements are too high for a single tube, a number of such tubes may be connected in parallel.   A power triode is frequently used for this purpose, although a pentode or beam tetrode connected as a triode will serve equally well.   Popular series control tubes include 6AS7G, 6B4, 6L6, 6V6, and 6Y6G.   These tubes will pass approximately 75 ma without seriously exceeding the plate dissipation of the tube.

The design of a potential regulator requires a knowledge of the characteristic curves of the control tube and also of the d-c amplifier tube. However, since small changes in potential and current are ordinarily involved, the circuit operation may be analyzed in terms of the slope of the tube characteristics—specifically, in terms of the mutual conductance and the internal resistance of the tubes at the operating points. Several cases of interest will be examined separately.

a. *Varying Input Potential—R_3 Connected to the Input Side of the Regulator.* Suppose that the output load remains constant but that the input potential to the regulator varies, either because of the poor regulation of the input a-c supply potential to the rectifier or because of the ripple in the output of the rectifier due to inadequate filtering. It is desired to determine the change in output potential under these conditions. This may be done by examining the change in potential across $T2$ due to the change in input potential.

Consider the changes that occur in $T2$ due to changes in electrode potentials. For small variations about the levels specified in Fig. 13-20,

$$i_{p2} = g_{m2}e_{g2} + \frac{1}{r_{p2}} e_{p2} \tag{13-59}$$

Note, however, that

$$e_{g2} = dE_1 - dE_2$$

and

$$e_{p2} = dE_i - dE_2 \tag{13-60}$$

Note also that

$$i_{p2} = \frac{dE_2}{R_l}$$

where R_l is the equivalent load resistance, which is assumed constant. By combining these equations, there follows

$$\frac{dE_2}{R_l} = g_{m2}(dE_1 - dE_2) + \frac{1}{r_{p2}} (dE_i - dE_2)$$

which becomes

$$dE_2 \left(\frac{r_{p2}}{R_l} + \mu_2 + 1 \right) = \mu_2\, dE_1 + dE_i$$

from which the change in output potential dE_2 is given by

$$dE_2 = \frac{\mu_2\, dE_1 + dE_i}{\mu_2 + 1 + r_{p2}/R_l} \tag{13-61}$$

To relate dE_1 to dE_2 and dE_i, an examination is made of the operation of $T1$. It should be observed that dE_1 is the resultant of two effects. One is an increase which arises from the change in input potential and is $+dE_i \dfrac{r_{p1}}{R_3 + r_{p1}}.$ This is the effect of the series circuit comprising R_3 and the tube $T1$ in series. The comparison potential source E_s does not appear, as it is assumed to be of constant potential and zero internal impedance. The second component is the amplified effect of the input to $T1$. This is $dE_2 \dfrac{R_2}{R_1 + R_2} K_1$, where K_1 is the gain of $T1$. That is, the total effective change dE_1 is

$$dE_1 = \frac{r_{p1}}{R_3 + r_{p1}} dE_i + \frac{R_2}{R_1 + R_2} K_1 dE_2 \qquad (13\text{-}62)$$

which is written as

$$dE_1 = \gamma \, dE_i + \beta K_1 \, dE_2$$

$$(13\text{-}63)$$

where $\qquad \gamma \equiv \dfrac{r_{p1}}{R_3 + r_{p1}} \qquad K_1 = \dfrac{-\mu_1 R_3}{r_{p1} + R_3} \qquad \beta = \dfrac{R_2}{R_1 + R_2}$

Now combine Eq. (13-63) with Eq. (13-61). This gives

$$dE_2 = \frac{\mu_2(\gamma dE_i + \beta K_1 \, dE_2) + dE_i}{(\mu_2 + 1) + r_{p2}/R_l}$$

which then becomes

$$dE_2 = \frac{dE_i(\mu_2 \gamma + 1)}{\mu_2(1 - \beta K_1) + 1 + r_{p2}/R_l}$$

The potential stabilization ratio S is given by

$$S = \frac{dE_i}{dE_2} = \frac{\mu_2(1 - \beta K_1) + 1 + r_{p2}/R_l}{\mu_2 \gamma + 1} \qquad (13\text{-}64)$$

which approximates under normal conditions to

$$S \doteq \frac{-\beta K_1 \mu_2}{\mu_2 \gamma + 1} \qquad (13\text{-}65)$$

The quantity S gives a measure of the effectiveness with which the regulator compensates for changes in potential in the input. For a regulator with a single d-c amplifier stage, S may be of the order of 300 to 1,000. If an improved value for S is required in order to achieve an almost ripple-free output, it is necessary that the gain of the d-c amplifier be increased. This is most easily done by adding a second stage of d-c amplification. Such circuits will be considered below. With such circuits, a value of S of 25,000 is possible.

b. Varying Input Potential—R_3 Connected to the Output Side of the Regulator. Somewhat improved results are theoretically possible if the plate-load resistor R_3 of the d-c amplifier stage $T1$ is connected to the output side of the regulator instead of the input side. That an improvement appears possible follows from the fact that one may now assume that the plate potential to which the amplifier $T1$ is connected is substantially constant and that the total change dE_1 is just the output from this stage, viz.,

$$dE_1 = \beta K_1 \, dE_2 \qquad (13\text{-}66)$$

All other conditions remain as in the foregoing analysis. As a result, the term involving γ does not appear, and the corresponding stabilization ratio becomes

$$S = \frac{dE_i}{dE_2} = \mu_2(1 - \beta K_1) + 1 + r_{p2}/R_l \qquad (13\text{-}67)$$

which approximates under normal conditions to

$$S = -\beta K_1 \mu_2 \qquad (13\text{-}68)$$

Owing to the denominator that appears in Eq. (13-65), the value of S appears to be higher in Eq. (13-68). Actually, however, the d-c amplifier $T1$ operates in a more linear manner under condition a, with somewhat higher gain K_1. Under normal circumstances, the two connections yield about equal results, and both are used.

   c. *Varying Load.* Suppose now that the change in the output potential when R_3 is connected as in case b results from a change in the load current, owing to the internal resistance of the supply. If this change in potential is again denoted as dE_2, then, as before, the potential appearing at the grid of the current control tube is

$$e_{g2} = dE_1 - dE_2$$

with

$$dE_1 = \beta K_1\, dE_2$$

If g_m denotes the mutual transconductance of the series control tube, the resulting change in current through this tube due to a change in potential e_{g2} at the grid is

$$dI_p = g_{m2}e_{g2}$$

which is

$$dI_p = g_{m2}(1 - \beta K_1)\, dE_2 \qquad (13\text{-}69)$$

The ratio of the change in output potential to the change in output current is denoted by R_0 and is the effective internal resistance of the regulated power supply. This is given by

$$R_0 = \frac{dE_2}{dI_p} \doteq \frac{1}{-g_{m2}\beta K_1} \qquad (13\text{-}70)$$

In a typical case the effective internal resistance of the regulated supply may be as low as 0.5 ohm.

   This calculation assumes, of course, that there is no change in the input applied potential with changes in output current, or, equivalently, that the internal impedance of the unregulated power supply is low. This condition is not often met in practice, and due account must be taken of this factor. If the internal resistance of the unregulated driving source is denoted by R_s, then by Eqs. (13-68) and (13-69) the total effective internal resistance of the regulated power supply is given by

$$R_0 = \frac{1}{-g_{m2}\beta K_1} + \frac{R_s}{S} = \frac{1}{-g_{m2}\beta K_1}\left(1 + \frac{R_s}{r_{p2}}\right) \tag{13-71}$$

For a typical case $R_s = 500$ ohms, $S = 1,000$, so that the added resistance due to the regulation of the input source may be only about 0.5 ohm.

13-11. Design Consideration. A typical circuit that yields satis-factory results over a wide range of input potential and over a wide range of load current is given in Fig. 13-21. Although the diagram of Fig. 13-20

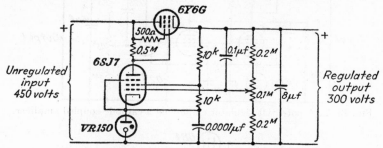

Fig. 13-21. An electronically regulated power supply.

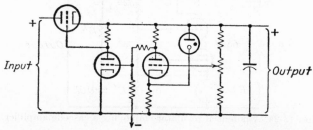

Fig. 13-22. An electronic potential regulator employing a two-stage d-c amplifier.

shows a triode as the d-c amplifier, it is found more desirable to use a pentode in this position and this has been done in the circuit of Fig. 13-21. The reason for this is that it frequently happens that the d-c regulation is not as good as one would expect when a triode is used, primarily because the grid impedance of a high-gain triode is quite low.   The grid imped-ance should be high, especially if the full gain capabilities are to be realized.   A 6SJ7 tube is superior in this respect and hence is frequently used.   The 6Y6G pentode called for in Fig. 13-21 gives satisfactory results.   The 6AS7G tube possesses some advantages over this, since it has a relatively high tube current rating (125 ma) with a relatively low tube drop.   Also, the heater-cathode insulation is sufficiently good to avoid the need for a separate filament heating transformer for this tube. The tube does have a rather low value of μ ($= 2.1$) which requires a rather large control potential.

If a potential regulator is required which is to provide a practically ripple-free output and an almost perfect regulation, it is necessary that the gain of the d-c amplifier be increased. This is most easily done by adding a second stage of d-c amplification to the regulator circuit. A variety of such circuits are possible, and several types are illustrated below. Figure 13-22 shows a simple two-stage resistance-coupled

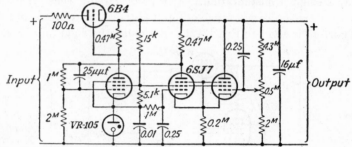

Fig. 13-23. A potential regulator employing a cathode-coupled amplifier.

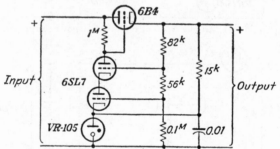

Fig. 13-24. A potential regulator employing a cascode amplifier.

amplifier; Fig. 13-23 utilizes a cathode-coupled amplifier; and Fig. 13-24 uses a "cascode" amplifier.

13-12. Special Precautions.[6] Although the principles of operation of the regulated power supply are straightforward, it frequently happens that the maximum performance will not be realized in practice. It is well to consider some of the reasons for this. The important factors to be examined closely are the degenerative d-c amplifier loop and the various sources of hum.

  a. The Degenerative D-C Amplifier Loop. For satisfactory operation, the d-c amplifier must be degenerative at all frequencies for which the loop gain is greater than unity. If this condition is not met, the system will oscillate (refer to Sec. 5-7) and the regulation properties will be greatly affected. One of the best ways to ensure that the power supply will not break into oscillation is to limit the h-f response of the amplifier. This is best done by including a large capacitor across the output (8 μf

or 16 μf). This will usually provide the necessary h-f cutoff and will still keep the power-supply impedance low at high frequencies. The 0.1-μf capacitor from the grid of $T1$ to B+ serves to prevent a phase lag at the grid of the d-c amplifier and also compensates somewhat for additional phase shift in the amplifier and increases K_1 for frequencies above a cycle or two.

b. *Sources of Hum.* Among the sources of hum which give rise to a higher ripple in the output than is expected, and their possible cures, are the following:

1. Ripple from a-c heated filaments in the d-c amplifier. By grounding the center tap of the heater transformer and by choosing tubes with low heater-hum characteristics, the hum in the output potential can be reduced to 4 or 5 mv rms or less.

2. Ripple from common leads. This may arise from coupling between the d-c supply and some a-c source, such as a filament supply. The use of the chassis as a common ground with grounds to various parts of the chassis may introduce this hum potential. This effect is ordinarily small, perhaps several millivolts rms, except when the common coupling appears in the input of the d-c amplifier in the regulator, in which case it may be appreciable. To avoid this difficulty, grounds should be separately returned to a single point.

3. Ripple from supply potential. The screen potential to the d-c amplifier must be ripple-free. This may require a filter at the screen terminal at the tube base.

4. Ripple in the comparison potential source. It might be necessary to include a filter in the CR circuit for this purpose, in addition to the 0.0001-μf condenser shown (which is to prevent any effects that might arise from the h-f plasma oscillations in the VR tube).

5. Induction loops. If coupling occurs between circuits by electrostatic or electromagnetic induction, it may be necessary to include a simple RC filter in the input circuit to the d-c amplifier and in the comparison-voltage circuit.

c. *Heater Supply.* When the heater of the d-c amplifier is fed from an unregulated source, changes in output with heater-potential changes may be quite noticeable. This can be eliminated by operating the heaters from the regulated d-c supply.

REFERENCES

1. Waidelich, D. L., *Trans. AIEE*, **60**, 1161 (1941).
     Schade, O. H., *Proc. IRE*, **31**, 341 (1943).
2. Overbeck. W. P.. *Proc. IRE*, **27**, 655 (1939).

3. Arguimbau, L., "Vacuum Tube Circuits," John Wiley & Sons, Inc., New York, 1948.
4. Berg, W. R., *Electronics*, **20**, 136 (October, 1947).
5. Mautner, L., *Electronic Eng.*, **66**, 894 (1947).
6. Lawson, J. L., *MIT Radiation Lab. Internal Rept.*, unpublished.
7. As general references, see:
    Hunt, F. V., and R. W. Hickman, *Rev. Sci. Instr.*, **10**, 6 (1939).
    Millman, J., and S. Seely, "Electronics," 2d ed., chap. XIII, McGraw-Hill Book Company, Inc., New York, 1951.

PROBLEMS

13-1. It is planned to use a type 83 gas diode in a single-phase full-wave rectifier circuit with capacitor filter. The transformer potential is 350 volts rms to center tap. The load consists of a 16-μf capacitor in parallel with a 2,500-ohm resistor. The tube drop and the transformer resistance and leakage reactance may be neglected.

a. Calculate the cutout angle.

b. Determine the cutin point.

c. Calculate the peak tube current. Should the type 83 tube be used? Compare the peak current per plate with that given (1 amp) in the tube manual.

13-2. Given two 20-henry chokes and two 16-μf capacitors. Calculate the output potential and ripple factor under each of the following conditions:

a. The two chokes are connected in series with the load.

b. The two capacitors are connected across the load.

c. A single L-section filter, consisting of the two chokes in series and the two capacitors in parallel, is used.

d. A double L-section filter, consisting of two sections, each of one choke and one capacitor, is used.

The load is 2,000 ohms, and a 375-0-375 transformer is used in a full-wave circuit. Assume a 25-volt drop occurs across the tube.

13-3. A power supply has the form shown in the diagram.

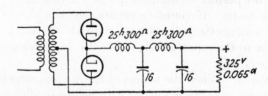

a. Determine the approximate secondary potential of the power transformer.

b. What would be the ripple potential if the power frequency is 60 cps; 400 cps?

13-4. In the power supply shown in the figure:

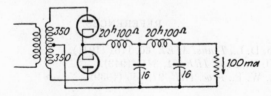

a. What is the output d-c potential?

b. What is the ripple potential in the output?

c. What is the minimum load current below which current cutout in the filter occurs? What is the corresponding load potential?

Note: Make allowance for the tube drop, but assume a perfect transformer.

13-5. A typical circuit for the high-potential supply for a cathode-ray tube is shown in the diagram. Estimate the output ripple potential.

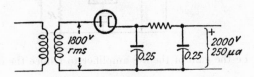

13-6. The circuit shown in the accompanying diagram is to supply two different potentials. If the transformer is 375-0-375, what are the output potentials?

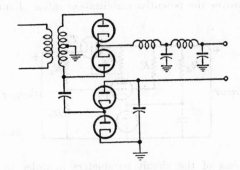

13-7. A simple shunt regulator is illustrated, with the ripple component of potentials and current specified. Suppose that $X_C \gg R_1$ at the ripple frequencies.

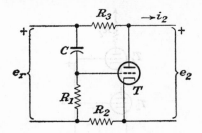

a. Derive an expression relating the circuit parameters to yield zero ripple potential e_2.

b. Suppose that tube T is a 6J5 which is biased at $E_{cc} = -8$ volts, so that $\mu = 20$, $r_p = 7,700$ ohms. The total d-c load is 50 ma at 250 volts. Find the values of R_2, R_3 and the total d-c potential drop through the regulator between input and output.

c. Discuss the limitations of the circuit, such as internal d-c resistance and internal a-c impedance.

13-8. Given the electronically regulated power supply shown in the diagram.

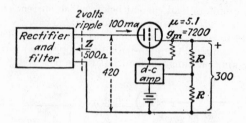

a. What must be the gain of the d-c amplifier to reduce the output ripple to 8 mv?

b. What must be the gain of the d-c amplifier to reduce the output impedance to 1 ohm?

13-9. The addition of a resistor R to the electronic voltage regulator, as shown in the figure, improves the potential stabilization ratio. Express the required

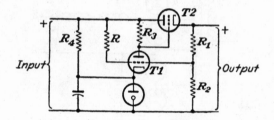

value of R in terms of the circuit parameters in order to achieve perfect stabilization.

13-10. Given the basic cascode circuit shown in the diagram, show that the

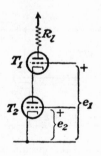

total current through the tubes is

$$i = \frac{\mu_2(\mu_1 + 1)e_2 + \mu_1 e_1}{r_{p1} + (\mu_1 + 1)r_{p2} + R_l}$$

Show that the over-all gain of this amplifier, when the grids are tied together in so far as the a-c signal is concerned, $e_1 = e_2 = e_g$, is

$$K = \frac{\mu(\mu + 2)R_l}{(\mu + 2)r_p + R_l}$$

13-11. Calculate the ripple potential and the per cent regulation in the regulators of Figs. 13-21, 13-23, and 13-24. A load of 75 ma at 300 volts is supplied. The rectifier and filter system supplies an input potential of 460 volts to the regulator. A II filter, consisting of two 8-μf capacitors and one 12-henry choke, is used. The effective output resistance of the filter is 650 ohms.

13-12. The circuit of a high-potential stabilizer is shown in the accompanying figure. Note that this circuit is similar in principle to that illustrated in Fig. 13-22. Calculate the stabilization ratio of this regulator.

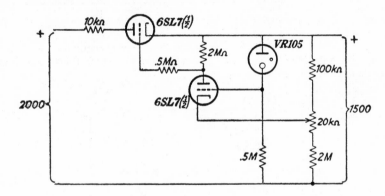

13-13. Given the voltage regulator shown in the figure.

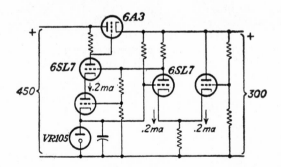

a. Specify the values of all circuit elements in the circuit, and give reasons for your choice. The load current is 75 ma.

b. Indicate on the diagram the d-c potentials at all points in the circuit.

c. There is a 3-volt rms ripple at the output of the rectifier and filter. The effective internal resistance of the source is 530 ohms. Calculate (1) the potential stabilization ratio of the regulator; (2) the output ripple potential; (3) the output resistance of the system.

13-14. Repeat Prob. 13-13 for the regulator shown in the accompanying diagram. Compare the corresponding results with those of Prob. 13-13. Such a

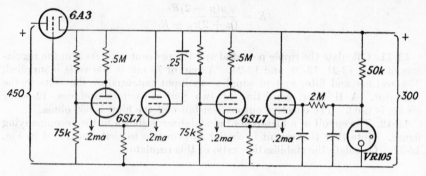

comparison is interesting since the two circuits require roughly the same components.

13-15. Repeat Prob. 13-13 for the electronic potential regulator shown in the accompanying diagram. Note that, from practical considerations, this is not a desirable circuit.

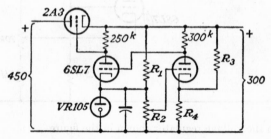

13-16. Design a regulated power supply that will supply 150 ma at 250 volts from a 450-volt rectified and filtered source, with a ripple not to exceed 0.1 per cent and with a stabilization ratio of 15,000. What is the rms ripple potential in the output of this regulated source if a Π filter consisting of two 8-μf capacitors and a 12-henry choke is used? The effective output resistance of the filtered supply is 650 ohms.

CHAPTER 14

ELECTRONIC INSTRUMENTS

A number of instruments have been developed which incorporate vacuum tubes as integral parts of these devices. These instruments possess certain advantages over the standard electromechanical varieties. In particular, most of the vacuum-tube types of instruments possess relatively high input impedance and also may be used over a very wide range of frequencies. These instruments are divided into the following general classes: voltmeters, ammeters, wattmeters, frequency meters, and phasemeters.

Perhaps the most versatile of all electronic instruments is the cathode-ray oscilloscope, which may be used as a voltmeter, ammeter, frequency meter, and phasemeter, depending upon the manner of its connection in a test circuit. The applications to these various services will be discussed below in the appropriate section.

14-1. Electronic Voltmeters. *The Oscilloscope.* The applicability of the oscilloscope as a voltmeter arises from the fact that the deflection sensitivity of the cathode-ray tube, for a given accelerating potential, is a constant and the deflection of the cathode-ray beam on the screen is directly proportional to the applied deflecting potential (see Sec. 1-33). Thus, by setting the gain of the amplifiers associated with the oscilloscope at some convenient value, the peak of any applied potential may be compared with a calibrating potential.

Such devices are very flexible but do have frequency limits, perhaps from 30 kc to 3 Mc, depending on the instrument, owing to the frequency distortion that occurs in the amplifiers at the higher frequencies. If connection is made directly to the plates of the tube, this frequency limitation is reduced and the tube may be used to the very high frequencies. However, as the deflection sensitivity is usually low, of the order of 40 volts/in. on a 5-in. tube with an applied accelerating potential of 2,000 volts, such a voltmeter would be limited to the higher potentials, in the range from 5 to 150 volts. For higher potentials, a potential divider might be used. Lower potentials cannot be measured, except with the aid of amplifiers, and with their consequent frequency limitations.

413

Vacuum-tube Voltmeters. The vacuum-tube voltmeter provides a convenient method for the accurate measurement across high-impedance sources of both d-c and also a-c potentials up to very high frequencies. The use of the conventional type of tube usually limits the operation to frequencies below about 1.5 Mc. For frequencies higher than this, the grid-circuit loading, resulting from the input capacitances of the tube and the electron transit time, usually becomes sufficiently serious to influence the operation. Where the loading effects are permissible, the use of suitable standard receiving-type tubes is permissible to frequencies of approximately 20 Mc without serious calibration errors.

For the measurement of potentials having frequencies above 1.5 Mc, to perhaps 30 Mc, acorn-type tubes in a special probe construction may be used without introducing appreciable loading. With such a probe construction, the lead impedance is reduced to zero by allowing direct connection to be made from the potential source to the grid of the tube. Also, the shunting effect of the grid resistor is made negligible either by neglecting it entirely or by using resistors of low self-capacitance in series to provide from 5 to 10 megohms across the grid to cathode.

A wider range of operation, perhaps to 100 Mc or higher, is possible by the use of the acorn-type diode rectifier. Such a circuit provides a low input capacitance and low transit time. A high efficiency of rectification is possible, and a high average impedance may be obtained when the load is of the order of 50 megohms. If the tube diode is replaced by one of the present-day crystals, the range of a vacuum-tube voltmeter is extended somewhat, to perhaps as high as 500 Mc.

All a-c voltmeters are essentially rectifiers, employing diode, grid-circuit, or plate-circuit rectification. They may be grouped according to the value of the waveform of the applied potential to which their readings are proportional, as rms, average, peak, or logarithmic. A number of circuits that are currently in use will be discussed.

RMS voltmeters. The response of this type of voltmeter is proportional to the rms value of the applied potential. To achieve such a response, the rectifier that is used must have a square-law relation between the applied input potential and the mean rectified current. Such voltmeters may therefore be used to measure the rms values of potentials, regardless of what the waveform may be.

The basic circuit of such an instrument is given in Fig. 14-1, which is essentially a conventional thermionic vacuum-tube circuit, except that an auxiliary d-c circuit is applied across the indicating milliammeter in the plate circuit in order to balance out the steady component of the tube current when the input potential is zero. In this way, the milliammeter reads the average rectified current that results when the a-c potential is applied to the input terminals.

It is possible to arrange the circuit in such a way that the tube forms one arm of a balanced Wheatstone bridge. In this way, the static operating current may be balanced out without the need for a separate d-c source. Two such circuits are illustrated in Fig. 14-2. In these

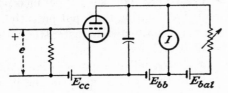

Fig. 14-1. The basic circuit of a vacuum-tube voltmeter.

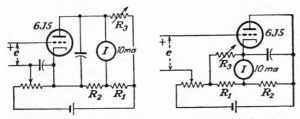

Fig. 14-2. Vacuum-tube voltmeters with balanced output.

circuits, to achieve good sensitivity, the resistor R_3 must be made large in comparison with the meter resistance.

A characteristic which is closely square law for a limited range of applied potential, and this is usually less than about 1 volt peak, may be obtained by operating a triode or a pentode on the curved portion of the characteristic curve. To ensure that the negative peak of the applied potential will not approach too closely to the cutoff bias of the tube, the static plate current must be slightly greater than twice the increment of plate current required to produce full-scale deflection of the indicating instrument. The situation is best understood by referring to Fig. 14-3, which illustrates the operation of the above circuits.

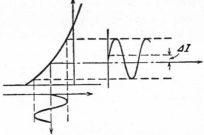

Fig. 14-3. Illustrating the operating characteristics of an rms voltmeter.

Values of applied potential higher than 1 volt peak may be measured without affecting the square-law property of the voltmeter by using a potential divider across the source of potential and applying a known small fraction of the total potential to the input terminals. When this is done, however, the desirable property of very high input impedance is lost. In general, also, the calibration of this type of instrument is dependent upon the tube maintaining its square-law characteristic. As a result, frequent calibration is usually necessary.

Use has also been made of materials other than tubes which possess a square-law characteristic, as the rectifying elements of a mean-square type vacuum-tube voltmeter. One such type[1] incorporates thyrite in a rectifier bridge circuit for squaring the input potential. Such a unit has been found to possess a square-law characteristic within ±2.5 per cent for a current range of 50:1.

Average-reading voltmeters. The response of an average-reading voltmeter is proportional to the average value of the input potential. To achieve such a response, there must be a linear relation between the

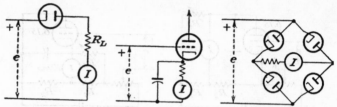

FIG. 14-4. The circuits of several average-reading vacuum-tube voltmeters.

applied input potential and the mean rectified current of the rectifier that is used. But as the mean rectified current is proportional to the mean of the positive excursions of the applied potential, the instrument is dependent on the waveform of the input potential.

The rectifier that is employed may be a simple diode rectifier without a shunt capacitor, a diode bridge circuit, or a biased triode or pentode that is operated from approximately cutoff over the linear portion of the dynamic curve. Owing to the fact that the dynamic curve is nonlinear at low potential levels, a substantially linear response is obtained only for relatively large values of applied potential. The linearity may be considerably improved by using a large load resistance in the diode circuit or by the use of a high plate resistance and negative feedback in the case of triodes or pentodes. Several circuits of such average-reading voltmeters are given in Fig. 14-4.

Since the reading of these voltmeters is dependent upon the waveform of the input potential wave, then, when the applied potential is not a sine wave or other symmetrical waveform, a reversal of the polarity of the input wave will, except for the bridge circuit, change the reading of the instrument. This effect is known as *turnover*.

Peak-reading voltmeters. The response of a peak-reading voltmeter is proportional to the peak value of the applied potential and is, therefore, independent of the waveform when it is calibrated in peak volts. Peak-reading voltmeters may be calibrated to read rms values for sinusoidal

voltages, which then correspond to 0.707 of the peak value.   A number
of peak-reading voltmeters are possible.   They include diode, grid-leak,
feedback, and slide-back types.

The *diode peak voltmeter* provides one of the most convenient and most
accurate methods of measuring peak potentials, especially at radio frequencies.   It consists of a conventional diode rectifier provided with a
capacitor input filter.   The capacitance that shunts the load resistance
is so chosen that the time constant of the circuit is large compared with
the period of the applied potential.   A nonlinearity exists for low input
potential which causes an error, but the indication is linear for voltages

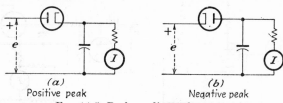

(a)   (b)
Positive peak   Negative peak
Fig. 14-5. Peak-reading voltmeters.

above about 10 volts.   The circuits of two such voltmeters are shown in
Fig. 14-5.

The shortcoming of these voltmeters is that the input impedance during
the conducting portion of the cycle is different from that during the nonconducting portion of the cycle.   This difference arises from the fact that
the diode consumes power during the conducting portion of the cycle.
This effect is precisely that which exists in the detector stage of a radio
receiver.   The effective input resistance of the diode is $R_e = R/2\eta$,
where η is the so-called detection efficiency.   Under the usual conditions
of large load resistance R, the input resistance is approximately $R/2$.
Consequently, fluctuations that might result from such a changing load
impedance would ordinarily be tolerable.

When the rectified current through the load resistance is too small to
be measured conveniently by a d-c microammeter, the potential developed across the load resistance may be applied to the input of a d-c
amplifier.   Several such circuits are illustrated in Fig. 14-6.   In circuit
a, a difference amplifier with $e_2 = 0$ is used as the d-c amplifier.   In
circuit b, a single-tube balanced amplifier is used.

The *grid-leak peak voltmeter* consists of a grid-circuit rectifier employing
either a triode or a pentode.   Rectification occurs in the grid-cathode
circuit in the same manner as in a diode, and grid current flows over the
positive half cycle of the applied potential.   The input impedance is substantially the same as that of the diode peak-reading voltmeter.

A *negative-feedback peak voltmeter* consists essentially of a self-biased
tube which operates from approximately cutoff over the linear portion of

the dynamic curve.   To maintain the tube almost at cutoff for all except the peak portions of the cycle, the bias resistor must be shunted by a capacitor which is adequate for essentially class B operation.   As a result, the plate current flows only at the positive peaks of the applied potential.   The indications on this type of voltmeter are dependent on the waveform.   Since the grid is not driven positive over any portion of the cycle of the applied potential, the input impedance of the voltmeter is high.

The circuit connections of such a voltmeter for use with either a 6J7 or a 954 acorn tube, depending upon the frequency range required, are

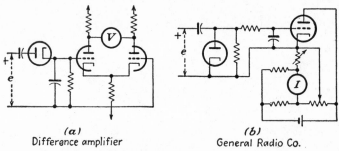

(a)
Difference amplifier

(b)
General Radio Co.

Fig. 14-6. Diode peak voltmeters with d-c amplifier.

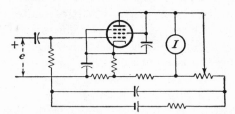

Fig. 14-7. A negative-feedback peak voltmeter.

shown in Fig. 14-7.   The 6J7 is satisfactory for use to several megacycles per second, but where the voltmeter is intended for use across high-impedance tuned circuits at frequencies as high as 10 Mc and where the input capacitance must be kept small, the 954 acorn tube is used.   Note that the tube is connected as a triode, with the suppressor connected to the cathode.   This instrument may be used to measure d-c potentials by omitting the blocking capacitor in the input, although a separate calibration must be used.

The *slide-back voltmeter* consists essentially of a threshold indicator, this threshold being indicated by a d-c voltmeter when the d-c potential is made equal to the peak value of the applied potential.   The circuit of the instrument is illustrated in Fig. 14-8.   The triode or pentode is operated at a very low value of plate current, and the bias is read on the d-c voltmeter.   The potential to be measured is then applied to the input terminals, and the grid bias is increased until the plate current is reduced to its initial value. The peak of the applied potential is then equal to the increase of grid bias, as obtained from the d-c readings.

This type of voltmeter is true peak-reading, and owing to the method of operation it is self-calibrating. It is completely independent of variations in operating potentials and tube characteristics. Moreover, it has a very high input impedance and operates over a very wide range of potentials simply by changing the slide-back potential. Because of the method of operation, such voltmeters are restricted to steady sources of potential.

Logarithmic voltmeter. A voltmeter with a logarithmic scale is possible by using a variable-mu tube in which the amplification factor is an exponential function of the grid potential. Thus for such a tube circuit

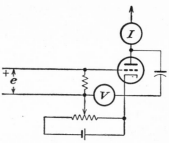

$$\frac{e_2}{e} = A e^{a E_c} \qquad (14\text{-}1)$$

Fig. 14-8. A slide-back peak voltmeter.

where a and A are constants and E_c is the d-c bias on the tube.

In this voltmeter, the output is maintained constant by rectifying and filtering the output and using the resulting d-c potential to bias the amplifier tube, as illustrated in block-diagram form in Fig. 14-9. That

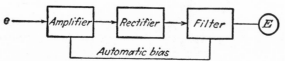

Fig. 14-9. Block diagram of a logarithmic voltmeter.

is, with e_2 constant,

$$E_c = K - \frac{1}{a} \log_e e$$

But since

$$db = 20 \log_{10} \frac{e_2}{e} = K' - 8.69 \log_e e$$

then

$$db = K' - 8.69a(K - E_c)$$

or

$$db = k + mE_c \qquad (14\text{-}2)$$

where K, K', k, and m are constants.

A logarithmic-reading voltmeter has been marketed which is essentially an average-reading instrument, except that the pole pieces of the indicating instrument have been so shaped that the scale indication is logarithmic.

In another type of instrument, illustrated in Fig. 14-10, use is made of the fact that the average diode current varies logarithmically with the input potential to the variable-mu pentode, over a large range of input potential.

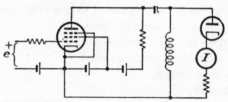

Fig. 14-10. A logarithmic voltmeter.

The desirable feature of logarithmic-reading voltmeters is that scale may be given as decibels, which is very convenient in some applications where the results are desired on the decibel scale.

D-c voltmeters. Most of the circuits considered as a-c voltmeters will operate to give a meter deflection for an input d-c potential applied directly to the grid of the tube. However, since rectification is not required for such an instrument, the tubes might be used for amplification and also to provide a very high input impedance.

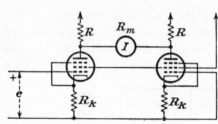

Fig. 14-11. A high-impedance d-c voltmeter.

The circuit of Fig. 14-11 is one which possesses a very high input impedance. The indicating instrument is a low-resistance milliammeter, having a resistance R_m. An analysis of the equivalent circuit shows that the meter current is

$$I_m = \frac{\mu R E}{[R + r_p + (\mu + 1)R_k](2R + R_m) - 2R} \qquad (14\text{-}3)$$

where E is the d-c potential being measured. However, for a pentode

$$r_p \gg R \gg R_m \qquad \mu \gg 1 \qquad R_k \gg \frac{1}{g_m}$$

and the current through the milliammeter is given by

$$I_m = \frac{E}{2R_k} \qquad (14\text{-}4)$$

This shows that a linear relation exists between the applied potential and the reading of the indicating instrument.

A voltmeter employing triodes, which utilizes a high-resistance voltmeter as the indicating instrument, may be built using the simple cathode-coupled difference amplifier. The circuit of such an instrument is given in Fig. 14-12. As shown in Sec. 6-1, the potential difference across the high-resistance indicating instrument connected between the two plates is given by [see Eq. (6-10)]

$$E = \frac{\mu R}{r_p + R} e \qquad (14\text{-}5)$$

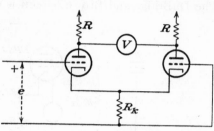

FIG. 14-12. A d-c voltmeter employing triodes.

14-2. Electronic Ammeters. The oscilloscope may be used to measure currents, although an indirect method must be adopted. In this measurement, the current to be measured is passed through a calibrated resistor, the resulting potential across the resistor being measured with the aid of the oscilloscope. The current may then be calculated from the known potential and resistance. However, owing to the fact that the input impedance of the oscilloscope is only moderately high, the oscilloscope is limited to the measurement of relatively high currents, of the order of that possible with good-quality d-c instruments, say 0.1 μa.

Electrometer Tubes. The amplification properties of a vacuum tube may be used to amplify extremely small currents, which are then indicated on a sensitive galvanometer. In order to measure these small currents, it is essential that the grid current of the tube be very small compared with the currents to be measured. Normal tubes, if selected for quality, and if operated at reduced electrode potentials, are satisfactory over rather wide limits. Special tubes with unusually small values of grid current are available. These include, among others,

General Electric Co. FP-54:　$I_g \sim 10^{-15}$ amp
Victoreen Inst. Co. VX-41:　$I_g \sim 10^{-15}$ amp
Raytheon Mfg. Co. CX-570A:　$I_g \sim 10^{-14}$ amp

A circuit utilizing a General Electric FP-54 electrometer tube and operating from a 12-volt storage battery is given in Fig. 14-13. Even though the FP-54 tube is a low-grid-current type, great care must be exercised in keeping leakage and surface currents to a minimum if high sensitivity and dependable operation are desired. This is frequently accomplished by incorporating the entire circuit in a suitable probe type of construction, which is shielded electrostatically and which is kept dry by the use of a drying agent. Also, the grid current is kept small by driving the circuit at low potential from batteries, the circuit being kept in continuous operation for long periods of time in order to reduce tube drift. With the simple circuit shown, the indicating instrument being a sensitive wall galvanometer, currents of the order of 10^{-14} amp may be reliably measured.

A number of other balanced electrometer circuits have been used. The DuBridge and Brown[2] circuit is illustrated in Fig. 14-14.

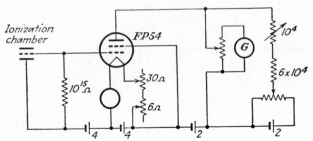

FIG. 14-13. An electrometer circuit using an FP-54 tube.

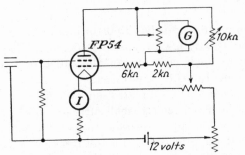

FIG. 14-14. An electrometer circuit using an FP-54 tube.

14-3. Phasemeters. *Lissajous Patterns.* A Lissajous pattern is the figure created on an oscilloscope screen when sine-wave potentials are applied to both the horizontal and vertical deflecting plates. If the frequencies of these two component potentials are the same but they differ in phase, the resulting pattern is a measure of the phase difference between the two waves.

To see that this is so, suppose that the potential across the horizontal deflecting plates of the oscilloscope is denoted as

$$e_x = E_1 \sin (\omega t + \theta_1)$$

and that across the vertical deflecting plates is given by

$$e_y = E_2 \sin (\omega t + \theta_2)$$

Then

$$\frac{e_x}{E_1} = \sin \omega t \cos \theta_1 + \cos \omega t \sin \theta_1 \qquad (14\text{-}6)$$

and

$$\frac{e_y}{E_2} = \sin \omega t \cos \theta_2 + \cos \omega t \sin \theta_2 \qquad (14\text{-}7)$$

Now eliminate the time factor ωt. To do this, multiply the first equation by $\cos \theta_2$, and multiply the second equation by $\cos \theta_1$. Subtract the two results to obtain

$$\frac{e_x}{E_1} \cos \theta_2 - \frac{e_y}{E_2} \cos \theta_1 = \cos \omega t (\sin \theta_1 \cos \theta_2 - \cos \theta_1 \sin \theta_2)$$

Similarly, multiplying the first by $\sin \theta_2$ and the second by $\sin \theta_1$, and subtracting, there results

$$\frac{e_x}{E_1} \sin \theta_2 - \frac{e_y}{E_2} \sin \theta_1 = \sin \omega t (\cos \theta_1 \sin \theta_2 - \sin \theta_1 \cos \theta_2)$$

Squaring and adding these equations gives

$$\frac{e_x^2}{E_1^2} + \frac{e_y^2}{E_2^2} - \frac{2 e_x e_y}{E_1 E_2} \cos (\theta_1 - \theta_2) = \sin^2 (\theta_1 - \theta_2) \qquad (14\text{-}8)$$

This is the equation of an ellipse whose principal axes coincide with the coordinate axes when $\theta_1 - \theta_2 = \pi/2$. Hence, in most cases the result is

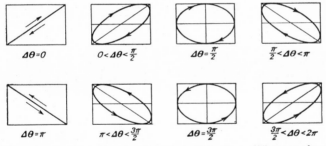

$\Delta\theta=0$ $0<\Delta\theta<\frac{\pi}{2}$ $\Delta\theta=\frac{\pi}{2}$ $\frac{\pi}{2}<\Delta\theta<\pi$

$\Delta\theta=\pi$ $\pi<\Delta\theta<\frac{3\pi}{2}$ $\Delta\theta=\frac{3\pi}{2}$ $\frac{3\pi}{2}<\Delta\theta<2\pi$

FIG. 14-15. Lissajous patterns showing the effect of the phase difference of two sources.

an ellipse, the orientation of which depends upon the phase difference between the two waves. The results have the form illustrated in Fig. 14-15.

If the amplitudes of the potential applied to the vertical and horizontal deflecting plates are equal, then the pattern at the phases $\Delta\theta = \pi/2$ and $3\pi/2$ will be circular. For the measurement of phase, it is customary to set the two amplitudes equal to each other, although this is not necessary.

The experimental procedure necessary for measuring the phase difference between the two potentials is quite direct and consists in measuring the two distances E_0 and E_m illustrated in Fig. 14-16. The distance E_0

is evidently the value of e_y when e_x is zero.   This requires that

$$E_0 = E_2 \sin (\theta_1 - \theta_2)$$

Likewise, the value of E_m is the maximum value of e_y and from Eq. (14-7) is given by

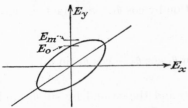

$$E_m = E_2$$

Solving these expressions simultaneously yields

$$\sin (\theta_1 - \theta_2) = \frac{E_0}{E_m} \quad (14\text{-}9)$$

Fig. 14-16. The phase difference between two potentials measured by means of the Lissajous pattern.

Electronic Phasemeter. The elements of a simple electronic phasemeter are illustrated in Fig. 14-17.   It will be observed that the circuit comprises in essence two diode peak-reading voltmeters which have been differentially connected.   With no input signal, the potentials appearing across the input of each diode-voltmeter circuit arise only from the impressed reference potential.   When the circuit is balanced, a zero reading appears on the zero-center high-resistance voltmeter.   This high-resistance voltmeter might be a d-c vacuum-tube voltmeter with a zero-center indicating instrument.

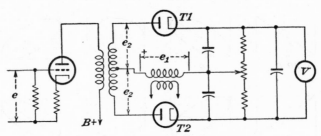

Fig. 14-17. An electronic phasemeter.

If now a potential of preset amplitude is impressed across the input, the potential at one anode decreases and becomes, say, $e_1 - e_2$, while the potential at the other anode increases and becomes $e_1 + e_2$.   As a result, the output potentials will no longer be the same, and a reading will appear on the output voltmeter.   The extent of the change will depend directly upon the phase of the input potential with respect to that of the reference potential, being a maximum in one direction for zero phase difference, and being a maximum in the other direction for 180 deg phase difference, there being a calculable phase difference for every intermediate reading.   The mathematical analysis parallels that of the f-m discriminator and follows below.

Suppose that the potentials e_1 and e_2 are

$$e_1 = E_s \sin \omega t \tag{14-10}$$

and

$$e_2 = E_s \cos (\omega t + \varphi) = E_s \sin \left(\omega t + \frac{\pi}{2} + \varphi \right) \tag{14-11}$$

The a-c potential that appears in the circuit of diode $T1$ is e_a and is

$$e_a = e_1 + e_2$$

and that in the circuit of $T2$ is e_b and is

$$e_b = e_1 - e_2$$

But e_a may be written explicitly as

$$e_a = E_s \sin \omega t + E_s \cos (\omega t + \varphi)$$

which reduces to

$$e_a = 2E_s \cos \frac{1}{2} \left(\varphi + \frac{\pi}{2} \right) \sin \left[\omega t + \frac{1}{2} \left(\varphi + \frac{\pi}{2} \right) \right]$$

Similarly

$$e_b = -2E_s \sin \frac{1}{2} \left(\varphi + \frac{\pi}{2} \right) \cos \left[\omega t + \frac{1}{2} \left(\varphi + \frac{\pi}{2} \right) \right]$$

The corresponding d-c output potentials are then given by

$$\begin{aligned} E_a &= 2\eta E_s \cos \frac{1}{2} \left(\varphi + \frac{\pi}{2} \right) \\ E_b &= 2\eta E_s \sin \frac{1}{2} \left(\varphi + \frac{\pi}{2} \right) \end{aligned} \tag{14-12}$$

where η is the detector efficiency. The corresponding indicating-volt-meter reading is then

$$E = E_a - E_b = 2\eta E_s \left[\left| \cos \frac{1}{2} \left(\varphi + \frac{\pi}{2} \right) \right| - \left| \sin \frac{1}{2} \left(\varphi + \frac{\pi}{2} \right) \right| \right] \tag{14-13}$$

The result has the form illustrated in Fig. 14-18.

A somewhat similar type of phasemeter is possible using triodes.[1] A circuit is shown in Fig. 14-19. It is supposed that the two potentials e_1 and e_2 are of equal frequency and of constant amplitude. The equal potentials appearing across the secondaries of the input transformers are connected in series opposition so that, when the input potentials are in phase, the potential across ab is zero. When the input potentials are slightly out of phase, a small potential appears across ab the magnitude of which is proportional to the phase angle. For small angles this potential may be considered to be 90 deg out of phase with either input.

The input e to the phase-shifting network is across terminals ab, and the output potential e' which appears across cd is 90 deg out of phase with e. The potential e' is applied across the grid resistor R and excites the grids of tubes $T1$ and $T2$, which are connected in push-pull. Owing to the initial 90-deg phase shift and the added 90-deg shift, then for an a-c potential applied to the plates the grid potential of one tube is in phase with its plate potential, whereas the grid potential of the other is in phase opposition with the plate. As a result, one tube conducts, while the other is cut off, either because of a highly negative grid potential or because of a negative plate potential. The conduction causes the zero-center instrument to deflect according to which tube conducts.

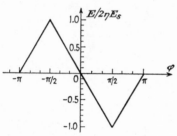

FIG. 14-18. The output of the phasemeter of Fig. 14-17.

The instrument must be zero-set initially with no signal on the grids, whence the unidirectional pulses of plate current through the tubes divide equally through the plate resistor, so that zero resultant potential appears across the d-c instrument. In this instrument, since e' is proportional to θ for small angles, the magnitude of the potential across the d-c instrument is proportional to θ.

Should either e_1 or e_2 drop below or exceed normal rated potential, the difference potential ab increases in length and rotates. This sinor may be resolved into two components, one of which is in phase with e, and

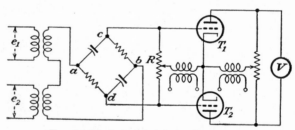

FIG. 14-19. A double-triode phasemeter.

will be effective in producing the potential across the indicating instrument. The other component, which is 90 deg out of phase with e, will not appreciably affect the accuracy of the instrument.

14-4. Wattmeters. The circuit of an electronic wattmeter is given in Fig. 14-20. In this circuit, the resistances R_2 are equal and sufficiently small so that the potential drop across them does not appreciably reduce the load potential. The resistance R_1 is high in order to prevent appreciable power loss.

To examine the operation, it is supposed that the first two terms of the series expansion adequately represent the dynamic characteristics of the tubes. Thus

$$i_{p1} = a_1(e_1 + e_2) + a_2(e_1 + e_2)^2 \qquad (14\text{-}14)$$

and

$$i_{p2} = a_1(e_1 - e_2) + a_2(e_1 - e_2)^2 \qquad (14\text{-}15)$$

The output meter reads the difference between i_{p1} and i_{p2}. Hence

$$i_0 \sim i_{p1} - i_{p2} = 2a_1e_2 + 4a_2e_1e_2 \qquad (14\text{-}16)$$

But with

$$ke_1 = kE_m \cos \omega t$$

$$\qquad (14\text{-}17)$$

and

$$e_2 = R_2I = R_2I_m \cos (\omega t + \theta)$$

and since the indicating instrument reads the average, then

$$
\begin{aligned}
I_0 &= \frac{1}{T} \int_0^T i_0 \, dt \\
&= \frac{2a_1}{T} \int_0^T R_2I_m \cos (\omega t + \theta) \, dt + \frac{4a_2R_2E_mI_mk}{T} \int_0^T \cos \omega t \cos (\omega t + \theta) \, dt
\end{aligned}
$$

so that finally

$$I_0 = 2ka_2R_2E_mI_m \cos \theta \qquad (14\text{-}18)$$

If the load contains harmonics, it can be shown that the reading of the d-c meter is proportional to the total load.

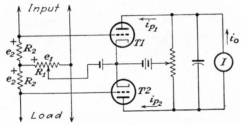

FIG. 14-20. An electronic wattmeter.

The foregoing wattmeter seeks to effect directly the product of the instantaneous potential across the load and the current through the load, the resultant product being averaged in time in order to achieve the average power absorbed by the load. Most techniques which provide the multiplication of two potentials could probably be adapted to this application (see Chap. 6 for a discussion of multipliers). A general-purpose electronic wattmeter has been developed[4] which modulates a carrier first with the current waveform and then with the potential waveform. The resultant modulated carrier is demodulated to yield the instantaneous product of e and i. The average value of the power is obtained by passing the instantaneous product p through a low-pass filter, to remove the carrier component. The peak power is also possible with this device, merely by passing p through a peak detector.

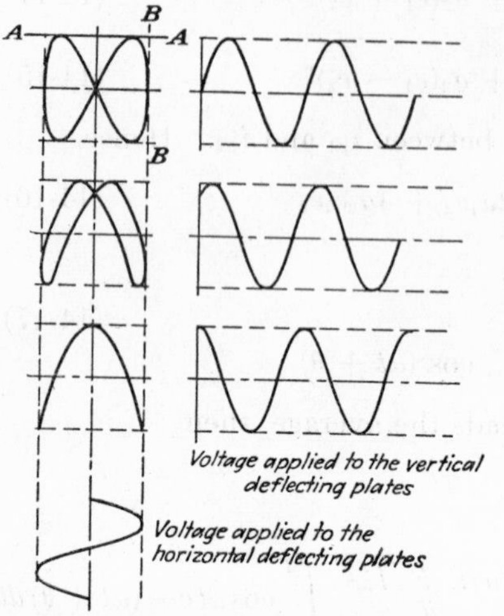

14-5. Frequency Meters. *Lissajous Patterns.* If the component potentials that are applied to the horizontal and vertical deflecting plates of an oscilloscope differ in frequency as well as in phase, the pattern that results is far more complicated than the simple ellipse that has already been considered. If the frequencies are in a constant ratio with each other, the resulting patterns permit a comparison of the ratio of these frequencies. If one of these frequencies is known, the method permits a comparison of the unknown frequency with the given standard.

Fig. 14-21. Lissajous figure for 1:2 frequency ratio.

Voltage applied to the vertical deflecting plates

Voltage applied to the horizontal deflecting plates

Suppose that a potential $e_x = E \sin \omega_1 t$ is applied to the horizontal plates and a potential $e_y = E \sin (\omega_2 t + \theta)$ is applied to the vertical plates. If the frequencies are in the ratio $\omega_2/\omega_1 = 2$, the form of the resulting patterns is readily calculated. The construction is illustrated

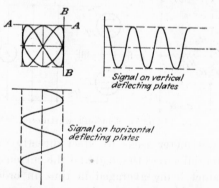

Signal on vertical deflecting plates

Signal on horizontal deflecting plates

Fig. 14-22. Lissajous pattern for 2:3 frequency ratio.

in Fig. 14-21. In a similar way, if the frequencies are in the ratio 2:3, the Lissajous pattern assumes the form shown in Fig. 14-22.

A feature that is common to all Lissajous figures is that the horizontal line AA and the vertical line BB are tangent to the pattern at a number of points, the number depending, respectively, on the frequency applied to the vertical and to the horizontal deflecting plates. Thus the frequency ratio

$$\frac{\omega_h}{\omega_v} = \frac{\text{no. of points at which figure is tangent to the vertical line}}{\text{no. of points at which figure is tangent to a horizontal line}}$$

A number of Lissajous patterns are contained in Fig. 14-23.

1:1   *2:1*   *1:5*   *5:3*

FIG. 14-23. A number of Lissajous patterns.

Electronic Frequency Meters. The circuit of an electronic device is given in Fig. 14-24. The input causes periodic switching from $T1$ to $T2$. When the current begins to flow in $T1$, the potential across R_{k1} causes C_1 to charge through the parallel paths R_1 and one plate of the rectifier $T3$. The average diode current is indicated by the instrument in series with the diode cathode. The diode current is proportional to the frequency, over the range for which C_1 and C_2 charge "fully" in less than the time of one half cycle of the impressed potential. For the circuit shown, the calibration of the instrument is linear to approximately 7,000 cps.

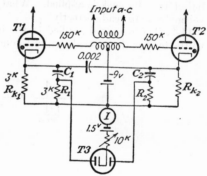

FIG. 14-24. An electronic frequency meter.

A rate meter[5] has been developed which is not limited to the measurement of periodically recurrent waveforms but may also be used to count random pulses such as those which occur in nucleonic processes. In this device the input signals are converted to pulses of the same amplitude and time duration. These pulses are applied to an integrating circuit, the

FIG. 14-25. The elements of a rate meter.

potential across the output of which is a measure of the average number of pulses per unit time. This potential is indicated on a vacuum-tube voltmeter. The elements of the circuit are illustrated in Fig. 14-25.

REFERENCES

1. Rosenthal, L. A., and G. M. Badoyamus, *Electronics*, **25**, 128 (September 1952).
2. DuBridge, L. A., and H. Brown, *Rev. Sci. Instr.*, **4**, 532 (1933).
3. Mikelson, W., *Gen. Elec. Rev.*, **41**, 557 (1938).
4. Garrett, D. E., and F. G. Cole, *Proc. IRE*, **40**, 165 (1952).
5. Smith, G. D., *Electronic Eng.*, **24**, 14 (1952).
6. As general references, see:
Reich, H. J., "Theory and Application of Electron Tubes," 2d ed., McGraw-Hill Book Company, Inc., New York, 1944.
Langsford-Smith, F., "Radiotron Designer's Handbook," 2d ed., Amalgamated Wireless Valve Co., 1953.

PROBLEMS

14-1. The plate current in a 6SK7 tube for $E_{cc2} = 100$ volts, $E_{bb} = 250$ volts is approximately expressed by the relation

$$i_b = 18e^{0.20E_c} \quad \text{ma}$$

This tube is used in the logarithmic voltmeter circuit of Fig. 14-9. An a-c potential of 18 volts peak is applied. What must be the shift in bias potential if the voltmeter is to read correctly?

14-2. The potential applied to the input of an average-reading vacuum-tube voltmeter has the form shown in the figure.

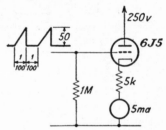

a. What is the zero-input reading of the d-c milliammeter?
b. Calculate the reading when the signal is applied.
c. If the input potential were sinusoidal with the same peak amplitude, what would be the corresponding reading?

14-3. A recurring potential having the waveform shown is applied to the input of a number of vacuum-tube voltmeters of different type, each of which

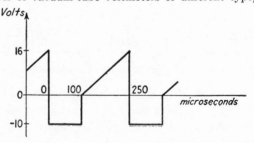

has been calibrated by means of a sinusoidal input waveform. Calculate the reading on the following instruments, for both directions of applied input:

    a. Single-diode average-reading instrument of Fig. 14-4.

    b. Bridge-diode average-reading instrument of Fig. 14-4.

    c. Peak-reading diode of Fig. 14-5.

    d. Rms-type voltmeter.

14-4. Show the connections for employing the multiplying circuit of Fig. 6-31 as an electronic wattmeter.

CHAPTER 15

SOLID-STATE THEORY

15-1. Electron Theory of Metals. An extensive statistical electron theory of metals has been developed over the past few decades based on the fundamental work of Fermi, Dirac, and Sommerfeld. This is not meant to imply that the theory of metals had not been developed to a high point prior to this time, but it was this later work which applied the quantum-statistical theory to the explanation of electronic phenomena of metals and provided analytical explanations of the important electronic phenomena. While analytic details of this theory will not be given,* some of the consequences of this theory will be discussed.

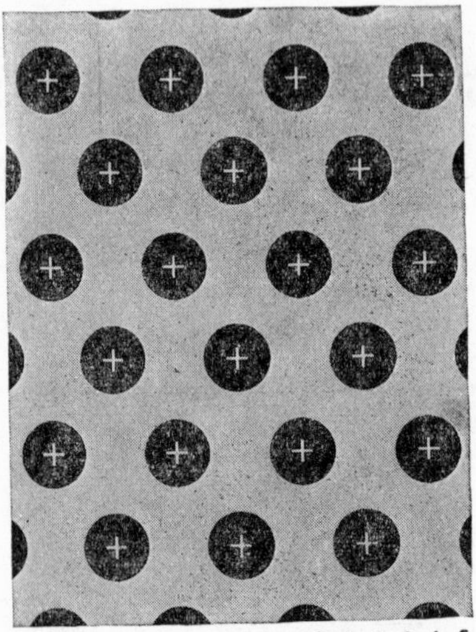

Consider therefore a simple metallic substance. X-ray and other studies reveal that most metals are crystalline in structure and consist of a space array of atoms or molecules (strictly speaking, ions) built up by regular repetition in three dimensions of some fundamental structural unit. The atoms of the elements are so close together that the electrons in the outer shells of the atom are associated with one atom as much as with its neighbor. As a result, the force of attachment of an outer electron with any individual atom is practically zero. Depending on the metal, at least one, sometimes two, and, in a few cases, three electrons per atom are free to move throughout the body of the metal under the action of applied forces.

Fig. 15-1. Arrangement of sodium atoms in the 110 plane of the metal. [W. Shockley, J. Appl. Phys., **10**, 543 (1939).]

Figure 15-1 shows the charge distribution for metallic sodium. The plus signs represent the heavy positive sodium nucleus of the atoms; the

---

* A fairly detailed discussion is given in J. Millman and S. Seely, "Electronics," 2d ed., McGraw-Hill Book Company, Inc., New York, 1951.

black regions represent the tightly bound electrons of the sodium atom; the lightly shaded regions represent the outer, or valence, electrons of the atom. It is these outer electrons which have lost a firm force of attraction to any particular atom and may move freely about from atom to atom in the metal. Thus a metal is visualized as a region of relatively fixed ions permeated with a swarm of electrons that may move about more or less freely. This is the "electron-gas" concept of the metal.

A detailed analysis of the potential-energy distribution within and at the surface of a metal will not be given here,* but the analysis shows the potential-energy variation to be somewhat as given in Fig. 15-2, when

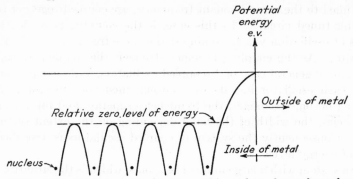

Fig. 15-2. The potential-energy distribution within and at the surface of a metal.

one singles out an entire row of nuclei from the metallic lattice. This picture shows that the potential energy varies considerably in the immediate neighborhood of the nuclei and is approximately constant over a substantial portion of the metal. Also, a potential-energy barrier exists at the surface of the metal. It is in fact the presence of this potential-energy barrier at the surface which prevents the internal free electrons from leaving the body of the metal. The total height of the potential-energy barrier at the surface will be of the order of 10 to 20 ev for most metals.

A correlation between Figs. 15-1 and 15-2 will show that electrons in the black regions are those below the "zero" level and are the bound electrons, as they are strongly bound to the nucleus and can move about only in the neighborhood of the nucleus. The free electrons are in the region above the zero level, and it is these which contribute to the bulk conductivity of the metal.

A number of factors affect the energies which may be possessed by the "free" electrons. A description of these requires considerations of the electron theory of matter. Before considering the consequences of this theory, an interesting and informative analogy is possible between the electron problem and the problem of a group of coupled oscillators. That is,

* *Ibid.*

each ion is firmly bound to its position of equilibrium in the crystal lattice, although the ion will vibrate about this equilibrium position owing to the effects of temperature. Consequently, each ion may be represented as an oscillator. Moreover, owing to the proximity of the ions, there will be some interaction among them, and this interaction may be represented by weak coupling springs. When the coupling is zero, each oscillator has its own normal mode of vibration, and if all ions are the same, the frequency of oscillation of each representative oscillator will be the same. As soon as coupling occurs, there is an effect on the resonant frequencies. The effect is not unlike that which occurs when two single-tuned circuits, each tuned to the same resonant frequency, are coupled together to form a double-tuned circuit. In this case, if the coupling is weak, the two modes of oscillation will have almost the same frequency as the isolated oscillator. As the coupling becomes stronger, the frequencies separate. In the more general case of N-coupled oscillators, if the coupling is very weak, each oscillator has its own normal mode of vibration. As the coupling becomes stronger, the frequencies separate and form a band of frequencies, the width of the band depending on the extent of the coupling. Consequently the system of coupled oscillators is described by a band of energy levels.

For a system with a large number of atoms, which is the situation under consideration, a number of quantum factors influence the process of splitting and the extent of the splitting. The result is a series of separated bands. In the case of a metal, the energy band of interest is the conduction band, which is illustrated in Fig. 15-3. The energy levels in

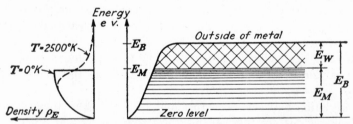

Fig. 15-3. The energy diagram of the free electrons of a metal.

the band are distributed in energy, the form of the distribution function being the so-called Fermi-Dirac-Sommerfeld (FDS) distribution. A graph of this distribution function shows the general form of the variation of the density of particles with energies in a specified energy range dE as a function of energy, and this function, with ordinate ρ_E, is also included in Fig. 15-3. The energy level labeled E_M is known as the Fermi level, or Fermi characteristic energy, and is the maximum possible energy of an electron at the absolute zero of temperature. It varies from roughly 5 to 10 ev for most metals. The sketch shows that the density function

oes not vary very markedly with temperature, although there will be a
mall number of electrons with energies above E_M. Note that it is only
hose surface-directed electrons with energies in excess of E_B, the height
f the potential-energy barrier at the surface of the metal, which possess
ufficient energy to overcome all force of attraction and hence are free
f the metal. It is these electrons which contribute to the surface emis-
ion current, whether it is thermionic-emission current, photoelectric
urrent, or the current due to any other process which removes electrons
hrough the surface of the metal.

The second curve of Fig. 15-3 defines a number of important concepts.
he array of horizontal lines and their spacing are intended to indicate
a a crude way the energy density. The progressively decreasing spacing
etween horizontal lines at the higher energies illustrates pictorially that
he density of the electrons is greatest in the neighborhood of the energy
J_M, in accordance with the density function. Not illustrated, but also
mplied, is that the crosshatched band also contains a distribution of
nergy levels, although they need not necessarily be inhabited by elec-
rons. In fact, at $T = 0°K$ all energy levels above E_M are empty. The
uantity E_W is the work function of the metal and represents the minimum
nergy that must be supplied to an electron in the metal at $T = 0°K$ for
; to overcome the potential-energy barrier and so escape from the metal.
t varies roughly from 2 to 6 ev for most metals.

15-2. Contact Potential. Consider two metals in contact with each
ther, as at the junction C in Fig. 15-4. The contact difference of potential
etween a point A just outside of metal 1 and a point B just outside of
netal 2 is denoted E_{AB}. That a difference of po-
ential should exist is evident from the fact that
vhen the two metals are joined at the boundary
', electrons will flow from the lower-work-function
netal, say 1, to the other metal 2. This electron
low will continue until metal 2 has acquired such
, negative surface charge that the electron flow
eases. The equilibrium condition of equal elec-
ron flow across the boundary in each direction is
ttained when the Fermi energies E_M of the two

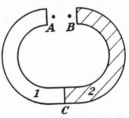

FIG. 15-4. Two metals in
contact at junction C.

netals are located at the same height on the combined energy-level diagram. The situation is illustrated in Fig. 15-5. It follows from this condi-
ion of common Fermi energy levels that the contact difference of potential
between the two metals equals the difference between their work functions.

If the metals are similar, the contact potential between them is zero.
f they are dissimilar metals, the metal with the smaller work function
becomes charged positively and the larger-work-function metal becomes
negatively charged.

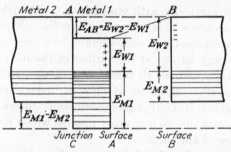

FIG. 15-5. The potential-energy system of two metals in contact.

15-3. Barrier-layer Rectification. A situation of considerable interest and importance appears evident, if in Fig. 15-5 it would be possible to include an extremely thin insulator between the two metals at the junction C. The insulator must be so thin that it does not interfere with the flow of electrons across the junction C but must be such as to permit the application of an external potential to the two metals to cause a shift in the potential-energy distributions of the systems. Under these circumstances, the possible situations would be somewhat like those indicated graphically in Figs. 15-6, which shows the effect of an external

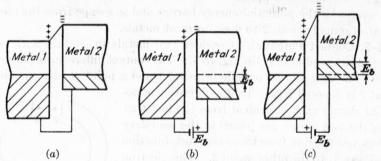

(a)   (b)   (c)

FIG. 15-6. Potential energy of a metal-insulator-metal boundary. (a) With no applied potential, the Fermi levels are on the same line, as in Fig. 15-5. (b) With a potential applied in the forward direction. (c) With a potential applied in the backward direction.

potential E_b, less than the work function of either of the two metals. Observe that the effect of the applied potential, as in Fig. 15-6b, is to cause the potential energy of metal 2 to move downward, whereas the reverse polarity produces the situation depicted in Fig. 15-6c. The applied potentials affect the degree to which the two metals become charged, and this effect is denoted graphically by the $+$ and $-$ signs shown on each diagram.

Note that there is no change in the height of the surface barrier as viewed from the metal of larger work function (metal 2 in this case). However, the height of the surface barrier as viewed from the metal of smaller work function varies linearly with the applied potential. In the case of Fig. 15-6b, the electron flow per unit time from metal 2 to metal 1 is increased because the effective barrier from metal 1 to metal 2 is decreased by the height E_b. Conversely for the case of Fig. 15-6c, the electron flow per unit time is decreased. The applied potential is said to be in the "forward," or "easy," direction in the former case and in the "reverse," or "blocking," direction in the latter case. The electron flow per unit time varies differently with potential polarity, being much greater in the forward than in the reverse direction. Consequently, conduction at such a boundary is nonlinear, and rectification is possible.

Attempts to construct satisfactory metal-insulator-metal rectifiers of the type here discussed have not been very successful. The use of a semiconductor in place of the insulator and one metal yields very successful rectifiers, and such devices have been fully exploited. These devices will be discussed below.

15-4. Insulators. There are characteristic differences between the energy bands of metals and of insulators. Whereas the metal is characterized by the conduction band, a portion of which is filled with electrons, as illustrated in Fig. 15-3, the insulator is represented by a valence band, which is fully occupied by the valence electrons, and the next higher conduction band, which is entirely empty. The energy gap between them is great, so that when in thermal equilibrium at room temperature none of the electrons from the filled valence band can acquire sufficient energy to pass through the forbidden (no energy-level) region. A sketch showing the energy-band distribution in the insulator is given in Fig. 15-7.

15-5. Semiconductors.[1] It appears reasonable, in the light of the discussion in the foregoing section,

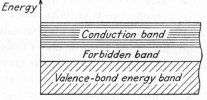

FIG. 15-7. The electronic-energy bands of an insulator.

to expect a class of materials for which the forbidden region is relatively narrow, say of the order of 1 ev or less. It would be expected that such a class of materials would exhibit the properties of an insulator at reduced temperatures but would exhibit conduction at higher temperatures, owing to the changing electron distribution with temperature and the fact that some electrons might then acquire sufficient energy to pass through the forbidden region. Materials of this class are known as semiconductors, and conduction of the type discussed known as *intrinsic* conduction. Intrinsic conduction is so named because the conduction is an intrinsic property of the pure material. Ultrapure germanium and silicon are semiconductors of this type.

A second class of semiconductors, known as the *extrinsic* type, is of extreme importance. In extrinsic semiconductors, which are also characterized by a band structure like that shown in Fig. 15-7, there is an additional feature caused by lattice imperfections or by the presence of impurities in the material. This is the presence of extra energy levels in the general neighborhood of the filled band, but in the normally forbidden region. In a second type, extra levels exist in the general neighborhood of the normally unfilled conduction band. In fact, a semiconductor with both sets of levels in the normally forbidden region is very important.

Suppose that these extra levels are filled at absolute zero of temperature. In this case, they may act as *donators*, or *donors*, at finite temperatures. That is, the electrons in these donator levels could be transferred to the conduction band. Once the electron is in the conduction band, then conduction is possible in the same way as for the metal.

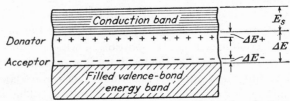

Fig. 15-8. The energy-level diagram of an extrinsic semiconductor, with donator levels (marked +) and acceptor levels (marked −).

If the extra levels were empty at absolute zero of temperature, they may act as *acceptor* levels at finite temperature. In this case, an electron from the normally filled band may transfer to the empty acceptor level. As a result, an empty level or hole exists in the normally filled band, and conduction is possible through the transfer of such holes.

An energy-level diagram of an extrinsic semiconductor is given in Fig 15-8. The donator levels (marked + in the diagram) are found to li below and near the empty conduction band; the acceptor levels (marked −) lie above and near the normally filled band. The energy separatio of the levels marked $\Delta E+$ and $\Delta E-$ from the conduction band and th filled band, respectively, may be quite small in a given case. Fo example, for silicon and germanium, the extra levels are about 0.1 e from the appropriate band edge.

A semiconductor that conducts principally by electrons that are i the normally empty conduction band is called an "n-type" (negativ semiconductor. The conduction in this case is also referred to a "excess" conduction. Correspondingly, a semiconductor that conduc principally because of the presence of holes or empty levels in the no mally filled band, is called a "p-type" (positive) semiconductor. Th process of conduction in this case is also called "deficit" conduction.

15-6. Some Physical Data on Semiconductors. Physical measurements of several types contribute to an understanding of the properties of semiconductors. Several of such physical properties will be discussed.

The conductivity of semiconductors exhibits quite different properties from that of metals. For metals, the electrical conductivity decreases with increasing temperature. Also, the conductivity increases with purification. The behavior of the conductivity of a semiconductor is strikingly different from that of the metal. These substances show low conductivity at low temperatures, and the conductivity increases as the temperature is raised. The conductivity reaches a maximum, decreases again, and finally increases a second time, and much more sharply when a higher temperature is reached. This behavior can be completely understood on the assumption that the number of current carriers in these substances is dependent on the temperature.

At low temperatures, the number of carriers is small and should be zero at absolute zero. In this case, the semiconductor becomes an insulator. As the temperature increases, dissociation of the impurity centers occurs and the conductivity increases. When all the carriers from the impurity centers have been released, their number remains constant. Owing to the increasing temperature, the resistance rises. At still higher temperatures, electrons are released from the semiconductor itself, and these intrinsic electrons are available in greater number than the carriers from the impurity centers, and the resistance at elevated temperatures decreases very rapidly. An expression has been developed by Wilson[2] that relates the resistivity of the material with the temperature and the width of the forbidden region. This expression, which is valid for the region where the conduction is intrinsic, is

$$\rho = A e^{\Delta E/2E_T} \tag{15-1}$$

where ρ is the resistivity in ohm-centimeters and E_T is the electron-volt equivalent of temperature ($eE_T = kT$, where e is the electronic charge, k is the Boltzmann constant, and T is the temperature in degrees Kelvin). Values of ΔE obtained from the use of this equation are given in Table 15-1.

TABLE 15-1[3]

WIDTHS OF FORBIDDEN REGIONS

Material	ΔE, ev
Diamond	7
Boron	2
Cu_2O	1.4
Silicon	1.2
Germanium	0.76

Over the range of temperatures for which both electrons and holes are present in the semiconductor, the conductivity is given by the relation[4]

$$\gamma = e(N_e u_e + N_h u_h) \tag{15-2}$$

where γ is the conductivity in mhos per centimeter, e is the electronic charge, N_e and N_h are, respectively, the electron and hole concentrations per cubic centimeter, and u_e and u_h are, respectively, the electron and hole mobilities (the average velocities attained by the electrons and holes in the direction of the field) in centimeters per second per volt per centimeter.

The Hall effect has been of tremendous importance in the measurements of the unknown quantities in this expression. This effect is the following: A magnetic field is applied in a direction perpendicular to the direction of flow of current in a long, thin semiconductor or conductor. Under the action of the magnetic field, electrons or holes are deflected transversely (see Sec. 1-35). Owing to the deflection, it is found that a transverse potential results. The deflection continues until the electric field that is produced just compensates the action of the magnetic field. The Hall constant is the ratio of the electric field normal to the current flow per unit magnetic field and per unit current density and is a direct measure of the number of carriers produced.

When the Hall effect has been measured, it gives an equation relating the four unknown quantities in Eq. (15-2). Moreover, with the careful choice of sample, for example, an n-type sample in the impurity-conduction temperature range, N_h may be taken as zero, and the Hall measurement allows a determination of N_e and u_e. Similarly, the use of a p-type sample permits a determination of N_h and u_h. Also, the measurement of conductivity provides another relation among the four unknown quantities in Eq. (15-2). From such measurements, the mobilities of germanium and silicon have the values shown[1] in Table 15-2.

TABLE 15-2

MOBILITIES

(In centimeters per second per volt per centimeter)

Semiconductor	Mobility	
	u_e	u_h
Germanium..........	2,600 (Hall mobility)	1,700
	3,600 (drift mobility)	1,700
Silicon..............	300	100

15-7. Crystal Structure of Semiconductors. A number of materials exhibit semiconductor properties, and these have become particularly important in the field of electronics.   In addition to silicon and germanium, already mentioned, some forms of carbon, selenium, copper oxide, certain other oxides, and certain ferrites are also becoming very important. Some aspects of the conduction characteristics are now examined.

Reference to the periodic table will show that carbon, silicon, and germanium have atomic numbers 6, 14, and 32, respectively.   Moreover, these elements are tetravalent, each having four valence electrons which may enter into chemical action, in addition to the inner tightly bound electrons.   In the crystalline form each atom is situated at the corner of a regular tetrahedron, the crystal being held together by "electron-pair bonds."   That is, each atom forms an electron-pair bond with four other surrounding atoms to form the crystalline structure, the resulting structure being electrically neutral and very stable.   A schematic two-dimensional representation of the system is shown in Fig. 15-9.

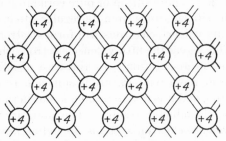

FIG. 15-9. A two-dimensional representation of the crystalline structure of diamond (also silicon and germanium), showing the electron-pair bonds.

In the diagram, each circle marked +4 is intended to represent the ion, consisting of the nucleus surrounded by its cloud of tightly bound electrons, with a resultant charge of four positive units.   The four outer electrons make up the electron-pair bonds.   Since in this structure every valence electron is tightly bound, an appreciable energy is required to release an electron from its bond in the structure.   The amount of energy required to release an electron from its bond is represented by the width of the forbidden band in Fig. 15-8.   When such an electron is released from its bond, it constitutes a localized negative charge and may move through the lattice of the crystal under the influence of an applied force. Since this electron may not be required to complete a bond in its immediate vicinity, it is an "excess" electron.

Whenever a valence electron is released from its bond, the resulting ion is positively charged.   This positive charge may also move through the crystal from atom to atom by the process of an electron from a neighboring bond completing the deficient bond of one ion, leaving behind its own positive ion.   Essentially, a transfer of charge from atom to atom takes place as the positive charge (or hole) migrates.   With the application of an electric field, the motion of these "holes" becomes systematic, and they drift in the general direction determined by the field. It has become common to consider the holes as "positive charges" somewhat like positive electrons (not positrons), but, because of their different drift characteristics in a field, their effective mass is different from the mass of the electron.

15-8. Impurity Semiconductors. The introduction of certain impurities into pure silicon or pure germanium may be used to produce conductivity by excess electrons or by holes. As already noted, when the conduction is due to excess electrons, the semiconductor is called n-type. When the conduction is due to holes, the material is called p-type. Any impurity which causes n-type material is called a donor, and, correspondingly, any impurity which produces p-type material is called an acceptor.

Consider then an impurity such as arsenic, which has five valence electrons, to be added to pure silicon or pure germanium. This atom will displace one of the silicon atoms from its regular site in the crystal structure, and four of its valence electrons will form electron-pair bonds with its neighbors. This leaves the fifth valence electron, which becomes very loosely bound to the arsenic ion. In the case of silicon and arsenic, thermal agitation at room temperature is sufficient to destroy the bond of this extra electron, and it is free to wander about in the crystal. Therefore an n-type semiconductor results. The impurity may be any of a number of five valence-electron systems, including arsenic, phosphorus, or antimony.

To produce a p-type semiconductor, an impurity which is trivalent, such as boron or aluminum, must be introduced into the pure metal. The impurity atom replaces one of the parent atoms in the crystal. But now one of the covalent bonds is not completed, and a hole is created in that particular bond. This bond can be completed by an electron from an adjacent atom, but the hole has then migrated to the ion from which the electron came. Thus the hole drifts from atom to atom, while the impurity atom becomes an immobile localized negative charge. These holes account for the acceptor states of Fig. 15-8.

15-9. Metal-semiconductor Barrier Layer. Consider now the situation which exists when a semiconductor, say of the n type, is placed in contact with a metal. Figure 15-10 shows the energy-level diagrams of the metal and the semiconductor which are widely separated so that the reference level for energy is that of an electron at rest at large distances from both bodies.

Consider that the semiconductor is placed in contact with the metal. A set of potential-energy curves corresponding to those in Fig. 15-6 for the metal-insulator-metal is desired. Theory shows that, for the metal-semiconductor contact, a redistribution of electrons results in the production of a surface-charge distribution, the equilibrium condition being reached when the two Fermi levels are located at the same height on the combined energy-level diagram. The Fermi level for the n-type semi-conductor is found to be approximately equal to the donor level. (It is approximately equal to the acceptor level for the p-type semiconductor.)

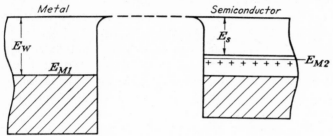

FIG. 15-10. Energy-level diagram for a metal and an n-type semiconductor which are widely separated.

If the work function E_S of the semiconductor is less than that of the metal E_W, electrons will flow from the semiconductor to the metal. This establishes a negative surface charge on the metal, with an equal positive space charge on the surface of the semiconductor. The approximate thickness of this positive-surface-charge distribution, which is called a "depletion" region, or "natural blocking layer," has been estimated to range from about 10^{-8} to 10^{-6} m. The situation is illustrated in Fig. 15-11a.

Rectification at the metal-semiconductor boundary is accomplished in much the same manner as for the metal-insulator-metal system, and the

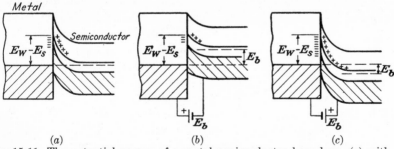

(a)   (b)   (c)

FIG. 15-11. The potential energy of a metal-semiconductor boundary, (a) with no applied potential, (b) with a potential in the forward direction, (c) with a potential in the backward direction.

situation is illustrated in Fig. 15-11. Suppose that a potential is applied in the forward direction (a negative potential is applied to the semi-conductor), as illustrated in Fig. 15-11b. This increases the potential energy of the semiconductor by an amount E_b. The height of the surface barrier as viewed from the metal to the semiconductor does not change with changes of E_b. However, when viewed from the semiconductor to the metal, the barrier has decreased by E_b. Since the electrons have a smaller potential barrier to hurdle, there will then be a resultant flow of electrons from the semiconductor to the metal. This situation is analogous to that in Fig. 15-6b. The limiting condition occurs when E_b equals the contact-barrier height, thereby wiping out the contact space charge. In this case the current is determined by the bulk resistance of the semiconductor.

When the potential is applied in the reverse direction, as illustrated in Fig. 15-11c, the potential energy changes in a manner to cause the height of the barrier, as viewed from the semiconductor to the metal, to increase by E_b. This results in a decrease in the electron flow from the semiconductor to the metal. Since the electron flow across the metal-semiconductor boundary responds differently for each polarity of the applied potential, being greater in the forward than in the reverse direction, the boundary is nonlinear and rectification is possible.

Two barrier-layer rectifiers appear possible on the basis of this model, depending on whether or not the natural blocking layer is thin compared with the electron mean free path in the semiconductor. If it is thin, then collisions of the electrons with the crystal structure in the blocking layer need not be considered and the assembly is analogous to a vacuum diode.

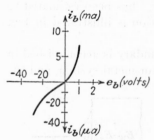

FIG. 15-12. Diode characteristic of a typical n-type germanium diode.

The metal is the anode, and the semiconductor is the cathode. This type of diode theory is applicable to germanium and silicon point-contact rectifiers. A typical diode characteristic of a germanium diode is shown in Fig. 15-12. For the thick natural blocking layer, a diffusion type of theory has been developed in which electron collisions with the crystal structure of the blocking layer are taken into account. The diffusion theory appears applicable to the selenium and cuprous oxide rectifiers.

It is of some interest to examine the situation that prevails when E_S of the n-type semiconductor exceeds E_W of the metal. Under conditions of equilibrium, the potential-energy diagram has the form illustrated in Fig. 15-13. The Fermi levels again line up, but now the electron flow has been from the metal to the semiconductor. A negative-surface-charge layer results, which lowers the semiconductor levels, as indicated. The potential step is inverted so that there is no impediment to electrons in the conduction band. Such a contact will obey Ohm's law.

Now consider a p-type semiconductor in contact with a metal. This case differs somewhat from that involving the n-type semiconductor, since, for barrier-layer rectification to take place, E_S must be greater than E_W. Refer first to Fig. 15-14a. If one now concentrates attention on the

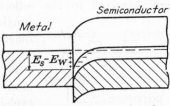

holes which move to the top of the full band, it can be seen that for the case illustrated an asymmetric resistance-potential characteristic results. That is, the application of a positive potential to the semiconductor lowers the Fermi level of the semiconductor relative to the E_M level of the metal. As a result the step that the holes pass under is decreased. This, therefore, is the forward direction. A

FIG. 15-13. An n-type semiconductor in contact with a metal which has a smaller work function than the semiconductor.

negative potential on the semiconductor is in the reverse direction.

Consideration of Fig. 15-14b, as for the analogous form in Fig. 15-11 for the n-type semiconductor, will show that in this case no blocking layer is formed. The contact is therefore ohmic.

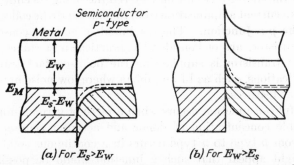

(a) For $E_S > E_W$ (b) For $E_W > E_S$

FIG. 15-14. A p-type semiconductor in contact with a metal.

15-10. Type A Transistor. In the type A transistor, two point contacts are placed near each other (only several mils apart) on the upper face of a small block of n-type germanium. A large area low resistance ohmic contact on the base provides the third element. Each of the two point contacts is separately connected to the base electrode through an external circuit. Each point contact with the base electrode has characteristics roughly similar to those of a contact rectifier. One point contact, the emitter, is biased in the forward or low resistance direction (emitter positive with respect to the semiconductor). Most of the current in this electrode is made up of electrons that are extracted from the valence bands of the germanium, thereby resulting in the injecting of holes into the semiconductor. The second point contact, the collector, is biased in the reverse or high resistance direction. The collector current comprises the sum of two components, each of which is of roughly comparable magnitude. One is the electron flow from the collector point to the base electrode through the semiconductor. The second component arises from the positively charged holes which were injected by the emitter, and which are attracted to the collector by the field that exists due to the proximity of the collector and the emitter. A diagram showing the flow of holes and electrons in the collector circuit is given in Fig. 15–15.

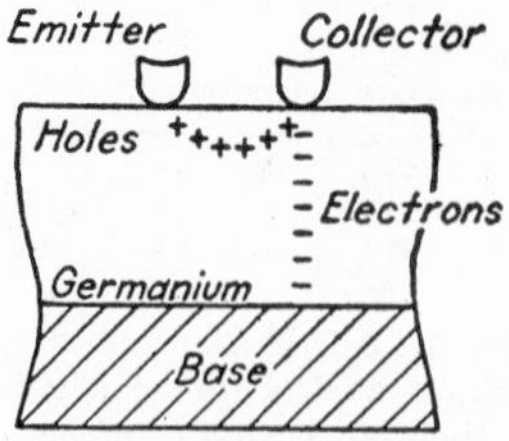

FIG. 15-15. The schematic diagram of a type A transistor, showing the flow of holes and electrons in the collector circuit.

It is found that the collector current may change more than the emitter current. This has been explained in the following manner: The density of the space charge in the barrier layer at the collector is increased by the hole current into that junction from the semiconductor. This increase in space-charge density and field strength makes it easier for electrons to flow from the collector, thereby increasing the collector-circuit current. The increase in hole current and electron current combined in the collector circuit may exceed the change in emitter current. The result is a current amplification from the emitter to the collector circuit.

15-11. The p-n Junction. The p-n junction, and the consequent p-n junction transistor, are of considerable practical importance, since the p-n junction transistor is supplanting the point-contact transistor for certain applications, such as l-f amplifiers where low noise and high gain are important features.

A successful p-n junction occurs when a piece of germanium or silicon has a variable concentration of donor and acceptor centers so that a transition from p type to n type occurs in a continuous solid specimen. While it might appear that such a junction would be possible if two separate pieces of germanium of opposite conductivity types were placed in contact, the presence of contaminants, surface states, roughness, etc., prevents a true p-n junction from being formed.

To examine the nature of the current flow across a p-n junction, refer to Fig. 15-16a, which shows the energy-band structure as a function of

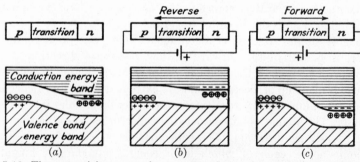

FIG. 15-16. The potential energy of a p-n junction under applied biases ($+$ hole, $-$ electron, $\ominus$ acceptor, $\oplus$ donor).

position under equilibrium conditions. It is convenient to think of the distortion of the energy bands as equivalent to a space-charge region between the p-type and n-type semiconductors. It is well to examine the situation that exists in each region of the junction.

In the p-type region at room temperature, the semiconductor is neutral in charge at all points. That is, the number of free holes moving about is just balanced by the number of negatively charged impurity (acceptor) ions. Similarly, in the n-type region, the number of free electrons is just balanced by the number of ionized donors. Now consider the transition region, which may be thought of as being caused by the gradual increase in the number of donors over the number of acceptors. A charge situated in this transition region will be acted upon by two fields, the electric field of the acceptor ions, and the field of the positively charged donor ions. Both these fields produce a force on the charge in the same direction. Thus any charge located in the transition region tends to be swept out of the region by the space-charge field. Under equilibrium conditions, holes and electrons move in both directions. That is, some of the holes in the p-type material acquire enough energy from thermal excitation of lattice ions to overcome the potential energy through the transition region to diffuse into the n region. Once in this region, they will combine with electrons. Similarly, holes which are thermally generated in the n region, as members of hole-electron pairs, will diffuse through the transition region into the p region. These hole currents balance each other. In a similar way, electron currents move in both directions across the transition region. The electron currents also balance each other.

Under conditions of reversed bias, perhaps a few tenths of a volt or more, the hole current from the p region into the n region and the electron current from the n region into the p region practically vanish. The hole current in the reverse direction, from n region into p region through the transition region, remains substantially as for the equilibrium state and, in fact, is substantially unaffected by the applied potential. The hole current saturates, and reaches a limiting value as the reverse potential is increased. A curve showing the theoretical current-potential variation for the p-n junction is given in Fig. 15-17.

In the forward direction, a relatively large hole current flows from the p region into the n region. Electrons will flow in the opposite direction. If there are many more holes than electrons, most of the current will flow in the form of holes. That is, such a junction will be a good emitter of holes. A curve showing the theoretical current-potential variation for this case is also given in Fig. 15-17.

15-12. The p-n-p Junction Transistor. A series of idealized curves which show details of a p-n-p transistor are given in Fig. 15-18. Consider the first series of curves which apply under equilibrium conditions. The equilibrium concentration of holes is shown in Fig. 15-18a-3, and this distribution remains sensibly constant, since the potential-energy system is such as to maintain this distribution of holes and electrons.

In the curves of Fig. 15-18*b* for the biased transistor a small forward

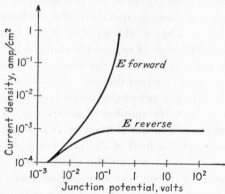

FIG. 15-17. Theoretical current-potential curves for a *p-n* junction.

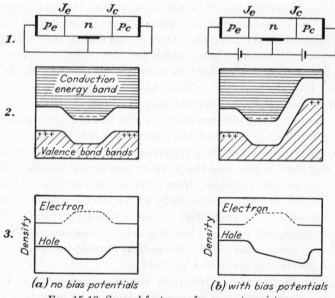

(a) no bias potentials   *(b)* with bias potentials

FIG. 15-18. Several features of a *p-n-p* transistor.

potential, positive for the *p*-type region, is applied across junction J_e, and a potential in the reverse direction is applied across J_c. If the *p*-type regions have much higher conductivity than the *n*-type region, most of the current across the junctions will be in the form of holes. In fact, if the *n*-type region is narrow, so that a hole can diffuse across it with only a small chance of recombination, the holes in the current across J_e will also flow across J_c. If the electron currents across the junctions are negligible and recombination in the n region is neglected, the transistor will draw no base current. In any case, owing to the fact that the collector is biased negatively (the reverse direction), very little current will flow in the collector circuit unless the emitter is biased in the forward direction, when the holes injected by the emitter will diffuse through the base and be attracted to the collector, thereby increasing the collector current. Clearly, the current in the collector circuit is controlled by the emitter circuit.

If the emitter is a-c grounded, a-c potentials applied to the base will require little current and the situation is quite like that of the ordinary triode, except that the carriers in the transistor are holes rather than electrons.

The n-p-n transistor is similar to the p-n-p transistor except that the polarities are reversed. Thus the negatively biased n-type emitter injects electrons which diffuse through the narrow p region and are collected by the positively biased collector.

15-13. Comparison of Point-contact and Junction Transistors. As noted in Secs. 15-10 and 15-11, amplification by transistors depends on the controlled injection of the minority carriers at the emitter contact or junction. To provide this injection, the emitter is biased in the forward direction, and the collector is biased in the reverse direction. For the point-contact transistor with an n-type semiconductor, the emitter is biased positively, and the current at the emitter contact is carried primarily by holes, as illustrated in Fig. 15-15. Moreover, in this case, the negatively biased collector collects the holes.

For the p-n-p transistor, the p-type emitter is biased positively, and the injected holes are driven toward the n-type region, with electrons moving toward the p region. With the collector biased negatively, some of the holes injected by the emitter will diffuse through the base and will be attracted to the collector, thereby increasing the collector current. That is, the current in the collector circuit is controlled by controlling the carrier injection at the emitter.

The n-p-n transistor is not unlike the foregoing, except that the polarities are reversed. Now the negatively biased emitter injects electrons. These electrons diffuse through the p-type region and are collected by the positively biased collector. Observe that the process of injection, diffusion, and collection of minority carriers is basic to transistor action.

REFERENCES

1. Shockley, W., "Electrons and Holes in Semiconductors," D. Van Nostrand Company, Inc., New York, 1950.

2. Wilson, A. H., "Semiconductors and Metals; An Introduction to the Electron Theory of Metals," Cambridge University Press, New York, 1939.
3. Pearson, G. L., *Trans. AIEE*, **66**, 209 (1947).
4. Shockley, *op. cit.*, chaps. 1 and 8.

PROBLEMS

15-1. The density of germanium is 5.46 g/cm^3, and its atomic weight is 72.60. Calculate:

a. The number of germanium atoms per cubic centimeter in solid germanium.

b. The number of electrons involved in the valence pair bonds per cubic centimeter.

Hint: Recall that one gram atomic-weight of any substance contains Avogadro's number ($= 6.023 \times 10^{23}$ molecules per mole) of atoms.

15-2. Suppose that 3.6 μg of antimony (pentavalent) are uniformly distributed throughout 100 g of pure germanium, by melting the two materials together. It is supposed that the antimony (Sb) atoms substitute for germanium atoms after solidification. Calculate:

a. The density of antimony atoms.

b. The density of donated electrons.

15-3. Assume that the excess electrons due to the antimony atoms of Prob. 15-2 are fully excited at room temperature. If the mobility of the electrons is $u_e = 3,600$ cm/(sec)(volt)(cm), calculate:

a. The conductivity of the resulting n-type semiconductor.

b. The resistance of a block of such n-type germanium 1 cm long and 1 mm square in cross section.

15-4. Suppose that 0.96 μg of gallium (trivalent) is used in Prob. 15-2 instead of the antimony. Atomic weight of gallium is 69.72. Calculate:

a. The density of gallium atoms.

b. The conductivity of the resulting p-type germanium, taking u_h as 1,700 cm/(sec)(volt)(cm).

15-5. Suppose that both the antimony and the gallium of Probs. 15-2 and 15-4 are added to the same sample of germanium.

a. Is the resulting sample n-type or p-type?

b. Calculate the conductivity.

15-6. If the concentrations of antimony and gallium were such as to provide, respectively, an equal number of electrons and holes, say 3.72×10^{14} per cubic centimeter, determine:

a. The conductivity of the material.

b. What such a material should be called.

CHAPTER 16

TRANSISTORS AS CIRCUIT ELEMENTS

16-1. Introduction.[1] In small signal applications, the analysis of the behavior of a transistor in a circuit is usually accomplished in terms of a four-terminal network equivalent of the transistor. In such an analysis, the performance is characterized by measurements at each of two pairs of terminals. Four variables are obtained, a current and a potential at each pair of terminals. If, therefore, two of the variables are fixed, the other two are thereby specified. Since three terminals are available in the transistor, viz., the emitter, collector, and base, six ways of describing the network exist, depending upon the dependent (or independent) variables which are chosen.

In the case of the vacuum tube, potentials are used as the independent variables, the grid and plate currents being the dependent variables. The d-c sources of power are of relatively low internal impedance in order to provide constant potential, independent of load. In those applications where truly constant potential may be required, electronically regulated power supplies are employed.

The transistor is analyzed as a current-controlled device, the electrode potentials being the dependent variables. It is not possible to generalize considerations for transistors, since the point-contact type transistor is sufficiently different in characteristics from the junction type to require separate considerations. The point-contact transistors are supplied from high impedance sources. This is necessary, since the feedback inherent in these devices is such that, with low source impedances, oscillations may occur. That is, the point-contact transistor may be short-circuit unstable. The junction transistor does not suffer from this limitation.

Although there are six possible sets of curves depicting the potential-current relationships of the transistor, four sets are sufficient to provide the significant properties of the device. A set of the four important static-characteristic curves of a typical point-constant transistor are given in Fig. 16-1. The important static characteristics of a p-n-p diffused junction transistor are given in Fig. 16-2.

As noted, the transistor is a current-controlled device, and its static

451

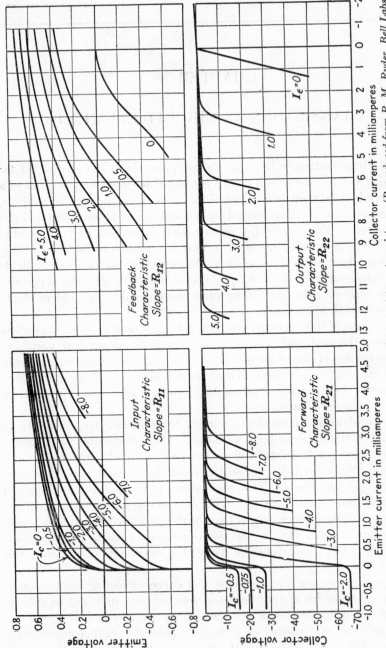

FIG. 16-1. Four sets of static characteristics for the type A contact-type transistor. *(Reproduced from R. M. Ryder, Bell Labs. Record, March, 1949, with permission.)*

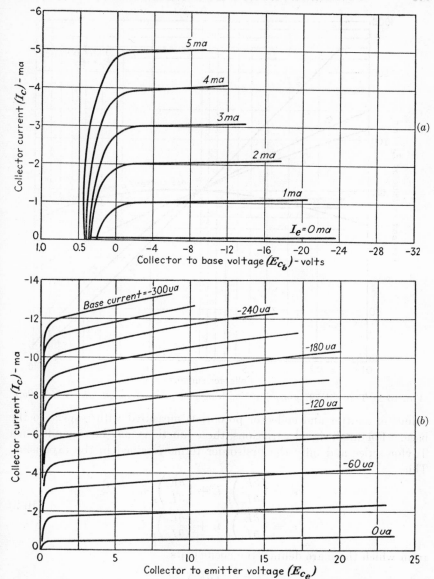

Fig. 16-2a, b.   Characteristics of a 2N64 *p-n-p* junction transistor. (*Raytheon Mfg. Co.*)

characteristics are expressed by the relations

$$E_e = E_e(I_e, I_c)$$
$$E_c = E_c(I_e, I_c)$$

(16-1)

where the independent variables I_e and I_c are the total values of emitter and collector currents, respectively, and E_e and E_c are the corresponding

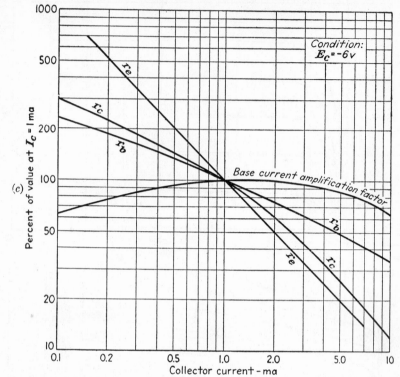

FIG. 16-2c. Type CK727 p-n-p junction-transistor parameters. (*Raytheon Mfg. Co.*)

values of emitter and collector potentials measured with respect to the base. For small signal variations, these functions may be expanded in a Taylor series and only the first-order terms retained in the expansion. Thus

$$e_e = \left(\frac{\partial E_e}{\partial I_e}\right)_{I_c} i_e + \left(\frac{\partial E_e}{\partial I_c}\right)_{I_e} i_c$$
$$e_c = \left(\frac{\partial E_c}{\partial I_e}\right)_{I_c} i_e + \left(\frac{\partial E_c}{\partial I_c}\right)_{I_e} i_c$$

(16-2)

from which there are defined the coefficients

$$r_{11} = \left(\frac{\partial E_e}{\partial I_e}\right)_{I_c}$$
$$r_{12} = \left(\frac{\partial E_e}{\partial I_c}\right)_{I_c}$$
$$r_{21} = \left(\frac{\partial E_c}{\partial I_e}\right)_{I_c}$$
$$r_{22} = \left(\frac{\partial E_c}{\partial I_c}\right)_{I_e}$$

(16-3)

In the light of these expressions, Eqs. (16-2) attain the form

$$e_e = r_{11}i_e + r_{12}i_c$$
$$e_c = r_{21}i_e + r_{22}i_c \tag{16-4}$$

These expressions admit of ready interpretation, as will be seen in the next section.

16-2. Four-terminal-network Considerations. Before considering the transistor equivalent network, certain of the general properties of a four-terminal network are examined. Refer therefore to Fig. 16-3. The general Z-system representation of this network is the equations

$$E_1 = Z_{11}I_1 + Z_{12}I_2$$
$$E_2 = Z_{21}I_1 + Z_{22}I_2 \tag{16-5}$$

Fig. 16-3. A general four-terminal network.

If the network is passive, $Z_{12} = Z_{21}$; but this reciprocal relation does not apply for an active network, or a network which contains vacuum tubes or transistors. In these expressions the currents and potentials are assumed to be sinusoidal, the subscripts 1 referring to the input terminals, and the subscripts 2 referring to the output terminals. The Z coefficients, Z_{11}, Z_{12}, Z_{21}, and Z_{22}, are the open-circuit driving point, feedback, transfer, and output impedances, respectively.

A number of equivalent circuits are possible, each of which is expressible in terms of these same general equations. Three such circuits are given in Fig. 16-4. The controlling equations are given by:

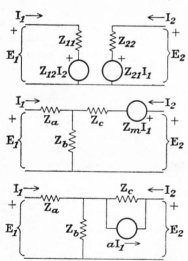

Fig. 16-4. Three networks which are potentially equivalents of the simple four-terminal network.

Fig. 16-4a:
$$E_1 = Z_{11}I_1 + Z_{12}I_2$$
$$E_2 = Z_{21}I_1 + Z_{22}I_2 \tag{16-6a}$$

Fig. 16-4b:
$$E_1 = (Z_a + Z_b)I_1 + Z_bI_2$$
$$E_2 = (Z_b + Z_m)I_1 + (Z_b + Z_c)I_2 \tag{16-6b}$$

Fig. 16-4c:
$$E_1 = (Z_a + Z_b)I_1 + Z_bI_2$$
$$E_2 = (aZ_c + Z_b)I_1 + (Z_b + Z_c)I_2 \tag{16-6c}$$

A number of other equivalent circuits are possible. However, it is found that the three circuits shown may be conveniently applied to the transistor.

In the adaptation of the foregoing general considerations to transistors, it is found convenient to assume that the transistor parameters are purely resistive. This is not a valid approximation at the higher frequencies, and some of the modifications necessary will be discussed later. Also, corresponding to the parameters that appear in Eqs. (16-6), the following transistor parameters, in addition to those already introduced in Eqs. (16-3) and (16-4), will be found important:

A resistance r_e associated with the emitter lead
A resistance r_c associated with the collector lead
A resistance r_b associated with the base lead
A resistance r_m [defined as in Eq. (16-6b)]
The current amplification α defined as $(\partial i_c / \partial i_e)_{E_c}$

The foregoing parameters vary considerably (see Fig. 16-2c) and must be specified at the operating point used; also they are usually positive. Typical values for a point-contact transistor and the junction transistors are given in Table 16-1.

TABLE 16-1

TYPICAL TRANSISTOR OPERATING PARAMETERS

Type		D-c operating points	Circuit parameters
Point contact, n-type		$I_e = 0.6$ ma $I_c = -2$ ma $E_e = 0.7$ volt $E_c = -40$ volts	$r_e = 240$ ohms $r_c = 19,000$ ohms $r_b = 290$ ohms $r_m = 34,000$ ohms $\alpha = 1.79$
n-p-n junction		$I_e = -1.0$ ma $I_c = +0.95$ ma $E_e = -0.1$ volt $E_c = +4.5$ volts	$r_e = 25.9$ ohms $r_c = 1 \times 10^6$ ohms $r_b = 240$ ohms $\alpha = 0.9785$
p-n-p junction		$I_e = 1.0$ ma $I_c = 0.95$ ma $E_e = 0.1$ volt $E_c = -5.0$ volts	$r_e = 32$ ohms $r_c = 1 \times 10^6$ ohms $r_b = 400$ ohms $\alpha = 0.98$

16-3. Grounded-base Equivalent Circuits. Consider a transistor with the emitter and base electrodes as the input terminals and the collector and base electrodes as the output terminals. It is assumed that the electrodes are biased at their prescribed d-c values. The a-c response of the system is specified by Eqs. (16-4), when the factors are appropriately specified. The transistor and three equivalent networks are given in Fig. 16-5. The corresponding controlling equations are the following:

Fig. 16-5b:
$$e_e = r_{11}i_e + r_{12}i_c$$
$$e_c = r_{21}i_e + r_{22}i_c$$
(16-7a)

Fig. 16-5c:
$$e_e = (r_e + r_b)i_e + r_bi_c$$
$$e_c = (r_b + r_m)i_e + (r_b + r_c)i_c$$
(16-7b)

Fig. 16-5d:
$$e_e = (r_e + r_b)i_e + r_bi_c$$
$$e_c = (ar_c + r_b)i_e + (r_b + r_c)i_c$$
(16-7c)

From this set of equations, the following relation is readily deduced:

$$a = \frac{r_m}{r_c} = \frac{r_{21} - r_b}{r_c} \qquad (16\text{-}8)$$

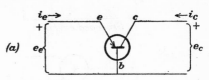

(a)

Also, from the second of Eqs. (16-7b), the quantity α is given by

$$\alpha = \left(\frac{\partial i_c}{\partial i_e}\right)_{E_c} = -\frac{r_{21}}{r_{22}} \qquad (16\text{-}9)$$

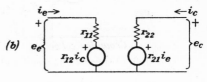

(b)

Then

$$a = \frac{\alpha r_{22} - r_b}{r_c}$$

which is

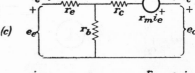

(c)

$$a = \frac{\alpha(r_b + r_c) - r_b}{r_c}$$

$$= \alpha + (\alpha - 1)\frac{r_b}{r_c} \qquad (16\text{-}10)$$

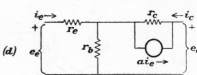

(d)

FIG. 16-5. The grounded-base transistor, and three potentially equivalent networks.

Attention is directed to the fact that, for the point-contact transistor, α may be greater than unity. For the junction transistor, α is slightly less than 1, whence in this case $\alpha \doteq a$.

A rough correspondence can be drawn between transistors and vacuum-tube triodes. If the emitter is considered to be roughly analogous to the cathode, the collector roughly analogous to the plate, and the base roughly analogous to the grid, then the grounded-base transistor is roughly analogous to the grounded-grid triode. The analogy is reasonably good, since both possess low input impedance and high effective internal impedance and no change in signal polarity occurs in transmission.

In fact, by extending the correspondence noted, the corresponding configurations for transistors and vacuum tubes are as illustrated in Fig. 16-6.

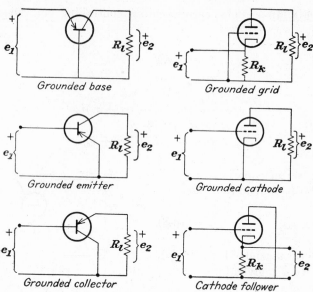

FIG. 16-6. Corresponding configurations for transistors and vacuum tubes.

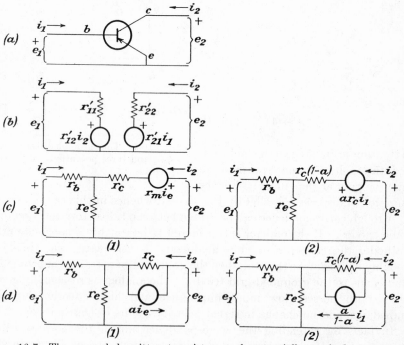

FIG. 16-7. The grounded-emitter transistor, and potentially equivalent network representations.

16-4. Grounded-emitter Equivalent Circuits. The schematic diagram of the circuit and five potentially equivalent networks are given in Fig. 16-7. Actually the two figures labeled c and the two figures labeled d are essentially the same, except that certain circuit parameters have been differently combined. Observe from Fig. 16-7b, c-1, and d-1 and the corresponding forms of Fig. 16-5 that the equivalent-circuit elements for each internal branch of the T equivalent are independent of the connection and depend only on the transistor element. For this reason the same elements r_b, r_e, r_c, and r_m appear in the network configurations, although the manner of interconnection depends on the transistor input and output terminals.

For the circuit of Fig. 16-7b

$$e_1 = r'_{11}i_1 + r'_{12}i_2$$
$$e_2 = r'_{21}i_1 + r'_{22}i_2 \qquad (16\text{-}11)$$

A comparison of Fig. 16-7c-1 with Fig. 16-5c is possible. Note that

$$e_1 = -e_e \qquad i_e = -(i_1 + i_2)$$
$$e_2 = e_c - e_e \qquad i_c = i_2 \qquad (16\text{-}12)$$

Now combine with Eqs. (16-7b) to get

$$e_1 = (r_b + r_e)i_1 + r_e i_2$$
$$e_2 = (r_e - r_m)i_1 + (r_c + r_e - r_m)i_2 \qquad (16\text{-}13)$$

Therefore it follows that

$$r'_{11} = r_b + r_e = r_{12} + (r_{11} - r_{12}) = r_{11}$$
$$r'_{12} = r_e = r_{11} - r_{12}$$
$$r'_{21} = r_e - r_m = r_{11} - r_{21} \qquad (16\text{-}14)$$
$$r'_{22} = r_c + r_e - r_m = r_{11} + r_{22} - r_{12} - r_{21}$$

This permits the elements of the equivalent network of the grounded-emitter transistor to be expressed in terms of the elements of the grounded-base transistor.

A word is in order regarding the grounded-emitter configuration and the corresponding grounded-cathode circuit, as indicated in Fig. 16-6. Both circuits possess comparatively high input impedance and high effective internal impedance, and there is a phase reversal of the signal potential in transmission. For the point-contact transistor for which $\alpha > 1$, the analogy is only moderately exact, since feedback exists. In fact, the open-circuit internal impedance is usually negative, unless resistance is added to the collector lead.

Another feature of the grounded-emitter point-contact transistor is its ability to transmit a signal in the reverse direction with some power gain. That is, power gain is possible with the positions of the input signal and the load reversed in a circuit.

16-5. Grounded-collector Equivalent Circuits. The third possible connection of the transistor is the grounded-collector configuration. A number of potentially equivalent networks of this connection are contained in Fig. 16-8.   Here the circuits c-1 and c-2 are substantially the

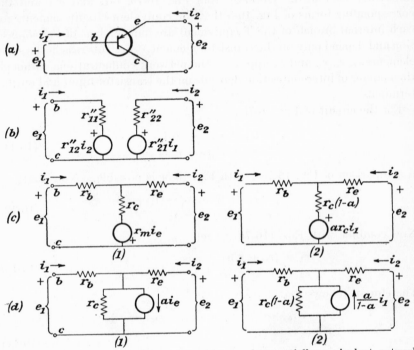

FIG. 16-8. The grounded-collector transistor, and potentially equivalent network representations.

same except for the different combination of several of the circuit parameters.   Similarly, d-1 and d-2 are substantially the same.

From Fig. 16-8b

$$e_1 = r_{11}'' i_1 + r_{12}'' i_2$$
$$e_2 = r_{21}'' i_1 + r_{22}'' i_2 \qquad (16\text{-}15)$$

Note from Figs. 16-5b and 16-8c-1 that

$$e_1 = -e_c \qquad i_c = -(i_1 + i_2)$$
$$e_2 = e_e - e_c \qquad i_e = i_2 \qquad (16\text{-}16)$$

Then Eqs. (16-7b) yield

$$e_1 = (r_b + r_c)i_1 + (r_c - r_m)i_2$$
$$e_2 = r_c i_1 + (r_c + r_e - r_m)i_2 \qquad (16\text{-}17)$$

Therefore

$$r''_{11} = r_b + r_c = r_{22}$$
$$r''_{12} = r_c - r_m = r_{22} - r_{21}$$
$$r''_{21} = r_c = r_{22} - r_{12} \qquad (16\text{-}18)$$
$$r''_{22} = r_c + r_e - r_m = r_{22} + r_{11} - r_{12} - r_{21}$$

The grounded-collector transistor amplifier is analogous to the grounded-plate triode amplifier (the cathode follower). When $a \doteq 1$, the analogy is reasonably good and the device may be used in much the same manner as the cathode follower. The characteristics are high input impedance, low output impedance, and no change in the polarity of the signal potential through the amplifier.

For the point-contact transistor, as a increases, the analogy deteriorates and transmission is possible in both directions. When $a > 2$, the transmission in the reverse direction becomes greater than that in the forward direction. Forward transmission occurs without change in signal polarity, while the polarity is inverted for transmission in the reverse direction.

When the emitter is the output electrode, it does not carry much a-c current. As a result, the power output is somewhat lower than that for other connections of the transistor.

16-6. Power Gain. A number of different power-gain definitions for use with transistor amplifiers are possible. They have been called (1) operating gain, (2) available gain, (3) maximum available gain, (4) insertion gain, and (5) power gain. These definitions are based on considerations of the transistor as a four-terminal network, with a potential generator E_g with internal impedance R_g connected to the input terminals and a resistance load R_l connected to the output terminals.

Refer to Fig. 16-9, which shows the transistor as a four-terminal network, with input source and output load. R_i is the input, or driving-

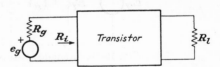

FIG. 16-9. The transistor as a four-terminal network for power-gain calculations.

point, impedance with the load resistance in place. The *available generator power* is defined as the maximum power that the generator can deliver when the transistor is not in the circuit. This occurs when $R_g = R_l$. Then, according to the definitions, with the transistor connected in the circuit,

1. Source operating gain
$$= \frac{\text{actual power delivered by generator}}{\text{available generator power}}$$

2. Available gain

$$= \frac{\text{actual power delivered when } R_l \text{ is adjusted for max output}}{\text{available generator power}}$$

3. Max available gain

$$= \frac{\text{max power output (by matching } R_l \text{ and } R_g \text{ to transistor)}}{\text{available generator power}}$$

4. Insertion gain

$$= \frac{\text{power developed in } R_l \text{ when connected to transistor output}}{\text{power in } R_l \text{ when connected directly to source of power}}$$

5. **Power gain**

$$= \frac{\text{power developed in } R_l \text{ when connected to transistor output}}{\text{actual power delivered by generator}}$$

$$= \frac{\text{insertion gain}}{\text{source operating gain}}$$

Analytical expressions for all five gains are possible for circuits with transistors. The normal power-gain information supplied by the manufacturer is essentially that given by (5). Some details of gain calculations are given in the next section.

16-7. The Grounded-base Amplifier. The equivalent circuit which is most directly analyzed for this configuration is shown in Fig. 16-10. Note that this is simply Fig. 16-5c with the driving source and the load

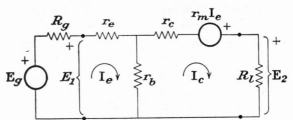

Fig. 16-10. Grounded-base amplifier, equivalent circuit.

in the circuit. It is noted that the following analysis is valid for the junction and point-contact transistors for small-signal l-f operation.

An application of the Kirchhoff potential law yields the equations

$$E_1 = (r_e + r_b)\mathbf{I}_e - r_b\mathbf{I}_c$$
$$0 = -(r_m + r_b)\mathbf{I}_e + (r_b + r_c + R_l)\mathbf{I}_c \qquad (16\text{-}19)$$

The network determinant Δ is

$$\Delta = \begin{vmatrix} r_e + r_b & -r_b \\ -(r_m + r_b) & r_b + r_c + R_l \end{vmatrix}$$
$$= r_b(r_c - r_m + R_l + r_e) + r_e(r_c + R_l) \qquad (16\text{-}20)$$

Expressions for the currents $\mathbf{I}_e$ and $\mathbf{I}_c$ are obtained directly from Eqs.

(16-19) by an application of Cramer's rule.   There results

$$I_e = \frac{\begin{vmatrix} E_1 & -r_b \\ 0 & r_b + r_c + R_l \end{vmatrix}}{\Delta}$$

which is

$$I_e = E_1 \frac{r_b + r_c + R_l}{\Delta} \tag{16-21}$$

Similarly, it follows that

$$I_c = \frac{\begin{vmatrix} r_e + r_b & E_1 \\ -(r_m + r_b) & 0 \end{vmatrix}}{\Delta}$$

which is

$$I_c = E_1 \frac{r_m + r_b}{\Delta} \tag{16-22}$$

The potential amplification K_e is given by

$$K_e = \frac{I_c R_l}{E_1} = \frac{(r_m + r_b) R_l}{r_b(r_c - r_m + R_l + r_e) + r_e(r_c + R_l)} \tag{16-23}$$

The current amplification K_i is given by

$$K_i = \frac{I_c}{I_e} = \frac{r_m + r_b}{r_b + r_c + R_l} \tag{16-24}$$

The input resistance R_i is, from Eq. (16-21),

$$R_i = \frac{E_1}{I_e} = \frac{r_b(r_c - r_m + R_l + r_e) + r_e(r_c + R_l)}{r_b + r_c + R_l}$$

which is

$$R_i = r_e + r_b \frac{r_c - r_m + R_l}{r_b + r_c + R_l} \tag{16-25}$$

The power gain is

$$K_p = \frac{I_c^2 R_l}{I_e^2 R_i} = K_i^2 \frac{R_l}{R_i}$$

By combining with Eqs. (16-24) and (16-25) there results

$$K_p = \frac{(r_m + r_b)^2 R_l}{(r_b + r_c + R_l)[r_b(r_c - r_m + R_l + r_e) + r_e(r_c + R_l)]} \tag{16-26}$$

The effective internal impedance is deduced in the regular way and requires an analysis of the circuit of Fig. 16-11.   The result, which is left as a problem for the student (see Prob. 16-1), is found to be

$$R_t = r_c - r_b \frac{r_m - R_g - r_e}{R_g + r_e + r_b} \tag{16-27}$$

Attention is directed to Table 16-1, which gives typical circuit parameters of point-contact and junction-type transistors. Thus, although the foregoing complete expressions must be used for point-contact transistors and in some circuits using junction transistors, approximate expressions may be deduced for most junction-transistor circuits. In particular for the case where the following approximations are valid:

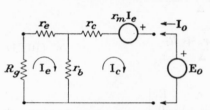

FIG. 16-11. Grounded-base amplifier arranged for determination of the effective internal impedance.

$$r_c - r_m \gg r_e$$
$$r_c \gg r_b \qquad (16\text{-}28)$$
$$r_c - r_m \gg R_l \gg r_e$$

then Eqs. (16-23) to (16-27) reduce to the following expressions:

$$K_e = \frac{aR_l}{r_e + r_b(1 - a)} \qquad (16\text{-}29)$$

$$K_i = a \qquad (16\text{-}30)$$

$$R_i = r_e + r_b(1 - a) \qquad (16\text{-}31)$$

$$K_p = \frac{a^2 R_l}{r_e + r_b(1 - a)} \qquad (16\text{-}32)$$

$$R_t = r_c \frac{r_e + r_b(1 - a) + R_g}{r_e + r_b + R_g} \qquad (16\text{-}33)$$

The foregoing results are tabulated for convenience in Table 16-2.

TABLE 16-2

GROUNDED-BASE FORMULAS

Factor	Exact formulas	Approximate formulas $r_c - r_m \gg r_e$; $r_c \gg r_b$ $r_c - r_m \gg R_l \gg r_e$
K_e	$\dfrac{(r_m - r_b)R_l}{r_b(r_c - r_m + R_l + r_e) + r_e(r_c + R_l)}$	$\dfrac{aR_l}{r_e + r_b(1 - a)}$
K_i	$\dfrac{r_m + r_b}{r_b + r_c + R_l}$	a
R_i	$r_e + r_b \dfrac{r_c - r_m + R_l}{r_b + r_c + R_l}$	$r_e + r_b(1 - a)$
R_t	$r_c - r_b \dfrac{r_m - R_g - r_e}{R_g + r_e + r_b}$	$r_c \dfrac{r_e + r_b(1 - a) + R_g}{r_e + r_b + R_g}$
K_p	$\dfrac{(r_m + r_b)^2 R_l}{(r_b + r_c + R_l)[r_b(r_c - r_m + R_l + r_e) + r_e(r_c + R_l)]}$	$\dfrac{a^2 R_l}{r_e + r_b(1 - a)}$

A similar series of calculations can be carried out for each of the other transistor configurations. The results of such calculations are given in Tables 16-3 and 16-4.

TABLE 16-3

GROUNDED-EMITTER FORMULAS

Factor	Exact formulas	Approximate formulas $r_e - r_m \gg r_e; r_c \gg r_b$ $r_e - r_m \gg R_l \gg r_e$
K_e	$-\dfrac{(r_m - r_e)R_l}{r_b(r_c - r_m + R_l + r_e) + r_e(r_e + R_l)}$	$-\dfrac{aR_l}{r_e + r_b(1 - a)}$
K_i	$\dfrac{r_m - r_e}{r_c - r_m + R_l + r_e}$	$\dfrac{a}{1 - a}$
R_i	$r_b + r_c\dfrac{r_e + R_l}{r_c - r_m + R_l + r_e}$	$r_b + \dfrac{r_e}{1 - a}$
R_t	$r_c - r_m + r_e\dfrac{R_g + r_b + r_m}{R_g + r_b + r_e}$	$r_e(1 - a) + r_e\dfrac{r_m + R_g}{R_g + r_b + r_e}$
K_p	$\dfrac{(r_m - r_e)^2 R_l}{(r_c - r_m + R_l + r_e)[r_b(r_c - r_m + R_l + r_e) + r_e(r_e + R_l)]}$	$\dfrac{a^2 R_l}{(1 - a)[r_e + r_b(1 - a)]}$

TABLE 16-4

GROUNDED-COLLECTOR FORMULAS

Factor	Exact formulas	Approximate formulas $r_e - r_m \gg r_e; r_c \gg r_b$ $r_e - r_m \gg R_l \gg r_e$
K_e	$\dfrac{r_c R_l}{r_b(r_c - r_m + R_l + r_e) + r_c(r_e + R_l)}$	1
K_i	$\dfrac{r_c}{r_c - r_m + R_l + r_e}$	$\dfrac{1}{1 - a}$
R_i	$r_b + r_c\dfrac{r_e + R_l}{r_c - r_m + R_l + r_e}$	$\dfrac{R_l}{1 - a}$
R_t	$r_e + (r_c - r_m)\dfrac{R_g + r_b}{R_g + r_b + r_c}$	$r_e + (r_b + R_g)(1 - a)$
K_p	$\dfrac{r_c^2 R_l}{(r_c - r_m + R_l + r_e)[r_b(r_c - r_m + R_l + r_e) + r_e(r_e + R_l)]}$	$\dfrac{1}{1 - a}$

16-8. Stability Considerations. Stability of a transistor circuit is assured if the input and internal resistances are always positive. Of course, a negative value of either does not necessarily imply oscillation. On the other hand, for completely stable operation, positive values of both R_i and R_t provide a sufficient condition. It is therefore of interest to examine the expressions for input and internal resistances for both junction and point-contact transistors.

For junction transistors under normal operation, the value of a is always less than unity. Thus $r_c - r_m = r_c(1 - a)$ is always positive. An examination of the expressions for R_i and R_t in Tables 6-2 to 6-4 indicates that these have positive values for all positive values of R_l and R_g. If the driving or load impedances are reactive, a calculation for Z_i and Z_t will have positive real parts. Consequently, for the low frequencies, the junction transistor is unconditionally stable.

The situation for the point-contact transistors is quite different, since a exceeds unity, in general; hence $r_c - r_m$ is ordinarily negative. As a result, there is a region of instability. The situation is examined in detail, for the grounded-base connection.

For a positive input resistance of the grounded-base connection, it is necessary that R_i in Eq. (16-25) be positive. Thus

$$r_e + r_b \frac{r_c - r_m + R_l}{r_b + r_c + R_l} > 0$$

But $r_b + r_c + R_l > 0$, whence

$$r_e(r_b + r_c + R_l) + r_b(r_c + R_l) - r_b r_m > 0$$

which becomes, by dividing by $r_b(r_c + R_l)$,

$$\frac{r_e}{r_c + R_l} + \frac{r_e}{r_b} + 1 - \frac{r_m}{r_c + R_l} > 0$$

or

$$1 + \frac{r_e}{r_b} > \frac{r_m - r_e}{r_c + R_l} \tag{16-34}$$

This expression shows that, for input stability, r_b should be as small as possible; R_l should be as high as possible; or add external resistance to r_e to increase this effective value.

For positive internal resistance, from Eq. (16-27), it is required that

$$r_c - r_b \frac{r_m - R_g - r_e}{R_g + r_e + r_b} > 0$$

Write this as

$$r_c(R_g + r_e + r_b) + r_b(R_g + r_e) - r_b r_m > 0$$

Divide by $r_c r_b$ to get

$$\frac{R_g + r_e}{r_b} + 1 - \frac{r_m}{r_c} + \frac{R_g + r_e}{r_c} > 0$$

or

$$1 + (R_g + r_c)\left(\frac{1}{r_b} + \frac{1}{r_e}\right) > \frac{r_m}{r_c} \tag{16-35}$$

To ensure a positive output resistance, r_b should be small; also, $R_g + r_e$ should be large.

The conditions for stability of the other connections are given without proof in Table 16-5. Observe from this table that the addition of resistance in the base lead will ensure a positive input resistance from the grounded-emitter and the grounded-collector circuits. Also, for a positive internal impedance, $R_g + r_b$ should be kept small, or r_e should be

TABLE 16-5

CONDITIONS OF STABILITY

Connection	For positive input resistance	For positive internal resistance
Grounded-base	$1 + \dfrac{r_e}{r_b} > \dfrac{r_m - r_e}{r_c + R_l}$	$1 + (R_g + r_e)\left(\dfrac{1}{r_b} + \dfrac{1}{r_c}\right) > \dfrac{r_m}{r_c}$
Grounded-emitter	$r_b > -\dfrac{r_e}{1 - \dfrac{r_m - r_c}{r_c + r_l}}$	$1 + \dfrac{r_e}{R_g + r_b} + \dfrac{r_e}{r_c} > \dfrac{r_m}{r_c}$
Grounded-collector	$r_b > -r_c\dfrac{r_e + R_l}{r_c - r_m + R_l + r_e}$	$1 + \dfrac{r_e}{R_g + r_b} + \dfrac{r_e}{r_c} > \dfrac{r_m}{r_c}$

made large.   The first of these conditions indicates that the cascading of grounded-emitter or grounded-collector stages might prove troublesome. It should perhaps be noted that this is one of several reasons why point-contact transistors are never used in amplifier applications. Another reason is to be found in the inherently higher noise figure of the point-contact transistor, being roughly 60 db above theoretical, whereas the junction transistor is roughly 20 db above theoretical.

16-9. Cascaded Amplifiers. A junction-transistor amplifier will ordinarily consist of several stages in cascade coupled by passive networks. Care must be exercised in the choice of stages so that one stage does not load the previous stage.   Several representative forms will be discussed in order to bring into focus important operating features of each.

The circuit of Fig. 16-12 illustrates a typical stage of an RC coupled transistor amplifier in a grounded-emitter connection.   As already noted, this connection cor-

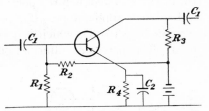

Fig. 16-12. A typical RC coupled amplifier stage.

responds roughly to the grounded-cathode triode circuit.   In this diagram resistors R_1, R_2, and R_3 provide the required bias to the collector and base. Resistor R_4 is employed to reduce the variation of the collector current with temperature.   Capacitors C_1 are coupling capacitors between stages, and C_2 serves to bypass resistor R_4.   Without C_2 in the circuit, the presence of R_4 would result in a reduced amplification.

If the stage is properly designed, resistances R_1 and R_2 are large compared with the input resistance of the stage.   Also, the capacitors C_1 and C_2 will have effectively zero impedance over the frequency range of interest.   Therefore, in so far as audio frequencies are concerned, the approximate circuit does not require the external R's and C's. Consequently, a representative multistage amplifier would have the form illustrated in Fig. 16-13.

The resistors R_c are not required for circuits utilizing junction transistors. They may be required when point-contact transistors are used.

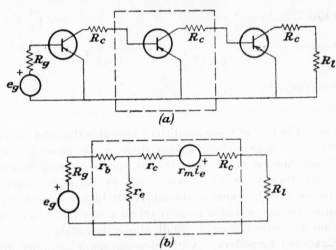

Fig. 16-13. (a) Schematic diagram of a cascaded grounded-emitter amplifier. (b) Equivalent circuit for a single stage.

However, as noted before, point-contact transistors are generally not used in such applications. The equivalent circuit for a single stage is given in Fig. 16-13b, which is precisely of the form illustrated in Fig. 16-10. The pertinent information is contained in Table 16-3. If no loading exists between stages, the over-all results follow from this table. A complete circuit diagram of a cascaded amplifier is given in Fig. 16-14.

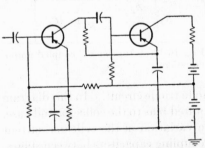

Fig. 16-14. A grounded-emitter grounded-emitter cascade amplifier.

A grounded-base cascaded amplifier may be sketched. In the light of the analogy between this transistor circuit and the grounded-grid triode amplifier, the direct cascading of grounded-base amplifiers is to be avoided, owing to the poor impedance-matching properties at both the input and output terminals. The use of coupling transformers which are designed to match the output resistance of one stage to the input resistance of the next stage permits the satisfactory operation of a cascaded chain of grounded-base amplifiers. Figure 16-15a shows such a trans-

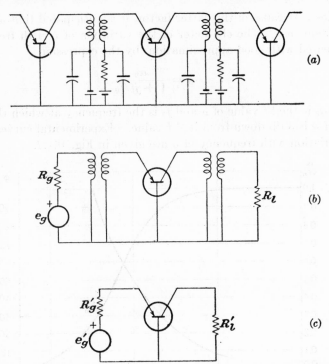

FIG. 16-15. (a) A grounded-base transformer-coupled amplifier, (b) an equivalent single stage, (c) a simplified single stage.

former-coupled amplifier. The equivalent circuit for a-c operation is given in Fig. 16-15b, and the simplified single-stage equivalent circuit is illustrated in Fig. 16-15c. This circuit is precisely that illustrated in Fig. 16-10, the results of importance being contained in Table 16-2.

As in vacuum-tube circuitry, transistor amplifiers of different types may be cascaded. The circuit of Fig. 16-16 illustrates a grounded-emitter grounded-base cascade. A grounded-collector cascade, which is analogous to a chain of cathode-follower circuits, would ordinarily not be used.

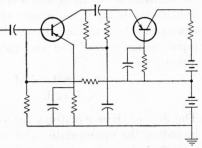

FIG. 16-16. A grounded-emitter grounded-base cascaded amplifier.

16-10. H-F Operation. A number of transistor parameters are frequency-dependent functions. In addition to such external effects as occur through capacitances and feedback, the internal effect resulting from the finite time for the electrons and holes to diffuse through the transistor also becomes important at the high frequencies. Because of this latter factor, it is anticipated that α will vary with frequency. The character of the variation of α with frequency is represented with good approximation[2] by the expression

$$\alpha = \frac{\alpha_0}{1 + jf/f_0} \qquad (16\text{-}36)$$

where α_0 is the l-f value of α and f_0 is the frequency at which the magnitude of α is 3 db down from its l-f value. Experimental curves showing the variation with frequency of α are given in Fig. 16-17.

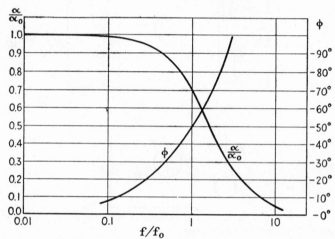

Fig. 16-17. The variation of α with frequency for a typical junction transistor. (*From "Principles of Transistor Circuits,"* [1] *with permission.*)

Consider, for example, the simple grounded-base transistor amplifier, the equivalent circuit of which is illustrated in Fig. 16-10. Owing to the relatively low input impedance of this circuit, the current $\mathbf{I}_e$ is almost a constant. Also in this circuit the $\mathbf{E}_1$ denotes the potential across the input impedance of the amplifier. The circuit equations thus follow directly as

$$\begin{aligned}
(r_e + r_b)\mathbf{I}_e - r_b\mathbf{I}_c &= \mathbf{E}_1 = \mathbf{I}_e\mathbf{Z}_i \\
-(r_b + r_m)\mathbf{I}_e + (r_c + r_b + R_l)\mathbf{I}_c &= 0
\end{aligned} \qquad (16\text{-}37)$$

The first of these equations reduces to the second, as may be shown by including the appropriate value for $\mathbf{Z}_i$ from Table 16-2. Therefore the ratio $\mathbf{I}_c/\mathbf{I}_e$ from the second of these equations is

$$\frac{\mathbf{I}_c}{\mathbf{I}_e} = \frac{r_b + r_m}{r_c + r_b + R_l} \qquad (16\text{-}38)$$

But from the definition of α and Eq. (16-7b),

$$\alpha = \frac{r_b + r_m}{r_b + r_c} \qquad (16\text{-}39)$$

Combine this expression with Eq. (16-38) to find

$$\frac{I_c}{I_e} = \frac{\alpha}{1 + R_l/(r_b + r_c)} \qquad (16\text{-}40)$$

Now combine this with Eq. (16-36) to get

$$\frac{I_c}{I_e} = \frac{\alpha_0}{1 + R_l/(r_b + r_c)} \frac{1}{1 + jf/f_0} \qquad (16\text{-}41)$$

This expression shows that the load cutoff characteristic varies directly with the variations in α.

The situation is actually more complicated[3] than that specified in Eq.

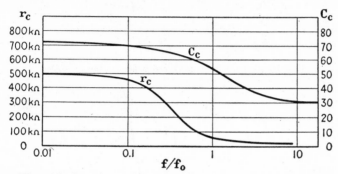

Fig. 16-18. The variation of r_c and C_c with frequency. (*From "Principles of Transistor Circuits,"*[1] *with permission.*)

(16-43) for I_2, since the capacitive component of the collector impedance becomes important at the higher frequencies. Thus at the higher frequencies r_c must be replaced by the parallel combination of r_c and C_c, both of which are functions of the frequency, as shown in Fig. 16-18.

Because of the several effects at the higher frequencies, the input impedance to the junction-transistor circuit will be complex, in general.[4] For the grounded-base circuit, the input impedance is inductive. For the grounded-emitter circuit, the input impedance is capacitive. Representative values of input impedance at $f_0/2$ are

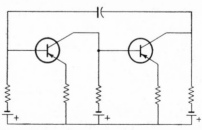

Fig. 16-19. A two-junction transistor multivibrator.

Grounded-base stage: $Z_i \doteq 80 + j50$ ohms
Grounded-emitter stage: $Z_i \doteq 400 - j150$ ohms

16-11. Switching Circuits.[5] The circuit of a junction-transistor multivibrator circuit is given in Fig. 16-19. The circuit makes use of one transistor to effect the switching of a second transistor, in a manner some-what analogous to the action of a two-tube multivibrator. Ordinarily, however, point-contact transistors are used in switching circuits.

The applicability of the point-contact transistor in switching circuits arises from the fact that the addition of resistance in the base circuit of this device will result in a negative input resistance (see Table 16-5). The general form of the results that exist is illustrated in Fig. 16-20,

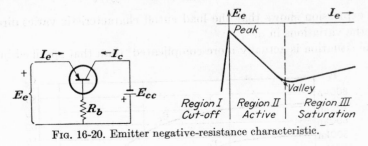

FIG. 16-20. Emitter negative-resistance characteristic.

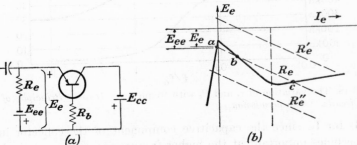

FIG. 16-21. Bistable or trigger characteristics showing trigger requirements.

which gives both the basic circuit and the negative-input-resistance characteristic.

Suppose now that the circuit is connected as shown in Fig. 16-21a. The situation now has the form illustrated in Fig. 16-21b. This figure shows a value of emitter bias E_{ee} and load resistance R_e such that there are three possible equilibrium values of emitter current and potential. Actually only points a and c are stable, being either cutoff (in region I) at a or at a saturation value at c (region III). If stable equilibrium exists at a, a small positive pulse will be enough to switch the circuit to c and a small negative pulse will cause the circuit to switch back to a.

Clearly, too high or too low a value of E_{ee} will raise or lower the R_e curve so that it intersects at only a single point, and no switching will be possible, as only a single equilibrium current exists. Likewise, if R_e is larger than the negative resistance, the load line will intersect at only one point with stable operation. It is important therefore that both E_{ee} and R_e be carefully chosen if bistable (trigger) operation is desired.

The addition of a capacitor to the basic trigger circuit leads to either monostable (gate) or astable (free-running) operation. The several situations are illustrated in Fig. 16-22.

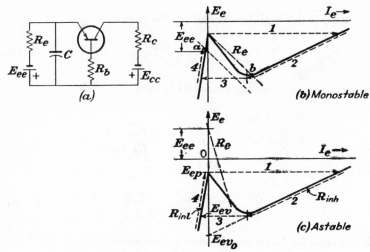

FIG. 16-22. Monostable and astable characteristics.

It is of some interest to analyze the circuit of the astable negative-resistance multivibrator. To do this, one makes the following assumptions,[6] as indicated on Fig. 16-22:

a. The transition along 1 from low-current to high-current negative-resistance region is instantaneous, resulting in zero rise time.

b. Transition along 3 is instantaneous, with zero fall time.

c. Emitter negative-resistance characteristic curve is linear along curves 2 and 4.

Under these assumptions the equivalent circuit for Fig. 16-22c becomes that illustrated in Fig.

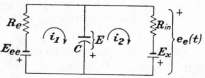

FIG. 16-23. The equivalent circuit of the emitter negative-resistance astable circuit or multivibrator.

16-23, where R_{in} is the emitter-ground resistance corresponding, respectively, to the regions 2 and 4. E_x is the d-c component of potential and corresponds to E_{ev0} for curve 2 and E_{ep} for curve 4.

The loop equations for the network are, in operational form,

$$-E_{ee} = i_1 R_e + \frac{1}{Cp} (i_1 - i_2)$$

$$-E_x = \frac{1}{Cp} (i_1 - i_2) - i_2 R_{in}$$

(16-42)

The solution of these equations is the expression

$$i_2(t) = \frac{E_x - E(0+)}{R_{in}} e^{-\beta t} + \frac{E_x - E_{ee}}{R_e + R_{in}} (1 - e^{-\beta t}) \qquad (16\text{-}43)$$

where $E(0+)$ is the initial potential on the capacitor and

$$\beta = \frac{R_e + R_{in}}{R_e R_{in} C} \qquad (16\text{-}44)$$

The instantaneous emitter potential is then

$$
\begin{aligned}
e_e(t) &= E_x - i_2 R_{in} \\
&= E_x + [E(0+) - E_x]e^{-\beta t} + \frac{E_{ee} - E_x}{R_e + R_{in}} (1 - e^{-\beta t}) \qquad (16\text{-}45)
\end{aligned}
$$

Solving for t gives

$$t = \frac{1}{\beta} \ln \frac{E(0+)(R_e + R_{in}) - (E_x R_e + E_{ee} R_{in})}{e_e(t)(R_e + R_{in}) - (E_x R_e + E_{ee} R_{in})} \qquad (16\text{-}46)$$

This is the time for the potential across the capacitor to change from one limiting value to another. Specifically, in region 4, the low-current region $e_e(t)$ varies from E_{ev} to E_{ep}, and

$$
\begin{aligned}
E(0+) &= E_{ev} \\
e_e(t) &= E_{ep} \qquad (16\text{-}47) \\
E_x &= E_{ep}
\end{aligned}
$$

and Eq. (16-47) yields

$$t_l = \frac{1}{\beta_l} \ln \frac{E_{ev}(R_e + R_{inl}) - (E_{ep} R_e + E_{ee} R_{inl})}{E_{ep}(R_e + R_{inl}) - (E_{ep} R_e + E_{ee} R_{inl})} \qquad (16\text{-}48)$$

Likewise in the high-current region 2, $e_e(t)$ varies between E_{ep} and E_{ev}, and $E(0+) = E_{ep}$; $e_e(t) = E_{ev}$; $E_x = E_{ev0}$; and Eq. (16-47) yields

$$t_h = \frac{1}{\beta_h} \ln \frac{E_{ep}(R_e + R_{inh}) - (E_{ev0} R_e + E_{ee} R_{inh})}{E_{ev}(R_e + R_{inh}) - (E_{ev0} R_e + E_{ee} R_{inh})} \qquad (16\text{-}49)$$

The total period is

$$t = t_l + t_h \qquad (16\text{-}50)$$

For the monostable circuit without the capacitor, the application of a trigger increases the effective E_{ee}, and the operating point a is raised by raising the load line. When it reaches the turning point, it would transfer to b, with a rapid change in potential and current, if stray capacitances are small. The capacitor potential E_e cannot change rapidly; so, instead of moving to b, it moves along line 1 to the characteristic. (In actual

practice, the transfer to *b* does not occur, because of the stray capacitances.)   The capacitor discharges along 2 to the second turning point,
where the emitter is again short-circuited.   The operating point snaps
along 3 to intersect region I portion of the curve.   This point slowly
moves along 4 back to the d-c stable
operating point.   Hence, a single
trigger causes a complete cycle of
operation.   The current and potential variations have the form illustrated in Fig. 16-24.   Observe that
the waveshape is not particularly
good.   An actual transistor monostable or gate circuit and its output
pulse are illustrated in Fig. 16-25.

When E_{ee} and R_e are chosen in the
manner illustrated in Fig. 16-22c so
that R_e intersects the negative-
resistance portion, astable or free-

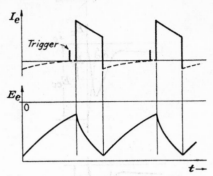

Fig. 16-24.   Idealized monostable re-
laxation-circuit waveforms.

running operation results.   Now C provides an a-c short circuit, so that
paths 1 to 4 are followed continuously.

It should be observed also from Table 16-5 that the internal impedance
of the grounded-base connection may be made negative by including a

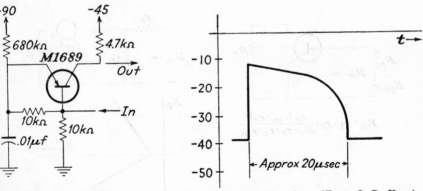

Fig. 16-25. A monostable gate circuit, and the output pulse.   [*From J. R. Harris,
Proc. IRE*, **24**, 1597 (1952).]

resistance in the base.   The general form of the internal-impedance characteristics is given in Fig. 16-26.   The effect of varying E_{cc} and R_c are
illustrated in these figures in providing different-type switching operations.

The negative-resistance characteristic of the grounded-emitter connection is illustrated in Fig. 16-27.   Therefore this connection may also
be used for switching operations.

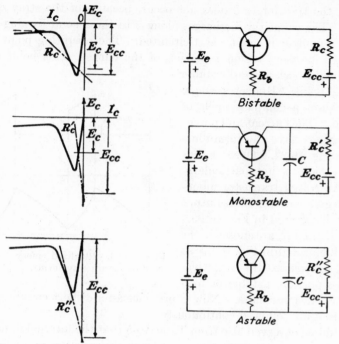

Fig. 16-26. Collector connection switching circuits.

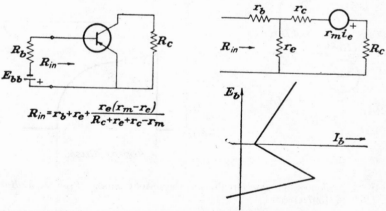

$$R_{in} = r_b + r_e + \frac{r_e(r_m - r_e)}{R_c + r_e + r_c - r_m}$$

Fig. 16-27. The base negative-resistance characteristics and switching circuit.

It should be noted that the foregoing circuits are temperature-sensitive, owing to the temperature sensitivity of point-contact transistors. The effect of temperature is to cause the displacement of the emitter negative-resistance characteristic, illustrated in Fig. 16-20, to move up or down, along the potential axis. The result of such displacements can cause a variety of undesirable features.   For example, the triggering sensitivity will change owing to the change of the intersection of the characteristic with the load line.   Also, such shifts might cause what is known as "lockup" of bistable circuits into either the high- or low-current position

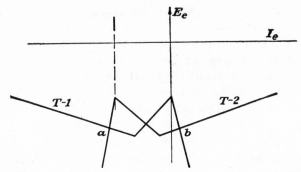

Fig. 16-28. The combined negative-resistance characteristic of the back-back connection of point-contact transistors.

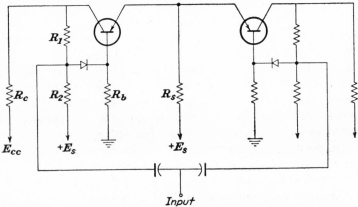

Fig. 16-29. The circuit diagram of a stabilized back-back trigger circuit.

by changing the bistable circuit into a monostable circuit.   The reverse process may also happen.

The foregoing temperature dependence can be largely removed by connecting two point-contact transistors in a back-to-back scheme.   The essential feature of this back-to-back scheme when used in a monostable connection is illustrated in Fig. 16-28, for the proper choice of circuit parameters.   With this connection, whenever transistor $T1$ is in an "off" state, $T2$ is in its "on" condition, as at the stable point b; and when $T1$ is "on," $T2$ is "off," as at stable point a.   The advantages of this type of circuit over the more usual single-transistor arrangement is its speed of operation and ease of triggering at high rates.   The complete schematic diagram of one possible arrangement is given in Fig. 16-29.*   Isolating crystal diodes are used.   The circuit responds to positive triggering pulses.

16-12. Duality between Triode and Transistors.[7] A critical examination of the properties of point-contact transistors will indicate some striking "dual" characteristics with the triode.   A number of such dual properties will be discussed.

Consider the grid and cathode as input terminals of a triode and the base and emitter as input terminals of a point-contact transistor.   The grid of the triode will conduct if biased in the forward direction (positively) and will normally not conduct if biased in the reverse direction. Correspondingly, the emitter of the transistor will conduct when biased in the forward direction and will show little conduction in the reverse direction.   However when both devices are to be used as amplifiers, the grid is biased in the reverse direction and the emitter is biased in the forward direction.

An inspection of the characteristics of the grounded-grid triode and the grounded-base point-contact transistor will indicate a number of properties which amount to an interchange of potential and current characteristics between the two.   For example, the grid and the plate of the triode are normally biased in the reverse and forward directions, respectively. This results in a high input impedance and a fairly low output impedance. The emitter and collector, on the other hand, are usually biased in the forward and reverse directions, respectively, with a resulting low input impedance and a relatively high output impedance.   The principal nonlinearity in the grid circuit in the triode occurs when the grid potential is allowed to swing through zero and the grid begins to draw current. The corresponding nonlinearity in the emitter circuit of the transistor occurs when the emitter current is allowed to swing through zero and the emitter potential begins to rise.

Another feature of importance is the duality between the amplification factor μ of the triode and the current amplification factor α of the transistor.   This follows from Eq. (1-18) for the triode and Eq. (16-9) for the transistor, where, in the case of the triode, μ is a measure of the ratio of the displacement of the plate characteristics to the right, for a specified change in E_c, whereas, for the transistor, α is a measure of the displacement of the current characteristic to the right for a specified change in I_e.

Actually, the dual properties are only approximately valid.   Despite this fact, the use of the principles of duality to find a circuit for use with a transistor in order to achieve operation reasonably like that for a given vacuum-tube circuit is often very useful and rewarding.

* This method of stabilization and the circuit illustrated were provided by James V. B. Cooper of the department of electrical engineering, Syracuse University.

16-13. Duality Principles and Circuit Design. As discussed in the foregoing section, a transistor is a reasonably approximate dual of a triode. It is possible to show* that, by replacing a given network by its dual, the response characteristics of two networks are the same. Consequently, by replacing a triode by its dual (the transistor), and by replacing the triode network by its dual, the response characteristics of the system are unchanged. Several examples of the use of duality principles in deducing transistor circuits will be given.

Before examining these examples, it is very important to call attention to certain significant consequences of duality. Specifically, the dual of a potential source with a high internal impedance is a current source with low shunting impedance. If a given transistor circuit is to be potential driven through a high impedance, one may then not desire an exact dual; otherwise the driving source will be virtually short-circuited. An alternative way of describing the same situation is the following: If the input impedance to an amplifier is high, the input impedance to its transistor dual will be low. Clearly, if a transistor circuit is desired which essentially replaces the triode with the transistor, it must also provide a high input impedance. Consequently, what is more often done is to replace the network by its dual, but the transistor connection is that which maintains the general impedance characteristics of the triode connection.

Specifically, the principles of duality are important in indicating the general character of a current-driven network which is dually related to a given potential-driven one. However, what is more often desired is to achieve circuits which are transistor equivalents of given circuits. If a transistorized version of a given network is desired, then often just a relatively simple replacement of a triode by a transistor is sufficient. In this case the transistor connection must be chosen to provide the proper impedance levels.

Several examples are given which illustrate these points.

Example 1. *The Cathode Follower.* Figure 16-30 illustrates the cathode follower, its dual, and the transistor analog. The input and output impedance levels are indicated on these diagrams.

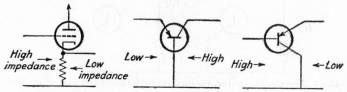

Fig. 16-30. The cathode follower, its transistor dual, the transistor analog.

* W. R. LePage and S. Seely, "General Network Analysis," McGraw-Hill Book Company, Inc., New York. 1952.

Example 2. *The Colpitts Oscillator.* Figure 16-31 illustrates the Colpitts oscillator and the dual with transistor analog.

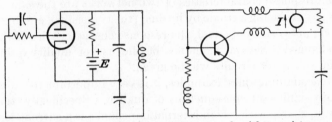

FIG. 16-31. The Colpitts oscillator; its dual network with transistor analog.

Example 3. *The Multivibrator.* Figure 16-32 shows the multivibrator, the dual circuit with transistor analog, and the modification for potential source drive. These circuits should be compared with that in Fig. 16-19.

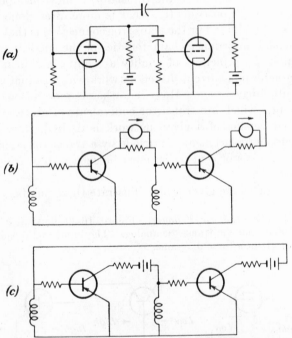

FIG. 16-32. (*a*) The multivibrator, (*b*) its dual with transistor analog, (*c*) the potential-driven equivalent of (*b*).

Example 4. The circuits of Fig. 16-33 are a group of transistorized triode circuits.

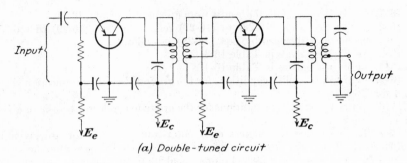

(a) Double-tuned circuit

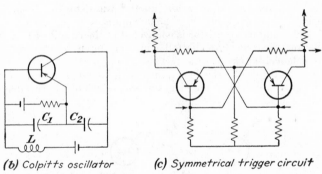

(b) Colpitts oscillator   *(c) Symmetrical trigger circuit*

FIG. 16-33. Transistorized triode circuits.

REFERENCES

1. For general references, see:
   Shockley, W., "Electrons and Holes in Semiconductors," D. Van Nostrand Company, Inc., New York, 1950.
   Shea, R. F., *et al.*, "Principles of Transistor Circuits," John Wiley & Sons, Inc., New York, 1953.
   Proc. IRE, Transistor Issue, **40**(11) (1952).
2. Pritchard, R. L., *Proc. IRE*, **40**, 1476 (1952).
   Thomas, D. E., *Proc. IRE*, **40**, 1481 (1952).
3. Shea, *op. cit.*, p. 198.
4. Early, J. M., *Bell System Tech. J.*, **32**, 1271 (1953).
5. Anderson, A. E., *Proc. IRE*, **40**, 1541 (1952).
   Lo, A. W., *Proc. IRE*, **40**, 1531 (1952).
6. McDuffie, Jr., G. E., *Proc. IRE*, **40**, 1487 (1952).
7. Wallace, Jr., R. L., and G. Raisbeck, *Bell System Tech. J.*, **30**, 381 (1951).

PROBLEMS

16-1. Verify that Eq. (16-27) results from an analysis of Fig. 16-11.

16-2. Verify that Eqs. (16-23) to (16-27) reduce to Eqs. (16-29) to (16-33) when the conditions specified by Eqs. (16-28) are valid.

16-3. Verify the entries in Table 16-3.

16-4. Verify the entries in Table 16-4.

16-5. Verify the stability conditions for the grounded-emitter connection given in Table 16-5.

16-6. Verify the stability conditions for the grounded-collector transistor given in Table 16-5.

16-7. The operating parameters of a point-contact transistor are given in Table 16-1. This transistor is used in a simple grounded-base amplifier with $R_g = 1,000$ ohms and $R_l = 20,000$ ohms. Calculate the following: (a) current gain, (b) potential gain, (c) power gain, (d) input resistance, (e) effective internal resistance.

16-8. Repeat Prob. 16-7 for an n-p-n junction transistor in a grounded-emitter circuit, with $R_g = 25,000$ ohms, $R_l = 25,000$ ohms.

16-9. A point-contact transistor is connected in the circuit of Fig. 16-13, with $R_c = 17,000$ ohms. Calculate the following: (a) input resistance, (b) effective internal impedance, (c) power gain.

16-10. A grounded-base cascade amplifier with interstage transformer coupling is illustrated in the accompanying diagram. Also included in this diagram is the equivalent circuit for one of the stages.

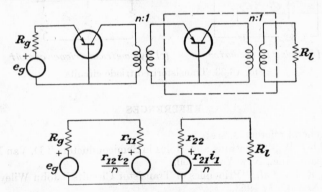

a. Verify that the equivalent circuit is that illustrated.

b. Show that the maximum insertion gain of the network exists when

$$r_{11} = r_{22}/n^2$$

and is $K_{\text{insert,max}} = \frac{1}{4}\alpha^2(r_{22}/r_{11})$.

16-11. Find an expression for i_2 of the grounded-emitter transistor amplifier under the conditions for which α is represented by Eq. (16-36).

16-12. The theoretically possible cascading arrangements are given in the following table:

GB-GB	GE-GB	GC-GB
GB-GE	GE-GE	GC-GE
GB-GC	GE-GC	GC-GC

Examine the practicability of each arrangement for point-contact transistors in the light of (a) inherent stability, (b) impedance mismatch.

16-13. Repeat Prob. 16-12 for junction transistors.

16-14. Consider the grounded-emitter junction transistor under conditions of a short-circuited output (zero resistance load).

 a. Show that the current gain K_{iss} under these conditions is nearly $a/(1 - a)$.

 b. Combine this expression with Eq. (16-36) for the variation of α with frequency, and deduce an expression which gives the h-f cutoff in terms of the mid-frequency value.

16-15. An n-p-n junction transistor has the parameter values given in Table 16-1, with the additional data at 1 kc: $C_c = 40\ \mu\mu f$, $\alpha = 0.9$, $f_0 = 1$ Mc, collector-base capacitance = 15 $\mu\mu f$. This transistor is used in a grounded-base tuned amplifier. A parallel resonant circuit with $Q = 50$ and shunt resistance of 50,000 ohms is used as the load. Calculate the input impedance over a 10-kc band, when the resonant frequency is 200 kc, 500 kc. Assume that the Q of the load is independent of the frequency.

16-16. The experimentally obtained emitter negative-resistance characteristic of an M-1689 point-contact transistor with the associated circuit is illustrated.*

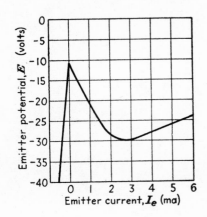

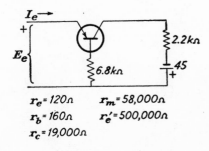

$r_e = 120\Omega$ $r_m = 58,000\Omega$
$r_b = 160\Omega$ $r_e' = 500,000\Omega$
$r_c = 19,000\Omega$

 a. Over what limiting values of R_e is an astable (free-running) circuit possible?

 b. For the value $R_e = 500$ kilohms, $C = 0.01\ \mu f$, evaluate the total period of oscillation.

* A. E. Anderson, *Proc. IRE*, **40**, 1541 (1952).

16-17. *a.* Draw the circuit of the tuned plate oscillator.

b. Draw a transistorized equivalent of the circuit.

c. Draw the circuit having the dual network and transistor analog.

16-18. Discuss the operation of the transistor crystal oscillator shown in the accompanying diagram. Show that the impedance looking into terminals a-a may be negative.

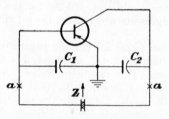

16-19. Consider the general operational amplifier of Fig. 6-13.

a. Draw the circuit of the dual network-transistor analog network.

b. Prove that the resulting network will have general operational characteristics.

APPENDIX A

NOTES ON GENERAL NETWORK ANALYSIS*

A-1. Reference Conditions and Notation. Mention is made at several points in the text of the reference positive polarity and reference current direction. It is important to examine the significance of these terms and their relationship to general network analysis.

The solution of a network problem amounts to the finding of expressions for the potentials and currents at various points in the circuit. Sometimes charges and flux linkages are required also. For the a-c case the directions of the currents and the polarities of the potentials are continually reversing. Algebraic notation must always be employed.

All measurable electrical quantities (current, potential, etc.) are called *physical entities*. Their algebraic representations (e, i, etc.) are called *algebraic quantities*. Physical entities change their direction or polarity, while their algebraic representation changes their sense (algebraic sign).

The direction of current, when the symbol which represents it is positive, is called its *reference direction*. Similarly, the polarity of a potential, when the symbol which represents it is positive, is called its *reference polarity*. In this latter case, the $+$ and $-$ signs not only are used to designate the potential but also are used in algebraic interpretations. The two uses should not be confused. The general term *reference condition* is used to imply either a reference direction or a reference polarity. Thus, in general terms, the reference condition of a physical entity corresponds with the positive sense of the algebraic quantity which represents it.

A-2. Notation for Sinors. It is customary in the discussion of amplifier response to assume that the input signal is sinusoidal and of the general form

$$e_1 = \sqrt{2}\, E_1 \sin\, (\omega t + \theta)$$

Ordinarily the calculations are not carried out in terms of the trigonometric functions, but use is made of complex-number theory in a-c network analysis. The use of complex-number theory stems from the fact

---

* For more detail, refer to W. R. LePage and S. Seely, "General Network Analysis," McGraw-Hill Book Company, Inc., New York, 1952.

that the sinusoid may be expressed in exponential form by the relation

$$e_1 = \sqrt{2}\, E_1 \sin\,(\omega t + \theta_1) = \mathrm{Im}\,\sqrt{2}\, E_1 e^{j(\omega t + \theta_1)} \qquad \text{(A-1)}$$

where Im denotes that the imaginary part of the Euler* expansion of this quantity is chosen. Now, it is found in subsequent analysis that the essential information relating to the sinusoid is contained in the quantity $E_1 e^{j\theta_1}$, which does not include the time. This permits the analysis to be carried out in terms of complex-number theory and the associated algebraic manipulations of this discipline, and, as a final step, the results may be correlated with, and written in trigonometric form involving the time.

Many of the results obtained by the use of complex numbers can be obtained through geometric means alone, by plotting the complex numbers as directed lines in a plane. The directed lines may be regarded as vectors in two dimensions. However, confusion with three-dimensional vectors can arise. Therefore, in electrical-engineering applications, quantities having two dimensions (complex quantities) are called *phasor* quantities. As discussed, therefore, phasor quantities can be used to represent symbolically sinusoidal functions of time. This is not the only use of them, however. For example, the impedance function $R + j\omega L$ of a simple series circuit is a complex number but represents quite a different quantity from the complex number which symbolically represents the sinusoid. Those complex quantities (phasor quantities) which symbolically represent sinusoidal functions are called *sinors*. Thus a sinor is a special type of phasor.

In setting up the correspondence between a sinor and a sinusoid, the sine form of writing the sinusoid is chosen arbitrarily. The correspondence between a sinor and sinusoid is written

$$E_1 e^{j\theta_1} \text{ symbolically represents } \sqrt{2}\, E_1 \sin\,(\omega t + \theta_1) \qquad \text{(A-2)}$$

The multiplier is introduced to make E_1 the effective value.

Emphasis is placed on the fact that either the sine or the cosine function could be used on the right-hand side of relation (A-2). However, in this text the foregoing symbolism *always* means the sine function. Without adherence to such a rule, the use of sinors and complex notation could lead to confusion.

Since a sinor is a complex quantity which symbolically represents a sinusoidally varying quantity, the previous definition of a reference condition would indicate that a sinor does not have a reference condition, since it is not a varying quantity. It is a directed line in a plane, but this direction is not an indication of a reference condition. It is related, however, to the reference condition in an indirect way, to be explained.

Figure A-1 illustrates how a potential or current is represented, first

* The Euler expansion of an exponential has the form $Ee^{j\alpha} = E(\cos\alpha + j\sin\alpha)$.

by a sinusoidal wave, and then in turn by a sinor. The meaning of the sinusoidal wave, in terms of the physical conditions shown on the circuit diagram, is discussed in Sec. A-1. The sinors **E** and **I** are interpreted by

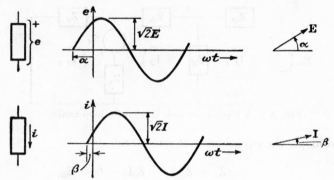

Fig. A-1. Interpretation of sinor notation in terms of a sinusoidal wave.

referring them to the sinusoidal waves; thus

$$\text{E symbolizes } e = \sqrt{2}\, E \sin\,(\omega t + \alpha)$$
$$\text{I symbolizes } i = \sqrt{2}\, I \sin\,(\omega t + \beta) \tag{A-3}$$

This gives meaning to the reference conditions, in terms of the instantaneous variables which are symbolized by the sinors.

A slightly different practice is shown in Fig. A-2. The sinor symbol is used on the circuit diagram, and the intermediate sinusoidal wave is omitted. This system is convenient, as it is more direct than that illustrated in Fig. A-1. In the event of any question of interpretation, the thought sequence indicated in Fig. A-1 is implied by Fig. A-2.

Double subscripts may be used on sinor symbols, to imply the reference condition for the variable which it symbolizes. In fact, it may be noted that identical systems of notation are applicable to instantaneous variables and sinors. The only difference is that, when applied to sinors, the connection with reference conditions

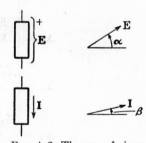

Fig. A-2. The use of sinor symbols on a circuit diagram to imply the reference conditions shown in Fig. A-1.

is indirect, through the intermediate variable quantity, as in Fig. A-1.

A-3. Loop Analysis. The general complete solution of a network by the loop method of analysis may be most easily presented in terms of a specific example. The circuit of Fig. A-3 serves this purpose. All sources are potential sources, and all have the same frequency. The impedances are drawn as boxes for simplicity. Each box is assumed to be no more complicated than a series combination of resistance, inductance, and capacitance.

By an application of the Kirchhoff potential law around each of the

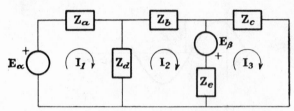

FIG. A-3. A typical network labeled for loop analysis.

indicated loops, the equations that result are

$$(Z_a + Z_d)I_1 - Z_dI_2 + 0 = E_\alpha$$
$$-Z_dI_1 + (Z_b + Z_d + Z_e)I_2 - Z_eI_3 = E_\beta \qquad \text{(A-4)}$$
$$0 - Z_eI_2 + (Z_c + Z_e)I_3 = -E_\beta$$

The solutions of Eqs. (A-4) are most easily written in terms of determinants, by the application of Cramer's rule. For writing these solutions, it is convenient to define certain symbols to represent determinants. These are

$$\Delta = \begin{vmatrix} Z_a + Z_d & -Z_d & 0 \\ -Z_d & Z_b + Z_d + Z_e & -Z_e \\ 0 & -Z_e & Z_c + Z_e \end{vmatrix}$$

$$\Delta_1 = \begin{vmatrix} E_\alpha & -Z_d & 0 \\ E_\beta & Z_b + Z_d + Z_e & -Z_e \\ -E_\beta & -Z_e & Z_c + Z_e \end{vmatrix}$$

$$\Delta_2 = \begin{vmatrix} Z_a + Z_d & E_\alpha & 0 \\ -Z_d & E_\beta & -Z_e \\ 0 & -E_\beta & Z_c + Z_e \end{vmatrix} \qquad \text{(A-5)}$$

$$\Delta_3 = \begin{vmatrix} Z_a + Z_d & -Z_d & E_\alpha \\ -Z_d & Z_d + Z_b + Z_e & E_\beta \\ 0 & -Z_e & -E_\beta \end{vmatrix}$$

In terms of these quantities, the three unknown currents are

$$I_1 = \frac{\Delta_1}{\Delta} \qquad I_2 = \frac{\Delta_2}{\Delta} \qquad I_3 = \frac{\Delta_3}{\Delta} \qquad \text{(A-6)}$$

by the application of Cramer's rule.

It should be realized that, even though the example above is for three loops, the general form of the equations will be similar for a circuit of N loops. For the network with N loops, the general equations will be of the form

$$\varrho_{11}I_1 + \varrho_{12}I_2 + \cdots + \varrho_{1N}I_N = E_1$$
$$\varrho_{21}I_2 + \varrho_{22}I_2 + \cdots + \varrho_{2N}I_N = E_2$$
$$\cdots \cdots \cdots \cdots \cdots \cdots \cdots \cdots \cdots \cdots$$
$$\varrho_{N1}I_1 + \varrho_{N2}I_2 + \cdots + \varrho_{NN}I_N = E_N \tag{A-7}$$

In these equations, the quantities E_1, E_2, . . . denote the algebraic sums of all the sources on the various loop peripheries or contours, with a potential rise in the loop-current direction taken as positive.

The factors ϱ_{pq} have the dimensions of impedance. When $p = q$, they are the sum of all impedances on a loop contour. When $p \neq q$, ϱ_{pq} is $+$ or $-$ the impedance in the branch common to loops p and q, according as these loop currents are in the same or opposite directions in the common impedance. The ϱ coefficients are given the name *copedance*, a contraction for the phrase, coefficient of impedance.

As an illustration, the analysis of Fig. A-3 may be written in the generalized notation of Eqs. (A-7). In this case

$$\varrho_{11}I_1 + \varrho_{12}I_2 + \varrho_{13}I_3 = E_1$$
$$\varrho_{21}I_1 + \varrho_{22}I_2 + \varrho_{23}I_3 = E_2$$
$$\varrho_{31}I_1 + \varrho_{32}I_2 + \varrho_{33}I_3 = E_3 \tag{A-8}$$

where

$$\begin{array}{lll} \varrho_{11} = Z_a + Z_c & \varrho_{21} = \varrho_{12} = -Z_d & E_1 = E_\alpha \\ \varrho_{22} = Z_b + Z_d + Z_e & \varrho_{31} = \varrho_{13} = 0 & E_2 = E_\beta \\ \varrho_{33} = Z_c + Z_e & \varrho_{23} = \varrho_{32} = -Z_e & E_3 = -E_\beta \end{array} \tag{A-9}$$

The resulting expressions are identical with those in Eq. (A-4), as they must be.

Special attention must be given when magnetic coupling exists, as the formulas for the copedances off the diagonal of the determinants are affected. In this connection, refer to Fig. A-4. Without proof, it is noted that the sign to be associated with the term $j\omega M$ representing the effect of the mutual coupling is positive if the currents enter or leave the dotted terminals and is negative if one current enters and the second current leaves the dotted terminal. For the case illustrated

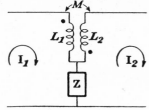

Fig. A-4. Example of magnetic coupling.

$$\varrho_{21} = \varrho_{12} = -Z + j\omega M \tag{A-10}$$

A-4. Junction Analysis. The presentation of the junction analysis follows the same scheme as used for the loop analysis. All sources have the same frequency, and all are current sources. The admittances are drawn as boxes for simplicity. Each box is assumed to be no more complicated than a parallel combination of resistance, inductance, and capacitance.

The rules for writing the equilibrium equations, which are based on the

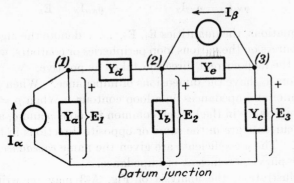

Fig. A-5. A typical network labeled for junction analysis.

Kirchhoff current law, are applied to the network of Fig. A-5. The equations are the following, when the current at each junction is equated to zero:

$$(\mathbf{Y}_a + \mathbf{Y}_d)\mathbf{E}_1 - \mathbf{Y}_d\mathbf{E}_2 + 0 = \mathbf{I}_\alpha$$
$$-\mathbf{Y}_d\mathbf{E}_1 + (\mathbf{Y}_b + \mathbf{Y}_d + \mathbf{Y}_e)\mathbf{E}_2 - \mathbf{Y}_e\mathbf{E}_3 = \mathbf{I}_\beta \qquad \text{(A-11)}$$
$$0 - \mathbf{Y}_e\mathbf{E}_2 + (\mathbf{Y}_c + \mathbf{Y}_e)\mathbf{E}_3 = -\mathbf{I}_\beta$$

The solution of this set of simultaneous equations is given by Cramer's rule. Write the determinants

$$\Delta = \begin{vmatrix} \mathbf{Y}_a + \mathbf{Y}_d & -\mathbf{Y}_d & 0 \\ -\mathbf{Y}_d & \mathbf{Y}_b + \mathbf{Y}_d + \mathbf{Y}_e & -\mathbf{Y}_e \\ 0 & -\mathbf{Y}_e & \mathbf{Y}_c + \mathbf{Y}_e \end{vmatrix}$$

$$\Delta_1 = \begin{vmatrix} \mathbf{I}_\alpha & -\mathbf{Y}_d & 0 \\ \mathbf{I}_\beta & \mathbf{Y}_b + \mathbf{Y}_d + \mathbf{Y}_e & -\mathbf{Y}_e \\ -\mathbf{I}_\beta & -\mathbf{Y}_e & \mathbf{Y}_c + \mathbf{Y}_e \end{vmatrix}$$

$$\Delta_2 = \begin{vmatrix} \mathbf{Y}_a + \mathbf{Y}_d & \mathbf{I}_\alpha & 0 \\ -\mathbf{Y}_d & \mathbf{I}_\beta & -\mathbf{Y}_e \\ 0 & -\mathbf{I}_\beta & \mathbf{Y}_c + \mathbf{Y}_e \end{vmatrix} \qquad \text{(A-12)}$$

$$\Delta_3 = \begin{vmatrix} \mathbf{Y}_a + \mathbf{Y}_d & -\mathbf{Y}_d & \mathbf{I}_\alpha \\ -\mathbf{Y}_d & \mathbf{Y}_b + \mathbf{Y}_d + \mathbf{Y}_e & \mathbf{I}_\beta \\ 0 & -\mathbf{Y}_e & -\mathbf{I}_\beta \end{vmatrix}$$

In terms of these determinants, the unknown potentials are given by the ratios

$$\mathbf{E}_1 = \frac{\Delta_1}{\Delta} \qquad \mathbf{E}_2 = \frac{\Delta_2}{\Delta} \qquad \mathbf{E}_3 = \frac{\Delta_3}{\Delta} \qquad \text{(A-13)}$$

by the application of Cramer's rule.

This type of solution can be written for a general network of N junctions plus the datum junction, by the set of equations

$$\delta_{11}E_1 + \delta_{12}E_2 + \cdots + \delta_{1N}E_2 = I_1$$
$$\delta_{21}E_1 + \delta_{22}E_2 + \cdots + \delta_{2N}E = I_{2N}$$
$$\cdots \cdots \cdots \cdots \cdots \cdots \cdots \cdots \cdots \quad (A\text{-}14)$$
$$\delta_{N1}E_1 + \delta_{N2}E_2 + \cdots + \delta_{NN}E_N = I_N$$

The coefficients δ represent the various branch admittances in the following way: If $p = q$, δ_{pq} is the sum of all admittances connected to the path junction. If $p \neq q$, δ_{pq} is the negative of the admittance connecting junctions p and q directly. These coefficients are called *comittances*, as a contraction of the phrase, coefficients of admittance. The currents I_N appearing on the right are junction current sources. A junction current source is the algebraic sum of all current sources connected to the junction. A current having a reference direction toward the junction is taken as positive in forming the algebraic sum.

A-5. Network Theorems. A number of network theorems are found to be of considerable assistance in solving the network problems involving vacuum tubes. Several such theorems will be given, although the proofs will not be given in all cases. The theorems which will here be given are the Helmholtz equivalent-source theorems (Thévenin and Norton theorems), the Millman theorem, and dual-circuit construction rules.

a. Helmholtz Equivalent-source Theorems. Let the rectangle of Fig. A-6 represent a general network with N independent loops, $M + 1$ junctions, N loop potential sources,

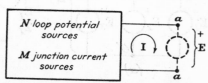

Fig. A-6. Circuit for illustrating the Helmholtz equivalent-source theorems (Thévenin and Norton theorems).

and M junction current sources, all of the same frequency. One branch of this general network is shown isolated. Let the outside terminals be closed by a fictitious potential source, which may be the potential drop

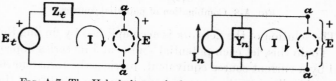

Fig. A-7. The Helmholtz equivalent-source representations.

across a passive element between these two points. A general analysis of such an active network leads to the conclusion that any two terminal linear network with any number of current and potential sources of the same frequency can be viewed as a source. This source can, in turn, be represented by either of the simple circuits of Fig. A-7. When the potential-source form is used, the network is said to be represented by a Helmholtz-Thévenin potential-source equivalent. The current-source form is called the Helmholtz-Norton current-source equivalent.

The series impedance Z_t, or the shunt admittance Y_n, appearing in Fig. A-7, are the inverse of each other, i.e., $Z_t = 1/Y_n$. Also, Z_t is the impedance of the network as measured at the terminals aa when all internal potential and current sources are reduced to zero.

The potential source E_t is the potential E which appears across the terminals aa when these terminals are on open circuit. Similarly, the current source I_n is the current in the short circuit which is placed across the terminals aa.

The parameters E_t, I_n, Z_t, Y_n can be found by any method of circuit solution. They may also be found experimentally for physical systems.

b. *Millman Theorem.* Certain simple combinations of potential-source equivalents are of use because they offer simplification in the solutions of more extensive networks in which the combinations occur. Consider Fig. A-8a, which is typical of the situation to be considered

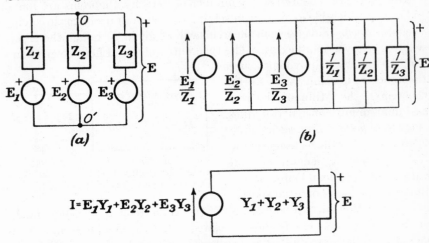

(a)   (b)

(c)

FIG. A-8. Combination of potential sources.

here. The solution of the network is accomplished by finding the potential E. To do this, let each potential source and its series impedance be replaced by a current-source equivalent, to yield the form shown in Fig. A-8b. In this diagram the sources have been separated from their individual admittances to give the grouped arrangement shown. This leads ultimately to the circuit of Fig. A-8c. The solution of this circuit for E is given directly by the relation

$$E = \frac{E_1 Y_1 + E_2 Y_2 + E_3 Y_3}{Y_1 + Y_2 + Y_3} \qquad (A\text{-}15)$$

c. Duality and Dual-circuit Construction. Throughout the development of network analysis a parallelism of statements is necessary, once for potentials and once for currents. There are potential sources and current sources; a Kirchhoff potential law pertaining to a loop, and a Kirchhoff current law pertaining to a junction, etc. These ideas are part of a larger pattern which exists in network analysis.

The simultaneous existence of two similar systems of analysis is given the name *duality* and is founded on the interchange of independent and dependent variables in the equations expressing the behavior of the circuit elements. Duality does not imply equivalence; it means only that the mathematical representations of the circuits are similar in form.

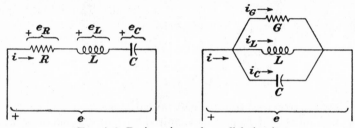

FIG. A-9. Basic series and parallel circuits.

Consider the basic series and parallel circuits illustrated in Fig. A-9. If the series combination is excited by a potential, and the parallel combination by a current, the appropriate relations for the respective circuits follow. For the series circuit,

$$e = e_R + e_L + e_C = Ri + L\frac{di}{dt} + \frac{1}{C}\int i\,dt \qquad (A\text{-}16)$$

For the parallel circuit,

$$i = i_G + i_C + i_L = Ge + C\frac{de}{dt} + \frac{1}{L}\int e\,dt \qquad (A\text{-}17)$$

Table A-1 contains the dually related quantities. Clearly, the two networks illustrated in Fig. A-9 are dually related.

It is of interest to compare Eqs. (A-4), which apply to Fig. A-3, with Eqs. (A-11), which apply to Fig. A-5. Since there is a systematic interchange of $\mathbf{Z}$ with $\mathbf{Y}$ and of $\mathbf{I}$ with $\mathbf{E}$ in these expressions, the two networks are dually related. Among the important dual relationships implied herein are those contained in Table A-1.

In the case of series or parallel circuits, the method of going from one circuit to its dual is illustrated in Fig. A-9. It is convenient to be able to construct a circuit which is the dual of another in the general case. A dual exists, and can be found, for any circuit, provided that it can be made flat and includes transformers in such a way that they can be replaced by equivalent circuits.

TABLE A-1

DUAL RELATIONSHIPS

Loop concept	*Junction concept*
Loop interior	Junction other than datum junction
Circuit exterior	Datum junction
Potential source in an external branch	Current source with one terminal connected to the datum junction
Potential source in series in a common branch	Current source shunting a common branch
Loop current	Junction potential to the datum junction
Branch impedance	Branch admittance

The essential problem to be solved is the following, and for convenience a typical three-loop network is to be considered. The network specified is represented by the equations of (A-18)

$$\varrho_{11}I_1 + \varrho_{12}I_2 + \varrho_{13}I_3 = S_{e1} - S_{e2}$$
$$\varrho_{21}I_1 + \varrho_{22}I_2 + \varrho_{23}I_3 = S_{e2} \qquad (A\text{-}18)$$
$$\varrho_{31}I_1 + \varrho_{32}I_2 + \varrho_{33}I_3 = S_{e3}$$

The symbols S_e are used to represent potential sources, and each I represents a loop current. It is now required to find the network which is represented by the equations

$$\delta_{11}E_1 + \delta_{12}E_2 + \delta_{13}E_3 = S_{i1} - S_{i2}$$
$$\delta_{21}E_1 + \delta_{22}E_2 + \delta_{23}E_3 = S_{i2} \qquad (A\text{-}19)$$
$$\delta_{31}E_1 + \delta_{32}E_2 + \delta_{33}E_3 = S_{i3}$$

in which each E is a junction response potential and each S_i is a current source. Each δ is to be the same form as the corresponding ϱ.

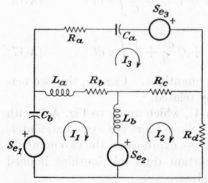

FIG. A-10. A typical circuit setup for loop analysis.

The details of the construction follow: The new network must have three junctions, in addition to the datum junction. A dot is then placed in each loop, and the network is enclosed by a continuous line. Each internal dot becomes a non-datum junction, and the outside line is the datum junction. The junctions are numbered to correspond with the loops in which they appear. Junctions 1 and 2 are to be connected by a branch which is the dual of that common to loops 1 and 2. When this branch is drawn, it in essence crosses the branch to which it is dually related. This procedure is carried out for each pair of junctions, including the datum junction.

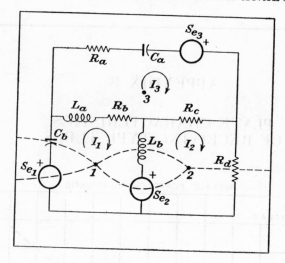

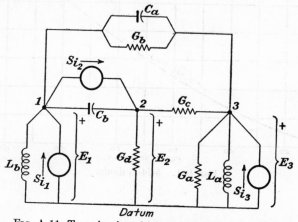

Fig. A-11. Two circuits which are duals of each other.

In setting up the dual circuit, it is necessary to choose reference conditions in accordance with a consistent set of rules. Two considerations are involved, (1) the reference direction of the current sources, and (2) the reference polarity at the junctions. The rules for a consistent representation are:

1. If a potential source in a loop is a rise in the clockwise direction, its dual is a current source directed toward the dually related junction.

2. If a current has a clockwise direction in a loop, its dual is a positive potential at the dually related junction.

Based on the above, Fig. A-10, appropriately marked, and its dual are given in Fig. A-11.

APPENDIX B

PLATE CHARACTERISTICS
OF RECEIVING-TYPE TUBES

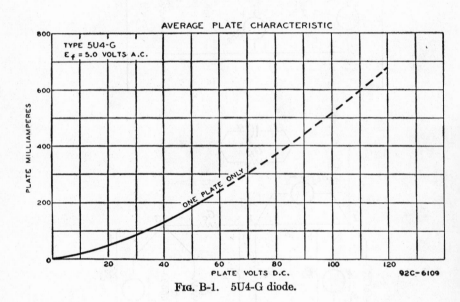

Fig. B-1. 5U4-G diode.

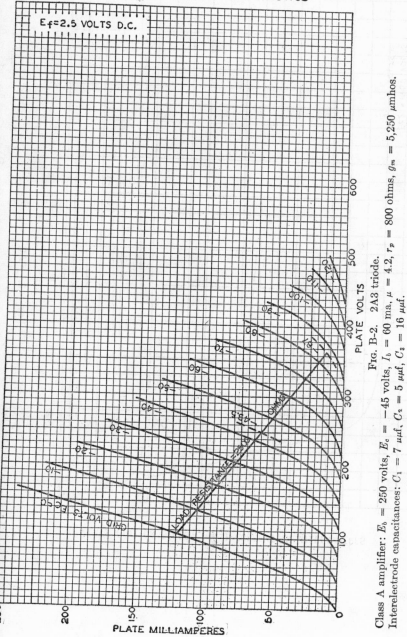

AVERAGE PLATE CHARACTERISTICS

Fig. B-2. 2A3 triode.

Class A amplifier: $E_b = 250$ volts, $E_c = -45$ volts, $I_b = 60$ ma, $\mu = 4.2$, $r_p = 800$ ohms, $g_m = 5{,}250$ μmhos.

Interelectrode capacitances: $C_1 = 7$ $\mu\mu f$, $C_2 = 5$ $\mu\mu f$, $C_3 = 16$ $\mu\mu f$.

497

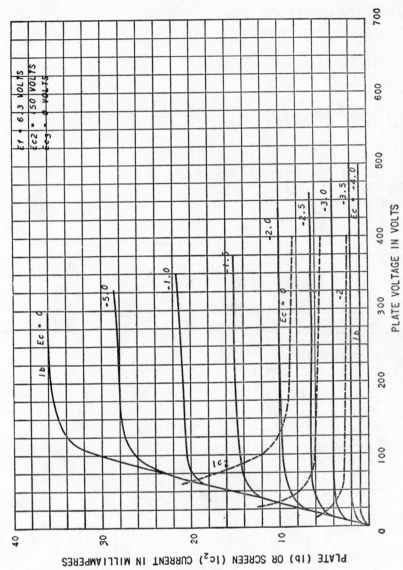

FIG. B-3. 6AC7 pentode.

Class A amplifier: $E_b = 300$ volts, $E_{c2} = 150$ volts, $E_c = -2$ volts, $I_b = 10$ ma, $I_{c2} = 2.5$ ma, $r_p = 1$

498

6AG7

AVERAGE PLATE CHARACTERISTICS
WITH E_CI AS VARIABLE

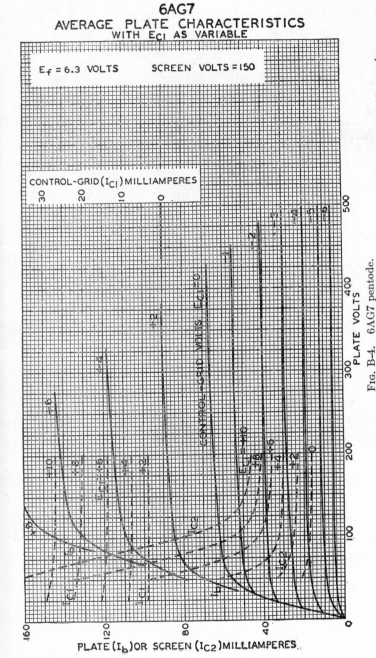

$E_f = 6.3$ VOLTS   SCREEN VOLTS = 150

CONTROL-GRID (I_{CI}) MILLIAMPERES

PLATE VOLTS

PLATE (I_b) OR SCREEN (I_{C2}) MILLIAMPERES

FIG. B-4. 6AG7 pentode.

Class A amplifier: $E_b = 300$ volts, $E_{c2} = 150$ volts, $E_c = -3$ volts, $I_b = 30$ ma, $I_{c2} = 7$ ma, $r_p = 0.13$ megohm approx; $g_m = 11,000$ µmhos.

Interelectrode capacitances: $C_1 = 13$ µµf, $C_2 = 7.5$ µµf, $C_3 = 0.06$ µµf.

499

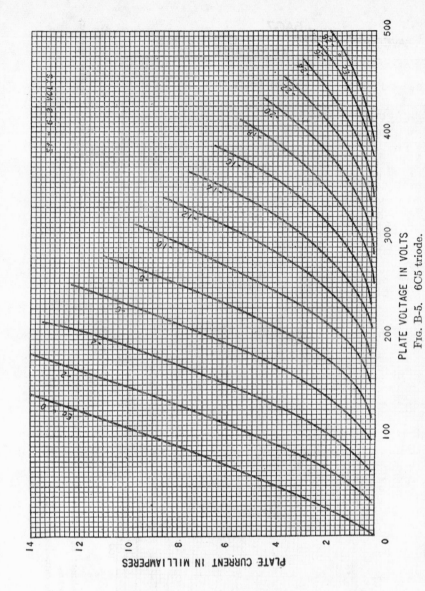

PLATE VOLTAGE IN VOLTS

Fig. B-5.   6C5 triode.

Class A amplifier: $E_b = 250$ volts, $E_c = -8$ volts, $I_b = 8$ ma, $\mu = 20$, $r_p = 10,000$ ohms, $g_m = 2,000$ μmhos.

Interelectrode capacitances: $C_1 = 3$ $\mu\mu f$, $C_2 = 11$ $\mu\mu f$, $C_3 = 2.0$ $\mu\mu f$.

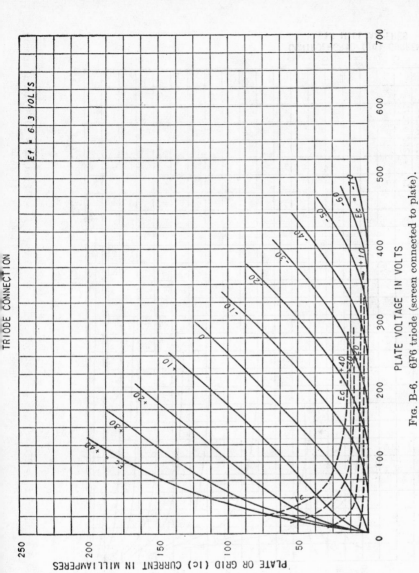

Fig. B-6. 6F6 triode (screen connected to plate).

Class A amplifier: $E_b = 250$ volts, $E_c = -20$ volts, $I_b = 31$ ma, $\mu = 6.8$, $r_p = 2{,}600$ ohms, $g_m = 2{,}600$ μmhos.

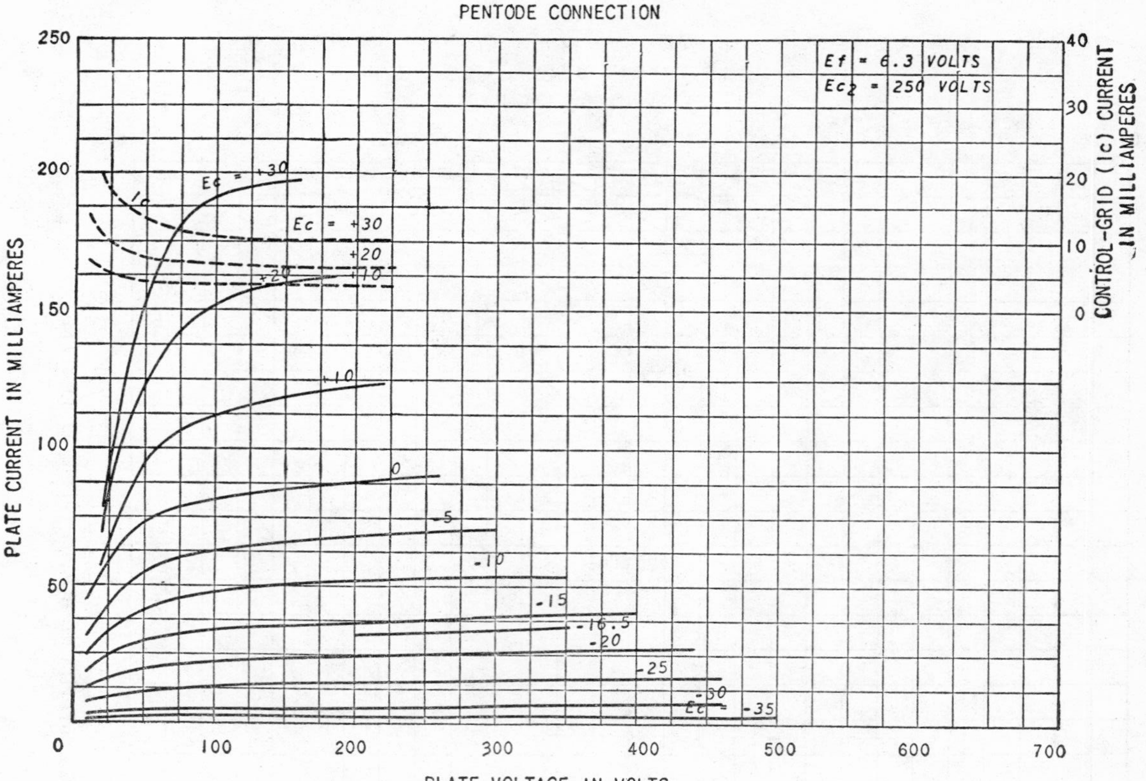

Fig. B-7. 6F6 pentode.

Class A amplifier: $E_b = 250$ volts, $E_{c2} = 250$ volts, $E_c = -16.5$ volts, $I_b = 34$ ma, $r_p = 80,000$ ohms approx, $g_m = 2,500$ μmhos. Interelectrode capacitances: $C_1 = 6.5$ $\mu\mu$f, $C_2 = 13$ $\mu\mu$f, $C_3 = 0.2$ $\mu\mu$f.

502

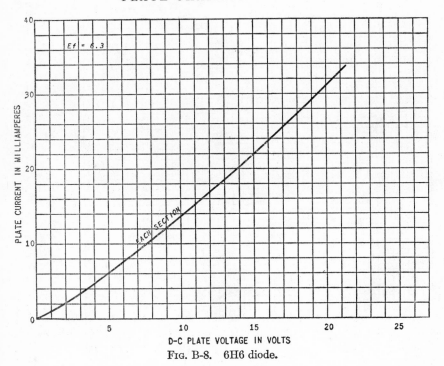

Fig. B-8. 6H6 diode.

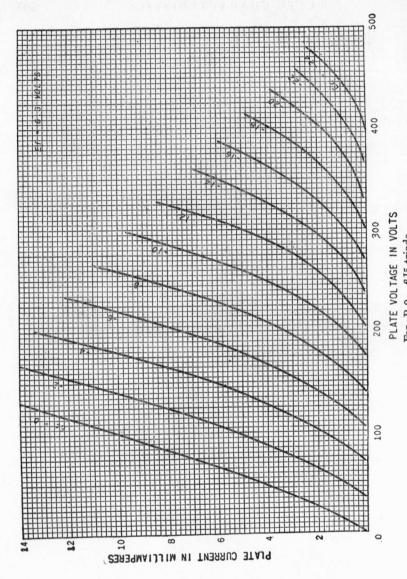

PLATE VOLTAGE IN VOLTS

Fig. B-9. 6J5 triode.

Class A amplifier: $E_b = 250$ volts, $E_c = -8$ volts, $I_b = 9$ ma, $\mu = 20$, $r_p = 7{,}700$ ohms, $g_m = 2{,}600$ μmhos.
Interelectrode capacitances: $C_1 = 3.4$ $\mu\mu$f, $C_2 = 3.6$ $\mu\mu$f, $C_3 = 3.4$ $\mu\mu$f.

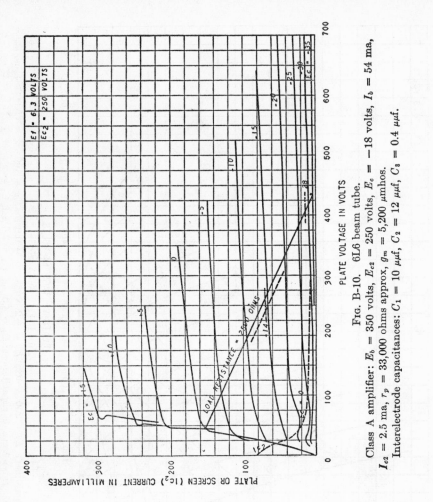

FIG. B-10. 6L6 beam tube.

Class A amplifier: E_b = 350 volts, E_{c2} = 250 volts, E_c = −18 volts, I_b = 54 ma, I_{c2} = 2.5 ma, r_p = 33,000 ohms approx, g_m = 5,200 μmhos.

Interelectrode capacitances: C_1 = 10 μμf, C_2 = 12 μμf, C_3 = 0.4 μμf.

505

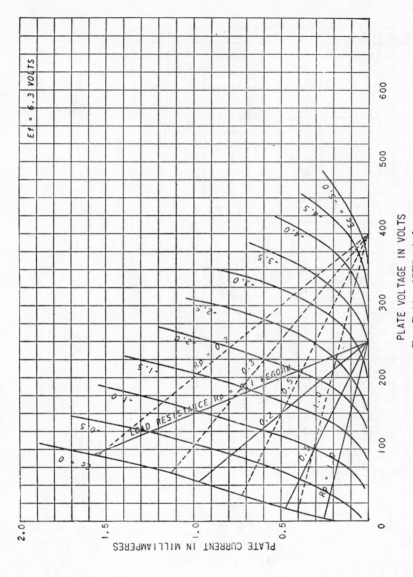

PLATE VOLTAGE IN VOLTS

Fig. B-11. 6SF5 triode.

Class A amplifier: $E_b = 250$ volts, $E_c = -2$ volts, $I_b = 0.9$ ma, $\mu = 100$, $r_p = 66,000$ ohms, $g_m = 1,500$ μmhos. Interelectrode capacitances: $C_1 = 4.0$ $\mu\mu$f, $C_2 = 3.6$ $\mu\mu$f, $C_3 = 2.4$ $\mu\mu$f

AVERAGE PLATE CHARACTERISTICS

PENTODE CONNECTION

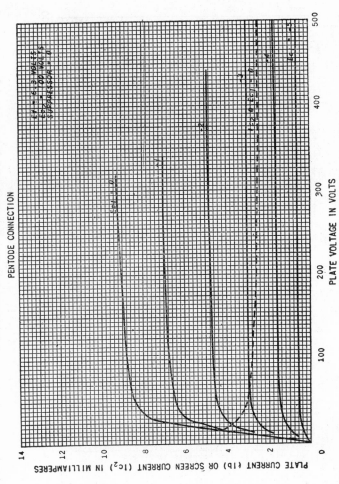

FIG. B-12. 6SJ7 pentode.

Class A amplifier: $E_b = 250$, $E_{c2} = 100$ volts, $E_c = -3$ volts, $I_b = 3$ ma, $I_{c2} = 0.8$ ma, $r_p = 1.0$ megohm approx, $g_m = 1,650$ μmhos.

Interelectrode capacitances: $C_1 = 6.0$ μμf, $C_2 = 7.0$ μμf, $C_3 = .005$ μf.

507

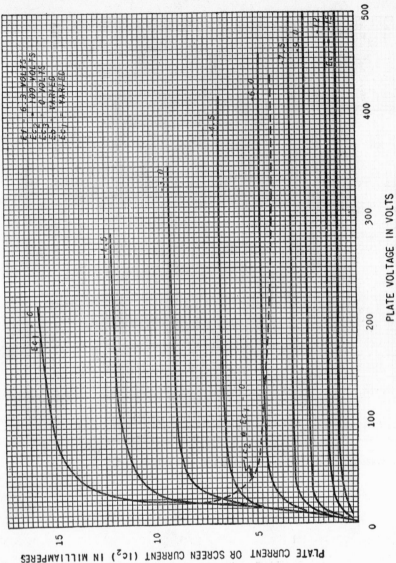

PLATE CURRENT OR SCREEN CURRENT (i_{c2}) IN MILLIAMPERES

PLATE VOLTAGE IN VOLTS

Fig. B-13. 6SK7 variable-mu pentode.

Class A amplifier: $E_b = 250$ volts, $E_c = -3$ volts, $I_b = 9.2$ ma, $I_{c2} = 2.6$ ma, $r_p = 0.8$ megohm approx, $g_m = 2,000$ μmhos. Interelectrode capacitances: $C_1 = 6.0$ μμf, $C_2 = 7.0$ μμf, $C_3 = .003$ μμf.

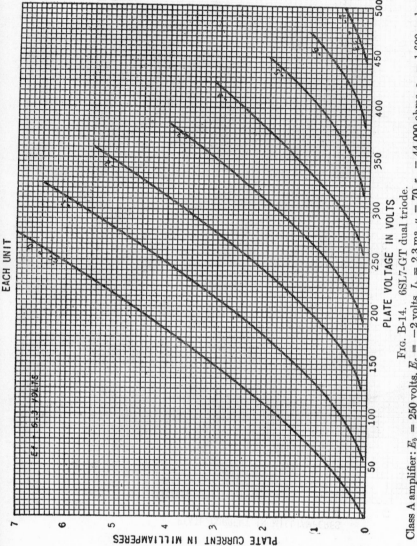

EACH UNIT

PLATE CURRENT IN MILLIAMPERES

PLATE VOLTAGE IN VOLTS

Fig. B-14. 6SL7-GT dual triode.

Class A amplifier: $E_b = 250$ volts, $E_c = -2$ volts, $I_b = 2.3$ ma, $\mu = 70$, $r_p = 44{,}000$ ohms, $g_m = 1{,}600$ μmhos. Interelectrode capacitances: Unit 1: $C_1 = 3.0$ $\mu\mu f$, $C_2 = 3.8$ $\mu\mu f$, $C_3 = 2.8$ $\mu\mu f$. Unit 2: $C_1 = 3.4$ $\mu\mu f$, $C_2 = 3.2$ $\mu\mu f$, $C_3 = 2.8$ $\mu\mu f$.

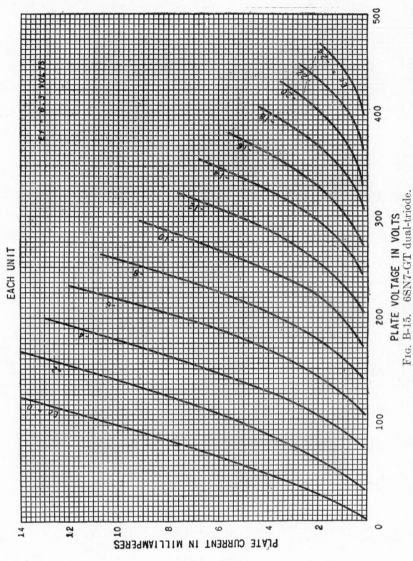

EACH UNIT

PLATE VOLTAGE IN VOLTS

Fig. B-15. 6SN7-GT dual-triode.

Class A amplifier: $E_b = 250$ volts, $E_c = -8$ volts, $I_b = 9$ ma, $\mu = 20$, $r_p = 7,700$ ohms, $g_m = 2,600$ μmhos. Interelectrode capacitances: Unit 1: $C_1 = 3.2$ μμf, $C_2 = 3.4$ μμf, $C_3 = 4$ μμf. Unit 2: $C_1 = 3.8$ μμf, $C_2 = 2.6$ μμf, $C_3 = 4$ μμf.

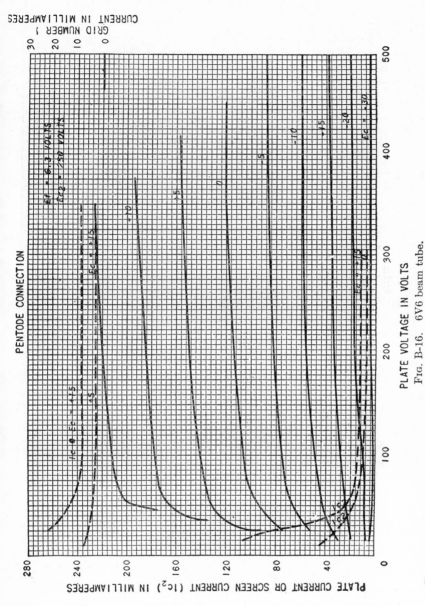

GRID NUMBER 1
CURRENT IN MILLIAMPERES

PENTODE CONNECTION

PLATE CURRENT OR SCREEN CURRENT (i_{c_2}) IN MILLIAMPERES

PLATE VOLTAGE IN VOLTS

Fig. B-16. 6V6 beam tube.

Class A amplifier: $E_b = 250$ volts, $E_{c2} = 250$ volts, $E_c = -12.5$ volts, $I_b = 45$ ma, $I_{c2} = 4.5$ ma, $r_p = 52{,}000$ ohms approx, $g_m = 4{,}100$ μmhos. Interelectrode capacitances: $C_1 = 10$ μμf, $C_2 = 11$ μμf, $C_3 = 0.3$ μμf.

511

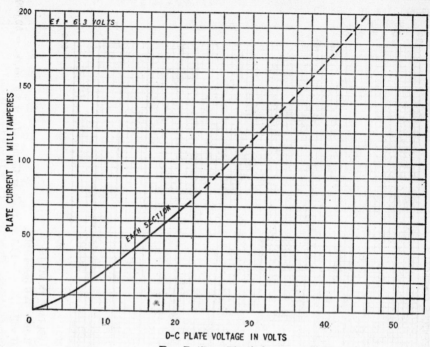

FIG. B-17.　6X5 diode.

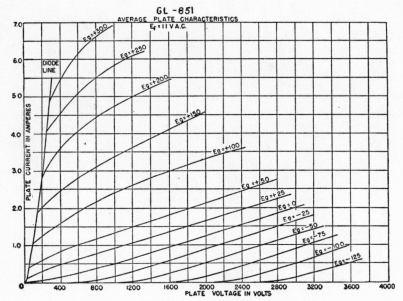

Fig. B-18. 851 triode.

INDEX

515